NATURAL EARTH, LIVING EARTH

NATURAL EARTH, LIVING EARTH

MIRANDA SMITH AND STEVE PARKER

COVENT
GARDEN
BOOKS

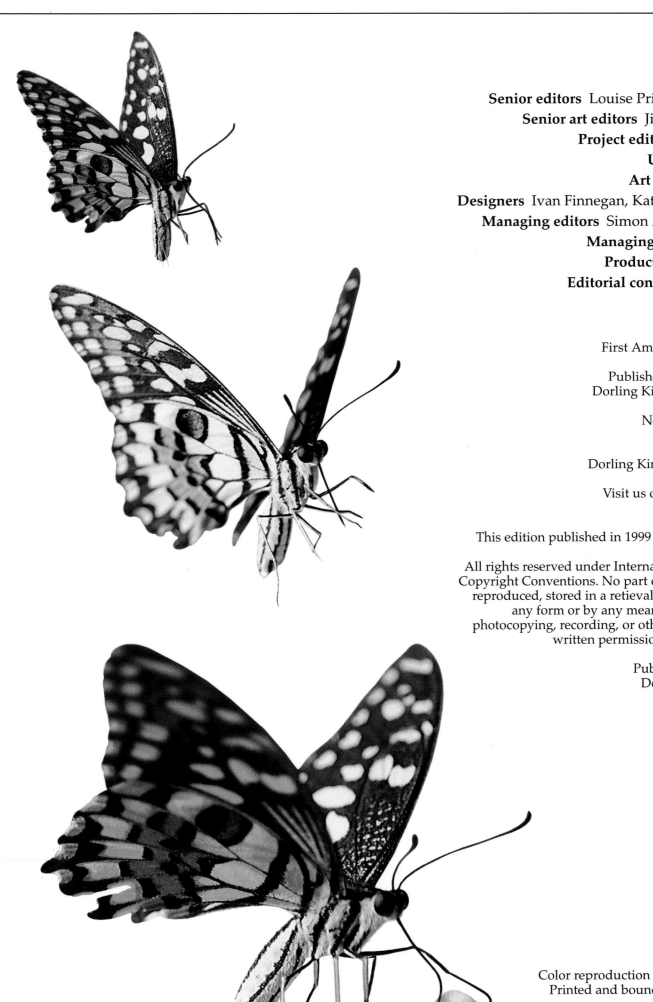

Senior editors Louise Pritchard, Miranda Smith
Senior art editors Jill Plank, Andrew Nash
Project editor Djinn von Noorden
US editor Jill Hamilton
Art editor Sharon Spencer
Designers Ivan Finnegan, Kati Poyner, Joseph Hoyle
Managing editors Simon Adams, Gillian Denton
Managing art editor Julia Harris
Production Catherine Semark
Editorial consultant Barbara Taylor

First American Edition, 1994/1996

Published in the United States by
Dorling Kindersley Publishing, Inc.,
95 Madison Avenue,
New York, New York 10016

Visit us on the World Wide Web at
http://www.dk.com

This edition published in 1999 for Covent Garden Books

Published in Great Britain by
Dorling Kindersley Limited

ISBN 0-7894-5098-4

Color reproduction by Colourscan, Singapore
Printed and bound in China by Dai Nippon

PART ONE
LIVING EARTH

CONTENTS OF PART ONE

INTRODUCTION

THE EARTH IS HOME to millions of species, all with different characteristics and needs. How these species behave and how they interact with their environment and with one another is a source of endless fascination. They survive in a variety of habitats and climates – from the frozen wastes of Antarctica to the tropical swamps of Southeast Asia, from the teeming Australian barrier reef to the arid sands of the Namibian desert. The life cycles of these animals and plants have been captured in superb detail by the photographers of the Eyewitness series, providing a unique insight into the living Earth.

FIRST FOSSILS

Fossils are the remains or impressions of living things that have hardened in rock. They tell scientists a great deal about the past, and the animals and plants that lived millions of years ago. The oldest fossils found so far are 4.5 billion years old and are of single-celled, bacterialike organisms. It was another million years before an oxygen-rich atmosphere developed on Earth, allowing more complex organisms to survive.

Fossil of rugose coral

Fossil of trilobite

Fossil of ammonite

FIRST STEPS

Four-legged animals took a major step forward when reptiles appeared. Unlike their amphibian ancestors, reptiles did not rely on an aquatic environment for survival. The land invasion from the swarming prehistoric seas that had begun with plants, arthropods, and amphibians was complete. Today's lizards, such as this tegu lizard from tropical South America, are not very different in shape or characteristics from prehistoric reptiles.

Spider preserved in amber

CHAPTER 1
FIRST LIFE

LIFE IS ONLY KNOWN here on Earth, and Earth's rocks contain fossils of past life. Paleontologists use these fossils to construct the story of that life. The first fossils date back to 4.5 billion years ago, when very diverse forms of life began to develop, eventually including reptiles, dinosaurs, and early mammals.

The Sun

THE SUN IS THE STAR at the center of the Solar System. It is 875,000 miles (1.4 million kilometers) in diameter and consists almost entirely of hydrogen and helium. The heat and light of the Sun sustain life on Earth. Without the Sun, there would be no weather. Because the Earth's surface is curved, the Sun's rays strike different parts at different angles, dividing the world into distinct climate zones, each with its own typical weather. Light from the Sun is the energy that fuels the world's great weather machine – its heat keeps the atmosphere constantly in motion.

A close-up view of the Sun, showing a violent storm erupting at the surface

Young stage of crab larva

Sample of zooplankton collected from northern Atlantic coast of Scotland

Shrimp

LIFE IN THE SEA
Zooplankton are tiny animals that drift in the oceans. They eat phytoplankton, minute, single-celled plants that use nutrients in seawater and sunlight to grow. Zooplankton in turn are eaten by larger fish, such as the dogfish, which are, in their turn, eaten by still larger fish or other predators such as dolphins. Some larger ocean animals (whale sharks and blue whales) feed directly on zooplankton.

Shaving brush tree
Pachira aquatica

ANIMAL LIFE
All life on Earth needs the Sun to survive. A lizard makes a dramatic example because it is cold-blooded. This does not mean that its body is always cold, but that its temperature rises and falls with that of its surroundings. A lizard needs to be warm to move around, and it heats up its body by basking in sunshine. If it gets too hot, it retreats into shade. Butterflies also adjust their body temperature in this way.

PLANT LIFE
The incredible variety of plant life on Earth relies on its ability to convert the energy from sunlight into food (pp. 46–47). In shape and form, leaves are adapted to the task of capturing light; pigments such as chlorophyll and carotenoids absorb the light energy. However, only a tiny fraction of the Sun's energy that reaches the Earth is actually used to create plant material.

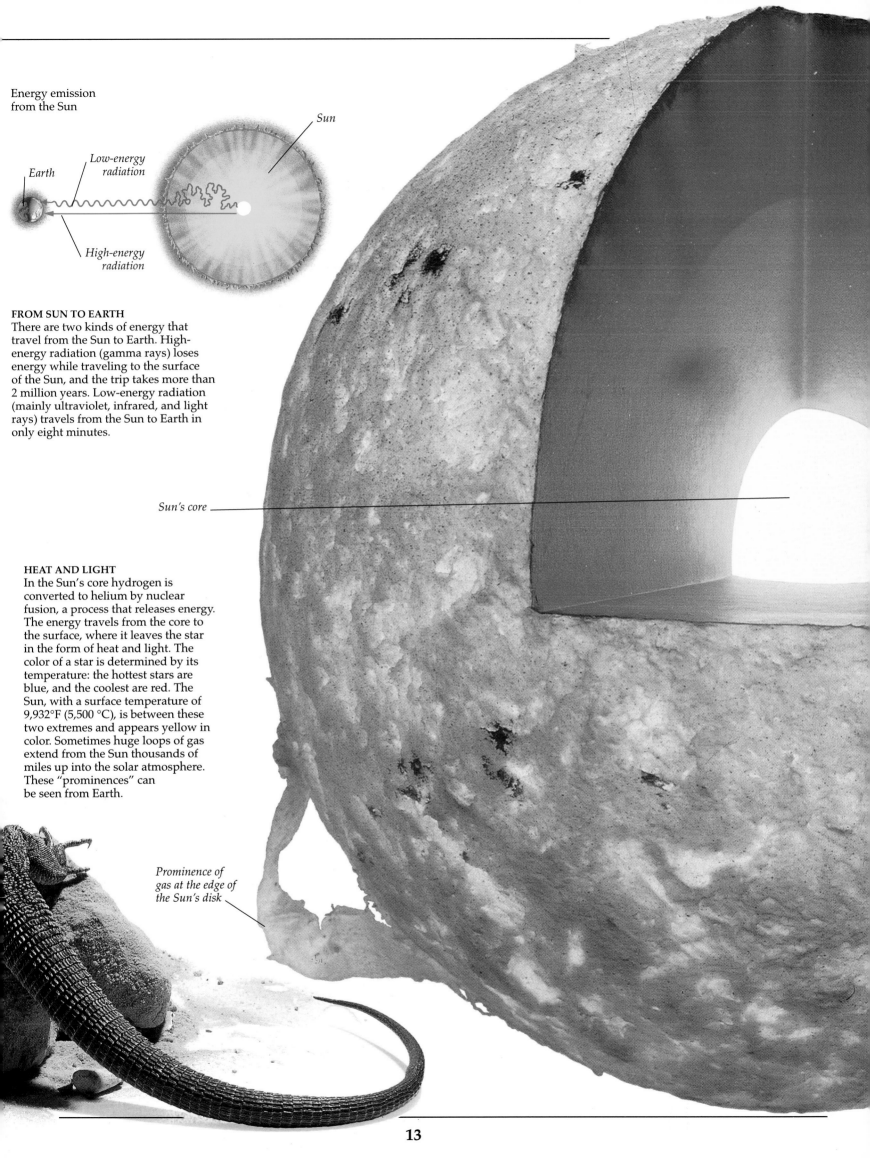

Energy emission
from the Sun

Sun

Earth

*Low-energy
radiation*

*High-energy
radiation*

FROM SUN TO EARTH
There are two kinds of energy that
travel from the Sun to Earth. High-
energy radiation (gamma rays) loses
energy while traveling to the surface
of the Sun, and the trip takes more than
2 million years. Low-energy radiation
(mainly ultraviolet, infrared, and light
rays) travels from the Sun to Earth in
only eight minutes.

Sun's core

HEAT AND LIGHT
In the Sun's core hydrogen is
converted to helium by nuclear
fusion, a process that releases energy.
The energy travels from the core to
the surface, where it leaves the star
in the form of heat and light. The
color of a star is determined by its
temperature: the hottest stars are
blue, and the coolest are red. The
Sun, with a surface temperature of
9,932°F (5,500 °C), is between these
two extremes and appears yellow in
color. Sometimes huge loops of gas
extend from the Sun thousands of
miles up into the solar atmosphere.
These "prominences" can
be seen from Earth.

*Prominence of
gas at the edge of
the Sun's disk*

Single-celled life

MOST FORMS OF LIFE consist of a single cell that carries out all the tasks involved in staying alive. With a few exceptions, single-celled organisms are so small that they cannot be seen with the naked eye. Until the 17th century, no one knew that they existed. The invention of the microscope revealed that single-celled creatures live almost everywhere, from pond water to household dust. Many exist on or in the human body. During the 20th century, scientists discovered that the many different forms of single-celled life fall into two distinct groups. Some cells have a nucleus and a range of special internal structures called organelles that harness energy and put it to work. Other cells are smaller and simpler, with very few internal structures. These organisms – the bacteria – are the most abundant life form that exists. It is estimated that the combined weight of all the bacteria in the world would be 20 times greater than the weight of all other living things put together.

EXPLORING A HIDDEN WORLD
The pioneering Dutch scientist Anton van Leeuwenhoek (1632–1723) designed and built this small single-lens microscope. In 1683, he used it to become the first person to see bacteria. He made these sketches of the movements of bacteria that he found living on his teeth.

ANCIENT LIFE
These wormlike strands, photographed in ultraviolet light, are clusters of single-celled organisms called cyanobacteria. They make their food by using sunlight, and are the oldest living things to be found on the Earth. Geologists have discovered huge fossilized mats of cyanobacteria, called stromatolites, that are more than 3 billion years old – almost three-quarters as old as Earth itself.

MICROBES AND DISEASE
Research by the German bacteriologist Robert Koch (1843–1910) helped prove that bacteria are one of the causes of disease. He found that certain bacteria cultured in the laboratory could produce the deadly disease anthrax when introduced into cattle.

THE RACE TO REPRODUCE
A bacterium reproduces simply by dividing to make two new cells. Under ideal conditions, each bacterium can split in two every 20 minutes. Each of these two will then do the same, and so on. Within just a few hours, a single bacterium can produce a teeming colony of millions, like the one below.

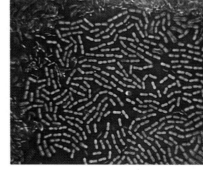

Fossilized plant-like organisms known as diatoms

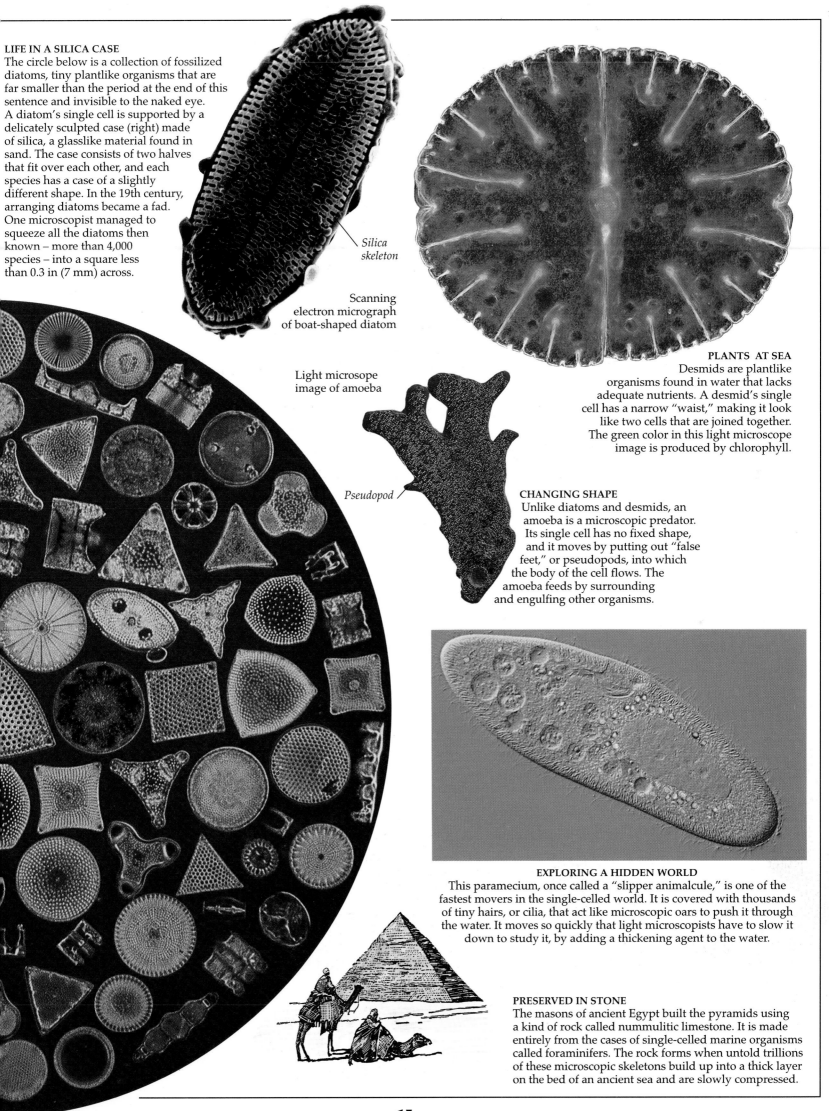

LIFE IN A SILICA CASE

The circle below is a collection of fossilized diatoms, tiny plantlike organisms that are far smaller than the period at the end of this sentence and invisible to the naked eye. A diatom's single cell is supported by a delicately sculpted case (right) made of silica, a glasslike material found in sand. The case consists of two halves that fit over each other, and each species has a case of a slightly different shape. In the 19th century, arranging diatoms became a fad. One microscopist managed to squeeze all the diatoms then known – more than 4,000 species – into a square less than 0.3 in (7 mm) across.

Silica skeleton

Scanning electron micrograph of boat-shaped diatom

Light microsope image of amoeba

Pseudopod

PLANTS AT SEA

Desmids are plantlike organisms found in water that lacks adequate nutrients. A desmid's single cell has a narrow "waist," making it look like two cells that are joined together. The green color in this light microscope image is produced by chlorophyll.

CHANGING SHAPE

Unlike diatoms and desmids, an amoeba is a microscopic predator. Its single cell has no fixed shape, and it moves by putting out "false feet," or pseudopods, into which the body of the cell flows. The amoeba feeds by surrounding and engulfing other organisms.

EXPLORING A HIDDEN WORLD

This paramecium, once called a "slipper animalcule," is one of the fastest movers in the single-celled world. It is covered with thousands of tiny hairs, or cilia, that act like microscopic oars to push it through the water. It moves so quickly that light microscopists have to slow it down to study it, by adding a thickening agent to the water.

PRESERVED IN STONE

The masons of ancient Egypt built the pyramids using a kind of rock called nummulitic limestone. It is made entirely from the cases of single-celled marine organisms called foraminifers. The rock forms when untold trillions of these microscopic skeletons build up into a thick layer on the bed of an ancient sea and are slowly compressed.

Carbon on the move

ALL LIVING THINGS contain the element carbon. It is also found in the oceans, in the air, and in the Earth itself. Carbon combines with other substances to take different forms. In the atmosphere, with oxygen, it exists as carbon dioxide (CO_2). In the ground and in the bones and shells of animals, carbon takes the form of chalky calcium carbonate. Carbon is passed around the biosphere, with plants as the main point of exchange. They convert atmospheric CO_2 into carbohydrates, a source of energy used to maintain their existence, through photosynthesis (pp. 40–41). When living things die, they are broken down by bacteria known as decomposers. The carbon that they needed to live is released back into the atmosphere to be used by other forms of life.

STORES OF CARBON
As plants grow, they absorb carbon from the atmosphere. Some is used immediately by the plant, but some is stored by being incorporated into the plant's structure, for example, as starch (p. 40). Every tree trunk is a store of carbon. If the tree is burned, its stored carbon is released back into the atmosphere as carbon dioxide.

THE CARBON CYCLE

Less than 1 percent of carbon on Earth is in active circulation in the biosphere. The rest is locked up as inorganic carbon in rocks and as organic carbon in fossil fuels. As growing plants take in carbon dioxide from the atmosphere and incorporate it as carbohydrates, carbon passes into the food chain. The plants release stored energy by breaking down the carbohydrates in a process called respiration. This releases energy and produces carbon dioxide as a waste product.

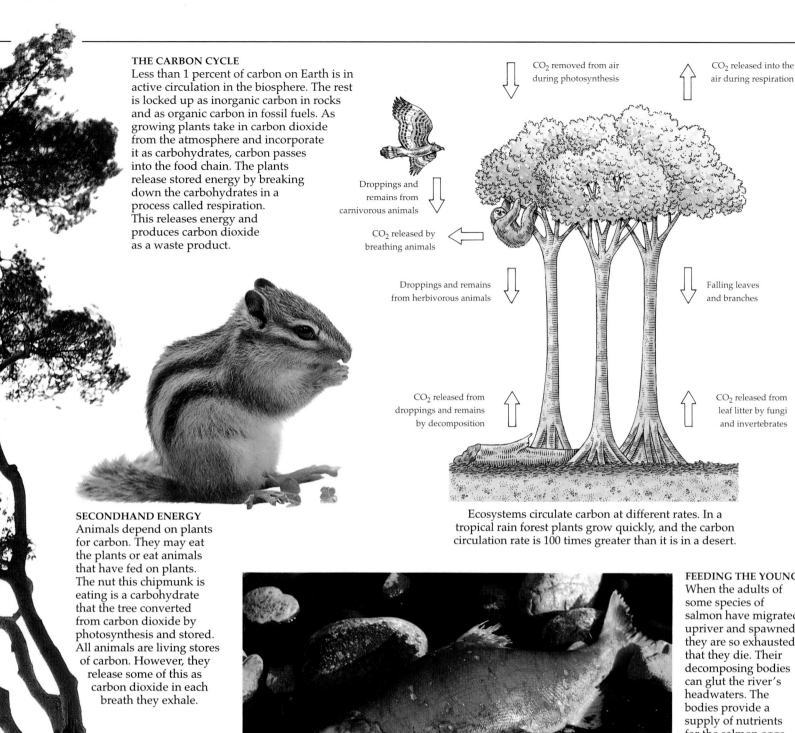

CO_2 removed from air during photosynthesis

CO_2 released into the air during respiration

Droppings and remains from carnivorous animals

CO_2 released by breathing animals

Droppings and remains from herbivorous animals

Falling leaves and branches

CO_2 released from droppings and remains by decomposition

CO_2 released from leaf litter by fungi and invertebrates

Ecosystems circulate carbon at different rates. In a tropical rain forest plants grow quickly, and the carbon circulation rate is 100 times greater than it is in a desert.

SECONDHAND ENERGY

Animals depend on plants for carbon. They may eat the plants or eat animals that have fed on plants. The nut this chipmunk is eating is a carbohydrate that the tree converted from carbon dioxide by photosynthesis and stored. All animals are living stores of carbon. However, they release some of this as carbon dioxide in each breath they exhale.

FEEDING THE YOUNG

When the adults of some species of salmon have migrated upriver and spawned, they are so exhausted that they die. Their decomposing bodies can glut the river's headwaters. The bodies provide a supply of nutrients for the salmon eggs and also for the young salmon when they hatch. The young are effectively made up of carbon from their parents.

CARBON AS A FOSSIL FUEL

Carbon is locked in the remains of living things that failed to completely decompose. During the Carboniferous period, 363–290 million years ago, plants died in shallow swamps, forming thick layers. Over millions of years, the heat of the Earth and the pressure of material building up above them turned this carbon into coal. In a similar way, vast deposits of tiny dead sea creatures became a liquid store of carbon – oil, which can be converted into gasoline. When these "fossil fuels" are burned, the carbon is finally released. About 50 times as much carbon is locked up in the Earth's coal and oil as there is in all living things. However, reserves of coal will only last about 250–300 years if they are used at the current rate. Oil reserves will probably only last 100 years.

The surface of the Earth

THE EARTH IS UNSTABLE. Over millions of years, its landscape has changed many times. The crust, or surface, of the Earth is made up of a number of pieces called tectonic plates. These plates move across the Earth's surface in response to forces and movements deep within the planet. The plate boundaries, where plates collide, rub shoulders, or move apart, are areas of intense geological activity. Most volcanoes and earthquakes occur at these boundaries. When two plates collide, one is forced beneath the other to form a subduction zone. The sinking plate partly melts and the light magma rises, feeding volcanoes just inside the plate boundary. The volcanoes take advantage of cracks in the plates, and molten rock bursts through to the surface.

Pangaea

Panthalassa

1 ONE LAND MASS
220 million years ago there was only one land mass, Pangaea, in a vast ocean called Panthalassa

Laurasia

Tethys Sea

Gondwanaland

2 TWO CONTINENTS
200 million years ago the growing Tethys Sea split Pangaea into Gondwanaland and Laurasia

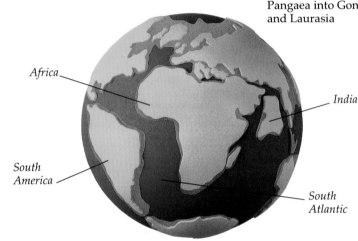

Africa

India

South America

South Atlantic

3 THE CONTINENTS DIVIDE
135 million years ago Gondwanaland split into Africa and South America as the south Atlantic opened up; India drifted toward Asia

FLASH POINT
Early volcano observers thought they saw flames or lightning flashes when a volcano erupted. This was probably the igniting of dangerous gases released by the volcano.

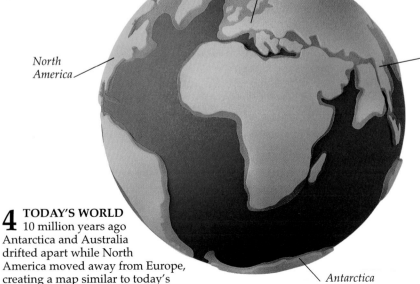

Europe

Asia

North America

Antarctica

4 TODAY'S WORLD
10 million years ago Antarctica and Australia drifted apart while North America moved away from Europe, creating a map similar to today's

TYPES OF VOLCANOES
There are different kinds of volcanoes. Most of the descriptions of volcanoes (right) refer to their shape. For example, during a large, ashy eruption, the empty magma chamber may not be able to support the weight of the volcano's slopes. These collapse inward, leaving a huge circular depression called a caldera. Some volcanoes, however, such as ash-cinder, are classified by their composition.

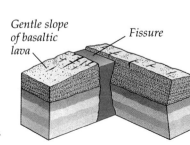

Gentle slope of basaltic lava

Fissure

Fissure volcano

Cutaway model showing how a composite volcano builds up as magma from the mantle erupts to the surface

Ash and gas clouds billow out of crater

Main volcanic vent or pipe

Volcano is built up from layers of lava and ash

Pressure forces magma up the main pipe and any branch pipes

Branch pipe

Magma collects in a magma chamber underground before it is forced up to the surface

VOLCANIC ERUPTIONS

Some 120 miles (200 km) below the surface of the Earth, the temperature is 2,732°F (1,500°C), and the rocks are white hot. But because of the intense pressure inside the Earth, the rocks, though soft, are not molten (liquid) until much deeper. Most of the molten rock, known as magma, erupted by volcanoes comes from the top of the mantle, 60 to 180 miles (100 to 300 km) down. Because magma is hotter and lighter than the surrounding rocks, it rises, melting some of the rocks it passes on the way. If it manages to find a way to the surface, the magma will erupt as lava.

Gentle slope of basaltic lava

Vent

Shield volcano

Steep, convex slope

Vent

Dome volcano

Fine ash

Cinder

Ash-cinder volcano

New cone

Caldera

Caldera volcano

The changing Earth

FOR ALMOST ONE BILLION YEARS, nothing lived on Earth. Nothing wriggled or ran, flew or swam. But as the early planet steadily changed – as new rocks formed, as mountains grew, as oceans spread and earthquakes and volcanoes shook and rattled, as continents slowly shifted, and as climates changed – the chance was created for life to exist. Today, evidence of that early life is preserved as fossils found on the Earth's rocky surface.

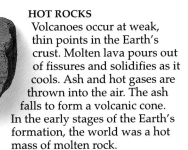

Granite solidified deep underground

Sandstone is made of eroded grains of quartz

HOT ROCKS
Volcanoes occur at weak, thin points in the Earth's crust. Molten lava pours out of fissures and solidifies as it cools. Ash and hot gases are thrown into the air. The ash falls to form a volcanic cone. In the early stages of the Earth's formation, the world was a hot mass of molten rock.

Metamorphic marble was once sedimentary limestone

Basalt is a common volcanic igneous rock

BUILDING BLOCKS
Igneous rocks form from molten rock material deep in the Earth. Sedimentary rocks are formed by rock particles, eroded by wind and water, that settle in layers in rivers, seas, and lakes. Changes in temperature and pressure can transform both igneous and sedimentary rocks into metamorphic rocks.

WATERY GRAVES
Rivers build thick sedimentary layers of sand and mud on flood plains and deltas. When it reaches the sea, the sediment sinks to the seafloor. Quickly buried, animal and plant remains may be preserved as the sediment slowly turns to rock.

The "part" of a trilobite

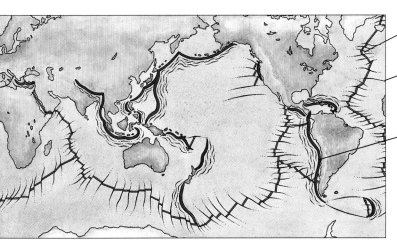

Volcanic ridge

Fault line

Plate-edge trench

MOVING PLATES
The Earth's surface is made of interlocking plates. Spreading out from volcanic ridges on the ocean floor, plate edges are constantly colliding. Some edges may sink, forming trenches where earthquakes and volcanoes often occur. Other collisions can produce huge mountain ranges, such as the Himalayas in Asia.

FOSSIL EVIDENCE
Splitting apart a fossil rock reveals the positive "part" (above) of the fossil and the negative "counterpart" (right), the natural mold. Fossils are evidence of ancient animal and plant life. They may preserve an organism's detailed inner structure as well as its outer shape. Flowers, feathers, and even footprints can be fossilized. The conversion of buried organisms into stony replicas takes millions of years, as the organic material is destroyed and minerals in the rocks slowly fill the microscopic shapes. Sometimes the buried fossil is completely destroyed in the rock, leaving only a natural mold.

How a fossil is formed

A decaying *Procolophon* (1) was covered in silt sediments swept in by shallow streams (2). Burial must have been rapid since the skeleton was not broken up, although the flesh rotted. Over millions of years, the skeleton was buried deep underground (3). Under pressure, sand became stone and chemicals turned the bones into fossil. Erosion brought the fossil back to the surface (4).

1. Decaying and dead *Procolophon* carcass lies exposed on Earth's surface

2. Silt sediments from shallow streams quickly bury the reptile's body

3. Sediment turns to rock around the fossil over millions of years

4. Fossilized skeleton is exposed at the surface

"Counterpart" of a trilobite, *Flexicalymene caractaci*

Procolophon trigoniceps South Africa

SMALL REPTILE
Procolophon was a small reptile that lived 245 million years ago. Its fossils, from the Karroo Basin in South Africa, are well known. Complete skeletons and skulls, perfectly preserved as white fossil bone, are buried in a red silty rock. This red color comes from the iron minerals that hold the quartz grains together, showing that the sediment was exposed to air and not continuously buried underwater.

HOT AND COLD
Rocks preserve clues about prehistoric climatic conditions that can help explain the shifting continents. Fossils of the large-leaved *Glossopteris* tree are found in abundance in Antarctic Permian rocks. During this period, Antarctica was part of a much larger continental mass and was not at the South Pole. Its climate was much warmer than it is today.

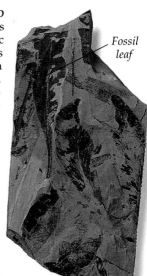

Fossil leaf

Glossopteris, Permian, New South Wales, Australia

MOLDED FROM LIFE
The natural mold left by a buried fossil fills with rock material and produces an accurate cast of the fossil's shape. This trilobite's overall shape has been preserved, but the hard fossil skeleton was destroyed over many years. Fossils are often flattened under the pressure of rock above and may be cracked and broken into many pieces.

OLD AGE
Evidence from meteorites and Moon rocks show that the Earth is about 4.5 billion years old. The oldest rocks on Earth, about 3.7 billion years old, are found in Greenland and are metamorphic. Originally sedimentary, some of these rocks were laid down at an even earlier date.

Turning to stone

FOSSILIZATION IS A VERY RISKY PROCESS that takes place over millions of years. As soon as animals and plants die, they begin to decompose, or rot. Any hard parts, such as shells, bones, and teeth in animals, or wood in plants, last longer than soft tissue, but they are often scattered by animals, wind, or flowing water. In order for something to be fossilized it must be buried quickly, before it decomposes. This is most likely to be accomplished by sediment, such as sand or mud, washing over the fossil in water. Some fossils dissolve later; others may be changed chemically or be distorted by high temperatures and pressures. Only a tiny fraction will survive to be found.

LAND SHAPES
Over millions of years, rocks are eroded and shaped by wind and water, bringing ancient fossils to the surface.

2 DECAYING MUSSEL
When the mussel dies, the two chalky shells open out into a "butterfly" position. The soft parts of the mussel enclosed by the shells soon begin to rot or are eaten by scavenging animals.

Living mussel

Living mussels attach themselves to rocks by byssal threads

1 LIVING MUSSEL
The soft parts of the mussel are enclosed by two chalky shells. Each individual may spend its entire life in one place, and dense masses form mussel beds. If a mussel becomes detached it may die, especially if it is swept into a different environment.

FROM PRESERVATION TO DISCOVERY
These four drawings show how animals can be preserved and their remains discovered millions of years later. It is a very slow process and the climate and shape of the land will probably change as much as the animal and plant life.

1. Dead animals sink to the seabed and their remains are buried by layers of sediment.

2. The lower layers of sediment turn to rock and the remains harden to form fossils.

3. The rock is gradually folded and eroded.

4. The fossils are exposed on the surface.

Soft parts have rotted away

3 HARD PARTS REMAIN
When the soft parts of the mussel have rotted away, the hard parts, the shells, remain.

Separated shell

4 TOWARD FOSSILIZATION
The shells of dead mussels are often carried along by currents in the water and dropped together in one area where they mix with pebbles and sand to form "mussel beaches." Some of the individuals shown here still have their two shells held together by a tough bit of tissue called a ligament. Constant battering by the sea may break some shells into small pieces. All these may then be buried and slowly fossilized.

Tough ligament holding shells together

Fossil mussel shell

5 FOSSILIZED MUSSELS
Many small mussels become firmly embedded in rock. Here, a natural mineral-cement binds the sediment grains and fossil shells together, making it difficult for a collector to take the shells out.

FOSSILS WITH COLOR
The shells of living mussels are deep blue. Some of the blue color is still visible in these fossil mussels, which are an incredible two million years old.

LOST COLOR
The color in shells is usually lost during the process of fossilization. The brown color in these fossils is from the rock in which they were fossilized.

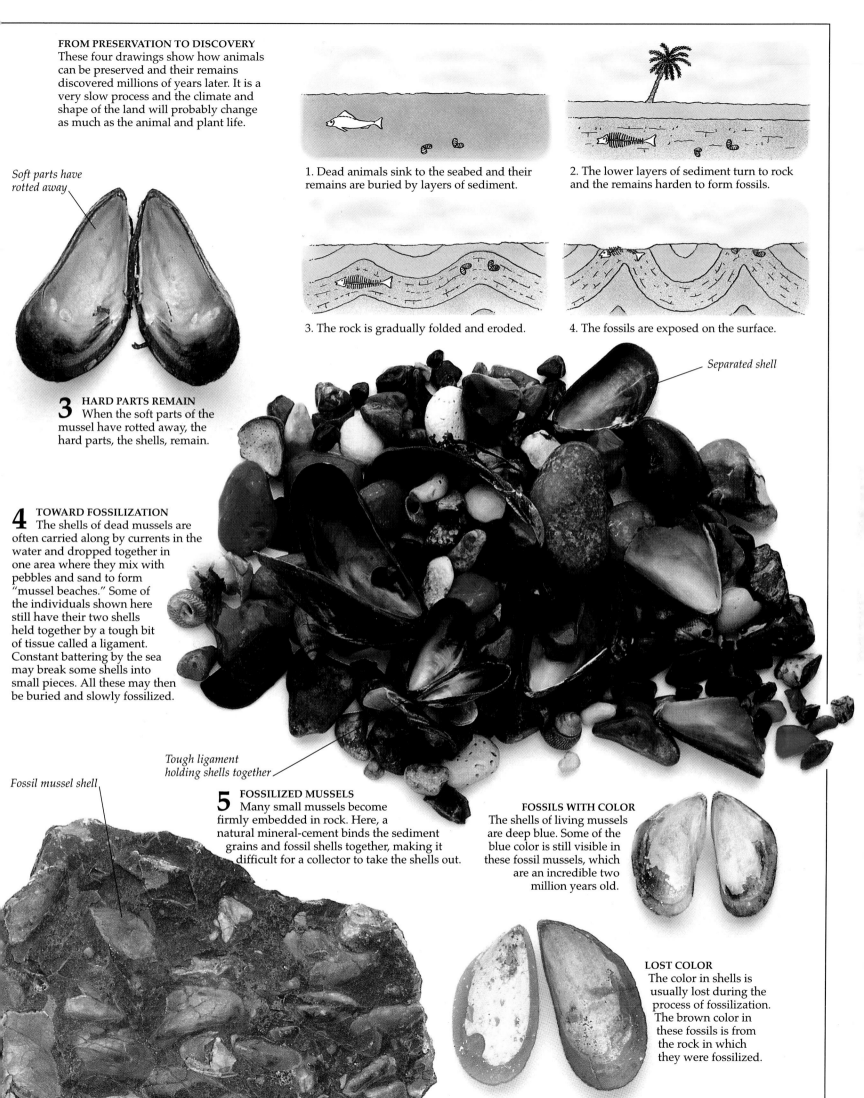

Life in the ancient seas

THE EARTH, WITH ITS VAST EXPANSES of ocean, has not always looked the way it does today. Over millions of years the land masses have drifted across the face of the Earth as new oceans have opened up and old oceans disappeared. Today's oceans only started to take shape in the last 200 million years of the Earth's 4.5-billion-year existence. Simple organisms first appeared in the oceans 3.3 billion years ago and were followed by more and more complex life forms. As the oceans changed, so too did life in the waters. Soft-bodied creatures evolved into animals with hard shells and trilobites flexed their external skeletons with internal muscles alongside gigantic marine reptiles such as plesiosaurs. Some forms of life eventually became extinct, while others still survive in the oceans today, more or less unchanged.

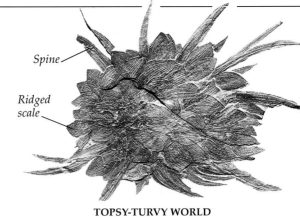

Spine

Ridged scale

TOPSY-TURVY WORLD
Wiwaxia lived on the seafloor 530 million years ago, yet this fossil was found high above sea level in the Rocky Mountains. This shows just how much the Earth's surface has changed, and how land originally formed under a sea has been forced upward to form mountain chains.

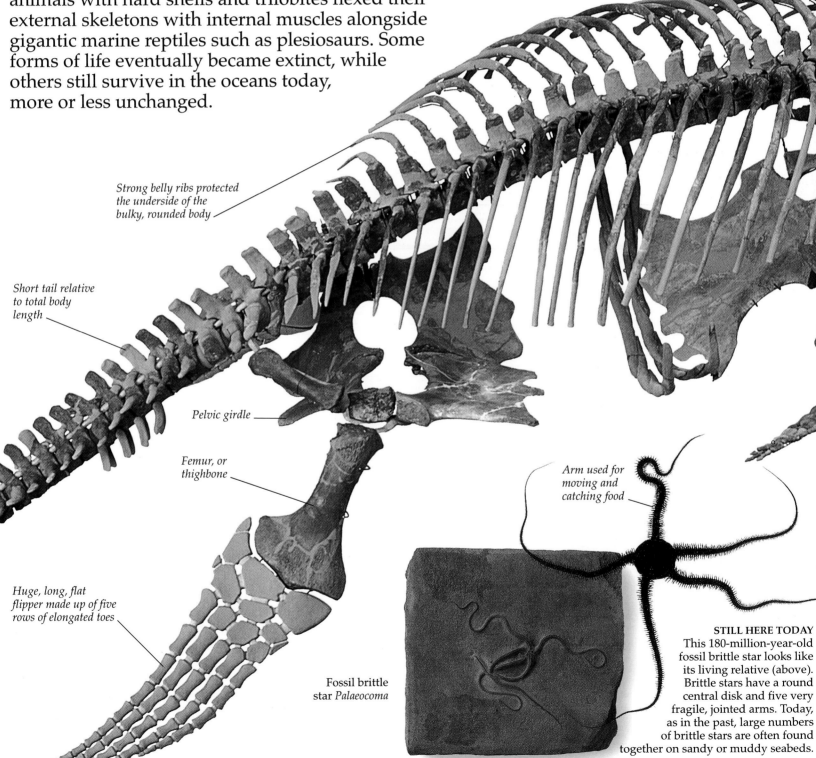

Strong belly ribs protected the underside of the bulky, rounded body

Short tail relative to total body length

Pelvic girdle

Femur, or thighbone

Huge, long, flat flipper made up of five rows of elongated toes

Arm used for moving and catching food

Fossil brittle star *Palaeocoma*

STILL HERE TODAY
This 180-million-year-old fossil brittle star looks like its living relative (above). Brittle stars have a round central disk and five very fragile, jointed arms. Today, as in the past, large numbers of brittle stars are often found together on sandy or muddy seabeds.

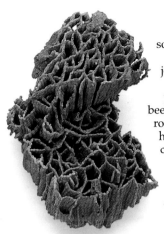

ANCIENT CORAL
Compared to their soft-bodied relatives, anemones and jellyfish, corals such as this 400-million-year-old fossil have been preserved well in rocks because of their hard skeletons. Each coral animal formed a skeleton that joined that of its neighbor, creating a network of chains with large spaces between them.

 1    2    3    4

CHANGING OCEANS
One giant ocean, Panthalassa, surrounded the super-continent Pangaea (1) 290–240 mya (million years ago). At the end of this period, many kinds of marine life became extinct. Pangaea broke up, with part drifting north and part south, with the Tethys Sea between.

CONTINENTAL DRIFT
The northern part split to form the North Atlantic Ocean 208–146 mya (2). The South Atlantic and Indian Oceans began to form 146–65 mya (3). The continents continued to drift 1.64 mya (4). Today the oceans are still changing shape – the Atlantic Ocean gets wider by an inch or two each year.

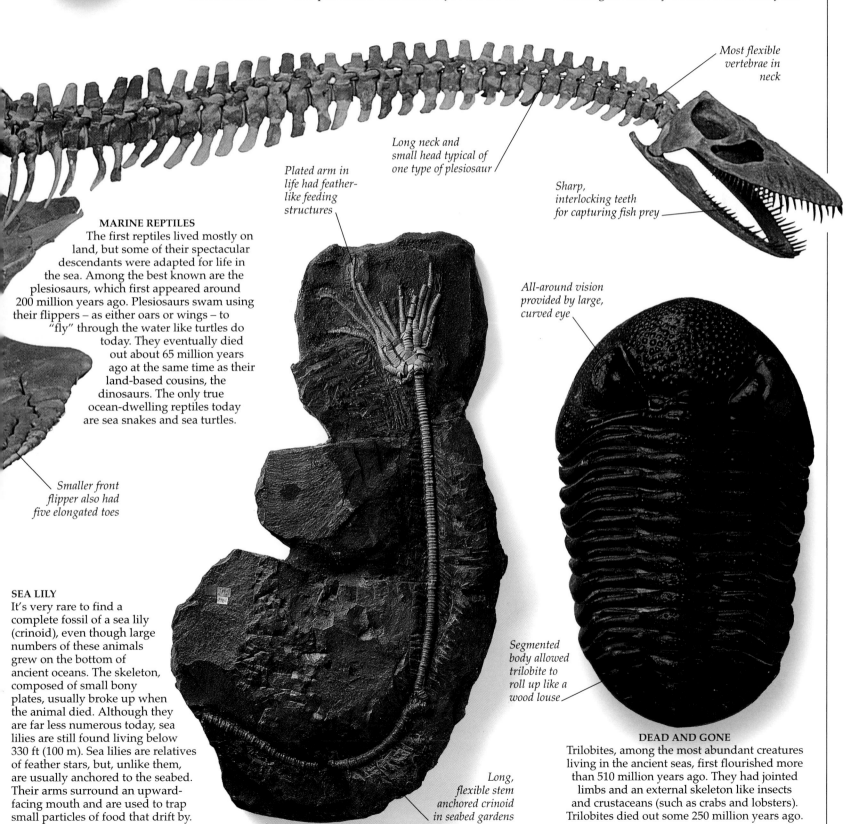

Most flexible vertebrae in neck

Long neck and small head typical of one type of plesiosaur

Plated arm in life had feather-like feeding structures

Sharp, interlocking teeth for capturing fish prey

MARINE REPTILES
The first reptiles lived mostly on land, but some of their spectacular descendants were adapted for life in the sea. Among the best known are the plesiosaurs, which first appeared around 200 million years ago. Plesiosaurs swam using their flippers – as either oars or wings – to "fly" through the water like turtles do today. They eventually died out about 65 million years ago at the same time as their land-based cousins, the dinosaurs. The only true ocean-dwelling reptiles today are sea snakes and sea turtles.

All-around vision provided by large, curved eye

Smaller front flipper also had five elongated toes

SEA LILY
It's very rare to find a complete fossil of a sea lily (crinoid), even though large numbers of these animals grew on the bottom of ancient oceans. The skeleton, composed of small bony plates, usually broke up when the animal died. Although they are far less numerous today, sea lilies are still found living below 330 ft (100 m). Sea lilies are relatives of feather stars, but, unlike them, are usually anchored to the seabed. Their arms surround an upward-facing mouth and are used to trap small particles of food that drift by.

Segmented body allowed trilobite to roll up like a wood louse

Long, flexible stem anchored crinoid in seabed gardens

DEAD AND GONE
Trilobites, among the most abundant creatures living in the ancient seas, first flourished more than 510 million years ago. They had jointed limbs and an external skeleton like insects and crustaceans (such as crabs and lobsters). Trilobites died out some 250 million years ago.

Fossil evidence

ABOUT 470 MILLION YEARS AGO, one group of animals – the vertebrates – escaped the restrictions of living in shells by developing internal, bony skeletons that anchored muscles and supported internal organs. Bones, teeth, and scales are tough and preserve well, so there is plenty of fossil evidence. The first vertebrates were jawless fish. Some of them, such as cephalaspids and placoderms, carried a heavy outer armor. Many were restricted to living on seabeds. Later fish had less of a bony covering on their heads and developed toothed, gaping jaws. The success of advanced bony fish, the teleosts, is obvious in the vast numbers of these mobile fish living today in the world's rivers, lakes, and seas.

Fossil of
Pterichthyodes milleri

Spiny pectoral fin for scooting along muddy seafloor

HEAVY ARMOR
One of the most armored placoderm fish – the 370-million-year-old, 5-in (13-cm) long *Pterichthyodes* – had no inner skeleton. Instead, it had a shell of bony plates that completely covered both its head and body. Even the pectoral fins were enclosed in a bony casing, which made them near-useless.

Large eye

Fossil of
Cephalaspis
pagei

SENSITIVE SUCKER
The first fish were jawless, sucking food and water through their mouths. *Cephalaspis* had a bony shield covering its jawless head, as well as a pair of pectoral fins protected by swept-back spines. Two eyes and a single nostril perched on the crest of the arched head shield, which had three sensitive, scale-covered patches connected to the brain. *Cephalaspis* was an ostracoderm – it had a "bony skin."

Symmetrical two-part tail fin

Fossil of
Lepidotes elvensis

Modern
African
lungfish

Dorsal fin supported on ray of fine bones

Armored head

Remains of concretion

EXPOSED WITH ACID
Unlike modern lungfish, which live in freshwater, the prehistoric lungfish *Chirodipterus* lived in shallow seas. It was covered in thick, bony scales and had an armored head. This specimen from Australia was preserved in a hard chalky mass called a concretion. The fossil was exposed by being bathed in acid, which dissolved the concretion, but not the fish inside.

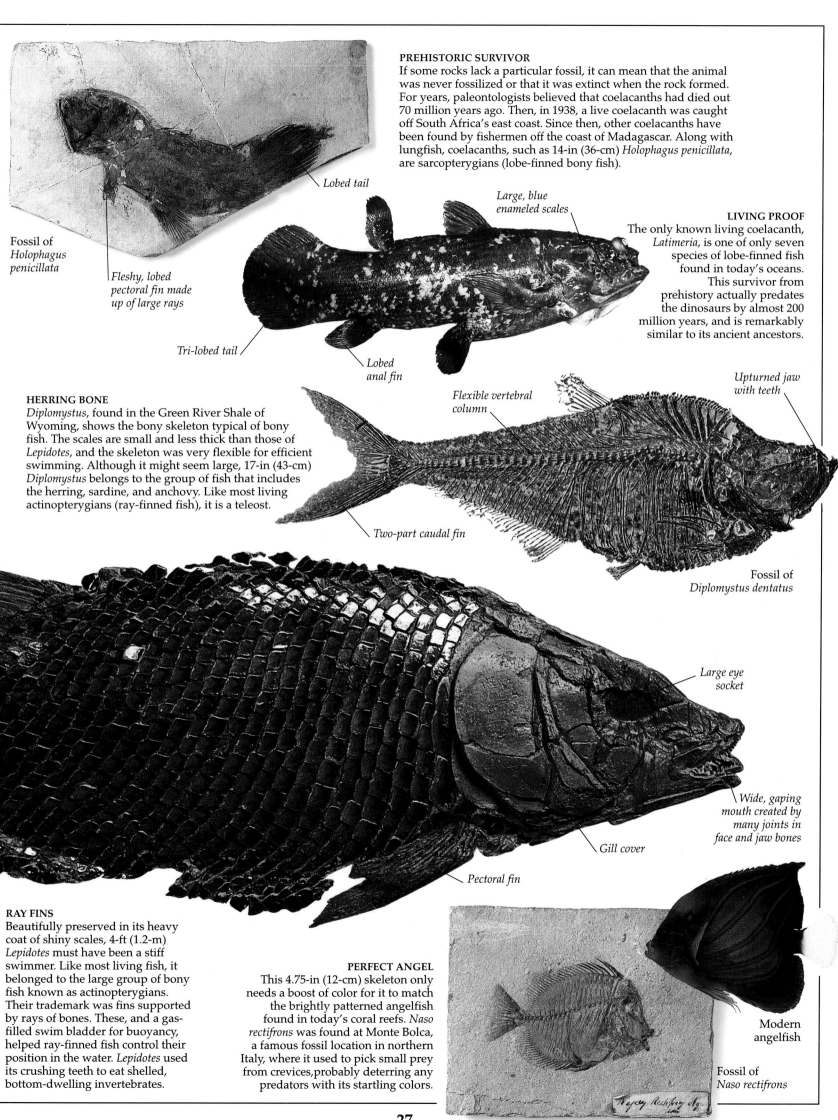

PREHISTORIC SURVIVOR
If some rocks lack a particular fossil, it can mean that the animal was never fossilized or that it was extinct when the rock formed. For years, paleontologists believed that coelacanths had died out 70 million years ago. Then, in 1938, a live coelacanth was caught off South Africa's east coast. Since then, other coelacanths have been found by fishermen off the coast of Madagascar. Along with lungfish, coelacanths, such as 14-in (36-cm) *Holophagus penicillata*, are sarcopterygians (lobe-finned bony fish).

Lobed tail

Fossil of
*Holophagus
penicillata*

*Fleshy, lobed
pectoral fin made
up of large rays*

Large, blue
enameled scales

LIVING PROOF
The only known living coelacanth, *Latimeria*, is one of only seven species of lobe-finned fish found in today's oceans. This survivor from prehistory actually predates the dinosaurs by almost 200 million years, and is remarkably similar to its ancient ancestors.

Tri-lobed tail

*Lobed
anal fin*

HERRING BONE
Diplomystus, found in the Green River Shale of Wyoming, shows the bony skeleton typical of bony fish. The scales are small and less thick than those of *Lepidotes*, and the skeleton was very flexible for efficient swimming. Although it might seem large, 17-in (43-cm) *Diplomystus* belongs to the group of fish that includes the herring, sardine, and anchovy. Like most living actinopterygians (ray-finned fish), it is a teleost.

*Flexible vertebral
column*

*Upturned jaw
with teeth*

Two-part caudal fin

Fossil of
Diplomystus dentatus

*Large eye
socket*

*Wide, gaping
mouth created by
many joints in
face and jaw bones*

Gill cover

Pectoral fin

RAY FINS
Beautifully preserved in its heavy coat of shiny scales, 4-ft (1.2-m) *Lepidotes* must have been a stiff swimmer. Like most living fish, it belonged to the large group of bony fish known as actinopterygians. Their trademark was fins supported by rays of bones. These, and a gas-filled swim bladder for buoyancy, helped ray-finned fish control their position in the water. *Lepidotes* used its crushing teeth to eat shelled, bottom-dwelling invertebrates.

PERFECT ANGEL
This 4.75-in (12-cm) skeleton only needs a boost of color for it to match the brightly patterned angelfish found in today's coral reefs. *Naso rectifrons* was found at Monte Bolca, a famous fossil location in northern Italy, where it used to pick small prey from crevices, probably deterring any predators with its startling colors.

Modern
angelfish

Fossil of
Naso rectifrons

Reptiles reign

THE FIRST REPTILES appeared 360–290 million years ago and probably did not look all that different from their amphibian ancestors. For 200 million years, they colonized the continents and dominated the Earth. Many reptiles evolved on land, like the dinosaurs. Others, such as the pterosaurs, took to the air, and some, such as the mesosaurs, lived in the sea. Many reptiles were amniotes: they produced an egg that enclosed the developing embryo in its own wet world, protecting it with a tough, waterproof shell. Reptiles were the first amniotes, followed by birds and mammals.

HOT STUFF
Reptiles were many different shapes. *Dimetrodon*, a carnivorous pelycosaur, was 10 ft (3 m) long and carried a huge fan of skin along its back, which it used as a giant radiator and heat absorber.

SETTING SAIL
The herbivorous *Edaphosaurus* had a skin sail supported on long, vertebral spines with cross pieces. It was a pelycosaur – a lizard with a basin-shaped pelvis.

Pelvis, legs, and five-toed feet separated from body

Individual spine in backbone

Neural spine of backbone helped form skin-covered sail of Edaphosaurus

Flattened skull

Backbone with ribs attached

REPTILE FIRST
Sandwiched between fine rock layers, this 338-million-year-old *Westlothiana lizziae* fossil is the oldest reptile and amniote ever found. Discovered in a small quarry in central Scotland, this distorted 8-in (20-cm) long fossil skeleton is nicknamed "Lizzie."

Very long body

Model of *Westlothiana lizziae* (viewed from above), based on scientific research and artist's rendering

Dry, scaly skin

UNDERSTANDING THE EVIDENCE
Westlothiana was discovered in ancient rocks formed in a lake once fed by hot, volcanic spring water. Four-legged, as well as legless, snakelike amphibian skeletons were also found, along with spiders, scorpions, and millipedes. Tree-sized seed ferns grew nearby. *Westlothiana* was about 1 ft (30 cm) long, its long body balanced on short legs. Some, but not all, features of the skull and limb bones match those found in later reptiles. It is not surprising that *Westlothiana*, so like its amphibian ancestors, is not easily distinguished from them.

Long, lizard-like tail

Tail made up a large part of the whole body length

Scales on its skin helped keep Westlothiana waterproof

Model of first known reptile, *Westlothiana lizziae*

Each foot had five toes

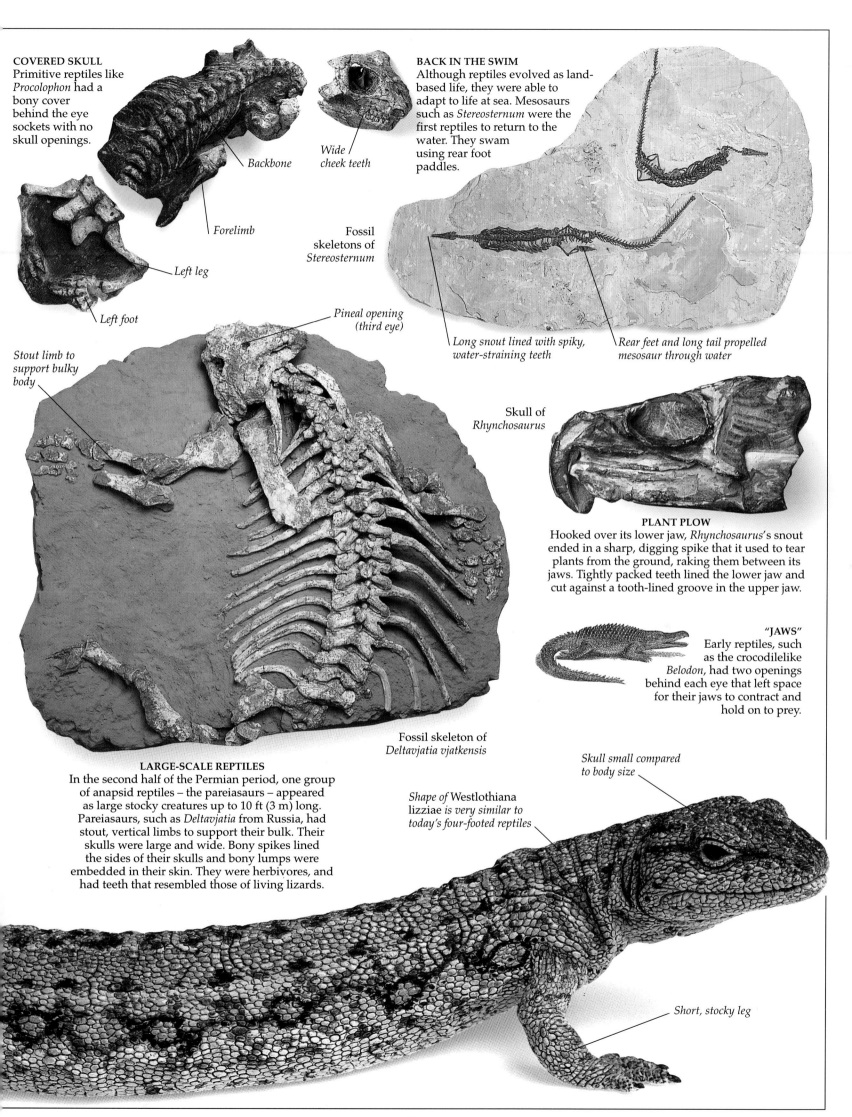

COVERED SKULL
Primitive reptiles like *Procolophon* had a bony cover behind the eye sockets with no skull openings.

Backbone

Forelimb

Left leg

Left foot

Wide cheek teeth

BACK IN THE SWIM
Although reptiles evolved as land-based life, they were able to adapt to life at sea. Mesosaurs such as *Stereosternum* were the first reptiles to return to the water. They swam using rear foot paddles.

Fossil skeletons of Stereosternum

Long snout lined with spiky, water-straining teeth

Rear feet and long tail propelled mesosaur through water

Pineal opening (third eye)

Stout limb to support bulky body

Skull of Rhynchosaurus

PLANT PLOW
Hooked over its lower jaw, *Rhynchosaurus*'s snout ended in a sharp, digging spike that it used to tear plants from the ground, raking them between its jaws. Tightly packed teeth lined the lower jaw and cut against a tooth-lined groove in the upper jaw.

"JAWS"
Early reptiles, such as the crocodilelike *Belodon*, had two openings behind each eye that left space for their jaws to contract and hold on to prey.

Fossil skeleton of Deltavjatia vjatkensis

LARGE-SCALE REPTILES
In the second half of the Permian period, one group of anapsid reptiles – the pareiasaurs – appeared as large stocky creatures up to 10 ft (3 m) long. Pareiasaurs, such as *Deltavjatia* from Russia, had stout, vertical limbs to support their bulk. Their skulls were large and wide. Bony spikes lined the sides of their skulls and bony lumps were embedded in their skin. They were herbivores, and had teeth that resembled those of living lizards.

Shape of Westlothiana lizziae *is very similar to today's four-footed reptiles*

Skull small compared to body size

Short, stocky leg

Birth of the dinosaurs

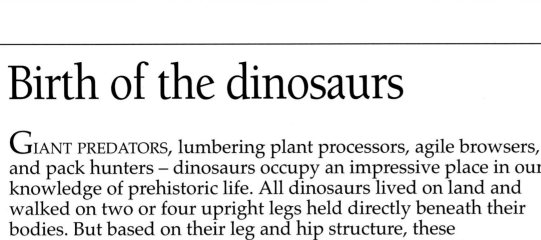

Bony crest

GIANT PREDATORS, lumbering plant processors, agile browsers, and pack hunters – dinosaurs occupy an impressive place in our knowledge of prehistoric life. All dinosaurs lived on land and walked on two or four upright legs held directly beneath their bodies. But based on their leg and hip structure, these amazing reptiles are split into two groups. The saurischians, or reptile-hipped dinosaurs, had the two lower bones of the pelvis (the pubis and the ischium) pointing in opposite directions below the pelvic upper bone, or ilium. The ornithischians, or bird-hipped dinosaurs, had pelvic bones with both the pubis and ischium pointing down and back. Dinosaurs appeared about 230 million years ago and quickly dominated life on land. Their ability to stand upright and move efficiently made them versatile and adaptable, but it did not save them from extinction 65 million years ago.

Cheek pouch

Toothless beak

CORYTHOSAURUS
This ornithischian dinosaur belonged to a group called the hadrosaurs that lived 97–65 million years ago in what is now North America, Asia, and Europe. Hadrosaurs had toothless beaks similar to ducks today. However, they had cheek teeth, sometimes more than 300 in each jaw, which they used for grinding tough vegetation. Hadrosaurs probably lived in herds, and their bony crests may have been displayed to attract mates.

Bony frill

Long brow horn

Model of *Triceratops*

Short nose horn

NESTING SITES
The most exciting discoveries of nesting sites have been made in Montana. The hadrosaur *Maiasaura* ("good mother lizard") laid its eggs in a raised and scooped-out hollow in sand, then covered them in vegetation to keep them warm. The 14-in (35.5-cm) long young would have stayed in the nest for a while after hatching and been fed by their parents. *Maiasaura* returned to their nesting colonies each season.

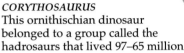

TRICERATOPS
This ornithischian dinosaur lived 100 million years ago. It was 6–30 ft (1.8–9.1 m) long and weighed up to 6 tons (5.4 tonnes). All ornithischian dinosaurs were herbivores, feeding on leaves, fruits, seeds, and even conifer needles. *Triceratops* had a large hooked beak, which it used for snipping and tearing at plants, while its teeth and powerful jaws sheared them. *Triceratops* lived in herds and used its large defensive horns to ward off threats as fierce as *Tyrannosaurus rex*. The bony frill around *Triceratops*'s head may have been used to scare predators, attract mates, or simply to protect the neck from attack.

Parrotlike beak

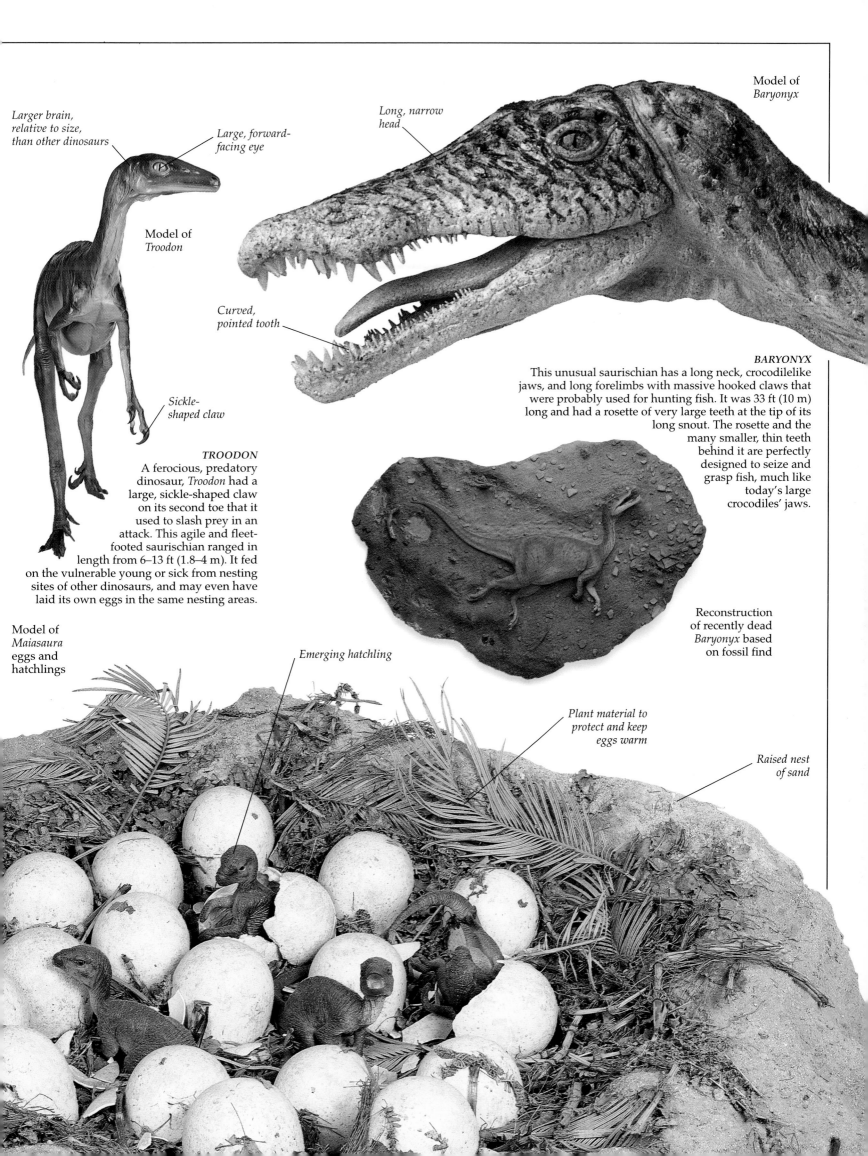

Larger brain, relative to size, than other dinosaurs

Large, forward-facing eye

Model of *Troodon*

Sickle-shaped claw

Model of *Baryonyx*

Long, narrow head

Curved, pointed tooth

TROODON
A ferocious, predatory dinosaur, *Troodon* had a large, sickle-shaped claw on its second toe that it used to slash prey in an attack. This agile and fleet-footed saurischian ranged in length from 6–13 ft (1.8–4 m). It fed on the vulnerable young or sick from nesting sites of other dinosaurs, and may even have laid its own eggs in the same nesting areas.

BARYONYX
This unusual saurischian has a long neck, crocodilelike jaws, and long forelimbs with massive hooked claws that were probably used for hunting fish. It was 33 ft (10 m) long and had a rosette of very large teeth at the tip of its long snout. The rosette and the many smaller, thin teeth behind it are perfectly designed to seize and grasp fish, much like today's large crocodiles' jaws.

Reconstruction of recently dead *Baryonyx* based on fossil find

Model of *Maiasaura* eggs and hatchlings

Emerging hatchling

Plant material to protect and keep eggs warm

Raised nest of sand

Winged wonders

THE FIRST ANIMALS TO FLY were insects – fossil dragonflies more than 300 million years old have been found in rocks. Flying vertebrates (animals with backbones) appeared almost 100 million years later, and true flapping flight has since evolved in three vertebrate groups: the now-extinct pterosaurs, living bats, and birds. These animals are not closely related, and their ability to fly evolved independently. Pterosaurs ("flying lizards") were reptiles. They were related to dinosaurs and had an elongated fourth finger. This supported the fleshy membrane, a thin, skin-covered sheet of muscle and elastic fibers covered by skin, that was the wing. In birds, the feathered wing is supported by several fingers and the lower part of the forearm. Bats are flying mammals. Their wings are made of a fleshy membrane similar to the pterosaurs', but bat wings are supported by four fingers.

WING SUPPORT
This is one of the long finger bones that supported the wing of a *Pteranodon*, one of the largest flying animals. The wingspan of this giant pterosaur was about 23 ft (7 m).

WELL BALANCED
Pteranodon was a pterosaur with a bony crest on its head that counterbalanced its long, toothless beak. It appears to have been a fish-eater that flew over the oceans like the albatross does today.

BIRDS OF FICTION
The discovery of fossil pterosaur remains fueled the imagination of many science fiction authors.

FURRY REPTILE
The sparrow-sized Jurassic pterosaur *Pterodactylus* had membranous wings, claws, a toothed beak, and a body covered by fine fur. Evidence of fur comes from Kazakhstan, where some pterosaurs were discovered with hairlike impressions around the body. This may indicate that pterosaurs were warm-blooded and used the fur as insulation. *Pterodactylus* had a short tail and a wingspan of only about 20 in (50 cm), but some pterosaurs had long tails, including *Rhamphorhynchus* with its 5-ft (1.5-m) wingspan.

Toothed beak

Greatly lengthened fourth finger

Membranous wing

Body covered by fine fur

Very short tail

Pterodactylus had sharp claws for catching and tearing apart prey

FLYING MAMMAL
It is easy to see the similarity between this bat and the pterosaurs. Because bats often roost in caves, their fossilized bones can be found in large numbers in cave deposits.

MISTAKEN IDENTITY
This small dinosaur belongs to a group that many scientists believe were ancestors of birds. In 1973, some museum paleontologists in Germany realized that one of their specimens, identified as *Compsognathus*, was really an *Archaeopteryx*!

Impression of birdlike
feathers

Reptilian clawed
fingers

Teeth, unlike a
modern bird

Archaeopteryx had a
wingspan of about 20 in (50 cm)

Fossil
feather

Modern
bird's
feather

THE FIRST BIRD
Archaeopteryx ("ancient
wing") lived 150 million
years ago. Specimens of
it, all found in Germany,
are generally regarded as the most
precious fossils in the world. Only
five more have been discovered
since the first was found, in
1861. *Archaeopteryx* was
intermediate between
reptiles and birds.
Some specimens
show clear feather
impressions.

RARE FIND
Only birds sport feathers and they are
very rarely fossilized. Very occasionally
they are found in fine-grained sediments
like this limestone.

Reptilian
bony tail

Claws

Elephant
bird egg

Ostrich
egg

Ostrich
*Struthio
camelus*

ELEPHANTINE EGG
The Madagascan
elephant bird *Aepyornis
maximus* stood over 6.5 ft
(2 m) high. Its fossil eggs
are the largest birds' eggs
known, reaching 35 in (90 cm) in
circumference. Here, one is compared
with an egg from the largest modern bird, the
ostrich, to show how enormous the eggs really are.

FINE SKULL
Fossilized remains of birds are rare. This finely preserved
skull comes from the bird *Prophaethon*. Some scientists think
that this was a close relative of the tropicbird of today.

Tropicbird
Phaethon lepturus

The elephant
bird, like today's
ostrich, was flightless

Elephant bird
Aepyornis maximus

The first mammals

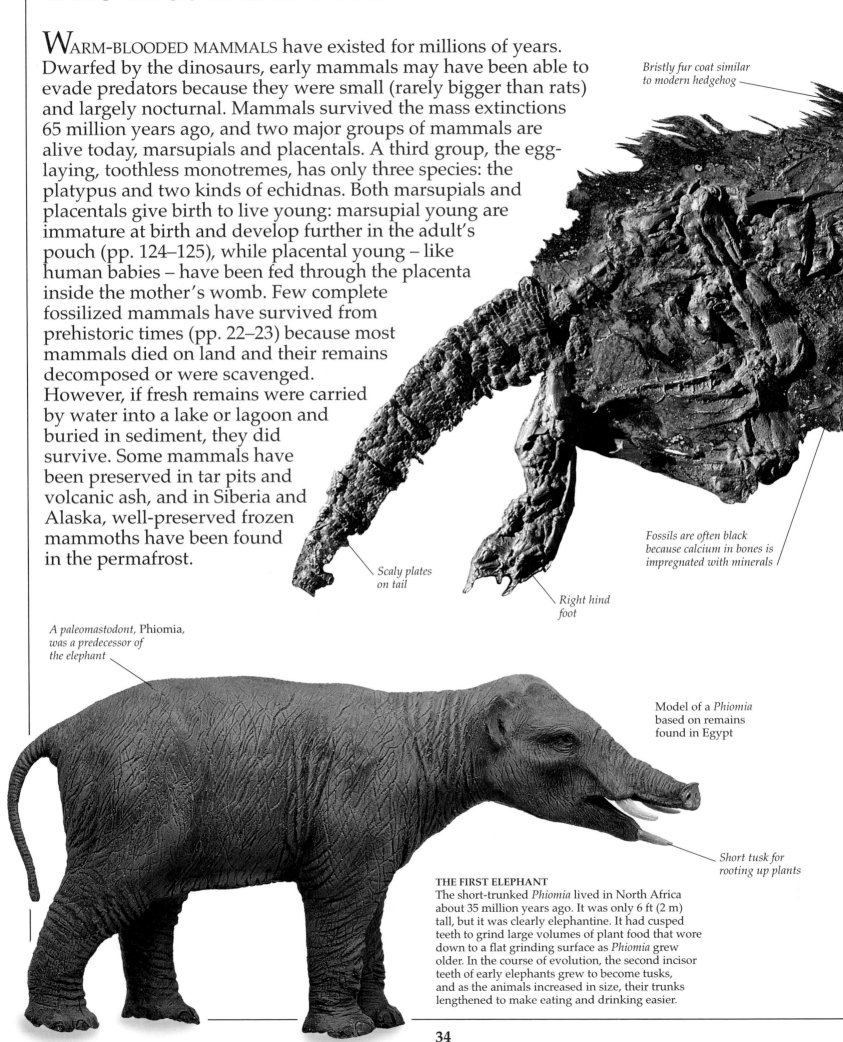

WARM-BLOODED MAMMALS have existed for millions of years. Dwarfed by the dinosaurs, early mammals may have been able to evade predators because they were small (rarely bigger than rats) and largely nocturnal. Mammals survived the mass extinctions 65 million years ago, and two major groups of mammals are alive today, marsupials and placentals. A third group, the egg-laying, toothless monotremes, has only three species: the platypus and two kinds of echidnas. Both marsupials and placentals give birth to live young: marsupial young are immature at birth and develop further in the adult's pouch (pp. 124–125), while placental young – like human babies – have been fed through the placenta inside the mother's womb. Few complete fossilized mammals have survived from prehistoric times (pp. 22–23) because most mammals died on land and their remains decomposed or were scavenged. However, if fresh remains were carried by water into a lake or lagoon and buried in sediment, they did survive. Some mammals have been preserved in tar pits and volcanic ash, and in Siberia and Alaska, well-preserved frozen mammoths have been found in the permafrost.

Bristly fur coat similar to modern hedgehog

Fossils are often black because calcium in bones is impregnated with minerals

Scaly plates on tail

Right hind foot

A paleomastodont, Phiomia, was a predecessor of the elephant

Model of a Phiomia based on remains found in Egypt

Short tusk for rooting up plants

THE FIRST ELEPHANT
The short-trunked *Phiomia* lived in North Africa about 35 million years ago. It was only 6 ft (2 m) tall, but it was clearly elephantine. It had cusped teeth to grind large volumes of plant food that wore down to a flat grinding surface as *Phiomia* grew older. In the course of evolution, the second incisor teeth of early elephants grew to become tusks, and as the animals increased in size, their trunks lengthened to make eating and drinking easier.

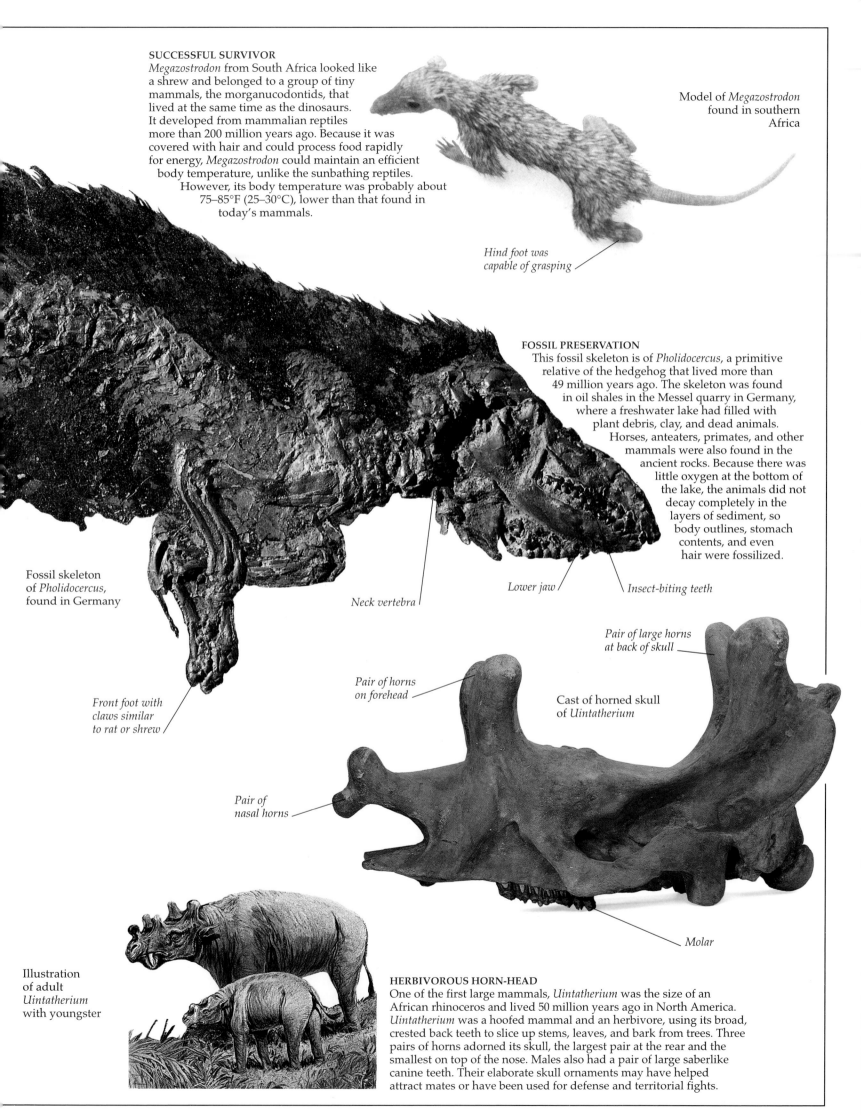

SUCCESSFUL SURVIVOR

Megazostrodon from South Africa looked like
a shrew and belonged to a group of tiny
mammals, the morganucodontids, that
lived at the same time as the dinosaurs.
It developed from mammalian reptiles
more than 200 million years ago. Because it was
covered with hair and could process food rapidly
for energy, *Megazostrodon* could maintain an efficient
body temperature, unlike the sunbathing reptiles.
However, its body temperature was probably about
75–85°F (25–30°C), lower than that found in
today's mammals.

Model of *Megazostrodon*
found in southern
Africa

*Hind foot was
capable of grasping*

FOSSIL PRESERVATION

This fossil skeleton is of *Pholidocercus*, a primitive
relative of the hedgehog that lived more than
49 million years ago. The skeleton was found
in oil shales in the Messel quarry in Germany,
where a freshwater lake had filled with
plant debris, clay, and dead animals.
Horses, anteaters, primates, and other
mammals were also found in the
ancient rocks. Because there was
little oxygen at the bottom of
the lake, the animals did not
decay completely in the
layers of sediment, so
body outlines, stomach
contents, and even
hair were fossilized.

Fossil skeleton
of *Pholidocercus*,
found in Germany

Neck vertebra

Lower jaw

Insect-biting teeth

*Front foot with
claws similar
to rat or shrew*

*Pair of large horns
at back of skull*

*Pair of horns
on forehead*

Cast of horned skull
of *Uintatherium*

*Pair of
nasal horns*

Molar

Illustration
of adult
Uintatherium
with youngster

HERBIVOROUS HORN-HEAD

One of the first large mammals, *Uintatherium* was the size of an
African rhinoceros and lived 50 million years ago in North America.
Uintatherium was a hoofed mammal and an herbivore, using its broad,
crested back teeth to slice up stems, leaves, and bark from trees. Three
pairs of horns adorned its skull, the largest pair at the rear and the
smallest on top of the nose. Males also had a pair of large saberlike
canine teeth. Their elaborate skull ornaments may have helped
attract mates or have been used for defense and territorial fights.

SUCCULENTS

No plant can survive entirely without water. Plants with fleshy leaves or stems for storing water are known as succulents and include the group of plants called cacti. There are three main kinds of succulents. Stem succulents store water in their stems, and are usually found in the driest climates. Leaf succulents store water in their leaves and grow in damper conditions. Root succulents have thickened roots that serve as water reservoirs.

CHAPTER 2
PLANT LIFE

MANY LIVING ORGANISMS depend on plants, either directly or indirectly, to survive. Plants grow in virtually every habitat on Earth, producing oxygen as a by-product and sustaining all animal life. They are an essential part of all food chains. After plants have grown and – many of them – burst into flower, they then ensure their own survival by spreading their seeds in an extraordinary and successful variety of ways.

GOLD DUST
The relationship between a plant and its pollinator (pp. 46–47) is often to their mutual benefit. A bumblebee helps carry the gold dust called pollen from one flower to another while it is feeding on the pollen and sugary nectar that the flowers produce. The bee combs the pollen from the hairs on its body and packs it into the pollen sacks on its back legs. It then carries the pollen back to its nest, where the young bees feed on the rich protein.

Parts of a plant

THE PART OF A FLOWERING PLANT that grows above the ground is the shoot, which stretches toward the light. It is supported by a complicated network of roots beneath the soil. These roots not only anchor the plant, they also absorb water and minerals from the soil, and are a vital part of a plant's supply system. Leaves are a plant's main sites of photosynthesis (pp. 40–41), and, via the plant stems, complete the supply system. The plant shoot eventually produces flowers, which make pollination and thus seed formation possible (pp. 46–47). Some plants also produce rhizomes, bulbs, corms, tubers, or other reproductive structures. Non-flowering plants, such as ferns and mosses, produce spores.

FUNGI
Fungi seem to grow like plants, but they have no roots or leaves and produce no seeds. Today they are classified separately by scientists, but are often described as plants. There are about 100,000 species of fungi in the world.

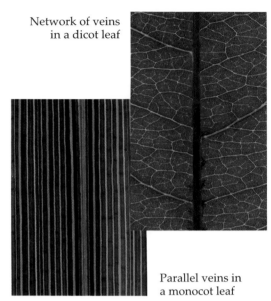

Network of veins in a dicot leaf

Parallel veins in a monocot leaf

LEAF VEINS
Flowering plants are either monocotyledons or dicotyledons. "Monocots" usually have parallel veins in their leaves. The leaves of "dicots" usually have a network of veins.

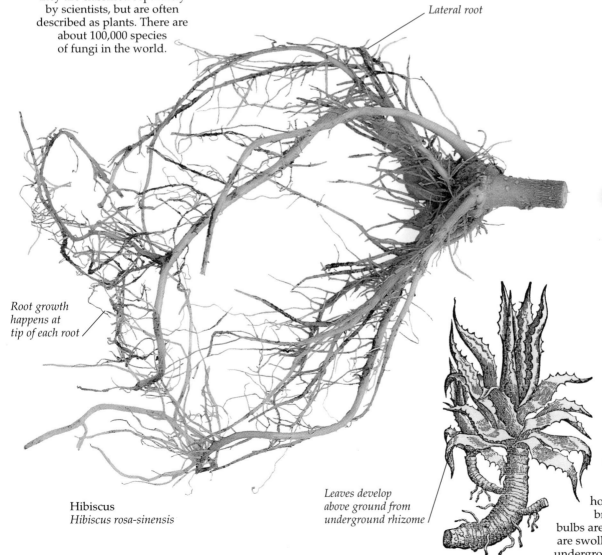

Lateral root

Midrib

Vein

Root growth happens at tip of each root

Hibiscus
Hibiscus rosa-sinensis

Leaves develop above ground from underground rhizome

STORAGE BINS
Rhizomes, bulbs, corms, and tubers are underground storage organs that various plants use to survive in adverse conditions and to reproduce. Rhizomes are horizontal underground stems that branch out to produce new plants; bulbs are joined swollen leaf bases; corms are swollen stems; and tubers are swollen underground stems. Gardeners are able to use these structures to propagate new plants.

Brightly colored tepal attracts insect pollinator

THE SUPPLY SYSTEM
Water, minerals, and sugars are carried up and down a plant in bundles of tubelike cells. One system, called the xylem, carries water and minerals upward. Another, called the phloem, can carry sugars either upward or downward to the parts of the plant that need them.

Large, colorful petals

Stigma

Anther

Filament

FLOWERS
Insects are drawn to a flower by the brightly colored petals. Once the flower has been pollinated, the petals fall off. The female part of the flower then grows larger to form a fruit containing seeds. The seeds are shed when the fully grown fruit opens.

Branch

Sepals are smaller and green

Stem

Node

Lateral bud

Pedicel (flower stalk)

Petiole (leaf stalk)

Bract (leaf-like structure)

Flower bud

Blade of leaf

A FLOWERING PLANT
The hibiscus is a dicotyledon. Its seedlings have two seed leaves, or cotyledons, and its leaves are broad with a central midrib and branched veins. Most species of hibiscus in the wild are pollinated by hummingbirds. A hummingbird hovers in front of the flower and inserts its long beak deep inside to reach the nectar. As it feeds, the anthers brush pollen on its head, while the stigma, also brushing its head, collects pollen from another flower.

A light diet

UNLIKE ANIMALS, plants do not need to find food – they can make it for themselves. The key is a green pigment called chlorophyll, which gives plants their characteristic green color. Chlorophyll allows plants to convert energy from sunlight into chemical energy, which can then be stored, usually as a carbohydrate, or starch. The stored energy is used to fuel the growth and development of the plant. In a process known as photosynthesis, the plant converts carbon dioxide and water into an energy-rich compound called glucose, which is then transported through a network of veins to the rest of the plant. Photosynthesis mainly takes place in the leaves of a plant. Many leaves have special adaptations, such as large, flat surfaces, to absorb more life-sustaining sunlight.

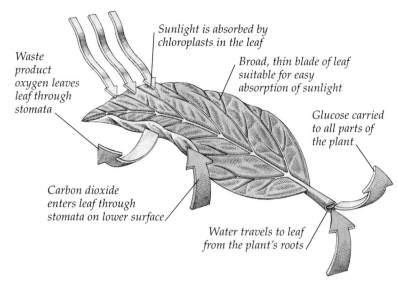

Waste product oxygen leaves leaf through stomata

Sunlight is absorbed by chloroplasts in the leaf

Broad, thin blade of leaf suitable for easy absorption of sunlight

Glucose carried to all parts of the plant

Carbon dioxide enters leaf through stomata on lower surface

Water travels to leaf from the plant's roots

THE PROCESS OF PHOTOSYNTHESIS
Photosynthesis takes place inside special structures called chloroplasts in the leaf cells. Chloroplasts contain the chlorophyll that traps energy from sunlight. Stomata (pores) in the lower surface of the leaves allow carbon dioxide and oxygen to pass into and out of the plant, while veins carry water into the leaves and transport glucose to the rest of the plant.

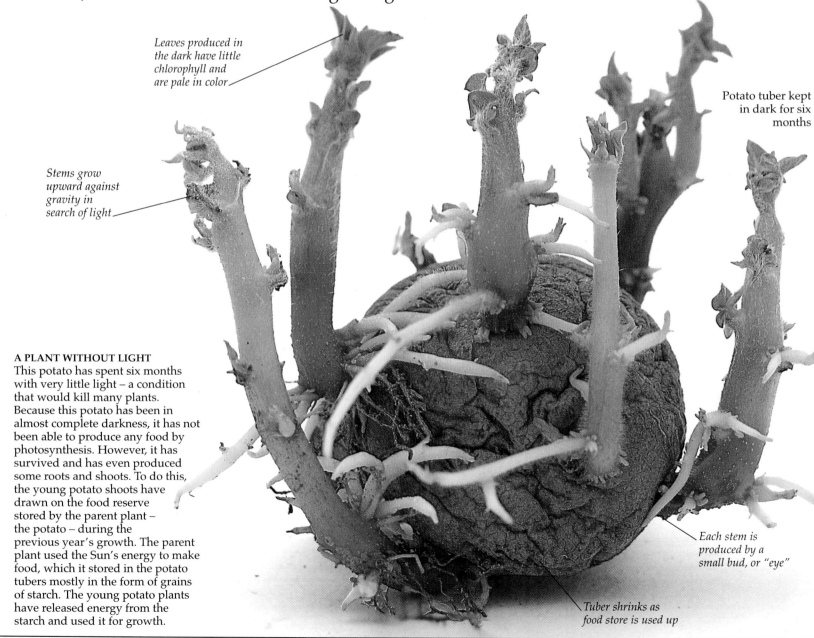

Leaves produced in the dark have little chlorophyll and are pale in color

Potato tuber kept in dark for six months

Stems grow upward against gravity in search of light

A PLANT WITHOUT LIGHT
This potato has spent six months with very little light – a condition that would kill many plants. Because this potato has been in almost complete darkness, it has not been able to produce any food by photosynthesis. However, it has survived and has even produced some roots and shoots. To do this, the young potato shoots have drawn on the food reserve stored by the parent plant – the potato – during the previous year's growth. The parent plant used the Sun's energy to make food, which it stored in the potato tubers mostly in the form of grains of starch. The young potato plants have released energy from the starch and used it for growth.

Each stem is produced by a small bud, or "eye"

Tuber shrinks as food store is used up

Chloroplast that collects sunlight

A PLANT'S SOLAR PANELS
Inside the cells that make up a plant's leaves are the tiny structures called chloroplasts. There may be 100 chloroplasts in a single cell. Chlorophyll is found inside the chloroplasts, which work like minute solar panels, collecting light energy and using it to make food.

Green leaves rich in chlorophyll

New shoots

New, healthier shoots

STORING FOOD
Plants store food in various ways – as starches, sugar glucose, or oils. In its first year, an onion plant stores sugars in the onion bulb, which is made up of swollen leaf bases around a shortened stem. In the second year, the sugars in the onion bulb are used up as the plant grows and flowers. The sugars "caramelize," or turn brown, when they are heated, which is why onions darken when sautèed.

Potato tuber after three weeks in the light

RAPID RECOVERY
Three weeks after emerging from the dark, the potato plant is growing rapidly. Its leaves have turned green because more chlorophyll has been made in the leaves to harness the energy of the sunlight falling on them. The growing potato plant can now collect enough light to build up its own reserves; it no longer needs the energy stored in the old tuber. If the potato were planted, the energy gathered by its leaves would be stored in new potato tubers, and the old tuber would shrivel and die.

Stems now growing rapidly upward and turning toward the light

Thickening root system with root hairs

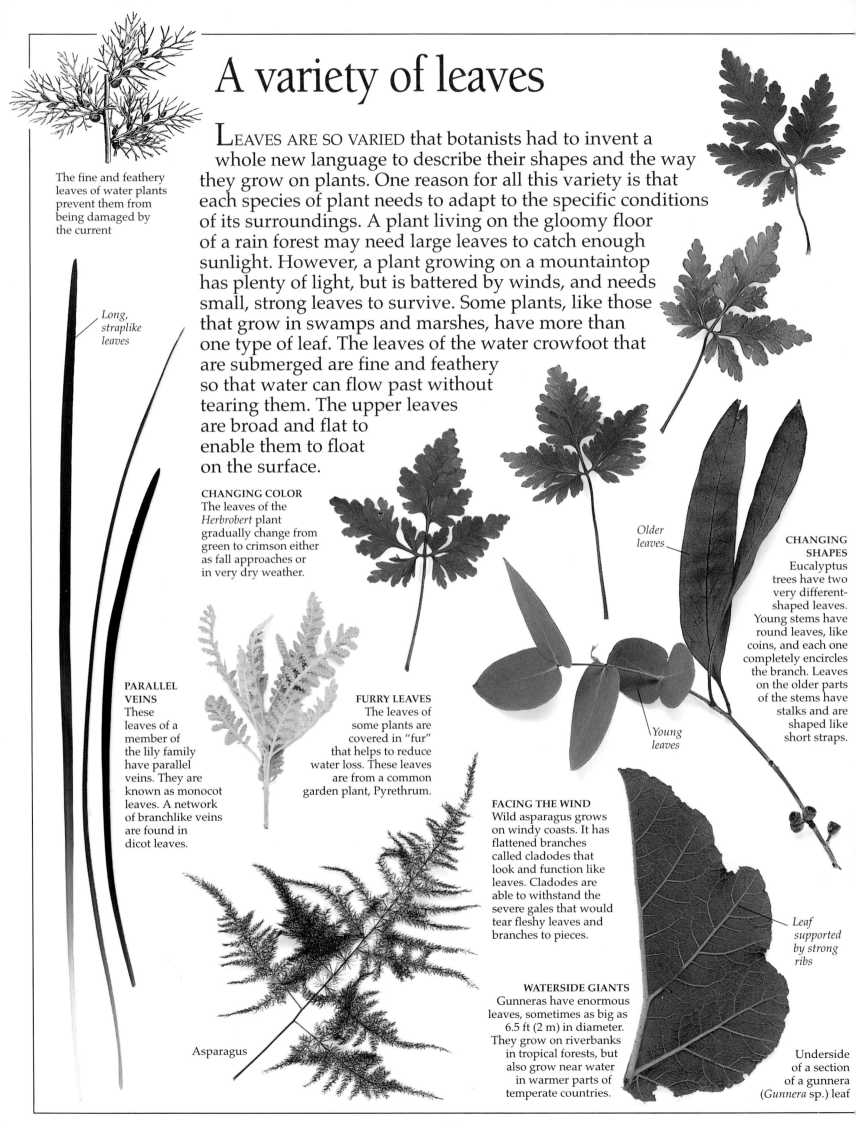

A variety of leaves

LEAVES ARE SO VARIED that botanists had to invent a whole new language to describe their shapes and the way they grow on plants. One reason for all this variety is that each species of plant needs to adapt to the specific conditions of its surroundings. A plant living on the gloomy floor of a rain forest may need large leaves to catch enough sunlight. However, a plant growing on a mountaintop has plenty of light, but is battered by winds, and needs small, strong leaves to survive. Some plants, like those that grow in swamps and marshes, have more than one type of leaf. The leaves of the water crowfoot that are submerged are fine and feathery so that water can flow past without tearing them. The upper leaves are broad and flat to enable them to float on the surface.

The fine and feathery leaves of water plants prevent them from being damaged by the current

Long, straplike leaves

CHANGING COLOR
The leaves of the *Herbrobert* plant gradually change from green to crimson either as fall approaches or in very dry weather.

PARALLEL VEINS
These leaves of a member of the lily family have parallel veins. They are known as monocot leaves. A network of branchlike veins are found in dicot leaves.

FURRY LEAVES
The leaves of some plants are covered in "fur" that helps to reduce water loss. These leaves are from a common garden plant, Pyrethrum.

Older leaves

CHANGING SHAPES
Eucalyptus trees have two very different-shaped leaves. Young stems have round leaves, like coins, and each one completely encircles the branch. Leaves on the older parts of the stems have stalks and are shaped like short straps.

Young leaves

FACING THE WIND
Wild asparagus grows on windy coasts. It has flattened branches called cladodes that look and function like leaves. Cladodes are able to withstand the severe gales that would tear fleshy leaves and branches to pieces.

Asparagus

WATERSIDE GIANTS
Gunneras have enormous leaves, sometimes as big as 6.5 ft (2 m) in diameter. They grow on riverbanks in tropical forests, but also grow near water in warmer parts of temperate countries.

Leaf supported by strong ribs

Underside of a section of a gunnera (*Gunnera* sp.) leaf

Slashes appear as leaf grows older

Leaflet

Compound leaves are made up of a number of individual leaflets

SLASHED LEAVES
The Swiss cheese plant *Monstera deliciosa* grows in tropical forests, clinging to trees for support. It probably gets its unusual name from its slashed and perforated leaves.

Simple leaves do not have leaflets

Peltate leaves are shield-shaped, with the stalk coming from the middle

Waxy upper surface

EVERGREEN LEAVES
Evergreen plants do not shed their leaves all at the same time, so they appear green all year round. They need to be tough to survive in the wind, sun, and rain. The leaves of the rhododendron have a waxy surface to keep them from drying out. They sometimes also have down on their undersides to retain moisture and ward off insects.

Lungwort *Pulmonaria officinalis*

Joseph's coat *Amaranthus tricolor*

LEAVES OF MANY COLORS
Variegated, or many-colored leaves, are frequent in nature. Lungwort is named after its spotty leaves, which resemble a human lung. The leaves of Joseph's coat are brightly colored, recalling the biblical Joseph and his multicolored coat.

Red underside

Feltlike downy underside

Rhododendron (*Rhododendron* sp.)

Flowers

A PROFUSION OF DIFFERENT SHAPES and colors of flowers has been produced in the course of evolution. To add to this, people have bred flowers that are even more brilliant – or bizarre – than those found in the wild. Behind this dazzling array of shapes and colors, however, there is a common pattern. All flowers use the same underlying structure for seed production. The male parts, the stamens, produce pollen. The female parts, the carpels, produce ovules, which eventually become seeds. Around both the male and the female parts are sepals and petals that attract pollinators like insects, birds, or bats (pp. 46–47). In the flowers of the lily or clematis, the sepals and petals look the same. Then they are known as tepals.

Honeysuckle
Lonicera

SCENTED TUBES
Honeysuckle is a vine with arching branches that uses trees and other surfaces to climb toward the light. The flowers of this plant have sweet-smelling petals that are fused to form long tubes, a further extension of the plant and one that is very visible and attractive to pollinators.

ROUND AND ROUND
The florets (small flowers) of this sunflower are grouped together to resemble a single, large flower. The outer, yellow ring is made up of ray florets, and surrounds the inner ring of disk florets. Toward the center of the whorl are the inner, immature disk florets, which appear darker in color.

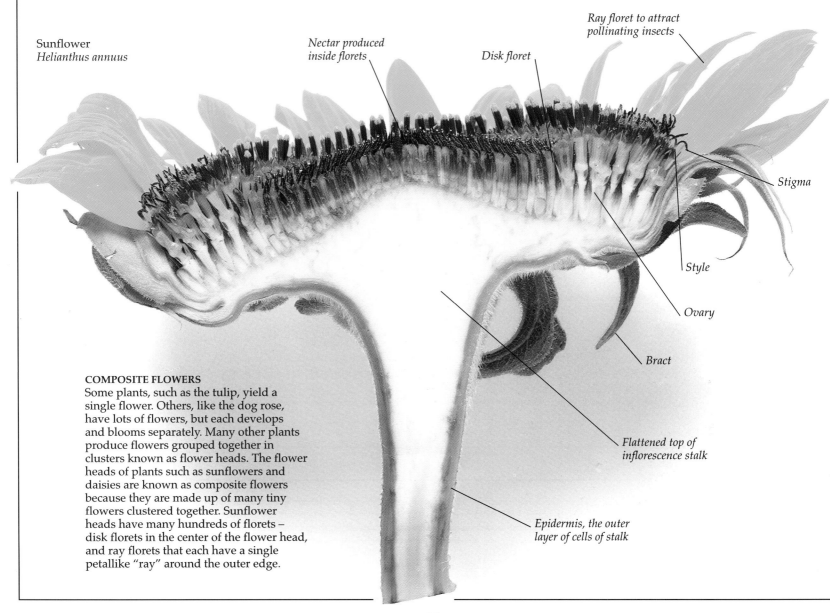

Sunflower
Helianthus annuus

Nectar produced inside florets

Disk floret

Ray floret to attract pollinating insects

Stigma

Style

Ovary

Bract

Flattened top of inflorescence stalk

Epidermis, the outer layer of cells of stalk

COMPOSITE FLOWERS
Some plants, such as the tulip, yield a single flower. Others, like the dog rose, have lots of flowers, but each develops and blooms separately. Many other plants produce flowers grouped together in clusters known as flower heads. The flower heads of plants such as sunflowers and daisies are known as composite flowers because they are made up of many tiny flowers clustered together. Sunflower heads have many hundreds of florets – disk florets in the center of the flower head, and ray florets that each have a single petallike "ray" around the outer edge.

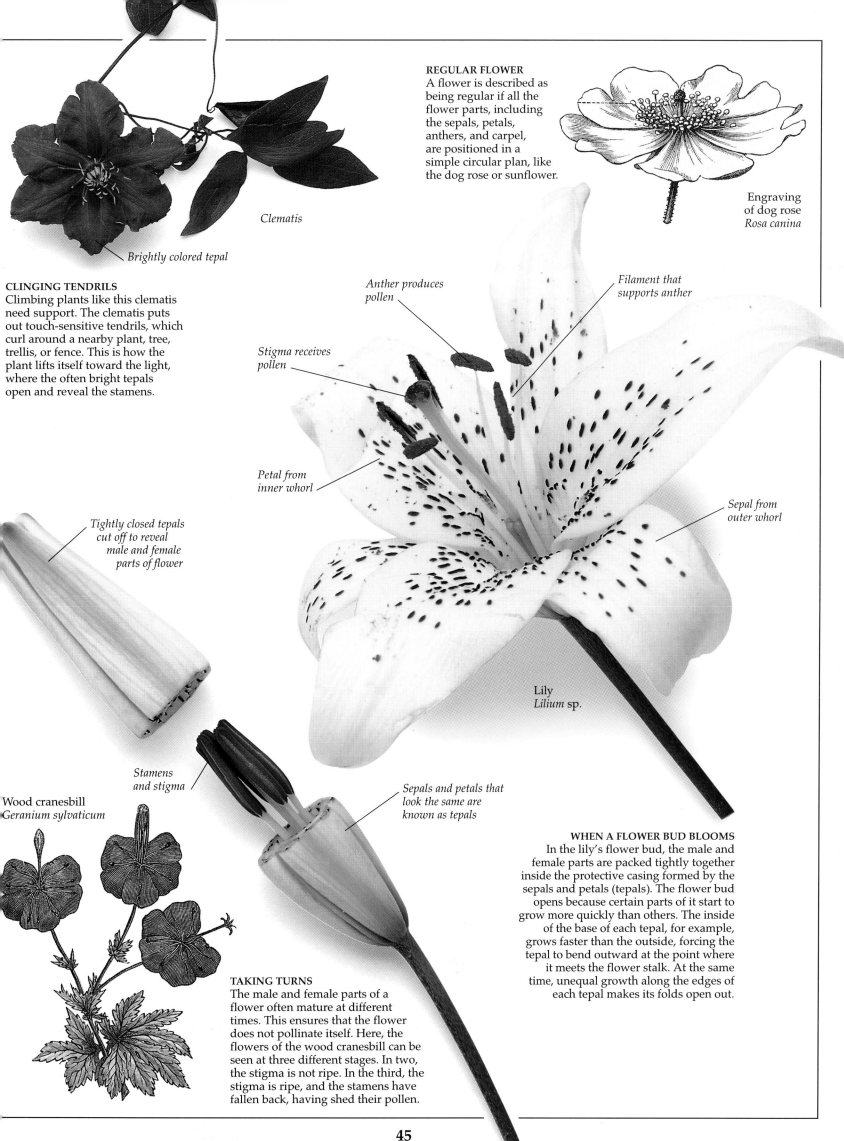

Clematis

Brightly colored tepal

REGULAR FLOWER
A flower is described as
being regular if all the
flower parts, including
the sepals, petals,
anthers, and carpel,
are positioned in a
simple circular plan, like
the dog rose or sunflower.

Engraving
of dog rose
Rosa canina

CLINGING TENDRILS
Climbing plants like this clematis
need support. The clematis puts
out touch-sensitive tendrils, which
curl around a nearby plant, tree,
trellis, or fence. This is how the
plant lifts itself toward the light,
where the often bright tepals
open and reveal the stamens.

*Anther produces
pollen*

*Filament that
supports anther*

*Stigma receives
pollen*

*Petal from
inner whorl*

*Sepal from
outer whorl*

*Tightly closed tepals
cut off to reveal
male and female
parts of flower*

Lily
Lilium sp.

*Stamens
and stigma*

*Sepals and petals that
look the same are
known as tepals*

Wood cranesbill
Geranium sylvaticum

WHEN A FLOWER BUD BLOOMS
In the lily's flower bud, the male and
female parts are packed tightly together
inside the protective casing formed by the
sepals and petals (tepals). The flower bud
opens because certain parts of it start to
grow more quickly than others. The inside
of the base of each tepal, for example,
grows faster than the outside, forcing the
tepal to bend outward at the point where
it meets the flower stalk. At the same
time, unequal growth along the edges of
each tepal makes its folds open out.

TAKING TURNS
The male and female parts of a
flower often mature at different
times. This ensures that the flower
does not pollinate itself. Here, the
flowers of the wood cranesbill can be
seen at three different stages. In two,
the stigma is not ripe. In the third, the
stigma is ripe, and the stamens have
fallen back, having shed their pollen.

45

Pollination

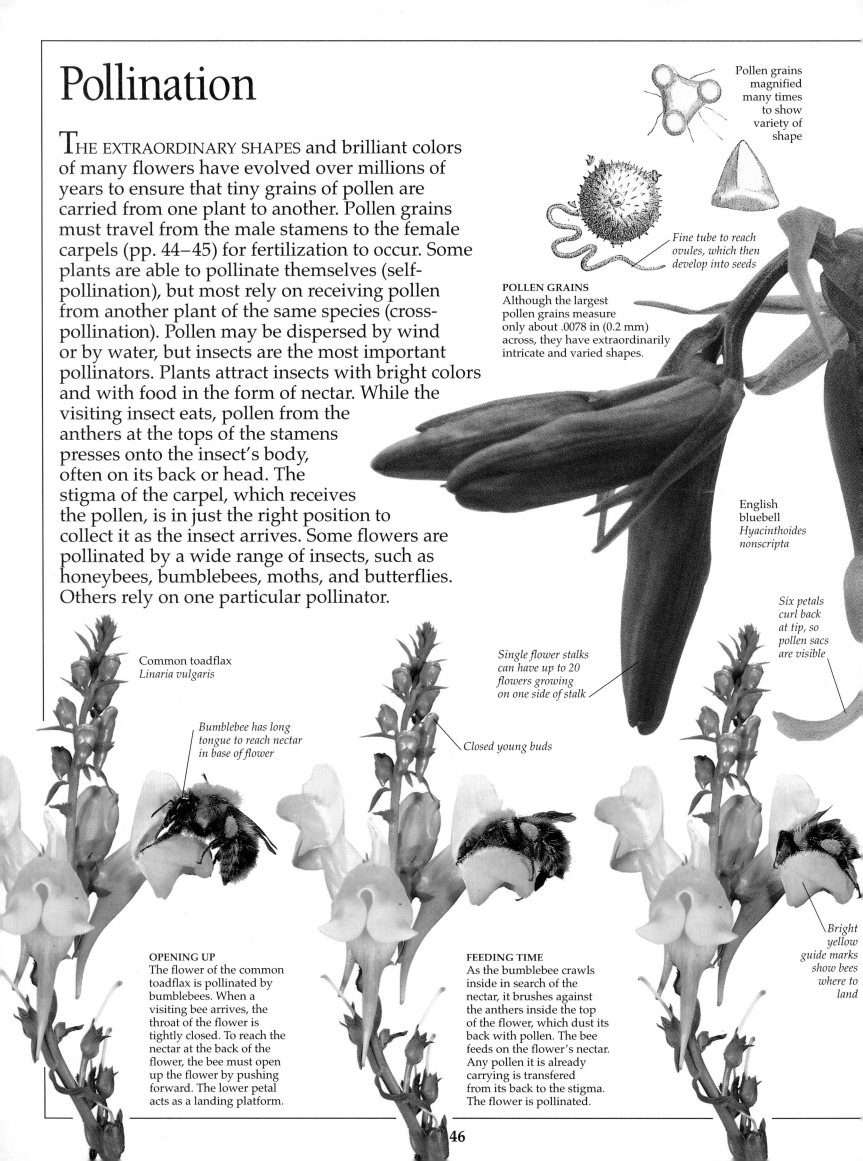

THE EXTRAORDINARY SHAPES and brilliant colors of many flowers have evolved over millions of years to ensure that tiny grains of pollen are carried from one plant to another. Pollen grains must travel from the male stamens to the female carpels (pp. 44–45) for fertilization to occur. Some plants are able to pollinate themselves (self-pollination), but most rely on receiving pollen from another plant of the same species (cross-pollination). Pollen may be dispersed by wind or by water, but insects are the most important pollinators. Plants attract insects with bright colors and with food in the form of nectar. While the visiting insect eats, pollen from the anthers at the tops of the stamens presses onto the insect's body, often on its back or head. The stigma of the carpel, which receives the pollen, is in just the right position to collect it as the insect arrives. Some flowers are pollinated by a wide range of insects, such as honeybees, bumblebees, moths, and butterflies. Others rely on one particular pollinator.

Pollen grains magnified many times to show variety of shape

Fine tube to reach ovules, which then develop into seeds

POLLEN GRAINS
Although the largest pollen grains measure only about .0078 in (0.2 mm) across, they have extraordinarily intricate and varied shapes.

English bluebell *Hyacinthoides nonscripta*

Six petals curl back at tip, so pollen sacs are visible

Common toadflax *Linaria vulgaris*

Single flower stalks can have up to 20 flowers growing on one side of stalk

Bumblebee has long tongue to reach nectar in base of flower

Closed young buds

Bright yellow guide marks show bees where to land

OPENING UP
The flower of the common toadflax is pollinated by bumblebees. When a visiting bee arrives, the throat of the flower is tightly closed. To reach the nectar at the back of the flower, the bee must open up the flower by pushing forward. The lower petal acts as a landing platform.

FEEDING TIME
As the bumblebee crawls inside in search of the nectar, it brushes against the anthers inside the top of the flower, which dust its back with pollen. The bee feeds on the flower's nectar. Any pollen it is already carrying is transferred from its back to the stigma. The flower is pollinated.

English bluebells are usually violet-blue, but can be white or pink

Pollen sacs, or anther

ATTRACTING INSECTS
Insect-pollinated flowers are brightly colored, scented, and produce nectar. In addition, these flowers usually have patterns on them that are not visible to the human eye. The patterns can be seen in ultraviolet light (below) and guide insect pollinators, since insects see ultraviolet light.

St. John's Wort, *Hypericum*, under normal light

Dark, central area with nectaries, anthers, and stigmas

Honey guide

St. John's Wort under ultraviolet light

INVISIBLE MESSAGES
Insects are attracted to the darkest, central part of the flower, visible in such dark colors here only because it is lit by ultraviolet light. The lines on the petals are honey guides that guide the insect to the central part of the flower where it will find pollen and nectar.

Green-veined white butterfly *Pieris napi*

Green color around veins gives this butterfly its name

BUTTERFLY POLLINATION
Butterflies and moths are also important pollinators but, unlike bees, they don't actively collect or eat pollen. When they land on a flower to feed on the nectar, pollen from the stamens sticks to their bodies, ready to be carried to the next flower. Because butterflies and moths have a highly developed sense of smell, flowers pollinated by these insects are often scented. Many bloom in the late summer, when butterflies and moths are most abundant. Butterflies and moths suck up nectar through their proboscis, which is hollow like a drinking straw. The proboscis may vary in length from a fraction of an inch to 1 foot (30 cm). It is coiled up under the butterfly's head when it's not in use.

Also known as wild hyacinths, English bluebells have single, thick, supporting stalks

47

Borne on the wind

ACCORDING TO TRADITION, if you blow on a dandelion's seed head, the number of puffs needed to blow away all the seeds will tell you the time of day. Whether or not it's true, the custom certainly helps the plant spread. The seeds of the dandelion are encased in tiny fruits and have their own special feathery parachutes to help them float through the air. The dandelion's flower is a composite flower head, composed of many tiny flowers, or florets, clustered together. Each of the tiny florets produces a single fruit. Like the dandelion, many other composite plants, such as hawkweeds, ragworts, and thistles, rely on the wind to disperse their seeds. The fruits of some of these have parachutes; others have fine hairs that stick out in all directions to form a feathery ball. Many of these plants are troublesome weeds because they quickly colonize bare soil in gardens and on farmland.

Dandelion's tiny fruits float away on the breeze

1 OPENING TIME
The dandelion's flower opens in the morning and closes in the afternoon or when it rains. The plant's name comes from the French *dent de lion*, meaning "lion's tooth," which describes the jagged edges of the leaves.

Flower closes before seeds form

Bracts protect developing seed head

2 THE SEEDS START TO FORM
After opening and closing for a number of days, during which time it can be pollinated, the flower finally closes, and seed formation begins. Gradually the yellow petals wither away, and the "pappus," which is the name given to the small circle of hairs attached to the top of each fruit, starts to grow longer. This is the beginning of the parachute.

Seed head opens
when parachutes
are formed

Bracts
fold back

3 OPENING OUT
The seed head begins to open
only in dry weather. At first, the
parachutes are squashed together,
but as the bracts around the edge
of the seed head fold back, the
parachutes can expand.

4 READY TO GO
In windless weather,
the fruits may spend
several days attached
to the seed head. This is
dangerous because seed-
eating birds like goldfinches are
likely to peck them off and eat them.

Fully
opened
seed head

Parachutes
attached to
tiny fruits

5 LIFT OFF
A slight breeze is all that is needed
to lift the parachutes into the air. They
may fall close by, but with enough
updraft they can travel long distances –
more than 6 miles (10 km) is an average
journey for a dandelion seed. When a
fruit lands, it no longer needs the
parachute that has carried it on its
journey, and this breaks off. Over the
winter months, the seeds inside the fruit
sink into the soil until the spring, when
they begin to germinate (pp. 52–53).

Scattering the seed

A PATCH OF BARE GROUND never stays bare for long. Within days, seedlings start to spring up, and, if the conditions are right, they eventually cover the ground. Even if the earth is sterilized by heat, so that all the seeds are killed, more somehow arrive and germinate (pp. 52–53). Plants have evolved very effective ways of spreading their seeds, often relying on transportation by wind, animals, and water. The fruit wall is part of a plant's dispersal method. In certain plants, exploding seed pods fling the seeds into the air. Some fruits are winged or cottony to help the seeds become airborne, and some air-filled seeds float on water. Animals also play their part. Many plants have fruits with hooks or burs that stick to fur, and the seeds some species develop inside tasty berries that are eaten by animals and birds. The seeds pass through these creatures unharmed and fall to the ground, where they germinate.

Seed heads
of lotus
*Nymphaea
nucifera*

*Seed held
in cup*

Dried lotus
head from above

*Seed protected
by fruit wall*

SPLITTING OPEN
The hard fruit walls of dry fruits such as money plant split open to release their seeds, which are then dispersed in the wind. The edges of the seed coats are flattened to make the seeds more aerodynamic.

*Flat edge
of seed
coat*

*Dry fruit
wall*

Money plant
Lunaria annua

Lotuses growing
in ancient Egypt

*Long tail
for climbing*

Ring-tailed
lemur
*Lemur
catta*

WASHED AWAY
The lotus is a water plant that produces its seeds in a flattened head. When the seeds are ripe, they fall to the water's surface and float away. Lotus seeds can be extraordinarily long-lived. Some have been known to germinate more than 200 years after they were shed.

FRUIT EATER
This ring-tailed lemur lives in tall trees near rivers in southern Madagascar. Fruit is the most important part of its diet, although it also eats insects and leaves. The seeds of the fruit are spread when the lemur spits them out, lets them fall, or passes them in its droppings.

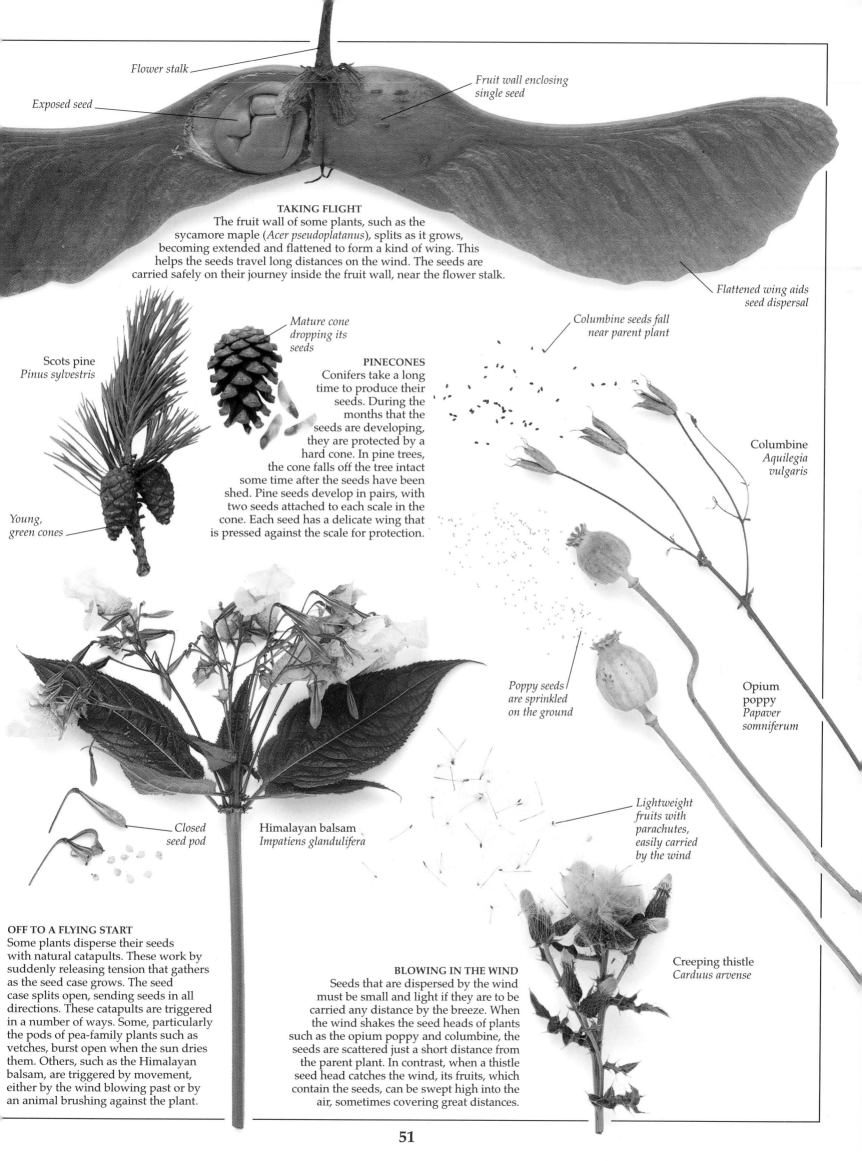

TAKING FLIGHT
The fruit wall of some plants, such as the sycamore maple (*Acer pseudoplatanus*), splits as it grows, becoming extended and flattened to form a kind of wing. This helps the seeds travel long distances on the wind. The seeds are carried safely on their journey inside the fruit wall, near the flower stalk.

Flower stalk

Exposed seed

Fruit wall enclosing single seed

Flattened wing aids seed dispersal

Columbine seeds fall near parent plant

Scots pine
Pinus sylvestris

Mature cone dropping its seeds

PINECONES
Conifers take a long time to produce their seeds. During the months that the seeds are developing, they are protected by a hard cone. In pine trees, the cone falls off the tree intact some time after the seeds have been shed. Pine seeds develop in pairs, with two seeds attached to each scale in the cone. Each seed has a delicate wing that is pressed against the scale for protection.

Young, green cones

Columbine
Aquilegia vulgaris

Poppy seeds are sprinkled on the ground

Opium poppy
Papaver somniferum

Closed seed pod

Himalayan balsam
Impatiens glandulifera

Lightweight fruits with parachutes, easily carried by the wind

OFF TO A FLYING START
Some plants disperse their seeds with natural catapults. These work by suddenly releasing tension that gathers as the seed case grows. The seed case splits open, sending seeds in all directions. These catapults are triggered in a number of ways. Some, particularly the pods of pea-family plants such as vetches, burst open when the sun dries them. Others, such as the Himalayan balsam, are triggered by movement, either by the wind blowing past or by an animal brushing against the plant.

BLOWING IN THE WIND
Seeds that are dispersed by the wind must be small and light if they are to be carried any distance by the breeze. When the wind shakes the seed heads of plants such as the opium poppy and columbine, the seeds are scattered just a short distance from the parent plant. In contrast, when a thistle seed head catches the wind, its fruits, which contain the seeds, can be swept high into the air, sometimes covering great distances.

Creeping thistle
Carduus arvense

Seeds of life

A SEED IS A TINY LIFE-SUPPORT package. Inside it is an embryo, which consists of the basic parts from which a seedling will develop, or germinate. Food is needed to keep the embryo alive and fuel the process of germination. It is either packed around the embryo in an endosperm, or stored in special seed leaves known as cotyledons. For weeks, months, or even years, the seed may remain inactive. But then, when the conditions are right, it suddenly comes alive and begins to grow. During germination, the seed absorbs water, the cells of the embryo start to divide, and eventually the seed coat, or testa, breaks open.

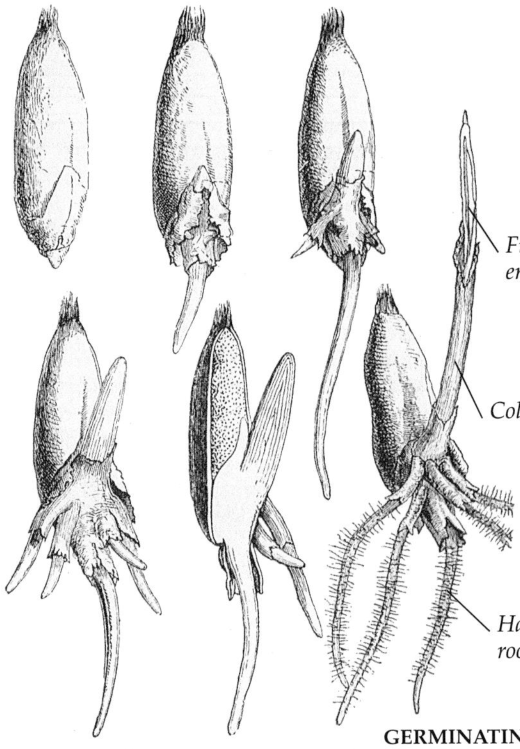

First leaves emerge

Coleoptile

Hairy roots

GERMINATING GRAIN
Wheat is a monocot – it has just one seed leaf. The young shoot grows upward through the soil, protected by a tube called a coleoptile. The growing point of a wheat plant remains at ground level and can continue to produce new shoots even if the leaves are removed.

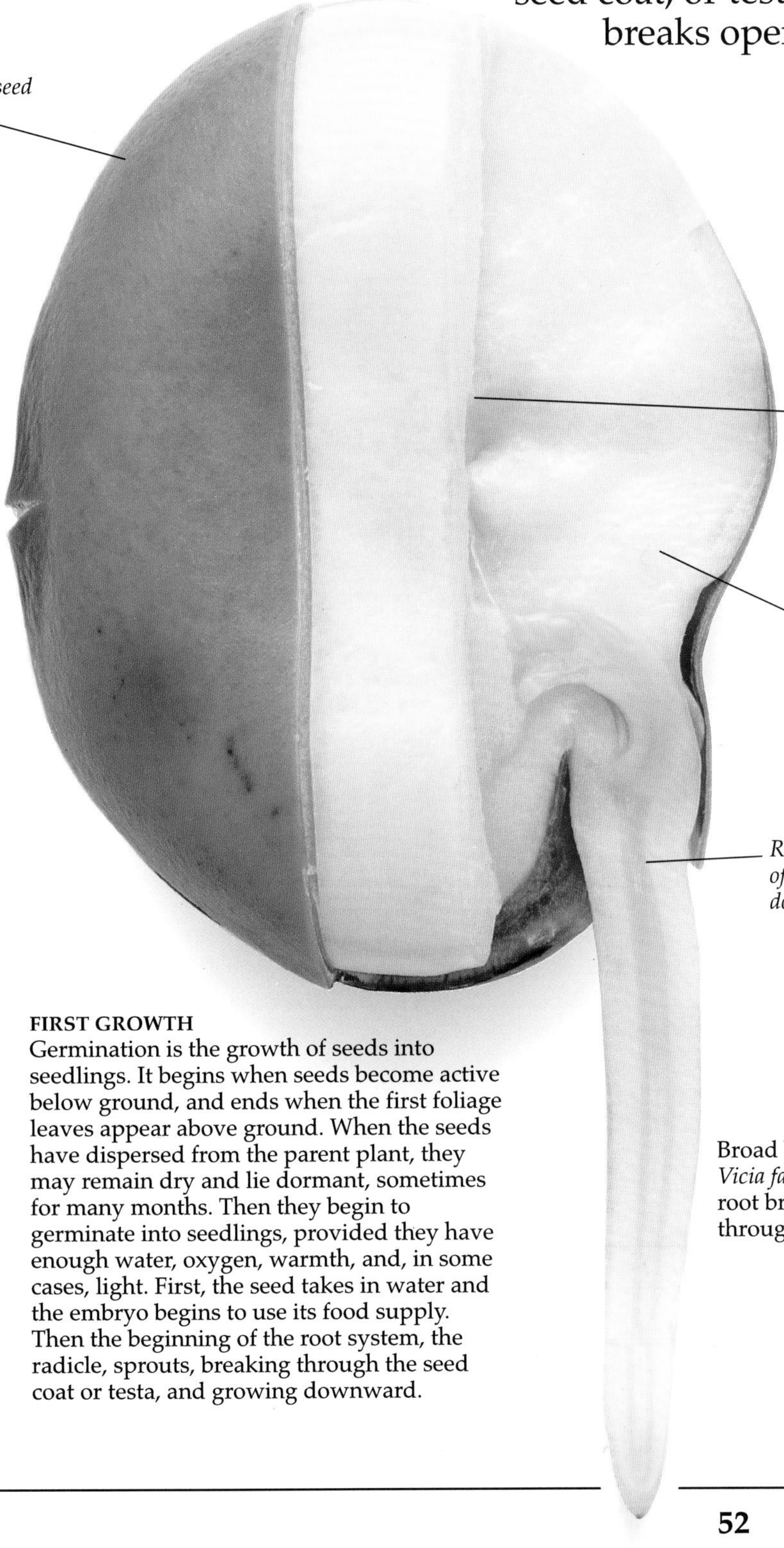

Testa (seed coat)

Cotyledon (seed leaf), where food is stored

Cotyledon (seed leaf)

First true leaves emerging

Plumule (shoot) straightening toward light

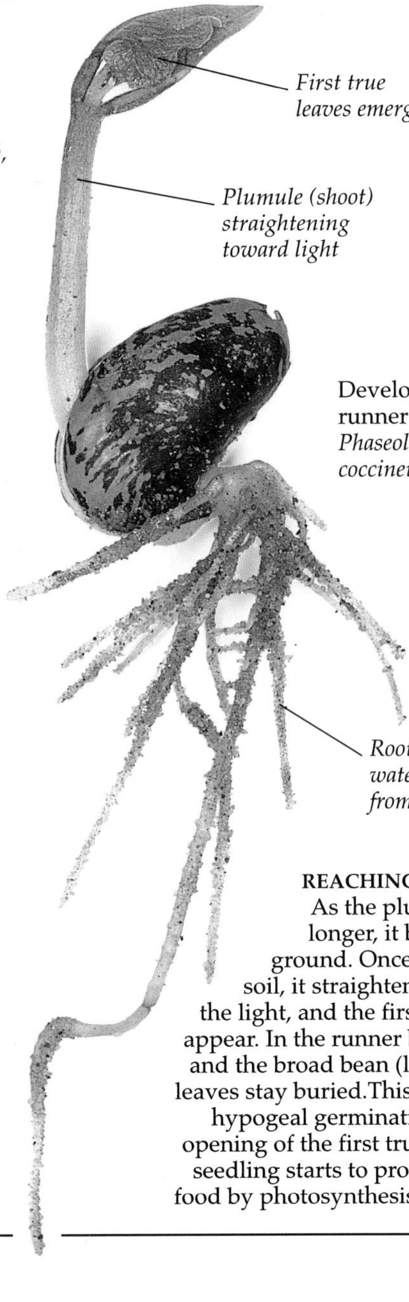

Developing runner bean *Phaseolus coccineus*

Radicle breaking out of testa and growing downward

Root hairs absorb water and salt from soil

FIRST GROWTH
Germination is the growth of seeds into seedlings. It begins when seeds become active below ground, and ends when the first foliage leaves appear above ground. When the seeds have dispersed from the parent plant, they may remain dry and lie dormant, sometimes for many months. Then they begin to germinate into seedlings, provided they have enough water, oxygen, warmth, and, in some cases, light. First, the seed takes in water and the embryo begins to use its food supply. Then the beginning of the root system, the radicle, sprouts, breaking through the seed coat or testa, and growing downward.

Broad bean
Vicia faba
root breaking through seed coat

REACHING THE LIGHT
As the plumule grows longer, it breaks above ground. Once through the soil, it straightens up toward the light, and the first true leaves appear. In the runner bean (above) and the broad bean (left), the seed leaves stay buried. This is known as hypogeal germination. With the opening of the first true leaves, the seedling starts to produce its own food by photosynthesis (pp. 40–41).

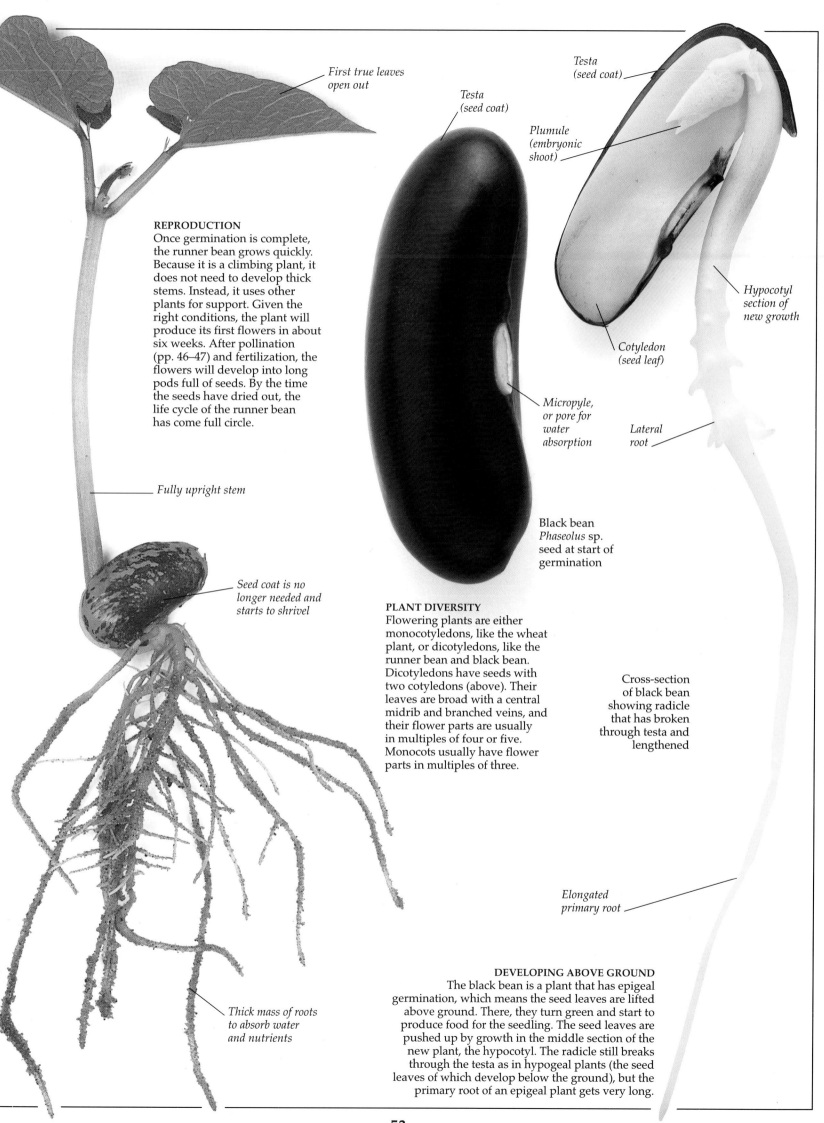

First true leaves open out

Testa (seed coat)

Testa (seed coat)

Plumule (embryonic shoot)

Hypocotyl section of new growth

REPRODUCTION
Once germination is complete, the runner bean grows quickly. Because it is a climbing plant, it does not need to develop thick stems. Instead, it uses other plants for support. Given the right conditions, the plant will produce its first flowers in about six weeks. After pollination (pp. 46–47) and fertilization, the flowers will develop into long pods full of seeds. By the time the seeds have dried out, the life cycle of the runner bean has come full circle.

Cotyledon (seed leaf)

Micropyle, or pore for water absorption

Lateral root

Fully upright stem

Seed coat is no longer needed and starts to shrivel

Black bean *Phaseolus* sp. seed at start of germination

PLANT DIVERSITY
Flowering plants are either monocotyledons, like the wheat plant, or dicotyledons, like the runner bean and black bean. Dicotyledons have seeds with two cotyledons (above). Their leaves are broad with a central midrib and branched veins, and their flower parts are usually in multiples of four or five. Monocots usually have flower parts in multiples of three.

Cross-section of black bean showing radicle that has broken through testa and lengthened

Thick mass of roots to absorb water and nutrients

Elongated primary root

DEVELOPING ABOVE GROUND
The black bean is a plant that has epigeal germination, which means the seed leaves are lifted above ground. There, they turn green and start to produce food for the seedling. The seed leaves are pushed up by growth in the middle section of the new plant, the hypocotyl. The radicle still breaks through the testa as in hypogeal plants (the seed leaves of which develop below the ground), but the primary root of an epigeal plant gets very long.

FIERCE FEEDER
In a typical food chain, the lion is the top predator. An adult male may eat 90 lb (40 kg) of meat in a sitting, although he may not feed again for several days. The lionesses in a group of lions, or pride, do most of the hunting. Often two or more will stalk and kill the antelope or zebras that are the pride's main food.

CHAPTER 3
ANIMAL LIFE

THERE IS AN INCREDIBLE VARIETY of animal life in the world, from brightly colored beetles and many-legged centipedes to waddling penguins, writhing snakes, scuttling brown rats, and fierce polar bears. The variety is reflected in the animals' lifestyles. They have all developed ingenious ways of protecting and feeding themselves and their young.

LAYING IN STORES
Female butterflies and moths lay batches of eggs on the plants that will provide food for the caterpillars when they hatch (pp. 60–61). Caterpillars are voracious and continuous feeders, eating and growing larger until they pupate. In the pupa, or chrysalis (pp. 58–59), a caterpillar develops further, eventually emerging as a fully grown butterfly.

Insect life

INSECTS ARE THE MOST ABUNDANT creatures on Earth – there are more than five million species. They first appeared 300 million years ago, and were the first animals to fly. All insects have six legs and a skeleton on the outside of their body. This outer skeleton, or exoskeleton, forms a soft, protective covering around the vulnerable internal organs. When a young insect, or larva, grows, it must shed its exoskeleton. As it grows too large, the skeleton splits, revealing a new one underneath. Most insects have two pairs of wings, each with a network of veins to give strength to their structure. Insects also have antennae, or feelers, which they use to investigate their surroundings. Some insects have very long antennae, used mainly for touch. Others have antennae that can sense airborne chemicals, even in minute quantities. These are often feathery, which provides a large surface area for collecting scent molecules from the air.

Back legs pulled in to push insect into air

JUMPING INSECTS
Grasshoppers, crickets, and locusts are all powerful jumpers. They bring the long, slender parts of their hind legs close under their bodies. The large muscles shorten, or contract, and the legs are suddenly straightened, throwing the insect into the air.

DANGER ON EIGHT LEGS
Although many people think they are, spiders are not insects. This red-kneed tarantula, *Brachypelma smithi*, stays in its silk-lined burrow during the day, emerging after dark to hunt for large insects or small invertebrates.

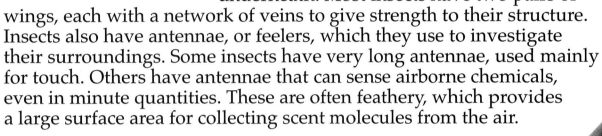

BUTTERFLIES AND MOTHS
There are hundreds of thousands of known species of butterflies and moths in the world. Together the two groups make up one group known as the Lepidoptera, from the Greek words for "scale" and "wing."

Orange albatross
Appias nero

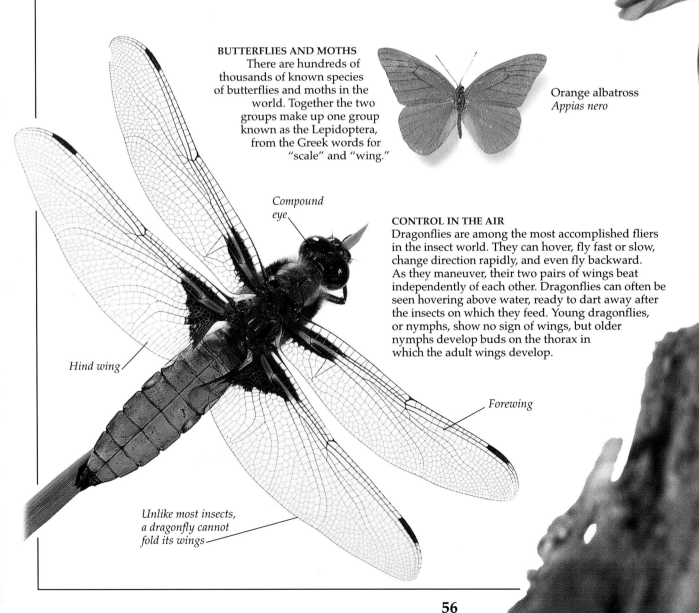

Compound eye

Hind wing

Unlike most insects, a dragonfly cannot fold its wings

Forewing

CONTROL IN THE AIR
Dragonflies are among the most accomplished fliers in the insect world. They can hover, fly fast or slow, change direction rapidly, and even fly backward. As they maneuver, their two pairs of wings beat independently of each other. Dragonflies can often be seen hovering above water, ready to dart away after the insects on which they feed. Young dragonflies, or nymphs, show no sign of wings, but older nymphs develop buds on the thorax in which the adult wings develop.

LIVING FOOD

Many insects practice a form of parasitism that involves laying eggs on or in another insect, which then acts as a living food supply for the insect's grubs to feed on. This striped field digger wasp is paralyzing a fly that it will carry back to its nest for its grubs to eat. Insects that carry out this kind of parasitism, indirect predation, can be used by humans to keep down the population of pests that attack many economically important crops. It is a natural form of biological control, which is less harmful than the use of poisonous chemicals.

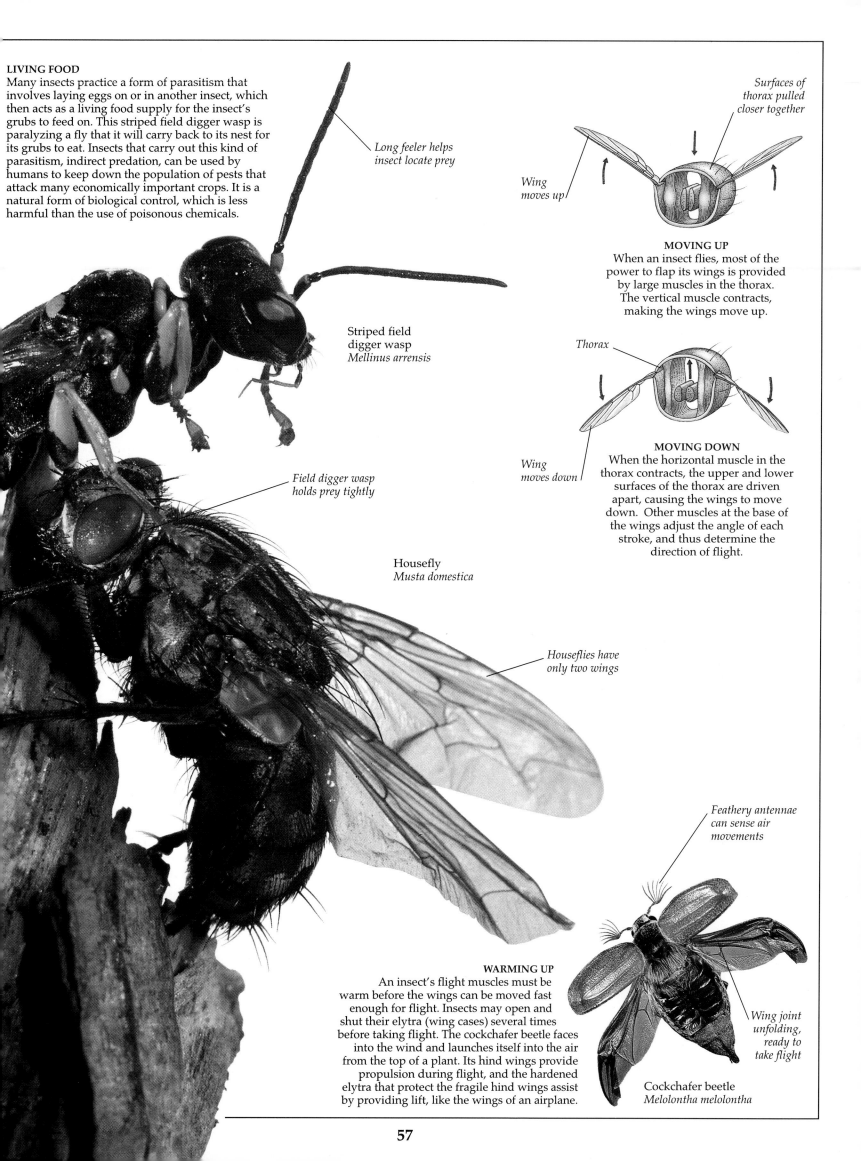

Long feeler helps insect locate prey

Striped field digger wasp
Mellinus arrensis

Field digger wasp holds prey tightly

Housefly
Musta domestica

Houseflies have only two wings

Surfaces of thorax pulled closer together

Wing moves up

MOVING UP

When an insect flies, most of the power to flap its wings is provided by large muscles in the thorax. The vertical muscle contracts, making the wings move up.

Thorax

Wing moves down

MOVING DOWN

When the horizontal muscle in the thorax contracts, the upper and lower surfaces of the thorax are driven apart, causing the wings to move down. Other muscles at the base of the wings adjust the angle of each stroke, and thus determine the direction of flight.

Feathery antennae can sense air movements

WARMING UP

An insect's flight muscles must be warm before the wings can be moved fast enough for flight. Insects may open and shut their elytra (wing cases) several times before taking flight. The cockchafer beetle faces into the wind and launches itself into the air from the top of a plant. Its hind wings provide propulsion during flight, and the hardened elytra that protect the fragile hind wings assist by providing lift, like the wings of an airplane.

Wing joint unfolding, ready to take flight

Cockchafer beetle
Melolontha melolontha

Insect transformation

METAMORPHOSIS MEANS "change of body form and appearance." The most advanced insects have a complex life cycle involving "complete" metamorphosis. The eggs hatch to produce larvae (caterpillars, grubs, or maggots) that are completely different from adult insects in both shape and appearance. The larvae grow and molt several times, producing a pupa, or chrysalis. Inside the pupa, the insect's whole body is reorganized, and a winged adult finally emerges. This life cycle enables larvae to specialize in feeding and adults to specialize in breeding and looking for new sites. Wasps, bees, ants, flies, beetles, butterflies and moths, caddis flies, fleas, lacewings, and scorpion flies all undergo complete metamorphosis. Grasshoppers, cockroaches, termites, mayflies, dragonflies, and many other bugs undergo "incomplete" metamorphosis. Like the original primitive insects, they transform gradually through a series of stages, the nymphs becoming more and more like the adults. There is no pupal stage.

MATING
Mexican bean beetles (*Epilachna varivestis*) are a species of plant-eating ladybug beetle. The adult males and females look very similar and mate frequently.

EGGS
Female Mexican bean beetles glue their eggs in groups of about 50 to the underside of leaves, where the eggs will be well protected. Each egg stands on its end and takes about seven days to hatch.

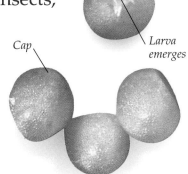

Cap

Larva emerges

1 EGG HATCHES
Even eggs have to breathe. Each egg has a ring of pores at the top, that allow air to reach the developing larva inside. About a week after the egg has been laid, the cap at the top is broken or chewed off and the larva emerges.

Old larval skin

New pupal skin

4 ABOUT TO CHANGE
When the larva has eaten enough food, it attaches itself to the underside of a damaged, netted leaf, ready to pupate. The larval skin is shed, and soft new pupal skin forms beneath it. This quickly hardens.

Larva feeding on plant shoot

DIET OF LEAVES
Mexican bean beetles feed on leaves both as larvae and adults. Because they only eat the fleshy parts between the veins, the leaf becomes netted and lacy.

Old larval skin with long spines

New pupal skin with short spines

Dead, lacy leaves that larvae have eaten

5 RESTING
A pupa is often called a "resting stage." But there is no rest for all the cells in the insect's body. The muscles, nerves, and other structures all dissolve, and new limbs, with new muscles and nerves, form. In this photo, the smooth yellow of the adult beetle's wing cases and the first segment of its thorax can be seen through the thin, spiny skin of the pupa.

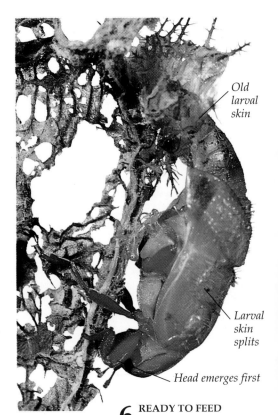

Old larval skin

Larval skin splits

Head emerges first

6 READY TO FEED
The thin, spiny pupal skin splits along the underside, and the smooth, young adult slowly pulls itself free, headfirst. It takes about an hour from the splitting of the pupal skin for the young beetle to free itself.

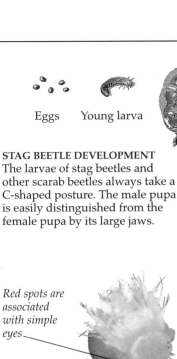

Eggs Young larva

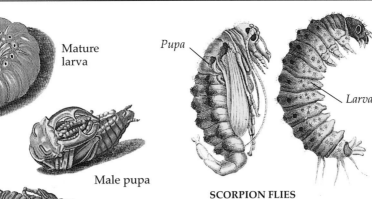

Mature larva

Male pupa

Female pupa

STAG BEETLE DEVELOPMENT
The larvae of stag beetles and other scarab beetles always take a C-shaped posture. The male pupa is easily distinguished from the female pupa by its large jaws.

Pupa

Larva

SCORPION FLIES
Scorpion flies undergo a complete metamorphosis. This drawing shows a pupa with well-developed wing buds (left) and a larva (right).

A MAN TRANSFORMED
This painting by Barbara Lofthouse depicts a scene from Kafka's *Metamorphosis*, in which a man is transformed into a cockroach.

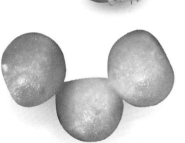

Red spots are associated with simple eyes

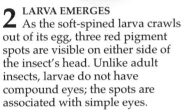

Soft spines harden quickly

PROTECTION FROM PARASITES
The spines on the surface of the larvae are branched, with hard, pointed tips. Spines like this are found on the larvae of all plant-eating ladybugs, but not on any of the more common predatory species. The spines make the larvae unpleasant for bird predators and may deter parasites from laying eggs.

2 LARVA EMERGES
As the soft-spined larva crawls out of its egg, three red pigment spots are visible on either side of the insect's head. Unlike adult insects, larvae do not have compound eyes; the spots are associated with simple eyes.

3 A FIRST MEAL
In many insect species, as soon as a young larva is free from its egg, it eats the nutrient-rich shell. The soft spines on the surface of the larva quickly harden.

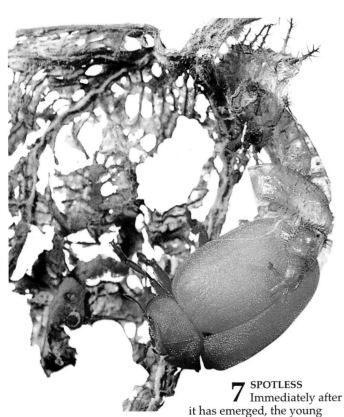

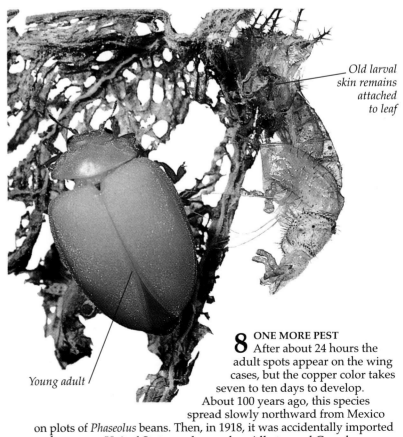

Old larval skin remains attached to leaf

7 SPOTLESS
Immediately after it has emerged, the young beetle is yellow and has no spots, although its wing cases quickly harden. Before the beetle can fly away to safety, there is a crucial drying stage that can last two to three hours. The young beetle holds its wing cases up and expands the wings below to allow them to dry in the air.

Young adult

8 ONE MORE PEST
After about 24 hours the adult spots appear on the wing cases, but the copper color takes seven to ten days to develop. About 100 years ago, this species spread slowly northward from Mexico on plots of *Phaseolus* beans. Then, in 1918, it was accidentally imported to the eastern United States and spread rapidly toward Canada. Today, it is a serious pest in bean crops in North and Central America, although it does not survive the harsher winters in central areas.

An emerging caterpillar

BUTTERFLIES AND MOTHS usually lay large numbers of eggs. The amount laid at one time varies greatly; some females lay more than 1,000, although only a few eggs will survive to become adults. Eggs also vary from one species to another in color and in surface texture, which can be smooth or intricately sculptured. The two main types are a flattened oval shape, usually with a smooth surface, and a more upright shape, which often has a heavily ribbed surface. In many cases, the eggs are laid on a leaf or stem, but species that feed on a wide variety of plants often scatter their eggs in flight. Both methods are designed to place the caterpillar as near as possible to the plant that is its food source. On these two pages, the caterpillar of a South American Owl butterfly (*Caligo idomeneus*) hatches from its egg.

Pattern of ridges can be useful aid to identification of eggs

Darker color shows egg will soon be ready to hatch

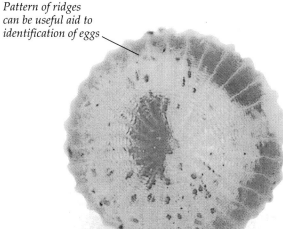

THE EGGS IN POSITION
The South American Owl butterfly lays its eggs in groups. The color of the individual eggs can vary in this species. The eggs get darker (top right) as the time of hatching approaches.

1 RESTING
Many butterflies and moths in temperate regions lay their eggs in fall. Once laid, the eggs enter a resting stage called "diapause" to survive the winter months. This state is disrupted by warm or fluctuating temperatures.

2 WARMING UP
Diapause ends when the environment is warm enough for the caterpillar to stand a chance of survival after the winter months. The egg darkens in color as the tiny caterpillar gets ready to emerge.

3 CUTTING A CIRCLE
In order to hatch, the caterpillar must bite its way through the shell of its egg. This is not a hard, brittle shell like a bird's egg, but it is still a tough task for the tiny caterpillar. Its jaws have to cut a circle big enough for the head to emerge, so it has enormous mouthparts.

4 EMERGING HEADFIRST
The caterpillar seems to have a disproportionately large head and jaws, but it can be difficult for the caterpillar to extract itself from the egg headfirst. The dark spots on each side of the head are simple eyes, or ocelli. The caterpillar also gets sensory information from its tiny antennae, which it uses for touch and smell.

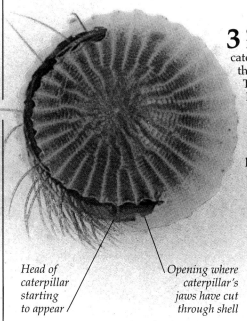

Head of caterpillar starting to appear

Opening where caterpillar's jaws have cut through shell

Ocellus

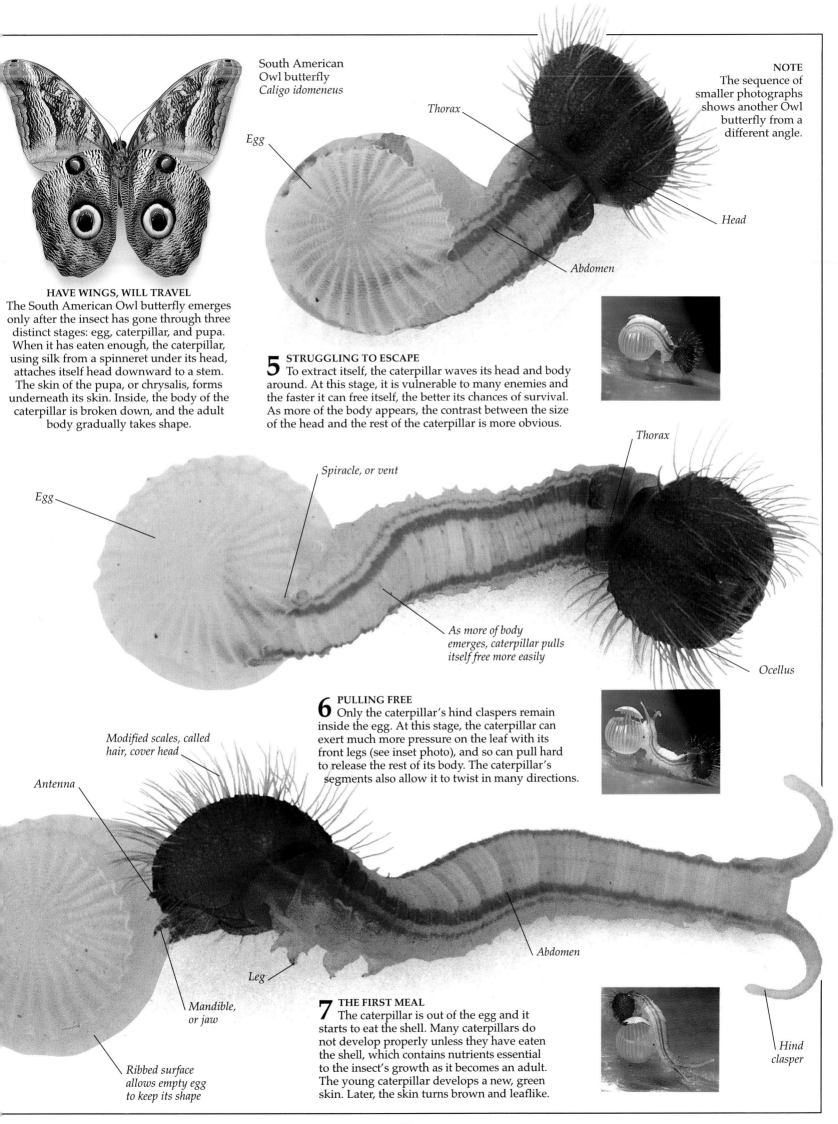

South American
Owl butterfly
Caligo idomeneus

Thorax

Egg

NOTE
The sequence of
smaller photographs
shows another Owl
butterfly from a
different angle.

Head

Abdomen

HAVE WINGS, WILL TRAVEL
The South American Owl butterfly emerges
only after the insect has gone through three
distinct stages: egg, caterpillar, and pupa.
When it has eaten enough, the caterpillar,
using silk from a spinneret under its head,
attaches itself head downward to a stem.
The skin of the pupa, or chrysalis, forms
underneath its skin. Inside, the body of the
caterpillar is broken down, and the adult
body gradually takes shape.

5 STRUGGLING TO ESCAPE
To extract itself, the caterpillar waves its head and body
around. At this stage, it is vulnerable to many enemies and
the faster it can free itself, the better its chances of survival.
As more of the body appears, the contrast between the size
of the head and the rest of the caterpillar is more obvious.

Spiracle, or vent

Thorax

Egg

*As more of body
emerges, caterpillar pulls
itself free more easily*

Ocellus

6 PULLING FREE
Only the caterpillar's hind claspers remain
inside the egg. At this stage, the caterpillar can
exert much more pressure on the leaf with its
front legs (see inset photo), and so can pull hard
to release the rest of its body. The caterpillar's
segments also allow it to twist in many directions.

*Modified scales, called
hair, cover head*

Antenna

Abdomen

Leg

*Mandible,
or jaw*

7 THE FIRST MEAL
The caterpillar is out of the egg and it
starts to eat the shell. Many caterpillars do
not develop properly unless they have eaten
the shell, which contains nutrients essential
to the insect's growth as it becomes an adult.
The young caterpillar develops a new, green
skin. Later, the skin turns brown and leaflike.

*Hind
clasper*

*Ribbed surface
allows empty egg
to keep its shape*

Anatomy of a butterfly

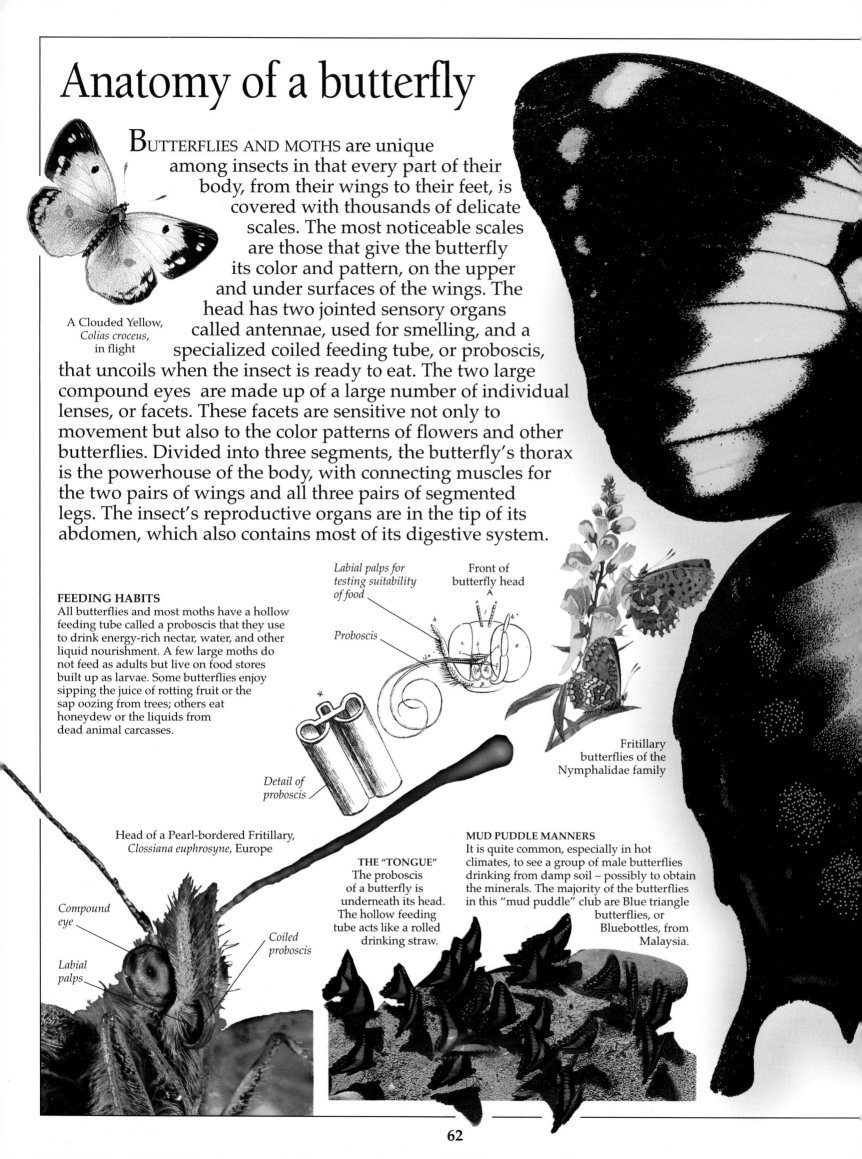

BUTTERFLIES AND MOTHS are unique among insects in that every part of their body, from their wings to their feet, is covered with thousands of delicate scales. The most noticeable scales are those that give the butterfly its color and pattern, on the upper and under surfaces of the wings. The head has two jointed sensory organs called antennae, used for smelling, and a specialized coiled feeding tube, or proboscis, that uncoils when the insect is ready to eat. The two large compound eyes are made up of a large number of individual lenses, or facets. These facets are sensitive not only to movement but also to the color patterns of flowers and other butterflies. Divided into three segments, the butterfly's thorax is the powerhouse of the body, with connecting muscles for the two pairs of wings and all three pairs of segmented legs. The insect's reproductive organs are in the tip of its abdomen, which also contains most of its digestive system.

A Clouded Yellow, *Colias croceus*, in flight

FEEDING HABITS

All butterflies and most moths have a hollow feeding tube called a proboscis that they use to drink energy-rich nectar, water, and other liquid nourishment. A few large moths do not feed as adults but live on food stores built up as larvae. Some butterflies enjoy sipping the juice of rotting fruit or the sap oozing from trees; others eat honeydew or the liquids from dead animal carcasses.

Labial palps for testing suitability of food

Front of butterfly head

Proboscis

Detail of proboscis

Fritillary butterflies of the Nymphalidae family

Head of a Pearl-bordered Fritillary, *Clossiana euphrosyne*, Europe

Compound eye

Labial palps

Coiled proboscis

THE "TONGUE"
The proboscis of a butterfly is underneath its head. The hollow feeding tube acts like a rolled drinking straw.

MUD PUDDLE MANNERS

It is quite common, especially in hot climates, to see a group of male butterflies drinking from damp soil – possibly to obtain the minerals. The majority of the butterflies in this "mud puddle" club are Blue triangle butterflies, or Bluebottles, from Malaysia.

Scarce swallowtail,
Iphiclides podalirius

Forewing

Hind wing

AT REST
This engraving shows a
Scarce swallowtail resting
in a typical swallowtail
position, with its wings
folded up above its body.

Thorax

Abdomen

Antenna

Rows of scales
form the patterns
and colors

Homerus swallowtail,
Papilio homerus

WHICH FAMILY?
The veins in the wings of
butterflies and moths help
keep the wing in the correct
flight position. The way the
veins are arranged also helps
scientists and butterfly
fanciers identify the family
to which a species
belongs.

A LARGE FAMILY
The Homerus swallowtail, found only in
Jamaica and an endangered species because
of its popularity with collectors, is one of 500
species belonging to a large family of butterflies,
the Papilionidae, that contains some of the most
beautiful butterflies in the world. Most of the
species are found in the tropics and are strong
fliers. They have large wings and three fully
developed pairs of legs. Swallowtails get their
name from the tapered shape of their hind wings.

COMING IN FOR A LANDING
With its wings slightly curved,
this Peacock butterfly is about to
land on a buddleia. Butterflies
have enormous control over
their flight movements
and can easily manage
sudden landings.

Spinning silk

Illustrations from *Vermis sericus*, a popular 17th-century book on silk moths

Sɪʟᴋ ɪs ᴘʀᴏᴅᴜᴄᴇᴅ by the caterpillars of most moths, but the finest silk is made by species of moths in the families Saturniidae and Bombycidae. In particular it is made by the caterpillars of the large white moth *Bombyx mori*, more commonly known as the Chinese silkworm. Today, this silkworm is so thoroughly domesticated that it no longer occurs in the wild. According to Chinese legend, silk fiber was first discovered as early as 2700 BC. However, the methods used to produce silk commercially were kept closely guarded for centuries and the export of silkworms or their eggs out of China was a crime punishable by death. Despite this, silkworm eggs, and the seeds of the mulberry trees on which the caterpillars feed, were eventually smuggled out of China, possibly hidden in a walking stick. In Europe, silk had been a highly valued material for making luxurious clothing for a long time. Even after Arabs introduced silkworms into Spain, and silk-weaving centers had been set up in Italy, silk continued to command high prices.

REELING OF THE COCOONS
The production of silk originated in China. This 19th-century engraving shows the thread being transferred to smaller bobbins as it becomes finer. The bobbins of silk were then dyed before being used to weave rich cloth. Today, silk-making is more mechanized, but the basic process remains the same.

UNWINDING THE THREAD
In 17th-century Europe, the methods used to produce silk changed little. Before they could hatch, the insects inside the cocoons were killed in boiling water to prevent them breaking the thread of silk and also to dissolve the gumlike substance that held the strands together. The threads from several cocoons were then caught up and twisted together.

Thread was wound onto a reel or frame

3 BUILDING UP THE WALLS
As the caterpillar works backward and forward between the leaves, the cocoon is made thicker. A fine thread of silk is forced out through the spinneret.

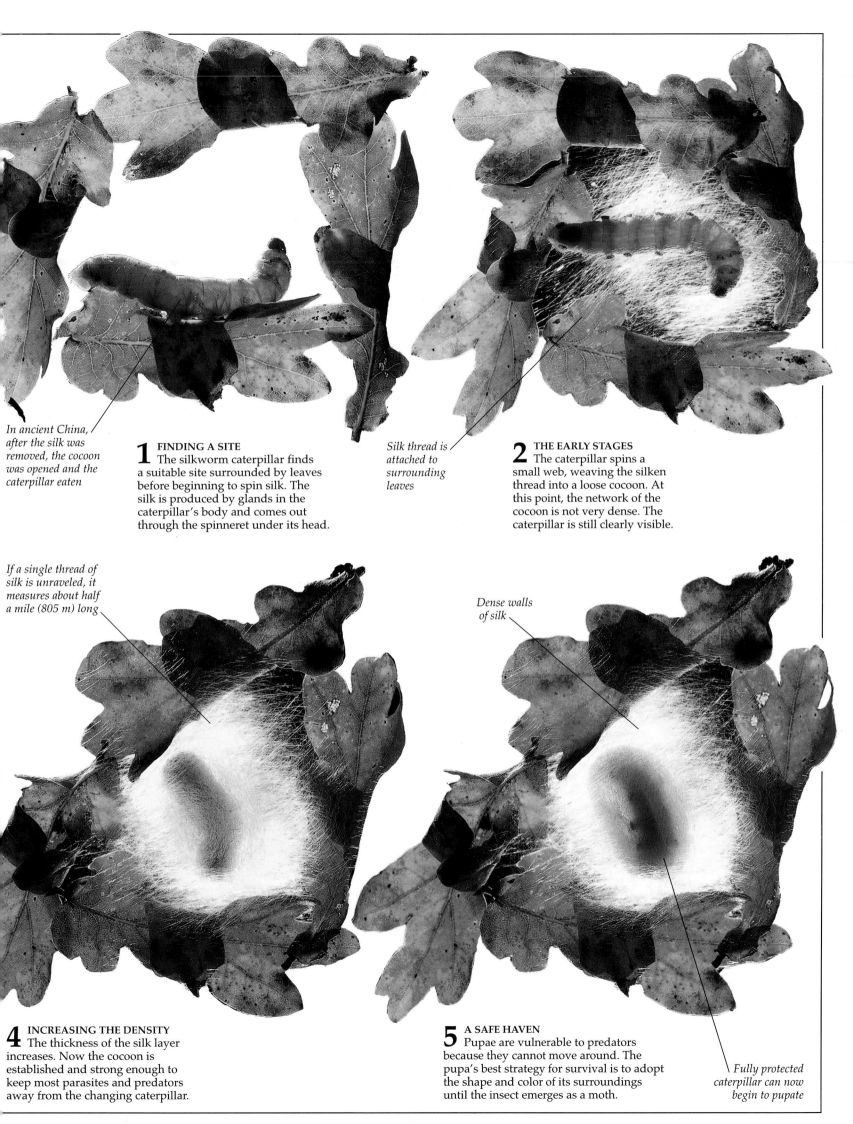

In ancient China, after the silk was removed, the cocoon was opened and the caterpillar eaten

1 FINDING A SITE
The silkworm caterpillar finds a suitable site surrounded by leaves before beginning to spin silk. The silk is produced by glands in the caterpillar's body and comes out through the spinneret under its head.

Silk thread is attached to surrounding leaves

2 THE EARLY STAGES
The caterpillar spins a small web, weaving the silken thread into a loose cocoon. At this point, the network of the cocoon is not very dense. The caterpillar is still clearly visible.

If a single thread of silk is unraveled, it measures about half a mile (805 m) long

Dense walls of silk

4 INCREASING THE DENSITY
The thickness of the silk layer increases. Now the cocoon is established and strong enough to keep most parasites and predators away from the changing caterpillar.

5 A SAFE HAVEN
Pupae are vulnerable to predators because they cannot move around. The pupa's best strategy for survival is to adopt the shape and color of its surroundings until the insect emerges as a moth.

Fully protected caterpillar can now begin to pupate

Moths

THERE ARE AT LEAST 170,000 DIFFERENT SPECIES of butterflies and moths, but the vast majority – more than 150,000 – are moths. The German word for moths, *nachtschmetterlinge* ("night-butterflies"), reflects what most people think of their behavior. Most moths are active at dusk or during the night, but a large number fly during daytime, too. Although many species of moths, such as the silkworm (pp. 64–65), are useful to people, a few species are harmful. These include the moths that destroy crops, fruit, or trees; the moths that nibble holes in wool; and moths that spread diseases in cattle by feeding on the moisture around their eyes. Most moths are harmless, pollinating flowers and forming a vital part of the complex web of life.

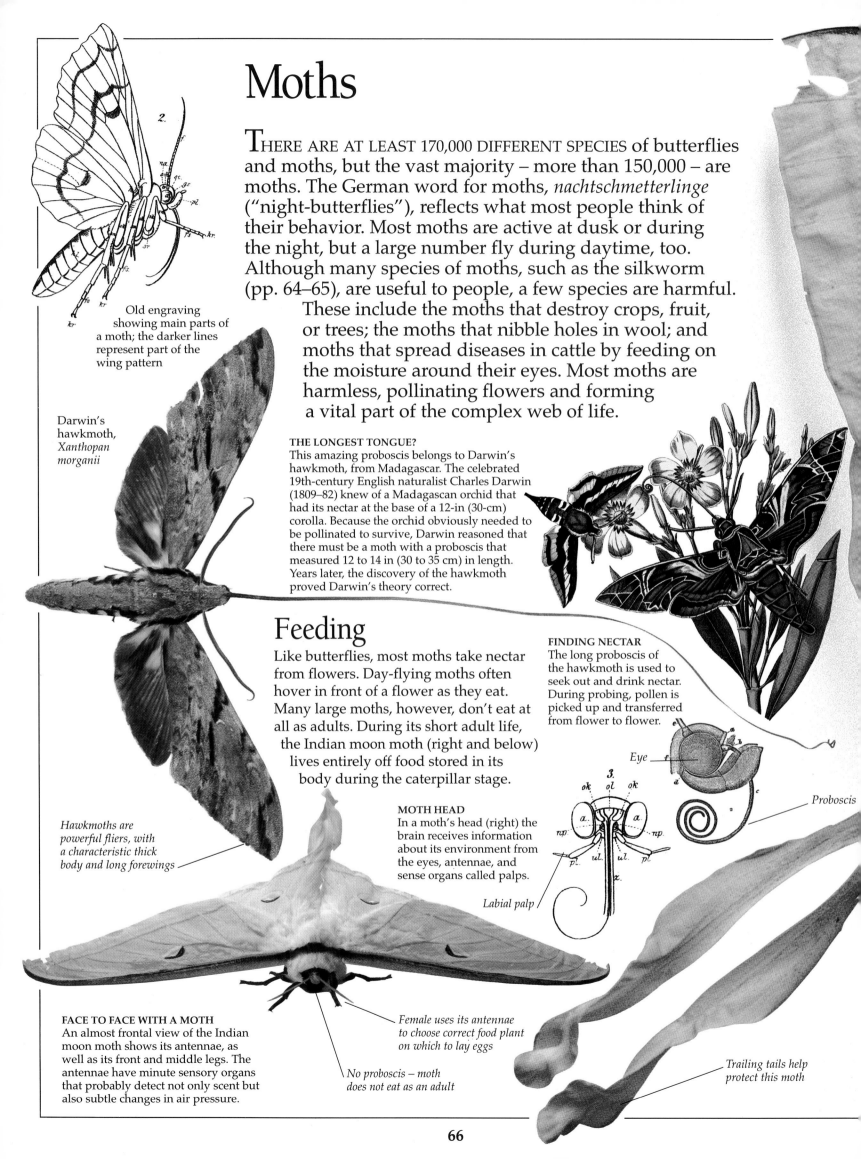

Old engraving showing main parts of a moth; the darker lines represent part of the wing pattern

Darwin's hawkmoth, *Xanthopan morganii*

THE LONGEST TONGUE?
This amazing proboscis belongs to Darwin's hawkmoth, from Madagascar. The celebrated 19th-century English naturalist Charles Darwin (1809–82) knew of a Madagascan orchid that had its nectar at the base of a 12-in (30-cm) corolla. Because the orchid obviously needed to be pollinated to survive, Darwin reasoned that there must be a moth with a proboscis that measured 12 to 14 in (30 to 35 cm) in length. Years later, the discovery of the hawkmoth proved Darwin's theory correct.

Feeding

Like butterflies, most moths take nectar from flowers. Day-flying moths often hover in front of a flower as they eat. Many large moths, however, don't eat at all as adults. During its short adult life, the Indian moon moth (right and below) lives entirely off food stored in its body during the caterpillar stage.

FINDING NECTAR
The long proboscis of the hawkmoth is used to seek out and drink nectar. During probing, pollen is picked up and transferred from flower to flower.

Eye

Proboscis

MOTH HEAD
In a moth's head (right) the brain receives information about its environment from the eyes, antennae, and sense organs called palps.

Hawkmoths are powerful fliers, with a characteristic thick body and long forewings

Labial palp

FACE TO FACE WITH A MOTH
An almost frontal view of the Indian moon moth shows its antennae, as well as its front and middle legs. The antennae have minute sensory organs that probably detect not only scent but also subtle changes in air pressure.

Female uses its antennae to choose correct food plant on which to lay eggs

No proboscis – moth does not eat as an adult

Trailing tails help protect this moth

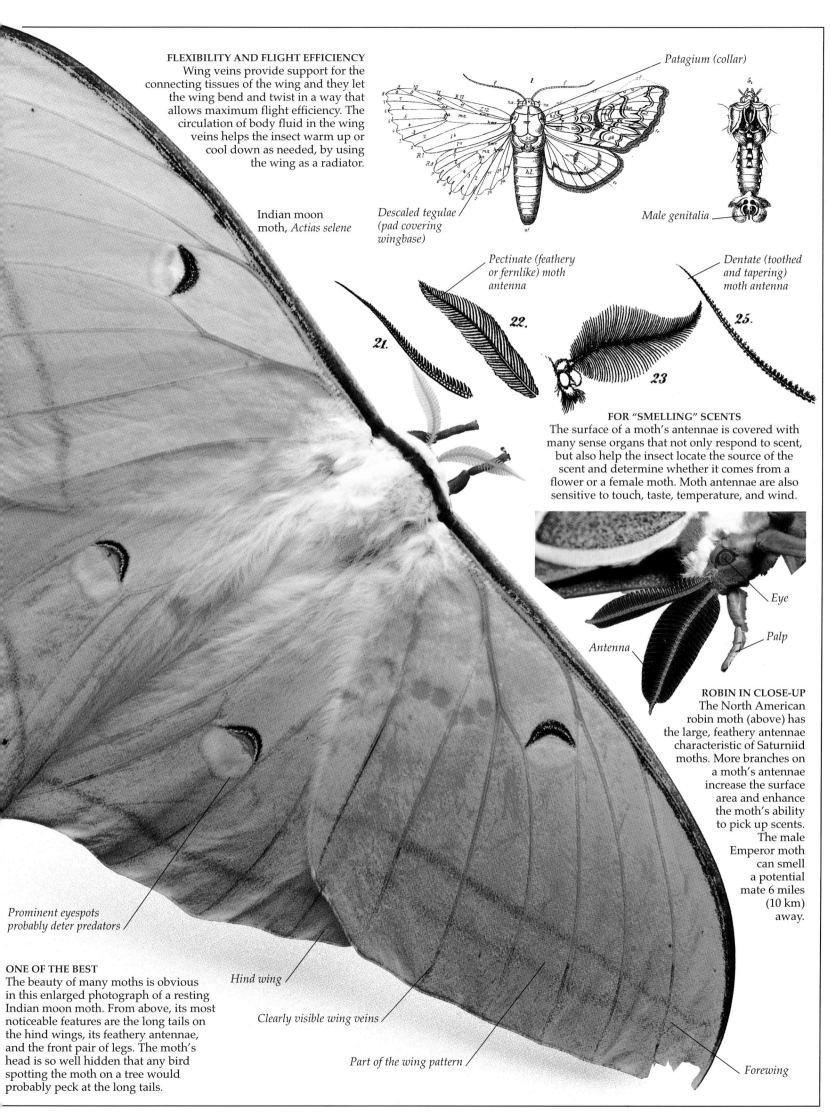

FLEXIBILITY AND FLIGHT EFFICIENCY
Wing veins provide support for the connecting tissues of the wing and they let the wing bend and twist in a way that allows maximum flight efficiency. The circulation of body fluid in the wing veins helps the insect warm up or cool down as needed, by using the wing as a radiator.

Patagium (collar)

Descaled tegulae (pad covering wingbase)

Male genitalia

Indian moon moth, *Actias selene*

Pectinate (feathery or fernlike) moth antenna

21.

22.

23

Dentate (toothed and tapering) moth antenna

25.

FOR "SMELLING" SCENTS
The surface of a moth's antennae is covered with many sense organs that not only respond to scent, but also help the insect locate the source of the scent and determine whether it comes from a flower or a female moth. Moth antennae are also sensitive to touch, taste, temperature, and wind.

Eye

Palp

Antenna

ROBIN IN CLOSE-UP
The North American robin moth (above) has the large, feathery antennae characteristic of Saturniid moths. More branches on a moth's antennae increase the surface area and enhance the moth's ability to pick up scents. The male Emperor moth can smell a potential mate 6 miles (10 km) away.

Prominent eyespots probably deter predators

ONE OF THE BEST
The beauty of many moths is obvious in this enlarged photograph of a resting Indian moon moth. From above, its most noticeable features are the long tails on the hind wings, its feathery antennae, and the front pair of legs. The moth's head is so well hidden that any bird spotting the moth on a tree would probably peck at the long tails.

Hind wing

Clearly visible wing veins

Part of the wing pattern

Forewing

Homes with hinges

BIVALVES ARE AMONG THE BEST KNOWN of all marine creatures. They are mollusks, but their shells are divided into two parts, or valves, that completely enclose and protect the soft body of the mollusk inside. The valves are attached by a shell-like ridge or by teeth that form a hinge, and can be opened and closed with strong muscles and ligaments. Bivalves do not lead very active lives – unable to extend far out of their shells to crawl, many live buried in sand and mud or hidden in rock crevices, while others attach themselves to a hard surface. They eat by opening their valves and filtering water through their gills to catch tiny creatures in the water around them.

THE BIRTH OF VENUS
This detail from Botticelli's famous painting shows the birth of Venus from an enormous scallop shell.

Royal cloak scallop

SCURRYING SCALLOPS
Scallops are very common bivalve mollusks. Some unique scallops can open and close their valves to swim away rapidly when disturbed.

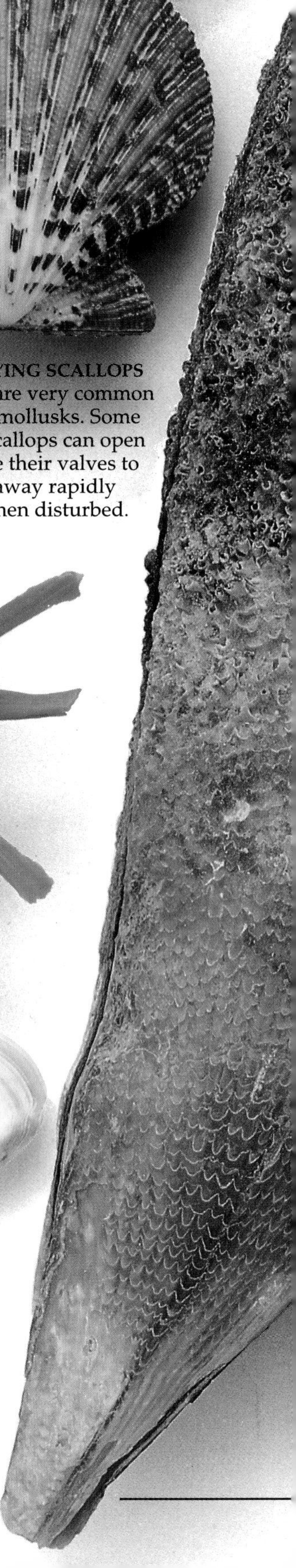

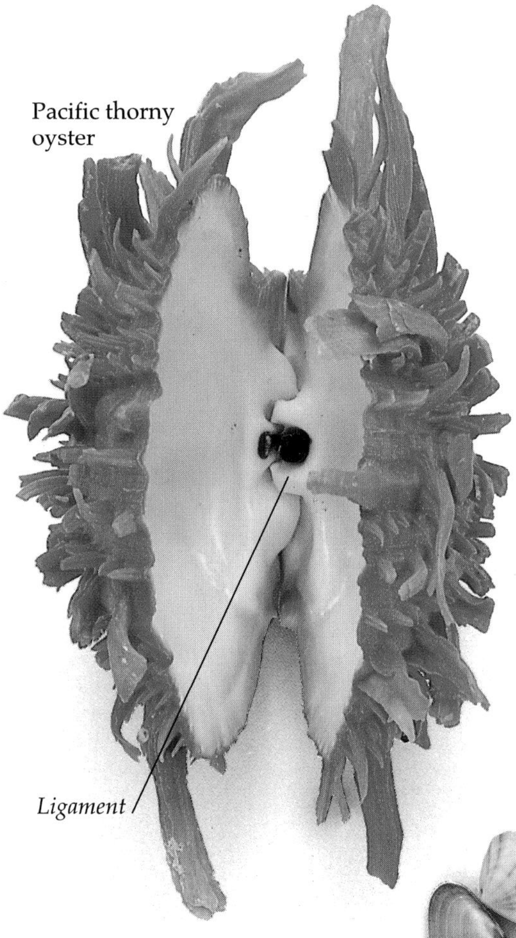

Pacific thorny oyster

Spiky exterior

Ligament

SPINY SHELL
Spiny, or thorny, oysters are also known as chrysanthemum shells because their spines resemble that flower's spiky petals. Although not related to the true oyster, they are similar in that they remain attached to a solid base throughout their lives.

BUTTERFLY WINGS
Shiny, colorful tellin shells often wash ashore still in pairs, resembling butterfly wings.

BEAN CLAMS
Generally tiny and wedge-shaped, these creatures live in large numbers on warm-water beaches. They are an abundant food source, and one often used in chowders and other soups.

Noble pen shell

THE GIANT PEN SHELL
The pinna, or pen shell, spends its life in an upright position with its tapered end half-buried in soft bases, usually among weeds. The giant pen shell, which lives in the Mediterranean Sea, is one of the largest bivalve mollusks, reaching a length of 2 ft (60 cm).

OPEN-AND-SHUT CASE
Although bivalves live mainly with their valves slightly apart, they must be able to close the gap quickly and securely to protect themselves from predators. For this purpose, the two halves of a bivalve shell match perfectly. When the valves clamp shut, the former opening is as impenetrable as the rest of the shell.

GIANT BATH
The enormous tridacna shell houses an animal that can feed up to 20 people! Common in the Molucca islands, the shell can be used as a child's bathtub.

Cock's-comb oyster

Fluted giant clam

Baby noble pen shell

Spiny sand cockle

MINIATURE PEOPLE-EATERS
There are many different types and sizes of clams, but the giant clam is the biggest of all shelled mollusks. Its valves can measure 4 ft (1.2 m), and it can outweigh most people, reaching weights of 550 lb (250 kg). These huge shells are put to many uses, including bathtubs and feeding troughs, and the shell is so strong that it can be made into ax-heads. Living clams are rumored to have killed pearl divers by trapping their arms or legs between the two valves.

Unusual partnerships

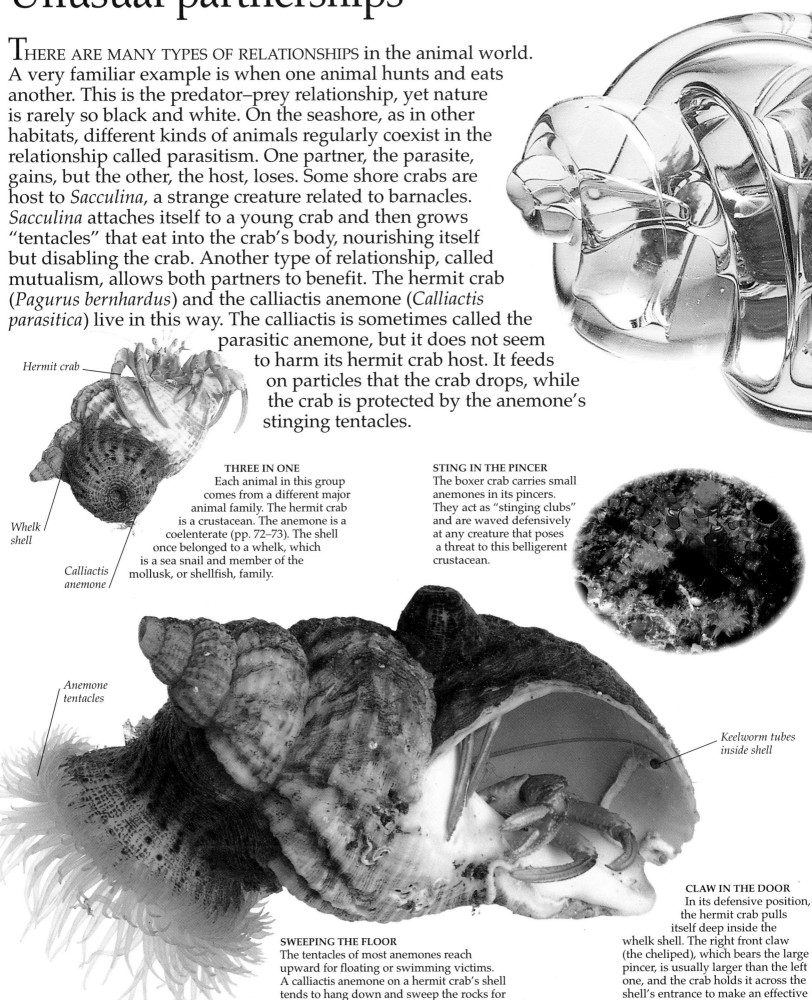

THERE ARE MANY TYPES OF RELATIONSHIPS in the animal world. A very familiar example is when one animal hunts and eats another. This is the predator–prey relationship, yet nature is rarely so black and white. On the seashore, as in other habitats, different kinds of animals regularly coexist in the relationship called parasitism. One partner, the parasite, gains, but the other, the host, loses. Some shore crabs are host to *Sacculina*, a strange creature related to barnacles. *Sacculina* attaches itself to a young crab and then grows "tentacles" that eat into the crab's body, nourishing itself but disabling the crab. Another type of relationship, called mutualism, allows both partners to benefit. The hermit crab (*Pagurus bernhardus*) and the calliactis anemone (*Calliactis parasitica*) live in this way. The calliactis is sometimes called the parasitic anemone, but it does not seem to harm its hermit crab host. It feeds on particles that the crab drops, while the crab is protected by the anemone's stinging tentacles.

Hermit crab

Whelk shell

Calliactis anemone

THREE IN ONE
Each animal in this group comes from a different major animal family. The hermit crab is a crustacean. The anemone is a coelenterate (pp. 72–73). The shell once belonged to a whelk, which is a sea snail and member of the mollusk, or shellfish, family.

STING IN THE PINCER
The boxer crab carries small anemones in its pincers. They act as "stinging clubs" and are waved defensively at any creature that poses a threat to this belligerent crustacean.

Anemone tentacles

Keelworm tubes inside shell

SWEEPING THE FLOOR
The tentacles of most anemones reach upward for floating or swimming victims. A calliactis anemone on a hermit crab's shell tends to hang down and sweep the rocks for bits of food dropped by the hermit crab.

CLAW IN THE DOOR
In its defensive position, the hermit crab pulls itself deep inside the whelk shell. The right front claw (the cheliped), which bears the large pincer, is usually larger than the left one, and the crab holds it across the shell's entrance to make an effective barrier against predators.

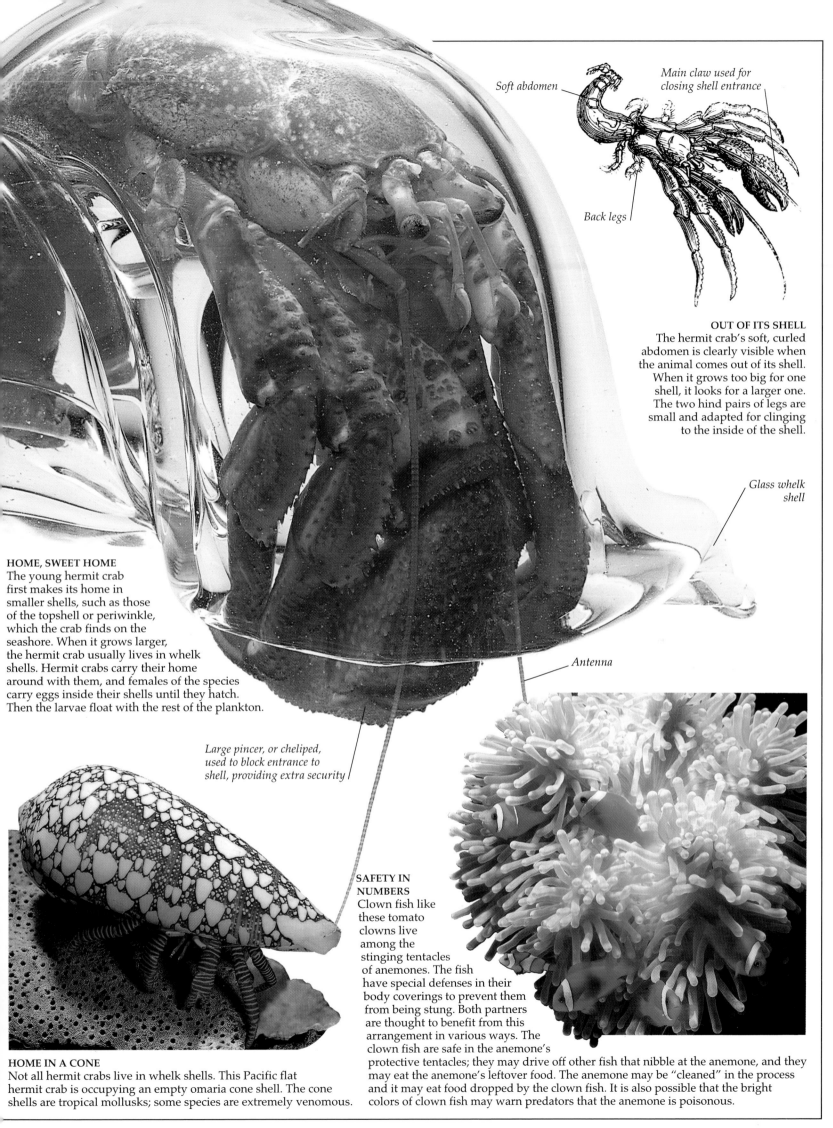

OUT OF ITS SHELL
The hermit crab's soft, curled
abdomen is clearly visible when
the animal comes out of its shell.
When it grows too big for one
shell, it looks for a larger one.
The two hind pairs of legs are
small and adapted for clinging
to the inside of the shell.

Main claw used for
closing shell entrance

Soft abdomen

Back legs

Glass whelk
shell

Antenna

HOME, SWEET HOME
The young hermit crab
first makes its home in
smaller shells, such as those
of the topshell or periwinkle,
which the crab finds on the
seashore. When it grows larger,
the hermit crab usually lives in whelk
shells. Hermit crabs carry their home
around with them, and females of the species
carry eggs inside their shells until they hatch.
Then the larvae float with the rest of the plankton.

Large pincer, or cheliped,
used to block entrance to
shell, providing extra security

**SAFETY IN
NUMBERS**
Clown fish like
these tomato
clowns live
among the
stinging tentacles
of anemones. The fish
have special defenses in their
body coverings to prevent them
from being stung. Both partners
are thought to benefit from this
arrangement in various ways. The
clown fish are safe in the anemone's
protective tentacles; they may drive off other fish that nibble at the anemone, and they
may eat the anemone's leftover food. The anemone may be "cleaned" in the process
and it may eat food dropped by the clown fish. It is also possible that the bright
colors of clown fish may warn predators that the anemone is poisonous.

HOME IN A CONE
Not all hermit crabs live in whelk shells. This Pacific flat
hermit crab is occupying an empty omaria cone shell. The cone
shells are tropical mollusks; some species are extremely venomous.

Flowerlike animals

ANEMONES ARE THE SURPRISING "FLOWERS" of the shore – surprising because they are not flowers at all. They are hollow, jellylike animals belonging to the coelenterate group, also called the cnidarian group, which includes jellyfish and corals. Anemones are unable to move quickly, so they cannot pursue prey or escape from predators. Their best form of attack and defense lies in their "petals," which are really tentacles equipped with specialized stinging cells. Inside each cell is a capsule called a nematocyst that contains a long, coiled thread. In some species these are barbed, in others they contain venom. Stimulated by touch or by particular chemicals, the threads flick out and either hold on to prey with the barbs, or inject venom into it. The prey is then pulled through the mouth into a digestive cavity where it is absorbed. Any remains are excreted through the mouth.

OPEN FOR DINNER
Anemones are beautiful but deadly. The waving tentacles of a colony are a forest of danger for any small sea creatures that float or swim near them.

Mouth in center of red beadlet anemone's body

Scallop shell

SWEEPING THE SEA
Fan worms are sometimes mistaken for anemones, but they belong to a different group of animals – the annelids, which include earthworms. The tentacles of the "fan" filter tiny food particles from the water and withdraw into the tube if danger threatens.

TRAFFIC-LIGHT ANEMONES
Like flowers, anemones have evolved many beautiful colors even within the species. Beadlet anemones are found in various colors, including red, amber, and green. When the tide recedes, they fold in their tentacles and look like overgrown jujubes scattered on the rocks. When fully grown, beadlet anemones have about 200 tentacles.

"FLOWER" ON A "STALK"
A side view of a beadlet anemone shows that it has a stubby "stalk" (body) with an iridescent sheen around the base. Beadlets can survive out of water for some time, and can live very high up on the shoreline.

A grayish beadlet anemone

FEATHERY PLUMES
The plumose, or frilled, anemone is brown, reddish, or white, and may grow up to 1 ft (30 cm) tall. Its feathery tentacles catch very small bits of food and waft them down to the mouth by the beating action of tiny hairs called cilia.

Snow-white tentacles and brown body of a beadlet anemone

Living cup coral with tentacles extended

Limy skeleton of dead cup coral

MEDUSA OF THE SEAS
Snakelock anemones range from gray with delicate sheens of pink or green to all-over deep green in color. The tentacles, tipped in deep pink, do not withdraw in this species, even when it is out of water.

LIVING CORAL
Corals are similar to anemones and members of the same overall group, the coelenterates. This cup coral lives alone, unlike its (mostly) tropical, reef-building cousins.

The body "warts" of this wartlet anemone are visible in this closed-up individual

Side view of dead cup coral

GIANT OF ITS KIND
The largest anemones may grow to more than 3.3 ft (1 m) across. This is a giant green anemone found in tropical waters. It can move, if only slowly, by sliding its muscular base along the rock surface.

TINY GHOSTS
There are many species of these tiny, ghost-white encrusting anemones, which cover areas of rocky shore. As the tide ebbs, most anemones pull in their tentacles and become jellylike blobs to avoid drying out.

Encrusted remains of barnacle shells

Coiled chalky remains of tube worm

Acontia (strings) of stinging cells

STINGING STRINGS
The colorful sagartia anemone (this is the "rosea" variety) ejects pale, stringy groups of stinging cells through its mouth or through slits in its body to defend itself or to catch a meal. The "stings" are in fact parts of the animal's guts.

A fish in water

MOST FISH LIVE IN WATER, breathe by means of gills, swim and maneuver with fins, and are covered in an outer layer of transparent plates called scales. These scales vary in size and shape, but most are small and rounded, flexible, and single-layered. The skin underneath the scales produces a special mucus that makes the fish seem slimy and helps it glide easily through water. All fish are vertebrates – they have a backbone and an internal skeleton. They use color as a means of camouflage and defense, or to advertise a territory.

PEARLY SCALES
In the pearl-scaled butterfly fish, the yellow and orange colors, typical of butterfly fish, are limited to the tail end. The large pearly scales create a rainbow effect of color, and the fish's eye is camouflaged by a black stripe. The deep body but thin profile of the butterfly fish allow it to slip easily between plant stems.

Tall dorsal fins

Strong spines on back

Yellow dorsal fin of ribbon eel

Large, gaping mouth

Pectoral fin

Flat back because fish hangs just below surface, waiting for flies

Silver hatchetfish
Argyropelecus lychnus

FRESHWATER COUSIN
The silver hatchetfish, with its extraordinary deep belly, can leap from the water while beating its large pectoral fins and "fly" short distances, skimming the surface of the water. It is a freshwater fish found in South America; other hatchetfish live in the deep sea.

European
John Dory
Zeus faber

HUNGRY PREDATOR
The European John Dory has a deep body but is extremely thin. It creeps up on smaller fish and prawns, keeping head on to make itself look inconspicuous. Then its great jaws suddenly lever forward and engulf the prey. The John Dory is well protected by the sets of spines in front of its dorsal and anal fins.

IN SHOALS
Young cod feed at the surface on small crustaceans. The adults feed in deeper water on small fish, crustaceans, and worms. They swim in shoals, making it hard for predators to target an individual.

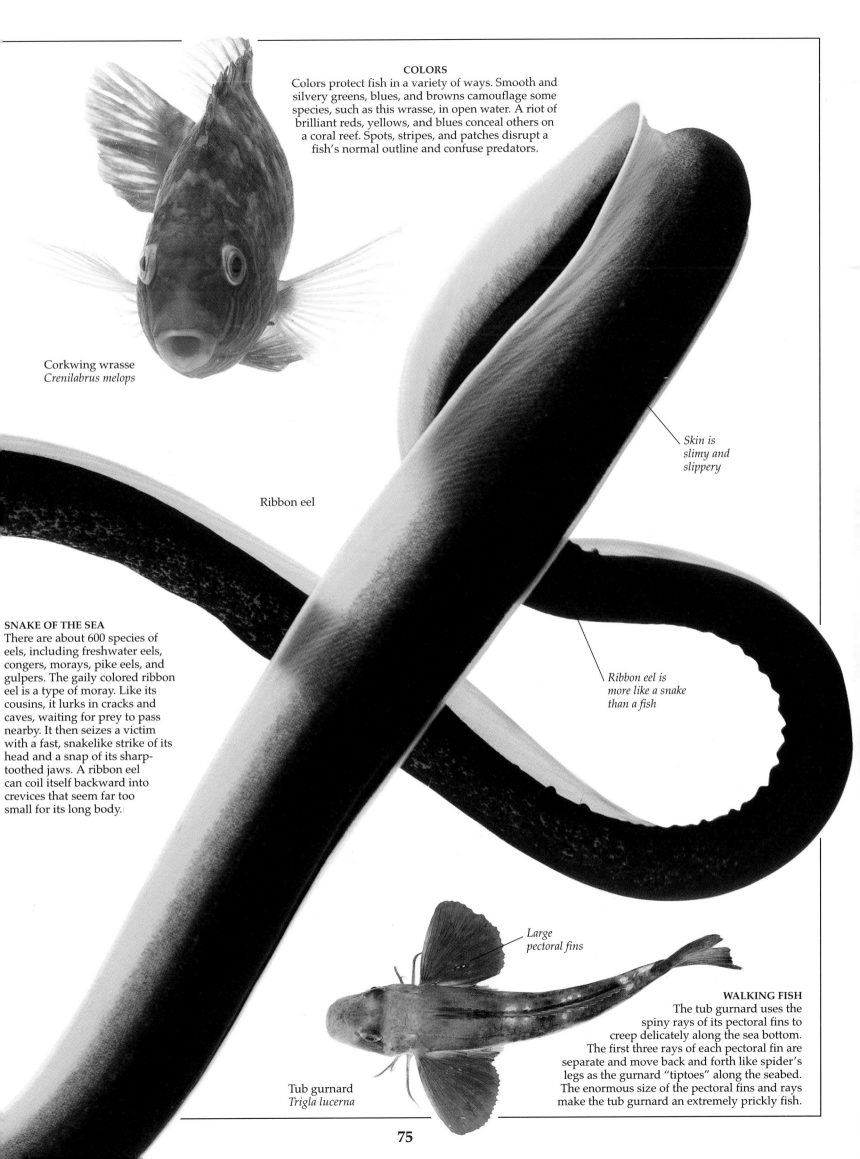

COLORS
Colors protect fish in a variety of ways. Smooth and silvery greens, blues, and browns camouflage some species, such as this wrasse, in open water. A riot of brilliant reds, yellows, and blues conceal others on a coral reef. Spots, stripes, and patches disrupt a fish's normal outline and confuse predators.

Corkwing wrasse
Crenilabrus melops

Ribbon eel

Skin is slimy and slippery

Ribbon eel is more like a snake than a fish

SNAKE OF THE SEA
There are about 600 species of eels, including freshwater eels, congers, morays, pike eels, and gulpers. The gaily colored ribbon eel is a type of moray. Like its cousins, it lurks in cracks and caves, waiting for prey to pass nearby. It then seizes a victim with a fast, snakelike strike of its head and a snap of its sharp-toothed jaws. A ribbon eel can coil itself backward into crevices that seem far too small for its long body.

Large pectoral fins

WALKING FISH
The tub gurnard uses the spiny rays of its pectoral fins to creep delicately along the sea bottom. The first three rays of each pectoral fin are separate and move back and forth like spider's legs as the gurnard "tiptoes" along the seabed. The enormous size of the pectoral fins and rays make the tub gurnard an extremely prickly fish.

Tub gurnard
Trigla lucerna

Moving along

EVERY SWIMMER KNOWS that moving through seawater is harder than moving through air. To be a fast, powerful swimmer like a dolphin, tuna, or sailfish, it also helps to have a streamlined shape to reduce drag (resistance to water). A smooth skin and few projections from the body allow an animal to move through the water more easily. The density of seawater has an advantage too, in that it helps support the weight of very heavy bodies, such as the heaviest animal to ever live on Earth, the blue whale, which weighs up to 165 tons (150 tonnes). Some heavy-shelled creatures, like the chambered nautilus, have gas-filled floats to buoy them. Some ocean animals, such as dolphins and flying fish, gather enough speed underwater to leap briefly into the air, but not all ocean animals are good swimmers. Many can only swim slowly, others drift along in the currents, crawl along the bottom, burrow in the sand, or simply stay put, anchored to the seabed.

FLYING FISH
Gathering speed underwater, flying fish leap clear of the surface to escape predators. They can then glide for more than 30 seconds by spreading out side fins.

AT SCHOOL
Fish often swim together in schools, like these blue-striped snappers. In schools, a single fish is less likely to be attacked by a predator than if it was swimming on its own. The moving mass of individuals may confuse the predator, and there are more pairs of eyes on the lookout for an attacker.

IN THE SWING
During the day, many electric rays prefer to stay hidden on the sandy bottom, relying on their electric organs for defense, but they do swim if disturbed and at night, when searching for prey. There are more than 30 kinds of electric rays, mostly living in warm waters. Most other rays have spindly tails (unlike the electric ray's broad tail) and move through water using their pectoral fins. Waves pass from the front to the back of the pectoral fins, that, in larger rays like mantas, become so exaggerated the fins actually beat up and down like watery wings.

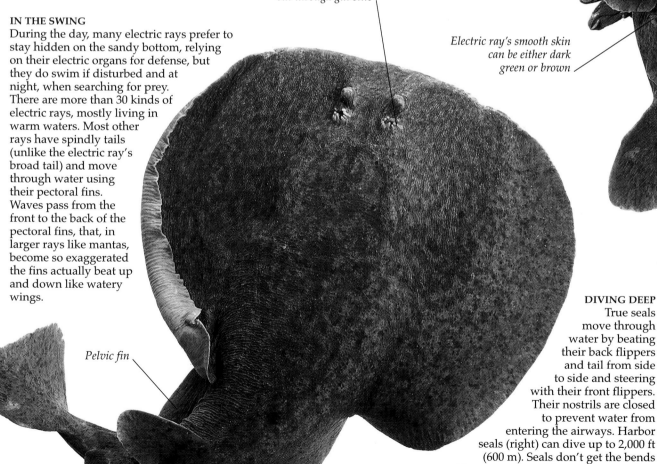

Spiracle (a one-way valve) takes in water, which is pumped out through gill slits

Electric ray's smooth skin can be either dark green or brown

Electric rays can grow to 6 ft (1.8 m) and weigh as much as 110 lb (50 kg)

Pelvic fin

DIVING DEEP
True seals move through water by beating their back flippers and tail from side to side and steering with their front flippers. Their nostrils are closed to prevent water from entering the airways. Harbor seals (right) can dive up to 2,000 ft (600 m). Seals don't get the bends (decompression sickness) because they breathe out before diving and, unlike humans, do not breathe compressed air. When underwater, seals use oxygen that is stored in their blood.

Broad tail fin, swinging from side to side, helps propel ray along

Pectoral fin provides extra propulsion as waves pass along flexible edges of its rounded side

Smaller second dorsal fin

Clasper (male reproductive organ)

Swimming sequence of an electric ray
Torpedo nobiliana

Electric organ, at base of pectoral fin, helps catch fish by stunning them – some species can deliver more than 200 volts

Model of great white shark
Carcharodon carcharias

TAKING OFF
Dolphins leap out of the water for fun, to signal to other dolphins, and when feeding. They can also porpoise (skim over the water for short distances) when moving quickly. They do this because it is easier to move in air, which puts less friction on their bodies.

Tall dorsal fin

Pectoral fin

Pelvic fin

Tail propels shark forward in water

Starry smooth-hound
Mustelus asterias

Undulations (S-shaped waves) pass down body, ending at the tail, which produces forward thrust

LEAN MACHINE
Sharks propel themselves through the water by beating their tails from side to side. The pectoral fins are held out away from the body. As water flows over them, the fins act like airplane wings and keep the shark from sinking. When the fins are tilted, they also act as brakes, just like the raised flaps on the wings of an airplane during landing. Some sharks that live on the seabed, such as horn sharks and epaulette sharks, use their pectoral fins to crawl along the ocean floor.

Mobile mollusks

MOLLUSKS ARE A LARGE GROUP of animals that includes cephalopods (octopuses, squid, and cuttlefish), bivalves (scallops, mussels, and oysters), and gastropods (snails, limpets, and abalones). Cephalopods move by jet propulsion. They have a small shell or no shell, and a muscular body wall that can expel water. Bivalves have a shell that is in two halves, and some, such as scallops, also "swim" using jet propulsion. Most clams, however, can only bury themselves in the sand or are anchored to the seabed. Gastropods usually have a coiled external shell, although some, like slugs, have a small internal shell or no shell at all. They travel by moving the muscles of their single, flat foot.

MOVING LIKE A SNAIL
Great pond snails move slowly, on a single, large, flat foot, among water plants looking for food. The muscles of the foot move in and out in waves, and the snail moves forward as each wave passes along the foot. Special glands produce a slime that helps the foot glide smoothly along.

INK SCREEN
Cephalopods like this squid produce a cloud of ink when threatened. This confuses an enemy and allows the squid to escape. The ink is produced in a gland linked to the gut and is ejected in a blast of water from the tubelike funnel near the squid's head.

JET PROPULSION
Squid are very efficient at swimming by jet propulsion. Their torpedo-shaped bodies are naturally streamlined so that they can swim fast to escape predators. It may be no coincidence that they are among the most common animals in the ocean.

Squid
Loligo forbisi

Eye with horizontal iris

Tentacle, also known as "leg" or "arm"

Funnel, or siphon, through which octopus squeezes water when swimming

Two rows of suckers under each tentacle

Powerful suckers grip rocky surfaces so octopus can pull itself along or hold prey

Common octopus
Octopus vulgaris

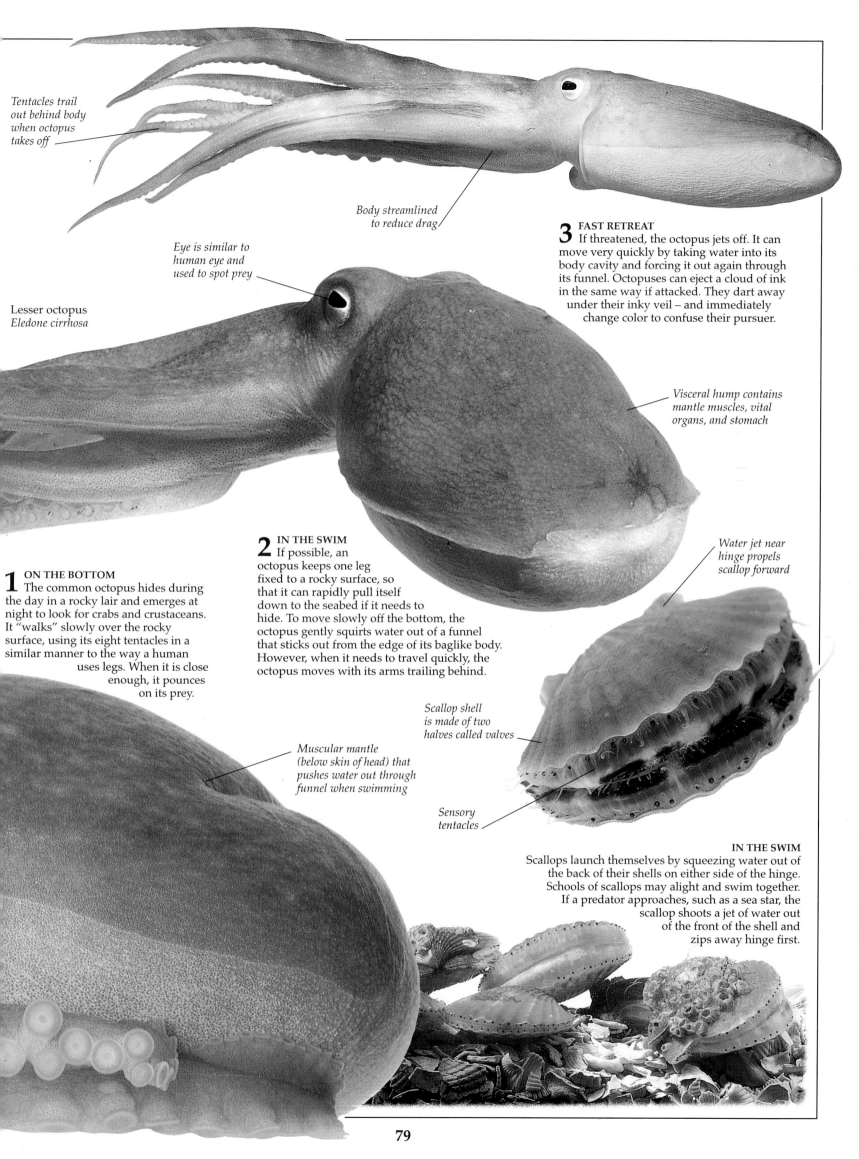

Tentacles trail out behind body when octopus takes off

Body streamlined to reduce drag

3 FAST RETREAT
If threatened, the octopus jets off. It can move very quickly by taking water into its body cavity and forcing it out again through its funnel. Octopuses can eject a cloud of ink in the same way if attacked. They dart away under their inky veil – and immediately change color to confuse their pursuer.

Eye is similar to human eye and used to spot prey

Lesser octopus
Eledone cirrhosa

Visceral hump contains mantle muscles, vital organs, and stomach

2 IN THE SWIM
If possible, an octopus keeps one leg fixed to a rocky surface, so that it can rapidly pull itself down to the seabed if it needs to hide. To move slowly off the bottom, the octopus gently squirts water out of a funnel that sticks out from the edge of its baglike body. However, when it needs to travel quickly, the octopus moves with its arms trailing behind.

Water jet near hinge propels scallop forward

1 ON THE BOTTOM
The common octopus hides during the day in a rocky lair and emerges at night to look for crabs and crustaceans. It "walks" slowly over the rocky surface, using its eight tentacles in a similar manner to the way a human uses legs. When it is close enough, it pounces on its prey.

Scallop shell is made of two halves called valves

Muscular mantle (below skin of head) that pushes water out through funnel when swimming

Sensory tentacles

IN THE SWIM
Scallops launch themselves by squeezing water out of the back of their shells on either side of the hinge. Schools of scallops may alight and swim together. If a predator approaches, such as a sea star, the scallop shoots a jet of water out of the front of the shell and zips away hinge first.

The importance of water

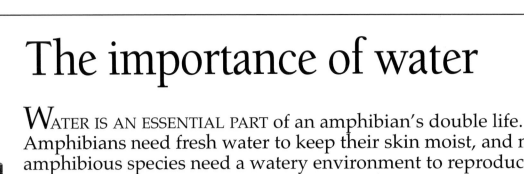

WATER IS AN ESSENTIAL PART of an amphibian's double life. Amphibians need fresh water to keep their skin moist, and most amphibious species need a watery environment to reproduce – especially those that spend all, or part, of their lives as larvae in water. In aquatic or watery habitats, water passes rapidly through the skin and has to be eliminated via the kidneys. In dry areas, amphibians risk losing more water than they can absorb. Frogs can reduce water loss by having a less porous skin, by seeking out damp, shady places, by burrowing, and by absorbing water from damp or wet surfaces. Some toads obtain almost three-quarters of the water they need through a baggy patch, or "seat," on their pelvis that they press against moist surfaces. Amphibians rarely drink water, although a little water may be consumed as part of their food. They have adapted their behavior and skin-surface structure to a surprising variety of habitats, from ponds and trees to high in the forest canopy where the only free-standing water collects in pockets formed by leaves. They have also adapted to life in the desert by burrowing and forming heat-sparing and water-conserving cocoons.

FLOWER POWER
Amphibians are popular subjects for stories. *Thumbelina* is a children's story about a flower fairy stolen by a toad who wants her to marry his ugly son. The toad imprisons Thumbelina on a lily pad in the middle of a river, but she escapes (with the help of fish) and eventually marries the Prince of the Flower People.

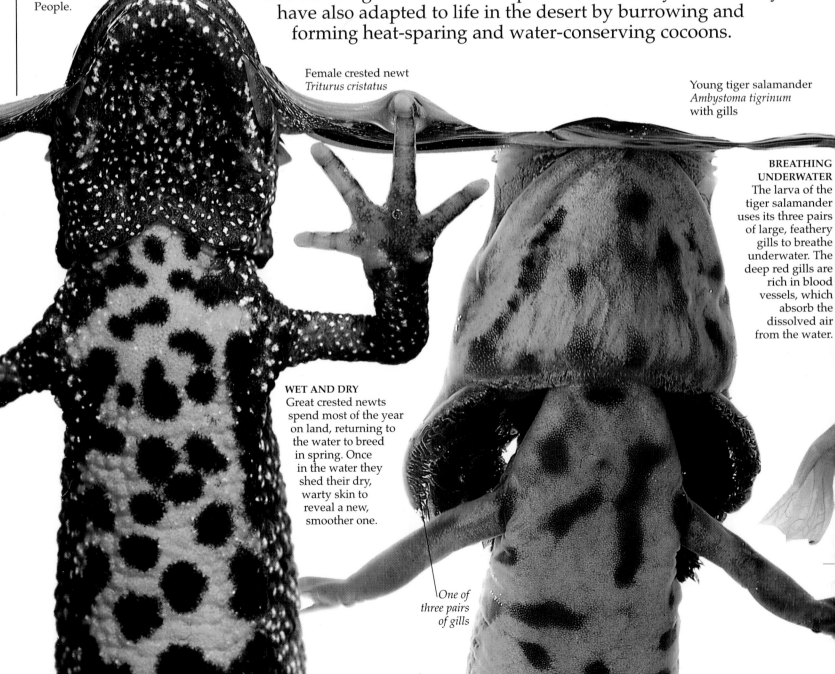

Female crested newt
Triturus cristatus

Young tiger salamander
Ambystoma tigrinum
with gills

BREATHING UNDERWATER
The larva of the tiger salamander uses its three pairs of large, feathery gills to breathe underwater. The deep red gills are rich in blood vessels, which absorb the dissolved air from the water.

WET AND DRY
Great crested newts spend most of the year on land, returning to the water to breed in spring. Once in the water they shed their dry, warty skin to reveal a new, smoother one.

One of three pairs of gills

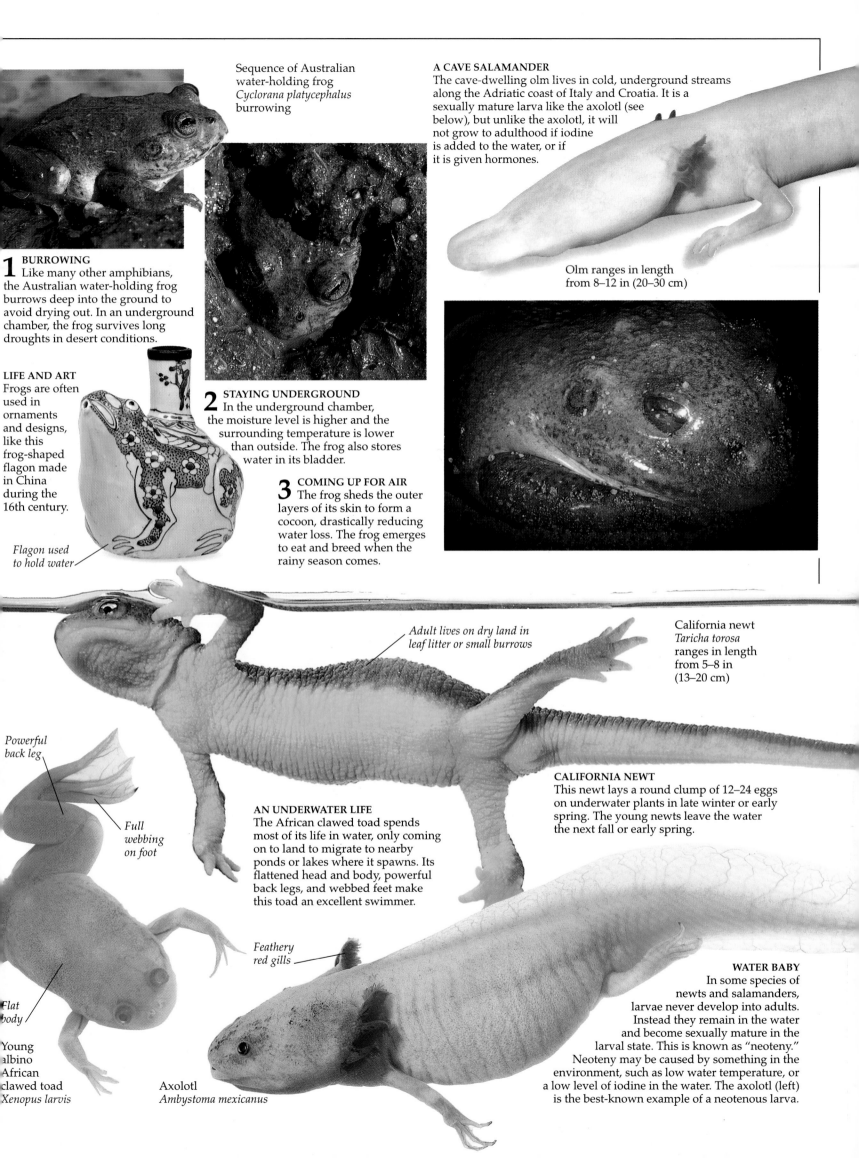

Sequence of Australian water-holding frog *Cyclorana platycephalus* **burrowing**

A CAVE SALAMANDER
The cave-dwelling olm lives in cold, underground streams along the Adriatic coast of Italy and Croatia. It is a sexually mature larva like the axolotl (see below), but unlike the axolotl, it will not grow to adulthood if iodine is added to the water, or if it is given hormones.

1 BURROWING
Like many other amphibians, the Australian water-holding frog burrows deep into the ground to avoid drying out. In an underground chamber, the frog survives long droughts in desert conditions.

LIFE AND ART
Frogs are often used in ornaments and designs, like this frog-shaped flagon made in China during the 16th century.

Flagon used to hold water

2 STAYING UNDERGROUND
In the underground chamber, the moisture level is higher and the surrounding temperature is lower than outside. The frog also stores water in its bladder.

3 COMING UP FOR AIR
The frog sheds the outer layers of its skin to form a cocoon, drastically reducing water loss. The frog emerges to eat and breed when the rainy season comes.

Olm ranges in length from 8–12 in (20–30 cm)

Adult lives on dry land in leaf litter or small burrows

California newt Taricha torosa *ranges in length from 5–8 in (13–20 cm)*

Powerful back leg

Full webbing on foot

AN UNDERWATER LIFE
The African clawed toad spends most of its life in water, only coming on to land to migrate to nearby ponds or lakes where it spawns. Its flattened head and body, powerful back legs, and webbed feet make this toad an excellent swimmer.

CALIFORNIA NEWT
This newt lays a round clump of 12–24 eggs on underwater plants in late winter or early spring. The young newts leave the water the next fall or early spring.

Feathery red gills

Flat body

Young albino African clawed toad *Xenopus larvis*

Axolotl *Ambystoma mexicanus*

WATER BABY
In some species of newts and salamanders, larvae never develop into adults. Instead they remain in the water and become sexually mature in the larval state. This is known as "neoteny." Neoteny may be caused by something in the environment, such as low water temperature, or a low level of iodine in the water. The axolotl (left) is the best-known example of a neotenous larva.

On all fours

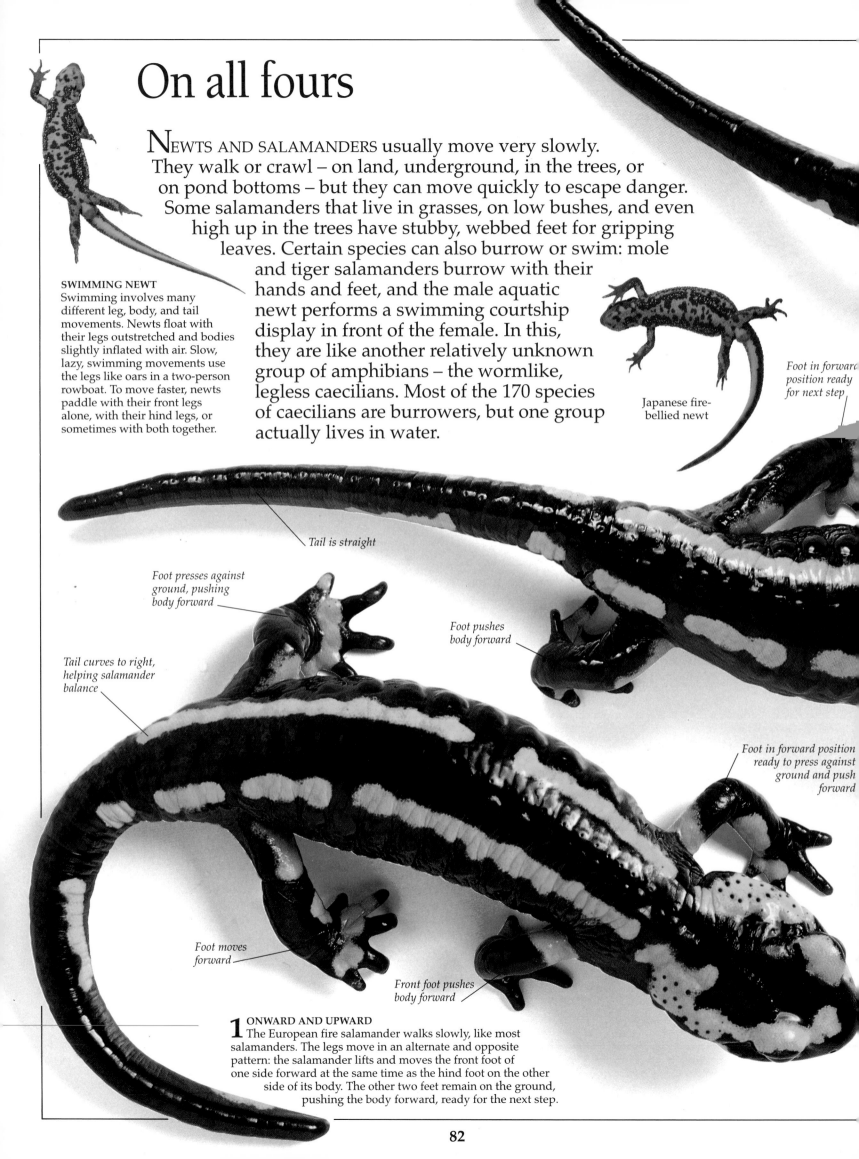

NEWTS AND SALAMANDERS usually move very slowly.
They walk or crawl – on land, underground, in the trees, or
on pond bottoms – but they can move quickly to escape danger.
Some salamanders that live in grasses, on low bushes, and even
high up in the trees have stubby, webbed feet for gripping
leaves. Certain species can also burrow or swim: mole
and tiger salamanders burrow with their
hands and feet, and the male aquatic
newt performs a swimming courtship
display in front of the female. In this,
they are like another relatively unknown
group of amphibians – the wormlike,
legless caecilians. Most of the 170 species
of caecilians are burrowers, but one group
actually lives in water.

SWIMMING NEWT
Swimming involves many
different leg, body, and tail
movements. Newts float with
their legs outstretched and bodies
slightly inflated with air. Slow,
lazy, swimming movements use
the legs like oars in a two-person
rowboat. To move faster, newts
paddle with their front legs
alone, with their hind legs, or
sometimes with both together.

Japanese fire-
bellied newt

*Foot in forward
position ready
for next step*

Tail is straight

*Foot presses against
ground, pushing
body forward*

*Foot pushes
body forward*

*Tail curves to right,
helping salamander
balance*

*Foot in forward position
ready to press against
ground and push
forward*

*Foot moves
forward*

*Front foot pushes
body forward*

1 ONWARD AND UPWARD
The European fire salamander walks slowly, like most
salamanders. The legs move in an alternate and opposite
pattern: the salamander lifts and moves the front foot of
one side forward at the same time as the hind foot on the other
side of its body. The other two feet remain on the ground,
pushing the body forward, ready for the next step.

3 FORWARD MARCH
The third step completes the sequence, with the left front and right hind feet together and the other two feet stationary. In addition to pushing the salamander forward, this alternate and opposite pattern pushes the middle of its body from side to side. The swaying motion increases with walking speed and looks like a crawling baby.

Foot ready to lift for next step

Foot about to push body forward

Foot ready to push body forward

Foot ready to lift and move forward

Foot about to lift and move forward

Foot in forward position

UNDULATING CAECILIANS
Most caecilians live in soft earth or in the leaf litter of the rain forest floor. About 20 species have moved back into the water and swim using undulating, wavelike movements. All caecilians can burrow by pushing their head into the soil and opening up a hole with movements of the neck. Then they either "swim" forward through the soil with undulating movements that pass back along the body, or use a special, wormlike concertina movement, in which the spine folds inside the body.

2 NEXT STEP
With the next step, the front right and left hind feet of the salamander move together, while the other two feet stay in the same position on the ground, getting ready to push the body forward.

Foot pressing on surface, ready to push body forward

Foot about to lift

Foot ready to lift and move body forward

Foot pressing down

NEWT WALK
When moving at slow speed on land, newts and salamanders walk in similar ways. This view from beneath shows which foot is actively pressing against the surface, pushing the newt forward, and which is being lifted off the surface before being set down again. In water, the newt is lighter and more buoyant (just as a person is in a swimming pool) and often uses just the tips of its fingers and toes to walk over the muddy bottom of its pond.

View from below of a newt walking

Foot ready to lift and move body forward

A tight squeeze

ALL SNAKES EAT MEAT, but they have had to develop many different ways of killing their food. Some kill their prey with venom, but boas and pythons feed mainly on mammals, which they kill by constriction. Constrictors do not crush their victims, as you might think. The snake coils its body around its struggling victim, making it harder and harder for the prey to breathe, until it finally suffocates. The snake applies just enough pressure to match the breathing movements of the prey. Any mammal from a mouse to a deer could be that prey, depending on the size of the snake. Giant snakes can swallow surprisingly large animals: an anaconda more than 26 ft (8 m) long can eat a caiman nearly 6.5 ft (2 m) long – it can take more than a week to digest its meal!

TO THE RESCUE!
Only a few Asian and African records exist of humans who have been killed and eaten by some of the larger species of pythons. In one of the famous Tintin books, Zorrino the guide makes a lucky escape (contrary to appearances), saved just in the nick of time by his friend, the redoubtable Tintin.

DANGEROUS ACT
Sideshow and circus performers who dance with constrictors do so at great risk. This dancer was nearly suffocated by a python, and was rescued only seconds before certain death.

2 DEADLY EMBRACE
The constricting snake reacts to every tiny movement of the rat, always tightening its grip. It responds to even the smallest vibrations produced by the rat's beating heart; the snake will not release its hold until the beating finally stops. Death is fairly quick and bones are rarely broken. The snake then shifts the rat so that it can be swallowed headfirst.

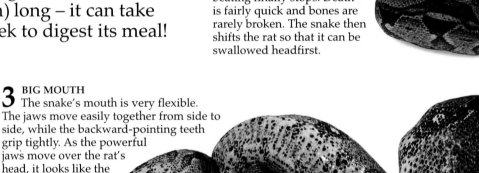

3 BIG MOUTH
The snake's mouth is very flexible. The jaws move easily together from side to side, while the backward-pointing teeth grip tightly. As the powerful jaws move over the rat's head, it looks like the snake is "walking over" its food.

4 SAFETY FIRST
A small animal can disappear completely in only one or two gulps, but it takes an hour or more for some of the larger victims. The swallowing action of the snake is mainly automatic, and the prey is drawn in by the trunk muscles of the snake. If the snake is frightened or disturbed while it is eating, it can regurgitate its meal in order to escape.

Body can expand to allow for large prey

5 TIGHT FIT
Most of the rat has disappeared. A flexible ligament, an elastic muscle that connects both halves of the snake's lower jaw, allows the snake to open its mouth very wide. As the lower jaws are forced apart, the muscle between them stretches to accomodate the shape of the prey.

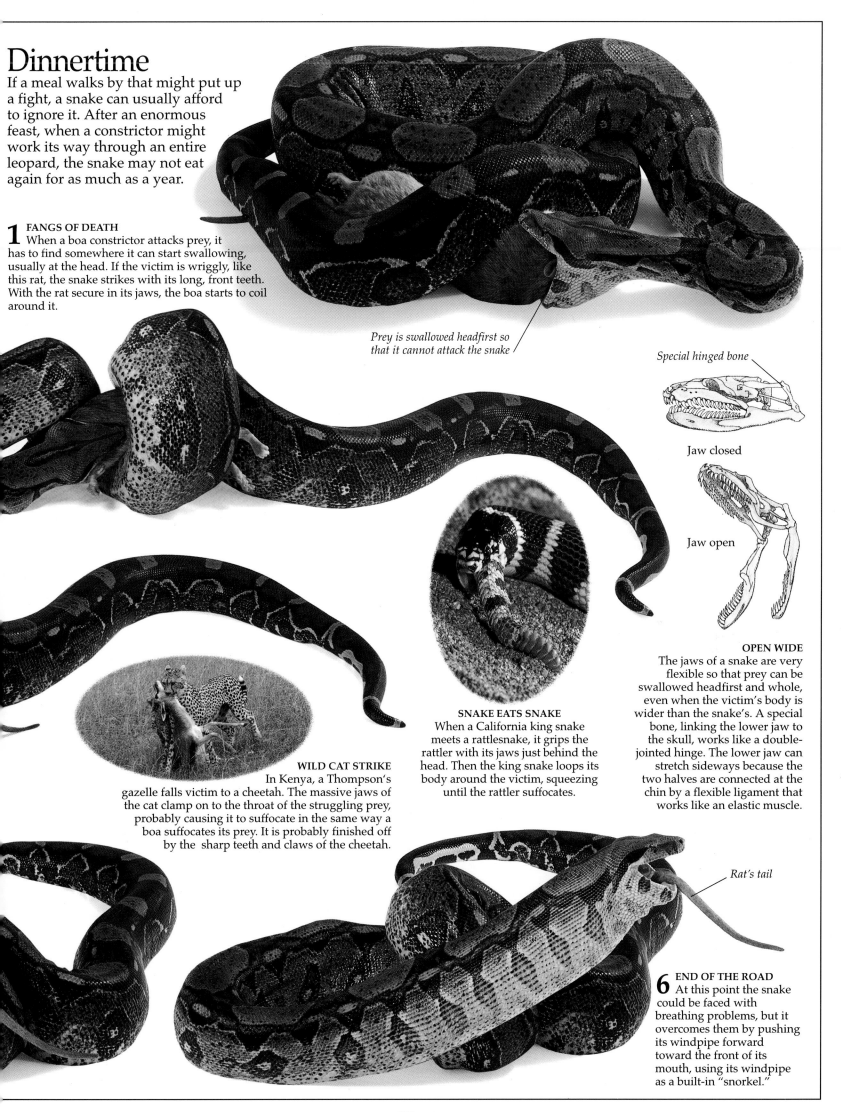

Dinnertime

If a meal walks by that might put up a fight, a snake can usually afford to ignore it. After an enormous feast, when a constrictor might work its way through an entire leopard, the snake may not eat again for as much as a year.

1 FANGS OF DEATH
When a boa constrictor attacks prey, it has to find somewhere it can start swallowing, usually at the head. If the victim is wriggly, like this rat, the snake strikes with its long, front teeth. With the rat secure in its jaws, the boa starts to coil around it.

Prey is swallowed headfirst so that it cannot attack the snake

Special hinged bone

Jaw closed

Jaw open

OPEN WIDE
The jaws of a snake are very flexible so that prey can be swallowed headfirst and whole, even when the victim's body is wider than the snake's. A special bone, linking the lower jaw to the skull, works like a double-jointed hinge. The lower jaw can stretch sideways because the two halves are connected at the chin by a flexible ligament that works like an elastic muscle.

SNAKE EATS SNAKE
When a California king snake meets a rattlesnake, it grips the rattler with its jaws just behind the head. Then the king snake loops its body around the victim, squeezing until the rattler suffocates.

WILD CAT STRIKE
In Kenya, a Thompson's gazelle falls victim to a cheetah. The massive jaws of the cat clamp on to the throat of the struggling prey, probably causing it to suffocate in the same way a boa suffocates its prey. It is probably finished off by the sharp teeth and claws of the cheetah.

Rat's tail

6 END OF THE ROAD
At this point the snake could be faced with breathing problems, but it overcomes them by pushing its windpipe forward toward the front of its mouth, using its windpipe as a built-in "snorkel."

Lizards

THERE ARE MORE THAN 3,000 species of lizards. They form the most successful of all the reptilian groups, having evolved many different lifestyles. Although most of them live on the ground, many live in trees, some are burrowers, and some are aquatic. Some lizards have no limbs and are snakelike; others can parachute or fly. The lizards on these two pages all live in desert regions, where they are more numerous than snakes. They like to bask in the sun in the early morning to warm up their muscles after a cold desert night. In the heat of the day, they retreat into the shade of rocks or plants or into cool burrows. Most desert lizards can change color to blend into their backgrounds and avoid being spotted by predators. When threatened, some lizards put on intimidating displays. If this does not work, then some lizards will bite, but most simply run away.

FIERCE FRILLS
The frilled lizard of the Australian desert spreads out the frill around its neck to make itself look larger to scare away enemies. The frill is supported by rods (like an umbrella's) that are attached to a bone at the base of the tongue.

FRINGE TOES
This fast-moving lizard can run across the sand dunes in the Sahara, where it lives. It has a fringe of scales on its feet that acts like a snowshoe to spread its weight and prevent it from sinking into the sand. To stay cooler on hot sand, it holds its head and body high above the surface of the ground.

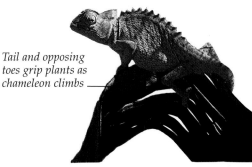

Tail and opposing toes grip plants as chameleon climbs

CHAMELEON
A chameleon sits on the stem of a welwitschia plant growing in the Namib Desert. Chameleons and other lizards are attracted to the plant because insects like to shelter under the shade of its leaves. They catch the insects by shooting out their long, sticky-tipped tongues.

GILA MONSTER
The Gila monster is one of only two lizards with a venomous bite, although it is seldom fatal to humans. Gila monsters live in desert scrub and are mainly active at night, feeding on small mammals, snakes, and other lizards.

Layer of skin under the scales changes color for camouflage

Bearded dragon

Beard not apparent when lizard is at rest

In places, the scales form spines

Color darker in morning to absorb heat of the Sun, and paler as day wears on

BEARDED DRAGON
A formidable-looking lizard, the bearded dragon from the dry interior of Australia has spiny skin to protect itself from predators. The beard under the chin expands to make the dragon look even more impressive. Bearded dragons feed on insects, birds' eggs, newborn small mammals, and some dew-soaked plants. They are active in the early morning and late afternoon. In the heat of the day, they climb into shrubs, where it is cooler.

Sturdy tail serves as a fat reserve

LIZARD EGGS
These eggs belong to the eyed lizard from northern Africa. It lays up to 20 eggs in sandy soil, which hatch out two to three months later. Eyed lizards grow more than 2 ft (60 cm) long. These large lizards feed on insects, small mammals, and other reptiles.

SPINY-TAILED, OR DAB, LIZARD
One of the hardiest desert lizards in the Sahara, the African spiny-tailed lizard tolerates high temperatures and survives on small amounts of water obtained from dew and the plants and few insects that it eats. This lizard is active in the day, but avoids the midday heat by staying deep in its burrow.

THORNY DEVIL
A spiny body helps protect this lizard from being attacked. It lives in the deserts in Australia and has a similar ant-eating lifestyle to horned toads. Thorny devils collect rain or dew on their backs, which finds its way down tiny channels into their mouths. These lizards are also known as molochs.

Keen sense of smell helps lizard hunt

Wide gape to deter predators

Collared lizard
Crotophytus collaris

The collared lizard can inflict a nasty bite with its sharp teeth

COLLARED LIZARD
In a defensive pose, the collared lizard opens its mouth in a wide gape. If attacked, the lizard will bite, but it would rather leap away over the rocks where it lives in the deserts of the southwestern United States. The collared lizard is an active predator. It hunts during the day for insects, smaller lizards, and small snakes and mice. Highly agile, it can even leap into the air to catch flying insects.

Sharp claws for gripping rocks

Birds of a feather

WADER
The black crake of East Africa has long, widely spaced toes to stop it from sinking into mud and to help it walk over floating water plants. The short, thick bill is used to peck small invertebrates and seeds off the surface of the water.

THERE ARE MORE THAN 9,000 species of birds in the world – flying and flightless, brightly colored and dull-hued, huge like the ostrich, or tiny like the hummingbird. Birds are the only creatures to have feathers, and these are lightweight, strong, and flexible. Birds also have two wings, a strong bill, no teeth, scaly legs and feet, and three or four toes with claws on the ends. Like mammals, birds breathe air, have a skeleton, and are warm-blooded. Unlike most mammals, they lay eggs. Bird colors help individuals of the same species identify each other, and they also help birds attract mates, threaten rivals, or camouflage themselves.

FLIGHTLESS
The brown kiwi, *Apteryx Australis*, is a medium-sized flightless bird that lives in New Zealand. It is nocturnal and eats worms, beetles, grubs, and berries, which it finds by smelling with the nostrils at the end of its long bill.

Zebra finch
Taeniopygia guttata

Short, seed-eating bill

SEED EATER
The colorful zebra finch lives on the dry grasslands of Australia, where it is one of the most common birds. Pairs of these gregarious birds mate for life, living in flocks of between 10 to 100 birds, and breeding within the group. In drier areas, they lay eggs whenever it is warm enough and there is enough rain to sustain their young. Zebra finches are perching birds as well as strong fliers. They feed on grass seeds and insects and are well known as songbirds.

Distinctive stripes around bill

Powerful grip for perching

Mandarin duck
Aix galericulata

Female

Short legs set well back on body

Male

WATERBIRD
Mandarin ducks live near ponds and lakes surrounded by woods, where they nest in tree holes. Like many other bird species, the male is more colorful than the female. However, once a year the mandarin molts his feathers, and at this time the female is the one who receives attention. Ducks have webbed feet and broad, flat bills.

Powerful hooked bill used to tear prey into bite-sized pieces

DIVING BIRD
Great white pelicans live in swamps and marshes, and usually fish in groups, making a circle and herding the fish together so they can scoop them up. A pelican's bill can hold more food than its stomach, and the bird has a daily intake of more than 2 lb (1 kg). Pelicans can hold prey in their throat pouches in order to transport it back to their nests.

Great white pelican
Pelecanus onocrotabus

Golden eagle
Aquila chrysaetos

BIRD OF PREY
Like all other birds of prey, the golden eagle uses its talons to catch and carry prey and its sharp, hooked bill to pull apart the animals it kills. It hunts for medium-sized mammals and birds, and will scavenge on carcasses as well. It is a very good flier, and the most numerous large eagle in the northern hemisphere. It makes its nest, called an eyrie, out of branches on high crags and rocky places. The eagle is named after the golden feathers on the top of its head and the back of its neck.

Large, webbed feet

Broad, rounded wings

Golden eagles can be 39 in (79 cm) tall

Sharp talons to hold prey

Primary flight feathers, used for power and steering

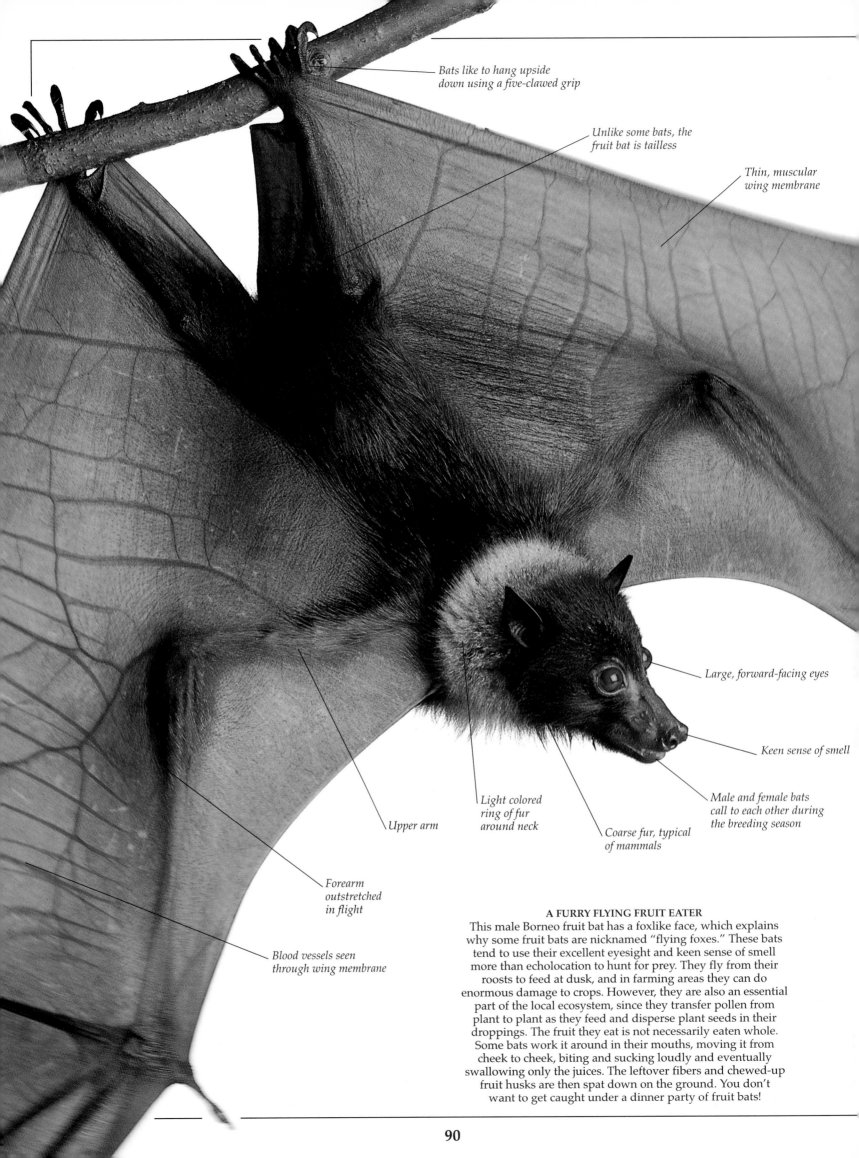

Bats like to hang upside
down using a five-clawed grip

Unlike some bats, the
fruit bat is tailless

Thin, muscular
wing membrane

Large, forward-facing eyes

Keen sense of smell

Male and female bats
call to each other during
the breeding season

Light colored
ring of fur
around neck

Coarse fur, typical
of mammals

Upper arm

Forearm
outstretched
in flight

Blood vessels seen
through wing membrane

A FURRY FLYING FRUIT EATER
This male Borneo fruit bat has a foxlike face, which explains
why some fruit bats are nicknamed "flying foxes." These bats
tend to use their excellent eyesight and keen sense of smell
more than echolocation to hunt for prey. They fly from their
roosts to feed at dusk, and in farming areas they can do
enormous damage to crops. However, they are also an essential
part of the local ecosystem, since they transfer pollen from
plant to plant as they feed and disperse plant seeds in their
droppings. The fruit they eat is not necessarily eaten whole.
Some bats work it around in their mouths, moving it from
cheek to cheek, biting and sucking loudly and eventually
swallowing only the juices. The leftover fibers and chewed-up
fruit husks are then spat down on the ground. You don't
want to get caught under a dinner party of fruit bats!

Fliers in the night

BATS ARE UNIQUE in that they are the only mammals that can truly fly. They are second only to rodents as the most numerous mammal species – there are about 950 different kinds. Bats vary enormously in size, ranging from the tiny hog-nosed bat, which measures just 5 in (13 cm) with its wings outstetched, to the large flying fox, which is the size of a small dog and has a wingspan of 6.5 ft (2 m). Bats' wings are made of thin, skin-covered sheets of muscle and elastic fibers. The bones of the arm and the second to fifth fingers support the wing. The first finger, or "thumb," sticks out like a claw and can be used to crawl, groom, fight, or hold food. Some bats can fly faster than 30 mph (50 km/h). Their wings are powered by the same muscles we use to "flap" our arms, but the bat's muscles are much stronger in proportion to the size of its body. Bats are some of the most sociable mammals. They roost together by the thousands in caves or trees, and some species help each other in the nightly hunt for food.

PEGASUS
People have always been fascinated by the possibility of flight. Observation of animals such as bats has led to the invention of many fanciful creatures, including the mythical flying horse Pegasus.

5th finger
4th finger
2nd finger
3rd finger
1st finger

OTHER FLIERS
Although bats are the only mammals capable of winged flight, other mammals – flying squirrels, opossums and flying lemurs – glide on the air. They use a membrane that acts as a kind of parachute.

MOTHER AND CHILD
A baby bat clings to its mother's furry abdomen and drinks milk, just like any other mammal.

FROM MOTHS TO BUDS TO BLOOD
Most bats are insectivores, eating moths, midges, flies, and other nocturnal insects. This fruit bat feeds on buds and the soft parts of plants. Vampire bats bite mammals and birds to drink their blood, but do not usually attack humans.

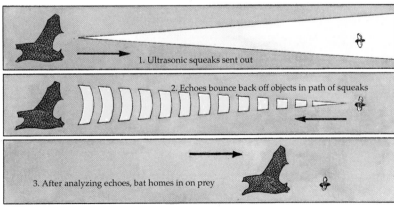

1. Ultrasonic squeaks sent out

2. Echoes bounce back off objects in path of squeaks

3. After analyzing echoes, bat homes in on prey

"SEEING" WITH SOUND
Bats hear in the dark using what is known as echolocation. Their mouths send out high-pitched squeaks (1). The sound waves bounce off anything in their path and return to the bats' ears as echoes (2). The bats' brains analyze the pattern of echoes to form a "sound picture" with which to locate and home in on prey (3).

FUNCTIONAL FACES
The curved flaps on the noses of horseshoe bats and leaf-nosed bats help with echo-location. A long, hairy tongue is useful for catching insects.

Horseshoe bat

Leaf-nosed bat

Bat with hair-fringed tongue

Rodent success

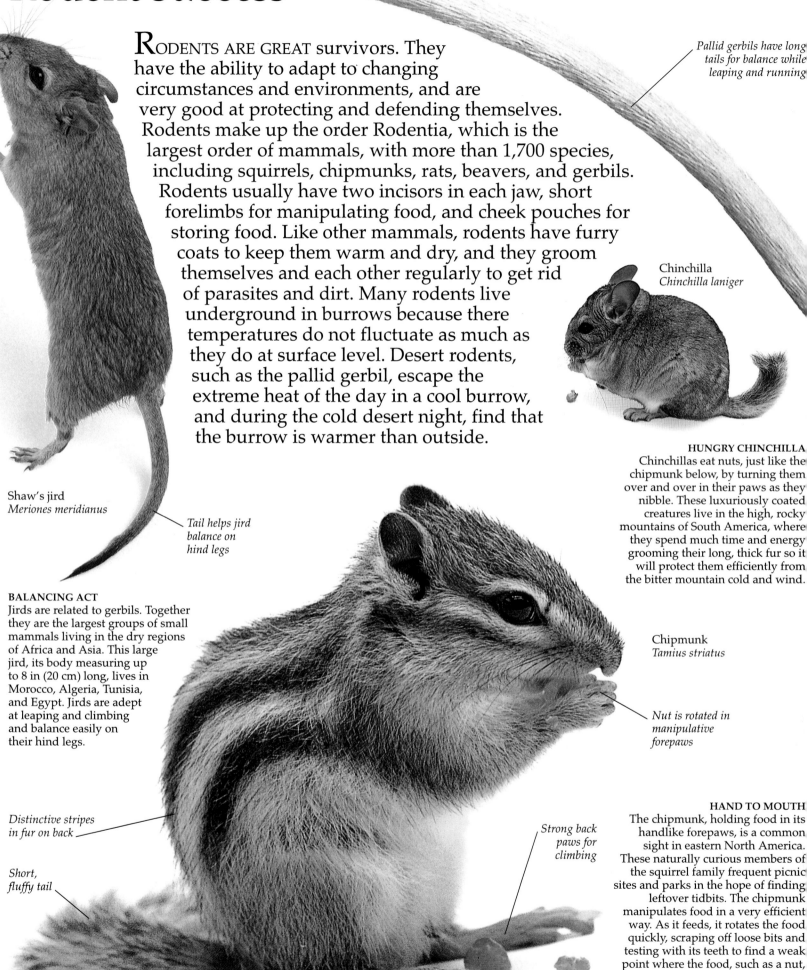

RODENTS ARE GREAT survivors. They have the ability to adapt to changing circumstances and environments, and are very good at protecting and defending themselves. Rodents make up the order Rodentia, which is the largest order of mammals, with more than 1,700 species, including squirrels, chipmunks, rats, beavers, and gerbils. Rodents usually have two incisors in each jaw, short forelimbs for manipulating food, and cheek pouches for storing food. Like other mammals, rodents have furry coats to keep them warm and dry, and they groom themselves and each other regularly to get rid of parasites and dirt. Many rodents live underground in burrows because there temperatures do not fluctuate as much as they do at surface level. Desert rodents, such as the pallid gerbil, escape the extreme heat of the day in a cool burrow, and during the cold desert night, find that the burrow is warmer than outside.

Pallid gerbils have long tails for balance while leaping and running

Chinchilla
Chinchilla laniger

HUNGRY CHINCHILLA
Chinchillas eat nuts, just like the chipmunk below, by turning them over and over in their paws as they nibble. These luxuriously coated creatures live in the high, rocky mountains of South America, where they spend much time and energy grooming their long, thick fur so it will protect them efficiently from the bitter mountain cold and wind.

Shaw's jird
Meriones meridianus

Tail helps jird balance on hind legs

BALANCING ACT
Jirds are related to gerbils. Together they are the largest groups of small mammals living in the dry regions of Africa and Asia. This large jird, its body measuring up to 8 in (20 cm) long, lives in Morocco, Algeria, Tunisia, and Egypt. Jirds are adept at leaping and climbing and balance easily on their hind legs.

Chipmunk
Tamius striatus

Nut is rotated in manipulative forepaws

Distinctive stripes in fur on back

Strong back paws for climbing

Short, fluffy tail

HAND TO MOUTH
The chipmunk, holding food in its handlike forepaws, is a common sight in eastern North America. These naturally curious members of the squirrel family frequent picnic sites and parks in the hope of finding leftover tidbits. The chipmunk manipulates food in a very efficient way. As it feeds, it rotates the food quickly, scraping off loose bits and testing with its teeth to find a weak point where the food, such as a nut, can be cracked. Like many other rodents, it carries surplus food back to its burrow in cheek pouches.

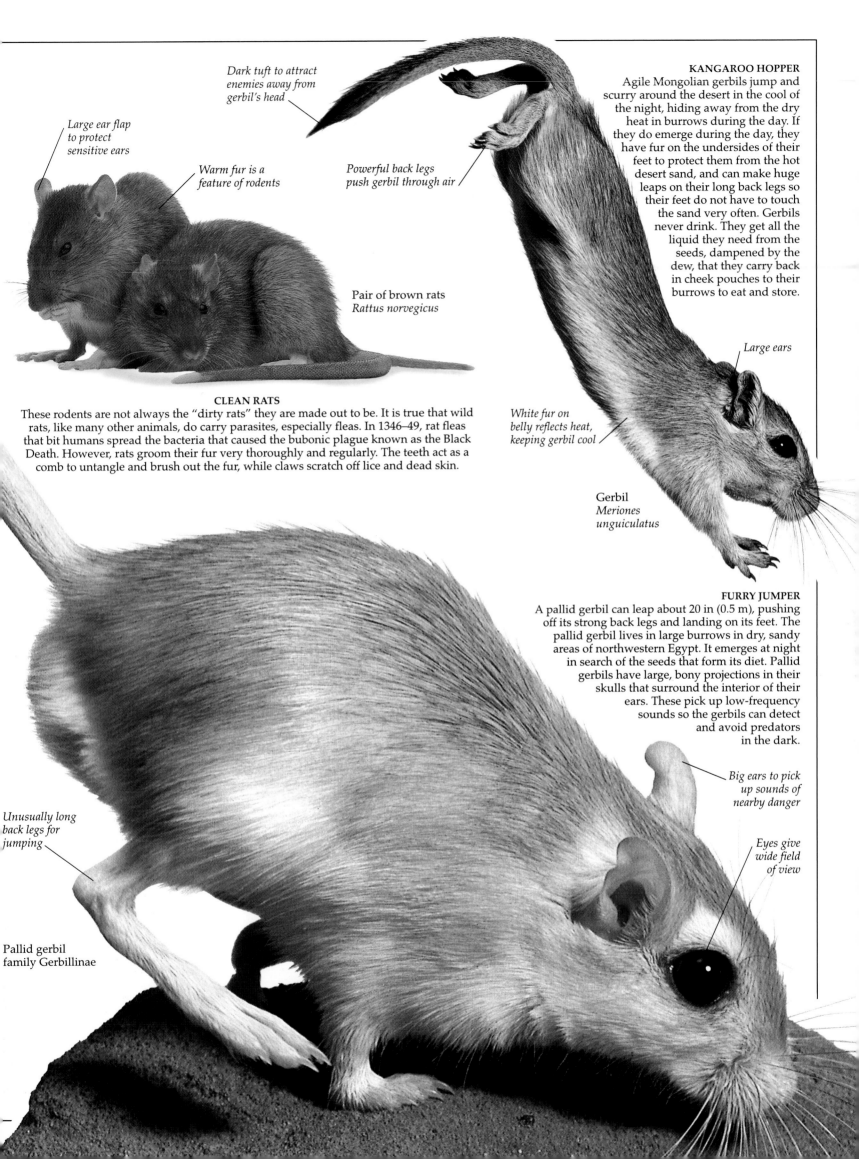

Large ear flap
to protect
sensitive ears

Dark tuft to attract
enemies away from
gerbil's head

Warm fur is a
feature of rodents

Powerful back legs
push gerbil through air

Pair of brown rats
Rattus norvegicus

KANGAROO HOPPER

Agile Mongolian gerbils jump and scurry around the desert in the cool of the night, hiding away from the dry heat in burrows during the day. If they do emerge during the day, they have fur on the undersides of their feet to protect them from the hot desert sand, and can make huge leaps on their long back legs so their feet do not have to touch the sand very often. Gerbils never drink. They get all the liquid they need from the seeds, dampened by the dew, that they carry back in cheek pouches to their burrows to eat and store.

Large ears

CLEAN RATS

These rodents are not always the "dirty rats" they are made out to be. It is true that wild rats, like many other animals, do carry parasites, especially fleas. In 1346–49, rat fleas that bit humans spread the bacteria that caused the bubonic plague known as the Black Death. However, rats groom their fur very thoroughly and regularly. The teeth act as a comb to untangle and brush out the fur, while claws scratch off lice and dead skin.

White fur on
belly reflects heat,
keeping gerbil cool

Gerbil
*Meriones
unguiculatus*

FURRY JUMPER

A pallid gerbil can leap about 20 in (0.5 m), pushing off its strong back legs and landing on its feet. The pallid gerbil lives in large burrows in dry, sandy areas of northwestern Egypt. It emerges at night in search of the seeds that form its diet. Pallid gerbils have large, bony projections in their skulls that surround the interior of their ears. These pick up low-frequency sounds so the gerbils can detect and avoid predators in the dark.

Big ears to pick
up sounds of
nearby danger

Eyes give
wide field
of view

Unusually long
back legs for
jumping

Pallid gerbil
family Gerbillinae

King of the Arctic

In EVERY HABITAT there is a dominant predator. In the Arctic, the polar bear is the largest and most powerful hunter. There are probably 20,000 polar bears wandering over the vast Arctic ice floes, some of them even roaming as far as the North Pole. Polar bears are solitary animals except during the breeding season. They do not hibernate, and in the long winter, when the Arctic ice pack extends farther out to sea, they hunt for seals beneath the ice. Their small ears help prevent heat loss, and they have a third eyelid, like a cat, which protects their eyes from snow blindness. Their dense fur keeps them warm even when the temperature drops to –40°C (–40°F). An undercoat of thick fur is protected by an outer coat of long guard hairs. These hairs stick together when wet, forming a waterproof barrier. Under the fur, a thick layer of blubber performs two roles, insulating the bear against the cold and acting as a food store to help the bear survive hard times.

Polar bear
Tharlactos maritimus

Small, rounded ears help prevent heat loss

HEAVYWEIGHT
Polar bears are twice the size of a tiger – an average adult male polar bear measures 8 ft (2.5 m) from head to tail and weighs more than 1,100 lb (500 kg). Female polar bears are much smaller than males, measuring 6.5 ft (2 m) and weighing about 700 lb (320 kg). To maintain this size, polar bears sometimes eat as much 150 lbs (68 kg) of seal blubber and entrails in one sitting. After feeding, they lick their fur and wipe their faces with their paws, very much like cats do.

Polar bears rely on scent and light reflected from the snow to guide them

Air vent scraped in roof lets stale air escape

GARBAGE DISPOSAL
When polar bears find it hard to hunt live food such as seals, they become omnivorous, and are often attracted by human garbage. The dumps on the edge of Churchill, Canada, are a favorite haunt for these enormous animals.

BEAR JOURNEYS
In their quest for food, polar bears make long journeys across the Arctic. In fact, they spend most of their lives walking on pack ice in a world of twilight and darkness. They are expert divers and swimmers, and often hitch rides on ice floes – one was even found swimming 200 miles (320 km) from land. They also dive from the tops of icebergs more than 50 ft (15 m) from the water.

CAVE CUBS
Polar bear cubs are born in December or January in a warm, cozy den dug in the snow by the mother. The cubs – usually two of them, sometimes one or three – grow rapidly on their mother's rich milk, which is about 30 percent fat. While in the ice cave, the mother has nothing to eat, and lives on the stored fat in her body.

POLAR PADDLE
Polar bears are slow but very strong and efficient swimmers underwater, and able to keep going for a long time. They use only their front legs to propel themselves; the back legs are held still and used to steer the body like a rudder.

FAVORITE FOOD
More than 90 percent of a polar bear's diet consists of seals. Waiting by a seal's blowhole in the ice, a polar bear will pounce as soon as a seal comes up for air. One stroke of the bear's massive paw and a bite at the back of the skull kills the seal. But most hunting trips are unsuccessful, and a bear may not eat for up to five days.

Yellow-white fur acts as camouflage

Powerful legs to outrun prey

Hollow hairs trap warm air near body

Thickly padded soles covered by rough skin and sometimes tough hair

Sharp claws for grabbing prey

Nonslip soles help grip slippery ice

Living in a troop

WESTERN LOWLAND GORILLAS (*Gorilla gorilla gorilla*) live in tropical rain forests in central Africa. A gorilla troop is usually made up of about 5 to 15 animals. The leader of the group is an adult male called a silverback because of his coloring. Apart from the silverback, the troop may include one or two young adult males, several adult females, and a number of juveniles and infants. The gorillas are fruit- and plant-eating, and their day begins just after dawn, when they set off through the forest to find food. The gorillas eat as they walk along, but if they find a ripe fruit tree, the younger ones will clamber into the branches. When they need to digest, the gorillas build day-nests on the ground and sleep for two or three hours. The troop moves off again, eating and traveling until dusk. The silverback decides when it is time to stop for the night and each gorilla then builds a new night-nest.

HIGH CLIMBER
This young zoo gorilla is playing on a climbing frame. For many years, scientists thought that gorillas were too heavy to climb trees. But when they actually studied them in the wild, they found that even adults are surprisingly agile and often climb high into trees to reach ripe fruit.

19th-century engraving of a gorilla family

White tail tuft helps mother locate infant in the jungle

A QUICK BITE
Gorillas sometimes crouch on two feet like this to gather up fallen fruit, or when there is not enough food in one place to make it worth sitting down! It is also a useful posture to adopt when feeding on fierce soldier ants, because it exposes less of the body to their painful bites.

Nimble fingers pick up fruit

Juvenile has lost its white tail tuft

THE FEMALE ROLE
Mature females like this one may be smaller than the males, but their role in the continuation of the group is vital. Female gorillas first give birth when they are eight years old, and the baby gorillas are weaned at the age of two. Females may leave their parents' group and join another group. This avoids inbreeding.

Weight rests on the knuckles while walking

96

A SLIMMER GORILLA
In the gorilla world it is not unhealthy to have a pot belly. It just means that the owner eats a hearty diet of bulky vegetation. Many zoo gorillas (right) look much slimmer than those in the wild because they are often fed on pellets of concentrated food, and given fewer fruits and vegetables.

Young gorilla can watch the world go by from its safe perch

Mother munches as she walks along

ON THE MOVE
The safest place for a young gorilla when traveling through the jungle is on its mother's back. From here it can watch the other members of the troop as they follow the broad silver back of the dominant male along the forest floor. Infant gorillas depend upon their mothers for transportation until they are about two and a half or three years old, by which time they are strong enough to walk by themselves for long distances.

Food picked from the wayside

LIFE AT THE TOP
The big silverback is lord of all he surveys. In addition to making all the day-to-day decisions for the troop, he can also take his pick of the breeding females. Serious fights among male gorillas are infrequent, but the silverback may take exception to another male when he becomes fully mature at about 11 or 12 years. The younger male may decide to leave the troop, and he will live alone or with other males until he can form his own troop.

Bare chest is a sign of maturity

JUNGLE EXPLORER
A gorilla learns to walk at about five to six months. When it is 18 months old, like this young gorilla, it can follow its mother on foot for short distances, often resting one hand on her rump for security. By the time it is two, it has enough confidence to follow the troop on its own. However, the young gorilla stays close to its mother so it can climb on her back if it gets scared or tired.

Gorilla leans forward to use his teeth on a stubborn plant

Pot belly is not an unhealthy sign

BREAKFAST IN BED
If food is within easy reach when a gorilla wakes up in its night-nest, it will have breakfast in bed before setting off into the forest. The silverback decides the pace and direction of the day's travel and will also indicate when it is time to stop and rest. Although he may look easygoing, the silverback is in fact keeping a constant lookout for dangers along the way.

Adapting to the dark

IN THE DARK OF AN AFRICAN NIGHT, the quiet background of insect noises may be pierced by a strange, childlike cry. This is the call of the bush baby, or galago, a small, nocturnal primate. Bush babies have sensitive, mobile ears to detect moving insects, and large eyes to focus on their prey in moonlight or starlight. They are very agile and move quickly, leaping from branch to branch. At the opposite end of the speed scale, but related to the galago, are the loris, the potto, and the angwantibo. These strange, slow primates are also nocturnal, and creep around the forest in search of fruit and creatures slow enough to be caught. There are no bush babies in Asia, but there is a fast-moving nocturnal primate – the tarsier. With their huge eyes, the three species of tarsier all look like tiny gremlins. In one species, a single eye weighs more than the animal's brain!

PRIMATE OWL
Don't be fooled by their large appealing eyes and cute faces – tarsiers are efficient and ruthless predators. Hunting at night, they silently drop onto large insects, roosting birds, and even venomous snakes. They kill their prey with a nip of their sharp teeth, and meticulously finish off every edible morsel.

SLOW MOVER
A slender loris creeps through the trees, grasping branches with each hand and foot. Lorises eat slow-moving caterpillars, beetles, and millipedes that faster insectivores leave behind.

Nocturnal spectral tarsier

Potto's specialized hand has small bump for second finger

A LEAP IN THE DARK
The nocturnal spectral tarsier is only the size of a squirrel, yet it can leap across gaps of 20 ft (6 m). Tarsiers spend most of their lives holding on to and jumping between upright stems, using the sticky pads on their toes to cling to even the smoothest wood. Using their tails to prop themselves up, they can even sleep clinging to vertical branches.

Enlarged thumb

PINCER FINGERS
This plaster cast of a potto's hand shows how the muscular thumb is set at 180 degrees opposite the other fingers. The hand works just like a pincer, allowing the potto to grasp branches and small trees in a clamplike grip.

Pincer-shaped hand can close tightly around branches

ALL EYES
The main feature of a loris's face are its eyes. Enormous eye sockets, or orbits, are set into the skull and protected by a thick, bony ring called the orbital margin.

Rounded cranium, or brain case

Postorbital bar protects side of eye

CRUNCHY SUPPER
This lesser bush baby is eating a praying mantis. After spending the day asleep, a bush baby sets off to hunt as soon as it is dark. Its large, mobile ears are sensitive to the sounds made by insects, scorpions, spiders, lizards, and nesting birds. Bush babies also eat fallen fruit, petals, nectar, and the sap of some trees.

Large, mobile ears for detecting movement of prey

Enormous eyes for sharp night vision

SCENT SIGNALS
This greater bush baby's powerfully built back legs suggest that it is a vertical clinger and leaper, like a tarsier. But scientists have found that different bush baby species move in different ways. Some bush babies move on all fours, while others seldom leap at all. However they move around their territory, bush babies let others know of their presence by anointing their hands and feet with their own urine. In this way, every hand- and foothold leaves a smelly message that clearly says "I was here."

Long, powerful legs for gripping on to and leaping from branch to branch

Protective pads on palm

Relatively short arms, with hands for grabbing prey

RECOGNIZING THE PATTERN
Zebras live in protective family groups and may recognize family members by their stripe patterns. No two zebras have the same pattern. The black-and-white stripes are confusing to predators. When zebras are moving, their coats blend together, making it difficult for predators to pick a target.

CHAPTER 4
LIFE ON THE LAND

ALTHOUGH LIFE MAY SEEM to be uniformly
distributed over the surface of the Earth, in reality
it is very uneven. In the extreme heat of some desert
areas, and in parts of the frozen continent of Antarctica,
there is no life at all. The complexity of life found in
other areas reflects the extraordinary variety of
habitats in which animals and plants live.

CATCHING THE EYE
To survive, species must procreate,
and many animals, birds, and insects
have evolved spectacular courtship displays.
The male peacock, *Pavo cristatus*, spreads out
his long, colorful feathers in a shimmering fan
to impress a female. After the breeding season
is over, the long tail feathers fall out.

Clouds of all kinds

TEN CATEGORIES OF CLOUDS were identified by the English pharmacist and amateur meteorologist Luke Howard in 1803. All the categories are variations on three basic cloud forms: puffy cumulus clouds, layered stratus clouds, and feathery cirrus clouds. This system proved so simple and effective that it is still used by meteorologists. Clouds form whenever moist air is lifted high enough above the ground to cool and condense. Cumulus clouds form because the Sun heats the ground unevenly, creating bubbles of warm air, or thermals, that drift upward through the cooler air. The bubbles cool as they rise until, high up, water vapor condenses to form a cloud.

FLYING SAUCERS
Lenticular clouds, so-called because they look like lenses, always form on wind-sheltered sides of mountains.

TRANSLUCENT CLOUD
Altostratus are high, thin sheets of cloud that can often completely cover the sky, so that the Sun looks as if it is behind misty glass. Altostratus usually appear at a warm front, where warm, moist air from the tropics slides up over a wedge of cold, polar air. The lower, thicker, nimbostratus rain clouds follow.

Strong updrafts carry billows of cloud high into atmosphere

Temperature here –40°F (–40°C)

FLEECY CLOUDS
Altocumulus are puffs and rolls of clouds, visible at medium heights. Unlike the higher, smaller cirrocumulus, they often have dark, shadowed sides.

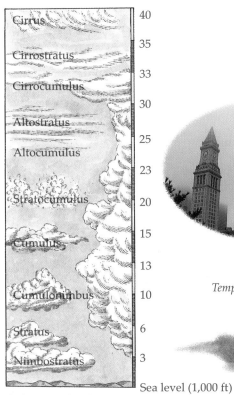

A GREY BLANKET
Stratus is a vast, dull type of cloud that hangs low in the sky and may produce a damp drizzle, but no real rain. Higher up, on hills or viewed from tall buildings, stratus simply appears as fog.

Temperature here 32°F (0°C)

Cloud	Height
Cirrus	40
Cirrostratus	35
Cirrocumulus	33
Altostratus	30
Altocumulus	25
	23
Stratocumulus	20
	15
Cumulus	13
Cumulonimbus	10
Stratus	6
Nimbostratus	3

Sea level (1,000 ft)

CLOUD HEIGHTS
Cirrus clouds, including cirrocumulus and cirrostratus, form at the top of the troposphere, where it is coldest. Altostratus and altocumulus are found at medium heights; stratocumulus, stratus, nimbostratus, and cumulus form closer to the ground. Cumulonimbus may reach up through the whole troposphere.

TRAILING VIRGA
Rain or ice crystals in cumulus clouds sometimes fall into drier, slower-moving layers of air. The streaks that result, known as virga, evaporate before they reach the ground. From below, they look as if they are vanishing into thin air.

MARES' TAILS
Cirrus clouds form high in the sky where the atmosphere is so cold that they are made entirely from ice crystals. Strong winds blow the crystals into wispy "mares' tails."

AN ICY VEIL
Cirrostratus occur when cirrus clouds spread into a thin, milky sheet. The Sun appears very bright and may have one or more colored rings, or haloes, around it and, occasionally, brilliant "mock suns."

HIGH, FLUFFY CLOUDS
Cirrocumulus are tiny, high clumps of shadowless clouds. Like all cirrus clouds, they consist of ice crystals, and often form in beautiful, regular waves and ripples known as a mackerel sky – because they look like the mottled scales of the mackerel.

Typical anvil shape

Mixture of ice crystals and water

A LAYER OF CUMULUS
Stratocumulus often form when the tops of cumulus clouds rise and spread out into broad sheets. Viewed from an airplane, they appear as an undulating blanket of cloud, with narrow breaks that sometimes allow a glimpse of the ground.

CLOUDS THAT BRING SHOWERS
Bigger and darker than cumulus, cumulonimbus usually bring rain – nimbus means "rain" in Latin. Sometimes they grow huge and unleash sudden, dramatic thunderstorms.

Violent updrafts and downdrafts in front wall of cloud create hailstones

CAULIFLOWER CLOUDS
Cumulus clouds often mass together and grow upward. They have dense, white heads that look just like cauliflowers. If they keep on growing, they may become rain-bearing cumulonimbus.

Mainly water droplets

Air drawn in here

Natural signs

WHAT'S THE WEATHER LIKE?
Everyone from travelers to sailors must know about the weather and be aware of natural signs around them.

SUNDAY OPENING
The scarlet pimpernel can foretell the weather from a flowerbed. Its tiny blossoms open wide in sunny weather, but close up when rain is coming.

SAILORS, FARMERS, AND OTHERS whose livelihood depends on the weather learned long ago that the world around them offers plenty of clues to the weather – as long as they know what to look for. Age-old advice has been passed down from generation to generation on everything from the color of the sky to the feel of your boots in the morning. Of course, most weather lore is little more than superstition and next to useless for weather forecasting. But some is based on close observation of the natural world and can give an accurate prediction of the weather. Tiny variations in the air, which we cannot feel, often affect plants and animals. A change in their appearance or behavior can be the sign of a change in the weather.

NOTHING BUT A GROUNDHOG
In the United States, February 2 is Groundhog Day. People say that if a groundhog sees its shadow, the weather will remain cold for six more weeks. Weather records have proved the groundhog wrong many times.

Sunset

Sunrise

SEEING RED
Old sea wisdom says: *Red sky at night, sailors' delight; red sky at morning, sailors take warning*. This means a fiery sunset should be followed by a fine morning, and a fiery dawn by storms. Weather experts are doubtful.

WOOLLY WARNING
Wool is very responsive to the humidity of the air. When the air is dry, wool shrinks and curls up. If rain is on its way, the air is moist, and wool swells and straightens out.

WEATHER WEED
People near the sea often hang out strands of kelp because seaweed is one of the best natural weather forecasters. In fine weather, the kelp shrivels and is dry to the touch. If rain threatens, the weed swells and feels damp.

Kelp is sensitive to changes in humidity

Cone in wet weather   Cone in dry weather

INSECT FORECASTING
Like many small creatures, grasshoppers are sensitive to changes in the weather, chirping louder and louder as the temperature rises. The chirping is not a real song, but the sound of the grasshoppers' hind legs rubbing rapidly against their hard front wings.

GLORIOUS MORNING
Like the scarlet pimpernel, morning glory flowers open and shut in response to weather conditions. These wide-open blooms indicate fine weather.

WEATHER CONES
A pinecone is a very reliable natural weather indicator. In dry weather, the scales on a pinecone open out; when they close up, it is a good sign that rain is on the way. This is because in dry weather, the scales shrivel and stand out stiffly. When the air is damp, the scales absorb moisture and become pliable again, allowing the cone to regain its normal shape.

Oak   Ash

SOAK OR SPLASH?
According to some, natural signs can indicate the weather, not just for the next few hours but for many days to come. There is an old English saying that says:
If the oak flowers before the ash, we shall have a splash (meaning only light rain for the next month or so).
If the ash flowers before the oak, we shall have a soak (meaning very wet weather). There is little evidence, however, to support these long-range predictions.

LYING COWS
When cows lie down in a field, it is often said that rain must be on the way. Apparently, the cows sense the dampness in the air and are trying to preserve their patch of dry ground. While many animals can sense changes in the weather before humans, this particular prediction is wrong as often as it is right.

SPRING IS HERE
Many natural signs are said to herald the end of winter, such as the first blooming of the white flowers of the horse chestnut. It is true that the flowers only appear when the weather is mild – but this is no guarantee that there will be no more winter storms.

WINTER'S TAIL
Some people expect a severe winter if squirrels have very bushy tails in the fall, or if they gather big stores of nuts. But scientists have found no evidence to support this.

Fiery rocks

WHEN VOLCANOES ERUPT, they may spout rivers of red-hot lava or spew great clouds of ash and gas into the atmosphere. Sometimes the lava oozes gently from a hole in the ground. At other times, lava is thrown into the air in spectacular fire fountains that run together when they land. In either case, the lava flows off the volcano in rivers of hot rock that may spread out over a large area before it cools. Fire fountains and lava flows are common in Iceland and Hawaii. They are easy to predict in these areas, and it is often possible to get close to them and take photographs. However, from time to time, volcanic gas that escapes the hot rock may cause explosions that throw out bombs and blocks – chunks of flying lava that litter the ground around the vent.

Weedy, flowering plant

Two species of moss

Lichen

GATHERING MOSS
How quickly plants recolonize lava depends on the nature of the erupted material. Climate and altitude are also important – recolonization is fastest in the tropics, for example. This piece of lava is from a flow on the western slope of Mount Vesuvius in Italy after an eruption in 1944. Some 50 years later, lichen covers much of the flow, and moss, grasses, and weedy, flowering plants are taking root.

BOMBS AND BLOCKS
Bombs and blocks can be as big as houses or as small as tennis balls. Bombs are usually more rounded, and blocks are more dense and angular. Their shapes depend upon how molten or gaseous the lava was during flight. Very liquid chunks of lava plop to the ground; denser, more solid chunks often shatter as they land.

Bomb thrown out by Mount Etna and covered with red crust of hematite

SPITTING MOUNTAIN
One of the highest mountains and most active volcanoes in Europe, Mount Etna rises 11,122 ft (3,390 m) over the Italian island of Sicily. Its barren summit is almost always bubbling with lava. Lava flows from an unusually long eruption destroyed several houses and threatened villages in 1992.

Dense, round bomb

Small, explosive eruption photographed at night on Mount Etna

Odd twists and tails of many bombs formed as they spin through the air

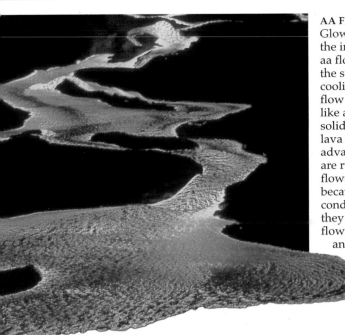

AA FLOWS
Glowing red at night, the intense heat of an aa flow shows through the surface crust of cooling lava. The flow moves forward like a bulldozer, as solidifying blocks of lava drop down the advancing front and are run over. Lava flows cool very slowly because rock is a poor conductor of heat. As they harden, the lava flows slow down and thicken.

Hardened chunk of pahoehoe lava

PAHOEHOE FLOWS
Pahoehoe flows are more fluid than aa flows and contain more gas. As its surface cools, the flow develops a thin, pliable skin. The hot lava on the inside distorts the skin, wrinkling it so that its surface looks like the coil of a rope. The skin of a pahoehoe flow may crust over into a roof thick enough to walk on. Hot lava continues to run in a tunnel or tube only a yard or so beneath the crusty roof.

Lava flows

Lava flows pose little danger to people because they rarely travel faster than a few miles an hour. There are two kinds of flows; they get their names from Hawaiian words. Aa (pronounced *ah-ah*) flows are covered in sharp, angular chunks of lava known as scoria. Pahoehoe (*pa-hoy-hoy*) flows grow a smooth skin soon after they leave the vent. Pahoehoe flows are rarely more than 3.3 ft (1 m) thick, while the thickest aa flows may be 330 ft (100 m) high.

Dribbles of remelted lava from roof of a pahoehoe tunnel

Chunk of scoria from surface of an aa flow

PAHOEHOE TOE
This photo shows red-hot pahoehoe bulging through a crack in its own skin. New skin is forming over the bulge. A pahoehoe flow creeps forward with thousands of little breakouts like this one. The chilled surface of the flow traps gas, keeping the flow in the tunnels hot and mobile. The lava often travels many miles from the vent in this way, engulfing farmland and houses as it goes.

FIRE AND WATER
Volcanic islands like Hawaii and Iceland are usually fringed by black beaches. The sand is formed when hot lava hits the sea and shatters into tiny, glassy particles. It is black because the lava is rich in dark minerals like iron oxides, and low in light-colored ones like quartz.

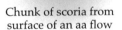

Black sand from volcanic island of Santorini, Greece

On the mountainside

THE HIGHER THE ALTITUDE at which a plant grows or an animals lives, the colder the temperatures it has to endure. The thin air holds little heat, and on exposed mountainsides, high winds create a chill factor that makes the cold even more penetrating. In addition, low rainfall and thin, frozen soils mean that water is scarce. However, mountain (alpine) plants are generally small and compact, so they can survive on high mountain peaks, often growing in dense cushions or flattened mats to give protection against the cold, drying wind. Animals and insects live on all levels of a mountain, sometimes moving up or down in search of food or greater warmth.

Canada lynx

Large neck ruff

Lady Amherst's pheasant
Chrysolophus Amherstiae

Western Himalayan spruce
Picea smithiana

HIMALAYAN CONIFER
Above the tropical forests of the southern Himalayan slopes are mixed forests containing many coniferous trees. This elegant spruce is found on the middle slopes. It has a narrow crown and drooping shoots, and the cones have smooth, notched scales

MOUNTAIN RANGES
There are mountains on all the continents. A few form great mountain ranges, such as the Rocky Mountains and the Himalayas. On the highest peaks of mountain ranges, snow lies frozen all year round. Below the high mountaintops with their snowy peaks, alpine meadows and scrub form cool coniferous forests and waterlogged moorlands. On the lower slopes, the warmer, deciduous forests are home to many animals and insects.

SEASONAL MIGRATION
Hardy pheasants such as this spectacular Lady Amherst's pheasant live in the mountain forests of Asia. They move up and down the mountains with the seasons. This shy, secretive bird rarely emerges from the bamboo thickets and dense forest where it lives. It eats bamboo shoots as well as small animals, insects, and spiders, and sometimes fishes under stones in streams for small aquatic animals.

Male has long and colorful tail feathers for display

*Himalayan
Mazus reptans
grows in mats*

Bhutan Glory
Bhutanitis lidderdalei

*Alpine daphne, or
garland flower, is
miniature shrub*

MOUNTAIN BEAUTY
Many butterflies and moths
have adapted to the harsh
climate of mountains. This
Bhutan glory lives in the
mountain forests of Thailand and
India. It is a dark brown because darker
colors absorb sunlight more easily, so the
insect can warm up rapidly in the early
morning when the air temperature is low.

*Butterfly has prominent
eyespots to startle
predatory birds*

*Moltkias have
small leaves to
withstand high winds*

*Brilliant colors of
North American phlox
stand out to attract
pollinating insects*

Mountain gorilla
*Gorilla gorilla
beringei*

*This St. John's wort
is much smaller than
its lowland relatives*

ALPINE PLANTS
Many plants have adapted to the harsh climate
of mountains. Some of them, such as *Mazus
reptans*, are "prostrate," or mat-forming. Others
are simply smaller than similar species in
warmer habitats. The leaves are often small
and tough to resist sharp frosts, and some are
covered with fine hairs to protect them from the
Sun's ultraviolet rays, which are more intense at
these heights. Mountain summers are short, so
the plants have to flower and produce seeds
quickly before the cold weather returns.

MOUNTAIN APE
Mountain gorillas live in the mountain forests of the Virunga volcanoes in
Africa. Their thick coats keep out the chill, while water runs off the outer
layer of hairs. Mothers like this female wrap their shaggy arms around
their babies to keep them warm and dry. Gorillas spend most of their time
on the ground, but will often climb trees to search for fruit, bark, or leaves.
Today, there are fewer than 650 mountain gorillas left in the world.

*Weight rests
on knuckles
when walking*

Lords of the skies

THE HUGE SUMMER BREEDING COLONIES of birds in both the Arctic and the Antarctic attract a number of predatory birds quick to enjoy easy meals of eggs and chicks. In the Arctic, the small mammals of the tundra lands, such as lemmings and hares, increase the range of food for birds to hunt. The variety of predatory birds is therefore greater in the Arctic than in the Antarctic and includes eagles, skuas, owls, falcons, and buzzards. The predators' breeding cycles are timed to coincide with that of their prey, ensuring that their chicks will always have plenty to eat.

GHOSTLY HUNTER
Snowy owls feed largely on the millions of lemmings living on the Arctic tundra, and their population is closely linked to the cyclical three to four year rise and fall in lemming numbers. Many of these superb owls wander south in winter.

Soapstone and ivory owl carved by Inuit craftsman in Cape Dorset, Canada

Feathers at tips of wings spread out like fingers to help the eagle push and steer through the air

Spread feathers help the bird reduce speed

Powerful wings give both speed and control in flight

Lethal curved talons grip, crush, and carry off prey

Strong legs to cushion impact of landing

The golden eagle slows in midair and spreads out its wings and tail to act as a brake

Eyes firmly focused on its destination, the eagle further brakes its flight by swinging out its lower body and legs

At the last moment, its feet swing down to grip the perch

LOOK OUT BELOW
Golden eagles fly at low altitudes while hunting, then swoop suddenly to pounce on their prey. This swoop-and-grab attack is effective because it happens so swiftly that the prey is often taken by surprise. Here, a golden eagle is landing on a branch in much the same way as it would dive for a meal.

KING OF THE CLOUDS
As the most powerful and majestic bird in the sky, the eagle is featured in countless stories, myths, and legends. Here a magnificent eagle perches in a tree in an illustration by British illustrator Reginald Knowles. It forms the title page of a collection of Norse legends.

Sharp eyesight to spot birds and animals moving on the ground below

Powerful hooked bill to tear flesh from prey

Golden eagle
Aquila chrysaetos

Huge chest muscles drive the enormous wings

Gyrfalcon
Falco rusticolus

BIGGEST AND BEST
The most powerful of the falcons, the gyrfalcon relies on power and speed to catch its victims. It usually kills its prey in flight.

A KILLING MACHINE
A magnificent flier, the golden eagle is a fierce predator of ptarmigan and other birds as well as small mammals such as ground squirrels and hares. Golden eagles usually kill their prey before carrying it off in their strong talons. They sometimes hunt in pairs, especially in winter.

FALCON FOOD
The rock ptarmigan (*Lagopus mutus*) is the gyrfalcon's main prey.

Mountain weather

Hɪɢʜ ᴜᴘ ɪɴ ᴛʜᴇ ᴀᴛᴍᴏsᴘʜᴇʀᴇ, pressure drops, winds are ferocious, and the air is bitterly cold. On mountain peaks like Mount Everest, the air pressure is very low, winds howl through the crags at up to 192 mph (320 km/h), and the temperature often drops to –94°F (–70°C). Because mountains jut so far into the atmosphere, they interfere with wind and cloud patterns, forcing air to move up or down as it passes over the peaks. Air rising up the windward side of a mountain means that the lower summits are often shrouded in mist and rain.

CLOUDS AND SNOW
In many mountain ranges, the highest peaks project above the clouds, basking in bright sunshine while clouds fill the valley below. However, though sunny, the peaks are usually icy cold. Any heat from the Sun is reflected back into the atmosphere by the snow. Near the equator, only the very highest peaks – above 16,400 ft (5,000 m) – are perpetually snow-covered, where it is too cold for rain. Toward the poles, however, the snow line creeps down the mountainside.

HIGH READINGS
Many weather stations are sited on the tops of mountains to record conditions high up in the atmosphere. On the summit of Mount Washington in New Hampshire, winds are frequently over 196 mph (60 km/h) and temperatures are often below –22°F (–30°C).

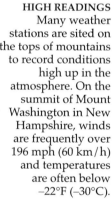

MEASURING AIR PRESSURE
In 1648, the French scientist Blaise Pascal proved that the atmosphere had its own weight, or pressure. Pascal reasoned that the air pressure would be lower at the top of a mountain because there was less air weighing down on it from above. When he took a barometer up a mountain, the mercury level showing air pressure dropped as he expected.

Barometer used for measuring air pressure

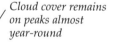
Air pushed up by mountain slopes often fills valleys with clouds

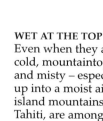
Cloud cover remains on peaks almost year-round

WET AT THE TOP
Even when they are not particularly cold, mountaintops are often wet and misty – especially if they poke up into a moist air stream. Pacific island mountains, like these in Tahiti, are among the dampest places in the world. Hawaii's Mount Wai-'ale-'ale is wreathed in moist clouds for 354 days a year. It is also drenched by more than 457 in (11,600 mm) of rain a year.

Barometer
very low

A little
cloud
cover

Winds of
99 mph
(165 km/h)
or more

ADAPTING
Tiny flowers
called alpines
have been
very successful
in adapting to
the sunny, cold
weather of
mountain ranges
such as the Alps
in Europe,
where they grow
plentifully in spring.

HIGH SIERRA
High up in the mountains, strong winds often
increase the chilling effect, even on sunny
days. Mountaintops are usually much more
windswept than open, low country, partly
because wind strength can be much stronger
at 3,280 ft (1,000 m) than at sea level. Winds
also rush over, rather than around, the tops
of mountains, and gain speed as they go.

*Air warms
and dries as
it descends*

Leeward
(sheltered)
side

Rain on summit

RISING AIR
When a moist air stream meets a
mountain range, it is forced upward, toward the
summit. As it rises, it cools and may condense into clouds
around the top. Higher-level clouds can then act as "feeder"
clouds, letting a little rain fall onto the summit clouds below.
Warm fronts may break up when they run up against a mountain
ridge, while cold fronts may drop so much rain that they die out
quickly on the far side. All this brings rain to the windward side
of mountains, and leaves the sheltered leeward side drier.

Windward
side

*Moist air forced
upward by
mountain range*

*Rising air cools and
condenses into clouds*

113

In the rain forest

TROPICAL RAIN FORESTS contain more species and a greater diversity of colorful plant and animal life than any other habitat on Earth. These forests are found in permanently wet, warm areas near the equator that get at least 60 in (1.5 m) of rain a year. The jungles have three layers – a layer of smaller plants on the forest floor, an evergreen canopy in the middle, and, towering above, scattered taller trees known as emergents. At all levels of the rain forest there is a host of wary creatures with strong survival instincts. In the canopy, many yards above the ground, harpy eagles swoop down on prey. Lower, hungry pitcher plants digest the insects that fall into their cups. In the dim light of the forest floor, scorpions and other poisonous creatures scuttle and slither their way through the maze of roots, fallen leaves, and branches.

A NASTY SHOCK
There are many ways that rain forest creatures protect themselves. Any predator that tries to sample this spiky leaf insect will receive a painful surprise because the insect has sharp spines all over its body. This female is an immature nymph; its wings are not yet fully formed.

Tomato frogs
Dyscophis antongili

RAIN FORESTS IN DANGER
Madagascar, off Africa's southeastern coast, is the world's fourth largest island. Like many other islands (pp. 122–123), most of its rain forest wildlife has evolved in isolation and is unique. However, many of the plants and animals, such as the rare comet orchid (*Angraecum sesquipedale*) and these tomato frogs, are endangered because their habitat – the rain forest – is being cut down and burned by farmers to clear the way for agriculture.

Four simple eyes on each side of the head

LIVING DANGEROUSLY
Heavy with moisture, the air near the shady forest floor is home to the poisonous tiger centipede, typical of the creatures that lie hidden in the dense vegetation. Tiger centipedes emerge only at night, when the forest grows cool. They have large poisonous claws, and feed on insects and spiders as well as small toads and mammals.

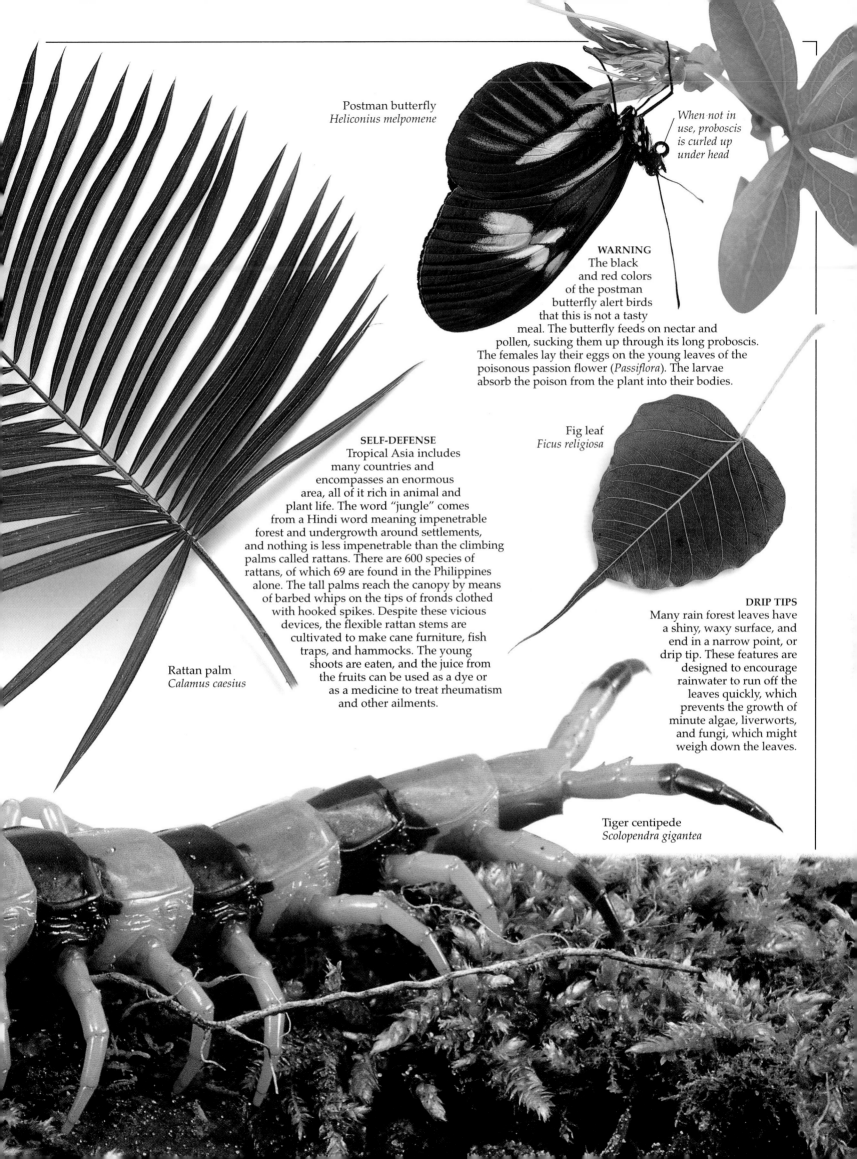

Postman butterfly
Heliconius melpomene

When not in use, proboscis is curled up under head

WARNING
The black and red colors of the postman butterfly alert birds that this is not a tasty meal. The butterfly feeds on nectar and pollen, sucking them up through its long proboscis. The females lay their eggs on the young leaves of the poisonous passion flower (*Passiflora*). The larvae absorb the poison from the plant into their bodies.

Fig leaf
Ficus religiosa

SELF-DEFENSE
Tropical Asia includes many countries and encompasses an enormous area, all of it rich in animal and plant life. The word "jungle" comes from a Hindi word meaning impenetrable forest and undergrowth around settlements, and nothing is less impenetrable than the climbing palms called rattans. There are 600 species of rattans, of which 69 are found in the Philippines alone. The tall palms reach the canopy by means of barbed whips on the tips of fronds clothed with hooked spikes. Despite these vicious devices, the flexible rattan stems are cultivated to make cane furniture, fish traps, and hammocks. The young shoots are eaten, and the juice from the fruits can be used as a dye or as a medicine to treat rheumatism and other ailments.

Rattan palm
Calamus caesius

DRIP TIPS
Many rain forest leaves have a shiny, waxy surface, and end in a narrow point, or drip tip. These features are designed to encourage rainwater to run off the leaves quickly, which prevents the growth of minute algae, liverworts, and fungi, which might weigh down the leaves.

Tiger centipede
Scolopendra gigantea

Living on the grasslands

MUCH OF THE AFRICAN continent is grassland, and most areas are hot savanna plains lying between tropical forests and desert land. Grasses, small trees, and shrubs are scattered across the savanna, with tall, thick grasses growing near the forests, and shorter, thinner grasses near the deserts. Grazing animals such as zebras, antelope, and wildebeests live in large herds that wander the plains, cropping the grass as they go. The trees and shrubs, such as acacias, have deep roots to reach water sources underground, and provide nourishment for many of the herbivores that live on the grasslands. Large browsing animals use their different heights to reach different parts of the foliage. Giraffes eat the tasty shoots at the treetops, elephants eat the leaves, twigs, and bark, and black rhinoceroses eat the lower branches. The water in the plants keeps these animals hydrated in this dry area – the animals may go up to a week without drinking.

Males' skulls strengthened for fighting

Small horns

Cloven hoof like that of a cow

Patas monkey
Erythrocebus patas

Males are twice as big as females

Long legs for sprinting

LIVING IN A HERD
Giraffes live in herds of up to 12 individuals, which may be spread out over a wide area, but always move together across the plains. The males average 16 ft (5 m) in height and weigh 3,080 lb (1,400 kg), while the females are usually 14 ft (4.3 m) tall and around 1,760 lb (800 kg). Giraffes move with some difficulty. They have trouble getting up from the ground, for instance, but when they gallop away, few predators can catch them. Unlike most large animals, they move with both legs on the same side working together, and they can gallop for hours without getting tired.

PLAINS MONKEY
The patas monkey, also known as the military monkey because of its reddish coat and impressive white mustache, lives on the dry plains of Africa in troops of about 15 to 20. It lives on the ground and its long legs let it bound along at 33 mph (55 km/h) if necessary. Patas troops spend most of the day moving around looking for leaves, fruit, and flowers to eat. At night, the monkeys climb into trees to sleep.

Spongy blood vessels near brain prevent blood pressure problems when giraffe bends down to drink

Reticulated giraffe
Giraffa melopardis

Because of its long neck, giraffe has to lower or raise its head slowly

RECORD HEIGHTS

No animal alive today is as tall as a giraffe. The long neck evolved to enable the animal to browse on the foliage of trees on the wide plains of the savanna. The extraordinary thing about a giraffe's neck is that it contains only seven vertebrae – exactly the same number as in the necks of other mammals, including our own. The vertebrae are simply long – 1 ft (0.3 m) long. When it reaches into the treetops, a giraffe's long tongue grasps leaves and twigs and pulls them within reach. Its canine teeth have two deep grooves to strip the leaves from their twigs.

Common zebra
Equus burchelli

HERDING TOGETHER

The main threat to the large herds of zebras on the African plains, apart from drought, is the efficient hunting of the large cats: the lion, leopard, and cheetah. Lions hunt in groups. The lionesses do most of the work, picking out and attacking the weakest animals in a herd. Zebras stay together for protection. Zebra herds contain family groups of about 12 females and their foals, led by a dominant male. By day, they graze on the long coarse grass and drink from waterholes regularly. They migrate to find water in the dry season.

Ostrich
Struthio camelus

Flexible neck

BIG BIRDS

The rhea lives on the South American grasslands, and can sprint at speeds of 50 km/h (31 mph) to get away from danger. It is related to the emu of Australia and the ostrich which lives on the grasslands of Africa. The ostrich is the heaviest bird in the world, at 90 kg (200–345 lb). It is also the tallest bird, 2.1–2.7m (7–9 ft), and the fastest two-legged animal, reaching speeds of up to 75 km/h (45 mph).

How plants survive in the desert

Pₗₐₙₜₛ ₜₕₐₜ ₗᵢᵥₑ ᵢₙ ₐₑₛₑᵣₜₛ PLANTS THAT LIVE IN DESERTS either spring up from dormant seeds after rain, or stay alive all year by adapting to the meager supply of water. The more permanent plants have a variety of methods of obtaining water. Some have long roots to reach moisture deep in the soil; some spread their roots to collect water over a wide area; others absorb dew through their leaves. Many desert plants, including cacti, are succulents, which are able to store water. A thick waxy layer on the succulents' stems and leaves also helps retain moisture and protects tissues from the Sun's intense heat. Growing smaller leaves, shedding leaves in times of drought, or even having no leaves at all, also helps reduce water loss by keeping the surface area of the plant to a minimum.

DATE PALMS
This grove of date palms is at an oasis in Oman. Only female trees produce dates, so just a few male trees are grown to produce pollen. Palm trees can live for up to 200 years.

Very long roots to seek out water

FLESHY LEAF
Haworthias grow in places with some shade, usually next to rocks. Only the tips of the leaves poke above the surface of the soil, the rest stays out of the sun. But leaves need light in order to make food by photosynthesis. This leaf has a translucent (clear) window in the tip to allow light through the leaf.

These agaves with varied patterns have been specially bred

FRESH DATES
There are many different varieties of dates. The most familiar are the ones that are dried and packed in boxes for export around the world. Dried dates are also part of the staple diet of villagers and desert nomads such as the Bedouin. They are very nutritious and do not rot easily.

CENTURY PLANTS
It takes 20 to 50 years for the century plant to produce flowers on a stem up to 30 ft (9 m) tall, growing out of the center of the plant. The flowers are pollinated by nectar-seeking bats. After flowering and producing seeds, the plant dies. The century plant belongs to the agave family, members of which are a source of sweet sap for drinks and of fibers for ropes and other products.

FIRETHORN BRANCH
Also called the ocotillo, or candlewood plant, the firethorn grows in the deserts of the south-western US. In dry times, it sheds its leaves to conserve moisture. After rain, new leaves grow among the spines; if the ground is wet enough, the firethorn flowers.

WELWITSCHIA
This bizarre plant has only two frayed, straplike leaves, and a huge taproot that may be up to 3.3 ft (1 m) wide at the top. It grows on the gravel plains in the Namib Desert. Welwitschia is actually a dwarf tree, and may live for 100 years or more, each leaf growing about 2 in (5 cm) a year.

Leaf absorbs dew

Welwitschia leaves usually split into many strips

When spread out, each leaf reaches up to 6.5 ft (2 m) long

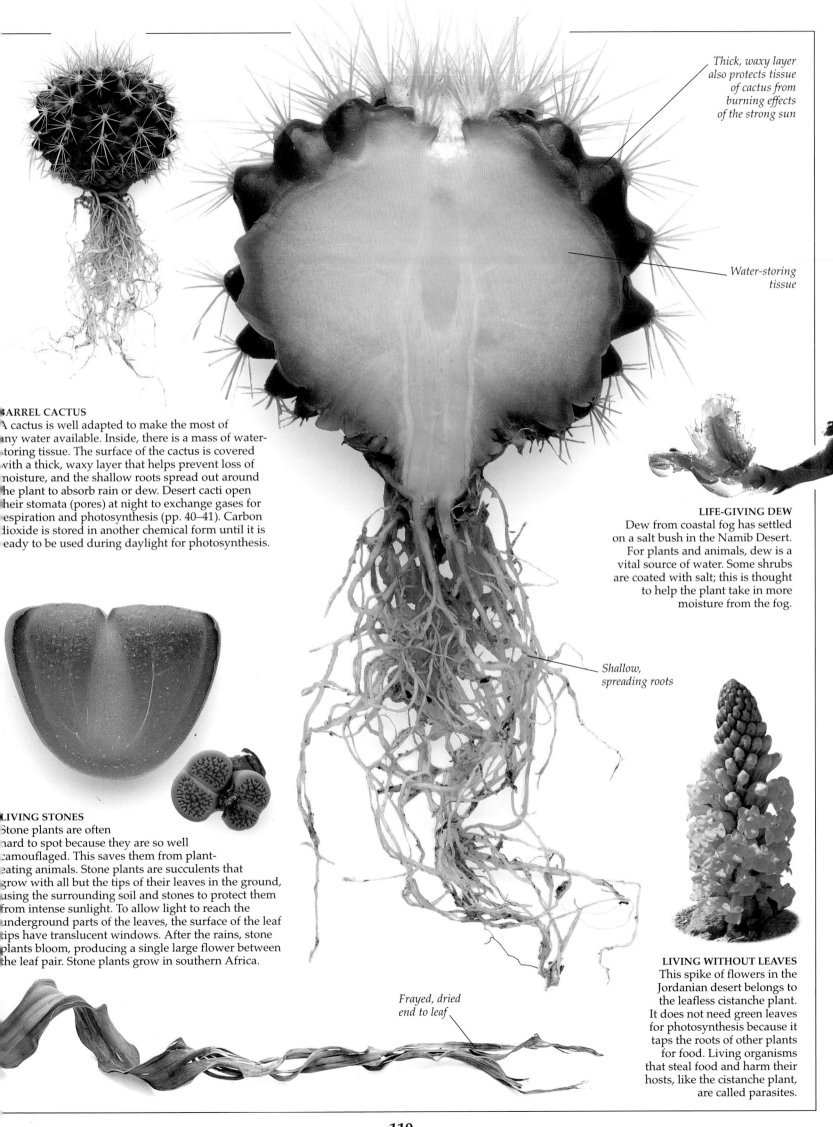

BARREL CACTUS

A cactus is well adapted to make the most of any water available. Inside, there is a mass of water-storing tissue. The surface of the cactus is covered with a thick, waxy layer that helps prevent loss of moisture, and the shallow roots spread out around the plant to absorb rain or dew. Desert cacti open their stomata (pores) at night to exchange gases for respiration and photosynthesis (pp. 40–41). Carbon dioxide is stored in another chemical form until it is ready to be used during daylight for photosynthesis.

LIVING STONES

Stone plants are often hard to spot because they are so well camouflaged. This saves them from plant-eating animals. Stone plants are succulents that grow with all but the tips of their leaves in the ground, using the surrounding soil and stones to protect them from intense sunlight. To allow light to reach the underground parts of the leaves, the surface of the leaf tips have translucent windows. After the rains, stone plants bloom, producing a single large flower between the leaf pair. Stone plants grow in southern Africa.

Thick, waxy layer also protects tissue of cactus from burning effects of the strong sun

Water-storing tissue

LIFE-GIVING DEW

Dew from coastal fog has settled on a salt bush in the Namib Desert. For plants and animals, dew is a vital source of water. Some shrubs are coated with salt; this is thought to help the plant take in more moisture from the fog.

Shallow, spreading roots

Frayed, dried end to leaf

LIVING WITHOUT LEAVES

This spike of flowers in the Jordanian desert belongs to the leafless cistanche plant. It does not need green leaves for photosynthesis because it taps the roots of other plants for food. Living organisms that steal food and harm their hosts, like the cistanche plant, are called parasites.

Desert wildlife

ANIMALS IN THE DESERT have a difficult problem to solve – they must find water in a dry, dusty environment. Some herbivorous animals and insects feed on fresh green plants that spring up after rain. Others get moisture and food from prey or from water and dew. To conserve water and avoid the drying effects of the Sun, many desert creatures are only active at night. Desert hedgehogs and foxes spend the heat of the day in burrows, emerging when it is dark to search for food. Members of the cat family that live in desert regions often hunt at night, sheltering in rocky lairs or any available shade during the day. There are desert animals that avoid the driest times, only becoming active after occasional rains. The eggs of desert crustaceans, such as brine and tadpole shrimps, need water just to bring them to life, and spadefoot toads remain inactive during the dry season, buried in the soil, only emerging when they hear rain falling above.

THE ANT LION
The larva of this winged insect is called an ant lion. As soon as it hatches, it digs a pit in the sand and hides at the bottom with only its jaws exposed, waiting for an insect such as an ant to come into the pit. When prey gets close enough, the ant lion flicks sand at it to make it lose its footing and slide down to certain death.

Long antenna

Jewel wasp

JEWEL OF THE DESERT
Hunting jewel wasps are solitary wasps, living on their own rather than in colonies. The adults feed on nectar from flowers, but their young eat cockroaches caught for them by the adult female. She hunts down the cockroach, stings it to paralyze it, and then drags the insect into a hole where she lays an egg on it. When the young hatches, it feeds on the paralyzed but alive cockroach.

Series of limbs push food into mouth

Tadpole shrimps are 1.2 in (3 cm) in length

Shield

THIRSTY SHRIMPS
The eggs of these tadpole shrimps can survive in dry sands for ten years or more, waiting for rain to bring them to life. The shrimps must grow quickly to reach maturity and produce eggs before the desert pool in which they live dries up and they die. Not all the eggs hatch the first time around. Some eggs are left for the next rain in case the pools dry out and the first shrimps die before they can complete their life cycle.

Distinctive ear tuft similar to that of lynx

DESERT CAT
The caracal lives in a wide range of habitats, including the deserts of Africa and Asia. These soft-footed cats are adept at catching birds, and can even leap into the air to swat a bird in flight. They also hunt reptiles, small mammals, and even larger prey such as gazelles. Caracals sleep in caves, rocky crevices, and the abandoned burrows of other animals.

Caracal
Lynx caracal

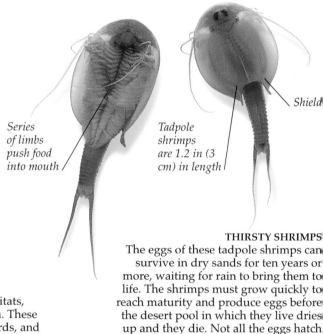

Desert hedgehog
*Paraechinus
aethiopicus*

Meerkat
Suricata suricatta

*A group of
meerkats is
capable of
warding off a
jackal or cobra*

LIVING TOGETHER
Meerkats live in the Kalahari
and Namib deserts, and in dry
open country in other parts of
southern Africa. They work
together as a group. A meerkat
with its head down looking
for food in the wide open
desert is an easy target for a bird
of prey, so one member of each
group scans the horizon from a high
place – on a raised sandbank, or in a
bush or tree. If a predator is spotted, the
guard barks in alarm and the group races
to the safety of a burrow. There are "nanny"
meerkats in each group that take turns
looking after the young while the mothers
are out feeding with the rest of the group.

DESERT HEDGEHOG
This spiny creature lives in the dry regions of
northern Africa, the Arabian peninsula, and Iraq.
When threatened, it rolls up to expose the spines
of its coat, like other species of hedgehog,
protecting its vulnerable underparts. Desert
hedgehogs dig individual burrows that they
live in during the day. In the breeding season,
the female looks after the young in the burrow,
suckling them for two months. Adult hedgehogs
eat birds, eggs, scorpions, and small mammals.

*Enlarged glands
secrete a strong
poison to deter
predators*

Green toad
Bufo viridis

TOADS IN THE HEAT
Green toads live in oases where there is a
permanent water supply in which to lay
their eggs. During the day, they hide
away from the heat of the desert under
stones. At night, they emerge to hunt
insects near water holes and around palm
trees. They have enlarged glands that
secrete a strong poison to deter predators.

Island life

MANY ISLANDS IN THE PACIFIC and Indian
Oceans were created by the flow of volcanic lava
or emerged from the sea at the summit of coral
reefs. Once formed, these isolated chunks of
land were populated by turtles, birds, and other
sea wanderers. Some small invertebrates and
seeds, such as those of the coconut, float there
by sea. Other creatures and plants establish
themselves after being carried by birds, blown
by the wind, or transported by swimming
reptiles. Because of their isolation, island
populations often evolve into unique forms.
Some island birds become flightless, like
the Galapagos cormorant and
the almost-flightless kakapo of
New Zealand. Because food is
plentiful and predators there
are few, many island-dwellers
grow to a great size. But their
isolation also makes them
vulnerable to invaders,
such as the cats and
rats introduced by
human visitors.

Coconut husk
broken by
robber crab

Powerful
claws to crack
open coconuts

Strengthened
carapace

Cook islander
holding a
robber crab

ROBBER OF THE TREES
The robber, or "coconut," crab is found on some Pacific
islands. This giant crustacean has adapted to its environment
by developing the ability to climb trees in search of coconuts, which
it cracks open with powerful claws. As a young adult, the crab carries
a mollusk shell, like a hermit crab, for protection. When the shell becomes
too small, it shields itself with half a coconut! Eventually, it relies on its claws
and hardened exoskeleton for protection. On some islands, the crab is hunted
for food. Once caught, however, the robber crab must be held carefully, as the
Cook islander is demonstrating (left), because it can inflict serious injury.

Leaf insect is 2.75 in (7 cm) long

Leg

LEAF WITH LEGS
This leaf insect lives on the island of Java and is very well camouflaged. Its skin has both the color and texture of a real leaf. There are marks that resemble the midrib and veins of a typical leaf, and it even has brown markings that make it look like an unappetizing, dying leaf.

Chameleon protected by ability to change color to match background

Toes of front foot grouped with two on outside and three on inside

Toes of back foot grouped with three on outside and two on inside

Cassowaries make a threatening, booming noise to scare invaders

FLIGHTLESS
Cassowaries, like many island birds, have lost the ability to fly. They have powerful legs for running and fighting, and daggerlike claws for defense, and so do not need to fly. These solitary birds blend easily into the dense jungles of New Guinea, where they feed on fruit, supplementing their diet with occasional reptiles, small birds, or mammals.

LIFE IN THE TREES
Chameleons have remarkable toes that are specialized for life in trees. The toes are arranged so the feet are able to grip branches securely while the tail offers extra support, twisting and twining itself around small twigs. This Madagascan chameleon has a sticky tipped tongue, which it is able to extend farther than the length of its body, guaranteeing it a good diet of insects and other small invertebrates.

In the outback

AUSTRALIA IS HOME to some of the most extraordinary animals in the world. It has been an island continent for millions of years, and its wildlife has developed in a very individual way. There are more than 150 kinds of pouched mammals, or marsupials, in Australia, and only 70 other such species in other parts of the world. Marsupials, including the largest, the kangaroo, are born tiny, naked, and blind, and wriggle from the birth opening to a teat in the mother's pouch. They stay in the pouch, well protected, feeding on the mother's milk until they are large enough to survive outside. In the case of the kangaroo, when it is big enough, the young, or joey, hops in and out of the pouch while its mother grazes. There are many other animals that live only in Australia, including some of the most poisonous snakes in the world.

TREE BOUND
The koala, *Phascolarctos cinereus*, is a marsupial and eats only the tough, leathery leaves of 12 species of eucalyptus gum tree. It is totally arboreal, only able to live in trees, because it has four hands to grip branches, and no feet suitable for walking.

Large, broad bill to catch and swallow prey

Large head with brown ear patch

Warm fur

Laughing kookaburra
Dacelo novaeguineae

BIRD WITH A SENSE OF HUMOR
The laughing kookaburra is named after its chuckling territorial calls, which are sometimes loud and booming, and sometimes quiet. It is a giant kingfisher that lives in the eastern half of Australia in family groups. The kookaburra has a very varied diet, pouncing on snakes, mammals, birds, and invertebrates. Despite the fact that it is a kingfisher, it only occasionally dives into water after fish. It is 16–18 in (40–45 cm) in length and has a large head and bill relative to its body size.

Stiff tail used as support

IN LEAPS AND BOUNDS
There are more than 40 species in the kangaroo and wallaby family. There is no real difference between a kangaroo and a wallaby: larger species tend to be called kangaroos, and smaller ones wallabies. The family name is Macropodidae, which means "big feet," and they certainly do have big feet, which they use to bound along in great leaps, while the tail acts as a counterbalance. Some large kangaroos can travel at nearly 40 mph (60 km/h)! These marsupials are herbivorous, grazing on plants as they move along slowly, resting their heavy tails and front paws on the ground for balance and swinging their back legs forward.

White's tree frog
Litoria caerulea

Doria's tree kangaroo
*Dendrolagus
dorianus*

STICKY-TOED AMPHIBIAN
White's tree frog has round toe-pads that are sticky with mucus. It lives in forests, although it is familiar to many Australians because it also lives in water barrels and lavatories. It is 2–4 in (5–10 cm) long and feeds on any moving creature small enough to be swallowed. These frogs spawn in water, producing 200 to 2,000 eggs.

Large ears

*Sharp
eyesight*

UP A TREE
Tree kangaroos have evolved from ground-living ancestors. They climb trees to browse on foliage, but most species can still hop over the ground. Doria's tree kangaroo is the most arboreal. It has strong forelegs, broad hind feet, and sharp claws, and can no longer hop like other kangaroos. It lives in the cooler forests of the New Guinea highlands and has a thick fur coat to keep warm.

*Powerful
shoulders*

*Long tail acts as
counterbalance
when kangaroo
climbs trees*

*Hands used for
pulling down
vegetation and
sparring with
other males*

*Powerful
claws*

*Deadly sting
in the tail*

DANGER UNDERFOOT
There are many poisonous creatures to be found in the outback. The marbled scorpion *Lychas marmoreus* lurks under bark and among leaf litter, where it hunts for small invertebrates. These are usually overpowered by its front claws and jaws, and it saves the venomous sting in its tail for defense.

Penguins of the Antarctic

THERE ARE 18 DIFFERENT SPECIES of penguins, all found south of the equator. Some live in cool waters off the coasts of New Zealand, South Australia, and South Africa. Others live off the west coast of South America and in the Galapagos Islands in the Pacific. But the vast majority prefer to live in the far south, in the frozen seas and islands off the coast of Antarctica. These flightless birds divide their time between the sea and the land. They travel up to 500 mi (800 km) in the winter months in search of krill, fish, and squid to eat, returning to rookeries on land to breed during the warmer summer months. A penguin has a thick, waterproof coat, with short, oily-tipped feathers that overlap to stop water from soaking through. Underneath is a thick layer of down that traps the warm air near the penguin's body. A layer of fat immediately under the skin also stops heat loss from the penguin's body.

KEEPING WARM
Emperor penguins are able to raise only one chick a year because the female lays the egg in the depths of winter on the icy surface of the Antarctic. The male penguin then incubates the egg under a brood patch, or flap of skin. The resulting chick – this one is about eight weeks old – benefits from the same extra warmth and protection as it grows.

The birds in the center are the warmest

Heat loss can be reduced by as much as 50 percent

Birds take turns in the most exposed positions

Incubating male Emperor penguins
Aptenodytes forsteri

Emperors often turn their backs to the constantly shifting wind

TOGETHERNESS
Incubating male Emperor penguins huddle together for warmth, moving very little to conserve energy. Even when the chicks are born, the birds still huddle together as much as possible. Some Emperor colonies contain more than 20,000 pairs.

After the females return from fishing, the hungry males head for the open sea

Penguin "flies" out of water to breathe

Penguin catches fish and krill in its beak

Penguin shoots onto land or ice in giant leap of up to 6.5 ft (2 m)

Under the water, penguin steers with its feet and tail

DUCKING AND DIVING
Over a long time, penguin wings have evolved to form flippers with which they "fly" through the water. When they are swimming fast, they often use a technique called porpoising, leaping out of the water like dolphins or porpoises. Air offers less resistance to movement than water, so porpoising penguins can travel at speeds of up to 18 mph (30 km/h).

Bill is small
to cut down
on heat loss

King penguin
*Aptenodytes
patagonica*

KING OF ALL THEY SURVEY
Nearly as big as an Emperor, at 3.3 ft (1 m) tall, the handsome King penguin breeds in huge colonies of thousands and thousands of birds. It breeds on Antarctica and the sub-Antarctic islands, but because it relies on a warmer breeding climate than the Emperor, it only raises, on average, two chicks every three years. The chicks take 10 to 13 months to fledge. When the chick has hatched, the parent birds go on fishing trips that last between four and eight days. The youngsters wait, huddled together in enormous outdoor nurseries or crèches. The average weight of an adult King penguin is 33 lb (15 kg), so parents need to catch between 50 and 90 squid or fish on each trip to the sea.

*Penguin feeds chick
by regurgitating
catch*

*Overlapping,
closely packed
feathers cover a
thick layer of blubber*

*King penguins lay
only one egg, carrying
it around on their feet,
covered by a brood patch*

*Small feet cut
down on heat loss*

Adaptable animals

To SURVIVE THE CHANGING SEASONS in some parts of the world, animals have to change, too. As winter approaches, some mammals grow thick fur coats, which may be white for camouflage against snow. They store a thick layer of fat in their skin to trap extra warmth and to act as a food supply in lean times. Some birds also gain layers of fat and a set of dense, fluffy feathers to keep out the cold. For many birds and mammals, the severe winter weather is just too much. They migrate south to warmer places, returning again in spring. Insects rest in soil over the winter, usually in the form of larvae, and are able to withstand the freezing temperatures. As summer arrives, birds and mammals molt, or shed, their thick coats. Animals that turn white in winter turn brown for summer camouflage.

FINE FURS
People in cold countries always wore fur clothes to keep warm through the coldest winters. They usually obtained them by snaring their original owners in traps.

Arctic fox
Alopex lagopus

DRESSED FOR SUMMER
In summer, the Arctic fox grows a thinner coat of brownish-gray fur over most of its body. These colors match the brownish-gray rocks of the tundra landscape, making the fox hard to see, so it can creep up on its prey, such as a lemming, without being spotted. The fox stores food under rocks during the summer and comes back to eat it in the winter months when food is hard to find. Arctic foxes have a varied diet, eating anything from berries, shells, and dead animals to garbage, birds, and eggs. But lemmings are vital to their diet and Arctic foxes will endure many weeks of starvation if few lemmings are available.

The chest and belly are usually a pale gray-white in color

Short legs lose less heat than long ones because there is less surface area exposed to the air

Thick, bushy tail can be curled around the body for warmth during blizzards or when resting

Antarctic ice fish
Chaenocephalus aceratus

ANTIFREEZE IN ITS VEINS
Many Antarctic fish have antifreeze molecules in their bodies that enable them to live in a "supercooled" state; their body fluids remain liquid at temperatures below the point at which ice forms. Antarctic ice fish (such as the fish to the left) have almost translucent blood.

Hair under paws stops the fox from sinking in snow; the fox's Latin name is Alopex lagopus – lagopus *means "hairy foot".*

A BIRD FOR ALL SEASONS
Ptarmigans change their plumage twice a year so that they are always well camouflaged. Their feather density also increases in winter. When resting overnight, ptarmigans sometimes burrow in snow to reduce heat loss.

Rock ptarmigan
Lagopus mutus

Dense fur coat with long hairs traps body warmth

Ears are furry inside and out for extra warmth

KEEPING WARM WITH FAT
Whales and seals are kept warm by a layer of thick fat called blubber. This fat walrus is in no danger of getting cold. Walruses can weigh up to 1.8 tons (1,600 kg), and have tusks 3.3 ft (1 m) long.

Small, round ears and a short muzzle cut down on heat loss; foxes from warmer places have larger ears and longer muzzles

Sharp, pointed teeth to grab animals such as lemmings

INSULATED FUR
The Arctic fox's white winter fur is made up of hairs that are hollow inside and full of air. The air in the hairs traps body warmth from the fox in much the same way as an insulated window traps warmth from a house. Air is a good insulator and does not let heat pass through it easily. The Arctic fox can tolerate temperatures of –40°F (–40°C), or even lower, quite comfortably.

Sharp claws used to dig through snow to find food

GIANT WEE
Many species of coastal kelps are found around th
world. Some are very large indeed – hundreds of fee
long. Waves and water currents pull on the enormou
fronds with great force, so the kelp is fastened to th
rocks of the shoreline by gnarled, rootlike structure
called holdfasts. These hold tight to the rock, like
tree's roots in soil. Well-anchored kelp protec
many ocean dwellers from the Sun and lesser
the force of waves and winds, so man
smaller plants and shore animals, suc
as crabs, fish, prawns, and mollusk
take advantage of the calme
conditions in forests of kel

CHAPTER 5
LIFE IN THE WATER

IN FRESHWATER rivers and lakes, and in saltwater seas
and oceans, a multitude of habitats exist. Water is a
rich environment, teeming with life, but tides, winds,
waves, water currents, temperature, and climate
can make it a difficult one in which to live.

SHAGGY SHELLS
Gaping file shells move by expelling
water from their shells and using their
masses of orange tentacles like oars.
They cannot withdraw the
tentacles inside the two
halves of their shells
for protection, so the
tentacles produce a sour-
tasting, sticky substance to
deter predators. Gaping file
shells build homes in
seaweeds, such as this maerl,
a chalky, red seaweed that
grows along the
stony seabed.

Freshwater fish

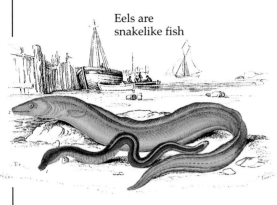

Eels are snakelike fish

Most people only ever see freshwater fish as dark torpedo shapes cruising silently below the surface of a river or pond. Their ability to remain elusive has served freshwater fish well, and an amazing variety of species are supremely suited to underwater life. They swim by flexing powerful muscles that move their bodies back and forth. This produces a thrashing motion and propels the fish along. The fins are used chiefly for stabilizing, steering, and braking. The stripe along a fish's side is called the lateral line. It is a groove of specialized tissue that detects vibrations in the water, in effect allowing the fish to "hear" and "feel" water movements. Most of the fish on these two pages demonstrate a clever camouflage trick called countershading. Their backs are dark and dull, so when viewed from above, they blend in with the murky water of their pond or riverbed. Their bellies are shiny and silvery, so that when seen from below, they merge with the ripples and flashes on the underside of the water's surface.

Lateral line for detecting water movements

Roach has red iris

RUDD
This fish likes still water, and the more weeds, the better. The rudd can be distinguished from the roach (above right) by its fins: in the rudd, the front edge of the dorsal (back) fin is farther back than the base of the ventral (belly) fin, while in the roach, these are in line. In some areas, rudd interbreed with roach or bream (bottom right). Rudd reach about 4.5 lb (2 kg) in weight.

Rudd
Scardinius erythrophthalmus

Rudd has orange iris

Ventral fins are bright orange

Young roach

YOUNG ROACH
When they are young, fish are very difficult to identify. This one is probably a young roach and bears very little resemblance to the older roach shown above.

TENCH
Tiny scales, a greenish sheen, an almost unforked tail, and a bulky, muscular body are characteristics of this still-water, bottom-feeding member of the carp family. A good-sized tench weighs around 9 lb (4 kg), and the fish is a powerful fighter.

Tench
Tinca tinca

Medieval ailments were treated with slime from tench skin

Unforked tail

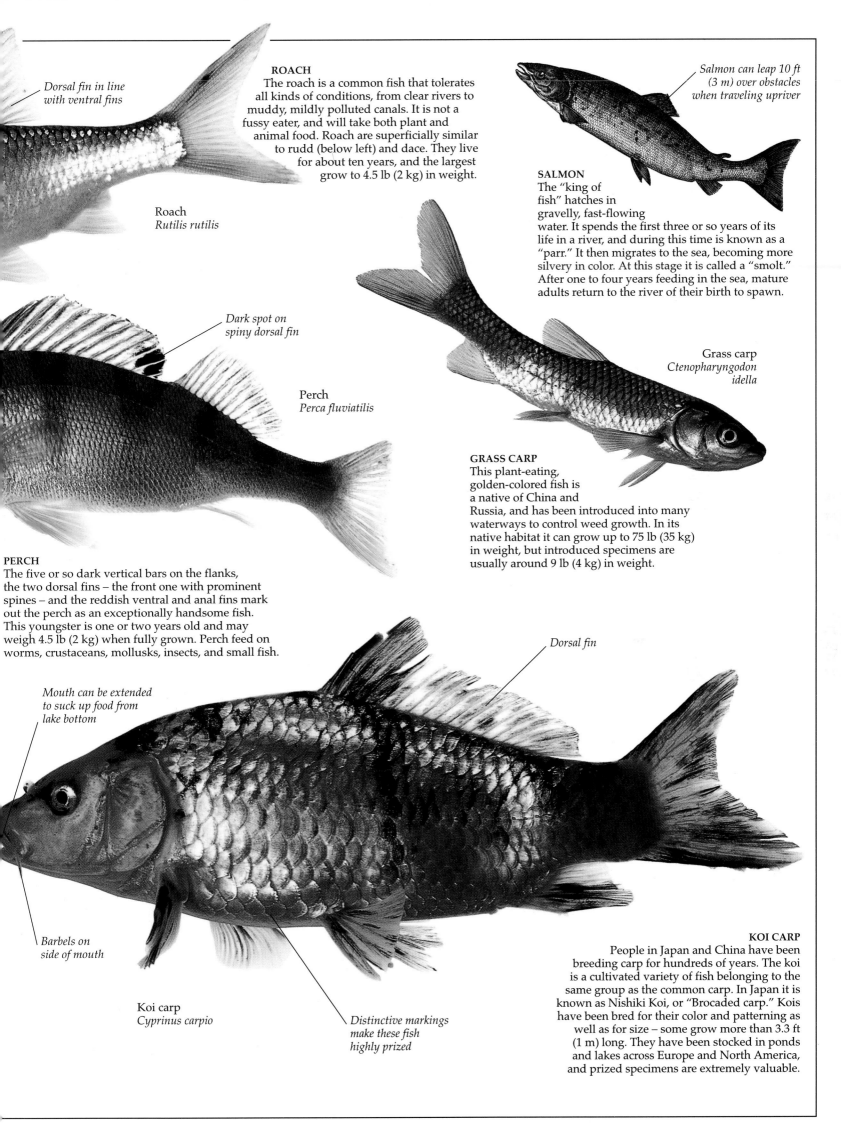

Dorsal fin in line with ventral fins

ROACH
The roach is a common fish that tolerates all kinds of conditions, from clear rivers to muddy, mildly polluted canals. It is not a fussy eater, and will take both plant and animal food. Roach are superficially similar to rudd (below left) and dace. They live for about ten years, and the largest grow to 4.5 lb (2 kg) in weight.

Roach
Rutilis rutilis

Salmon can leap 10 ft (3 m) over obstacles when traveling upriver

SALMON
The "king of fish" hatches in gravelly, fast-flowing water. It spends the first three or so years of its life in a river, and during this time is known as a "parr." It then migrates to the sea, becoming more silvery in color. At this stage it is called a "smolt." After one to four years feeding in the sea, mature adults return to the river of their birth to spawn.

Dark spot on spiny dorsal fin

Perch
Perca fluviatilis

Grass carp
Ctenopharyngodon idella

GRASS CARP
This plant-eating, golden-colored fish is a native of China and Russia, and has been introduced into many waterways to control weed growth. In its native habitat it can grow up to 75 lb (35 kg) in weight, but introduced specimens are usually around 9 lb (4 kg) in weight.

PERCH
The five or so dark vertical bars on the flanks, the two dorsal fins – the front one with prominent spines – and the reddish ventral and anal fins mark out the perch as an exceptionally handsome fish. This youngster is one or two years old and may weigh 4.5 lb (2 kg) when fully grown. Perch feed on worms, crustaceans, mollusks, insects, and small fish.

Mouth can be extended to suck up food from lake bottom

Dorsal fin

Barbels on side of mouth

Koi carp
Cyprinus carpio

Distinctive markings make these fish highly prized

KOI CARP
People in Japan and China have been breeding carp for hundreds of years. The koi is a cultivated variety of fish belonging to the same group as the common carp. In Japan it is known as Nishiki Koi, or "Brocaded carp." Kois have been bred for their color and patterning as well as for size – some grow more than 3.3 ft (1 m) long. They have been stocked in ponds and lakes across Europe and North America, and prized specimens are extremely valuable.

Underwater weeds

Submerged weeds grow in ponds and rivers like trees in a miniature underwater forest. They provide shelter for some animals and hiding places for others from which to pounce on unwary victims. Underwater weeds are food for many creatures, from pond snails to ducks, and provide vital oxygen. As a plant carries out photosynthesis (pp. 40–41), released oxygen is the essential by-product. The oxygen diffuses into the water and is used by both plants and animals for respiration. On a sunny day, tiny oxygen bubbles coat the leaves of underwater plants and occasionally rise to the water's surface.

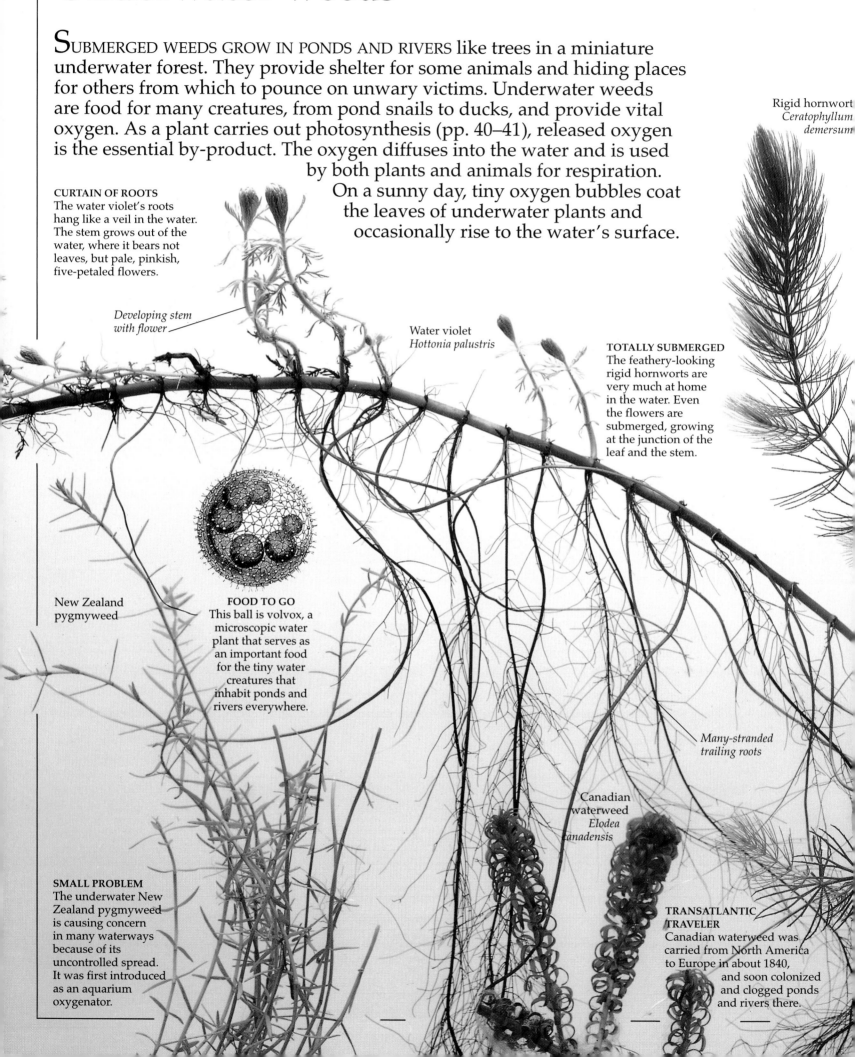

Rigid hornwort
Ceratophyllum demersum

CURTAIN OF ROOTS
The water violet's roots hang like a veil in the water. The stem grows out of the water, where it bears not leaves, but pale, pinkish, five-petaled flowers.

Developing stem with flower

Water violet
Hottonia palustris

TOTALLY SUBMERGED
The feathery-looking rigid hornworts are very much at home in the water. Even the flowers are submerged, growing at the junction of the leaf and the stem.

New Zealand pygmyweed

FOOD TO GO
This ball is volvox, a microscopic water plant that serves as an important food for the tiny water creatures that inhabit ponds and rivers everywhere.

Many-stranded trailing roots

Canadian waterweed
Elodea canadensis

SMALL PROBLEM
The underwater New Zealand pygmyweed is causing concern in many waterways because of its uncontrolled spread. It was first introduced as an aquarium oxygenator.

TRANSATLANTIC TRAVELER
Canadian waterweed was carried from North America to Europe in about 1840, and soon colonized and clogged ponds and rivers there.

INVISIBLE TO THE EYE
At 25 x magnification, the microscopic world of underwater plants is revealed. This drop of pond water is teeming with plankton.

PERCH IN THE GRASS
Tape grass is one of the popularly named "river grasses." It provides a hideout for many fish, particularly the perch, which is well camouflaged by the vertical stripes on its sides.

Tape grass
Vallisneria spiralis

Narrow leaves resemble needles of a fir tree

Bulbous rush

Tall, grasslike stems grow close together

SLENDER WATERWEED
The pale green water starwort sways in large clumps in the water. Water starwort is a favorite shelter for the shy loach, which only emerges to forage for food at dusk.

RUSHED GROWTH
The bulbous rush is usually rooted on the pond side, but sometimes it grows underwater, becoming very elongated.

Water starwort
Callitriche stagnalis

Floating flowers

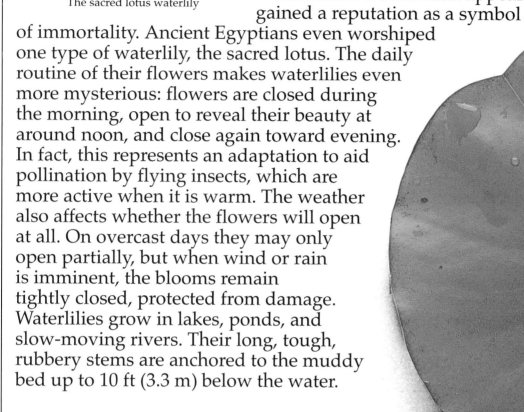

The sacred lotus waterlily

IN ANCIENT TIMES, people saw that when a previously dry watercourse filled with rain, the lush blooms of waterlilies would soon appear. These aquatic plants gained a reputation as a symbol of immortality. Ancient Egyptians even worshiped one type of waterlily, the sacred lotus. The daily routine of their flowers makes waterlilies even more mysterious: flowers are closed during the morning, open to reveal their beauty at around noon, and close again toward evening. In fact, this represents an adaptation to aid pollination by flying insects, which are more active when it is warm. The weather also affects whether the flowers will open at all. On overcast days they may only open partially, but when wind or rain is imminent, the blooms remain tightly closed, protected from damage. Waterlilies grow in lakes, ponds, and slow-moving rivers. Their long, tough, rubbery stems are anchored to the muddy bed up to 10 ft (3.3 m) below the water.

NUISANCE OR FRIEND?
The flowering water hyacinth floats freely on the surface of the water, carrying its roots below. It is borne along by the water currents and breezes, spreading rapidly – and often clogging rivers and canals. However, the roots are good at trapping the harmful substances that pollute rivers and lakes. They are often planted by scientists to "strain" water and clean it of toxins.

Waxy coating repels water droplets

Red hybrid – "Escarboucle"

Yellow waterlily leaves are patterned with a red tinge

Silky hairs cover leaf surfaces, preventing them from becoming waterlogged and sinking underwater

Leaves may be heart-shaped, oval, or round

Conspicuous yellow stamens

LILIES AND THEIR HYBRIDS

There are more than 60 species of waterlilies around the world. In some areas thay are known as lotuses. Their magnificent waxy-looking flowers and bold circular leaves have made them favorites for growing in ponds, ornamental water gardens, and lakes. A wide variety of different-colored flowers known as hybrids have been bred by horticulturalists.

Waxy petals

Yellow hybrid – "Chromatella"

FLOATING SAUCERS

The Amazonian waterlily has some of the largest leaves in the plant world. A single leaf may measure more than 5 ft (1.5 m) across and has an upturned rim with reinforcing ribs beneath.

WATER LILY LEAF CASE

The china mark moth caterpillar cuts out an oval of leaf and fastens to the underside with silk thread to form a case in which it stays, underwater, until it emerges as a moth.

Waterlily leaf

WELL-USED LEAVES

The leaves, also known as lily pads, are used by many creatures that live in the water. In the spring, pond snails lay their speckled, jellylike egg masses on the undersides of lily pads. Frogs rest on or under them, waiting to snap up unwary insects. Lily pads can grow dense enough to allow some creatures to walk across them. The African jaçana, a bird with long, widespread toes, is known as the "lily trotter" because it steps delicately from pad to pad as it searches for insects and seeds.

Waterfowl

WATER AND ITS RESIDENT WILDLIFE attract an amazing variety of birds. There are about 150 species of wildfowl, including swans, geese, and ducks, which are quite at home on the ponds, lakes, rivers, and seashores of the world. These generally heavy-bodied birds have webbed feet for swimming, and long, mobile necks for dabbling in the water and rummaging in the muddy bed for food. During spring, the dense bank vegetation provides many species with safe and sheltered nesting sites. In summer, the proud parents can be seen leading their fluffy chicks across the surface of the water. Aquatic plants and animals are a ready source of food for most of the year. In winter, when ponds and some lakes freeze over, many wildfowl fly south, often covering vast distances to find a more favorable climate in which to spend the winter. Others retreat to parks and gardens where they feast on scraps donated by well-wishing humans.

Nest and eggs of
eider duck
Somateria mollisima

*Soft down feathers
insulate eggs in nest*

Nest and eggs
of Common teal
Anas crecca

TEAL NEST
The teal makes its nest in dens
undergrowth, using twigs an
grasses. The female is very
careful not to attract predator
when visiting her chicks.

SPECIALLY GROWN DOWN
Ultrasoft eiderdown feathers grow
on the female eider duck's breast.
She plucks them to cocoon her
eggs as she nests on sea- or
lakeshore, or on the
riverbank.

TUFTED DUCK EGG
The six to fourteen eggs of th
tufted duck are laid in a nest
close to the water's edge. The
chicks hatch after 25 days an
are swimming within a day.

Teal is one of the
smallest ducks

MUTED COLORS
Out of the breeding
season, the pintail drake
molts to the inconspicuous
"eclipse" plumage, resembling
the female's colors.

Pintail
wing

PLUMAGE
In the breeding
season, most male
ducks, like the pintail
(far right), sport bright
plumage to catch the eye
of the female. The female
(right) is a duller color for
camouflage on the nest.

ON THE WING
Pintails, like
most ducks,
can escape
danger with
a twisting and
turning flight.
They open and
close their pointed
wings (right) to change
direction. All wildfowl are strong
fliers, many covering vast distances
during annual migrations.

TUFTED DUCK FOOD
The tufted duck feeds on freshwater
mussels, as well as small fish, frogs,
and any insects it can catch.

Tufted duck
*Aythya
fuligula*

Tufted
duck skull

MUSCOVY DUCK BILL *below*
This native of Central and South
American ponds and marshes has
a broad bill that allows it to feed
on aquatic plants and animals.

Muscovy duck
Cairina moschata

Muscovy
duck skull

MUTE SWAN THREAT
The mute swan's bill (below) is normally
covered by an orange sheath. Male swans
can be extremely vicious, particularly in the
breeding season, when defending territory.

*uter vane
windward
ge of
ather)*

Mute swan
Cygnus olor

*Broad bill of
swan suitable
for dabbling for
water vegetation*

Mute
swan skull

Flight
feathers

*ong
uill*

FEATHER CARE
Water-dwelling birds
rely on feathers to stay
dry. They spend a lot of time
preening their feathers to keep them
in good condition and free of parasites.

River life

FROM THE COLD, RUSHING WATERS of mountain streams to the warm, sluggish coastal swamps of the tropics, the rivers of the world are home to a wealth of wildlife. The rainwater that falls on mountaintops and forms streams is chemically pure, but as it travels down toward the sea, it gradually collects particles and dissolved nutrients from the rocks and plants over which it rushes, becoming warmer and oxygenated and able to sustain animal life. Plants take root and animals dig burrows in the soft, damp soil of riverbanks, crustaceans, amphibians, and fish eat insect larvae underwater, and adult insects mate and feed above the surface. In turn, these flying insects are eagerly snapped up by hungry birds and bats.

Gray wagtail
Motacilla cinerea

BUSY BIRI
The gray wagtail snaps up flies
midges, small dragonflies, anc
water beetles with its long beak
It often catches insects in flight

GOOD SHOT
Although archer fish usually live around the coasts of Southeast Asia and Australia, they come into mangrove swamps and even freshwater rivers to seek prey. This aptly named fish presses its tongue against a groove running along the roof of its mouth to form a narrow tube. Through this it spits out a powerful jet of water, knocking insects down to eat.

Archer fish
Toxotes chatereus

Draws head and legs inside shell for protection

Long, thin snout to search for insect larvae in mud

Young Chinese soft-shelled turtle
Trionyx sinensis

FLAT SHELL
River turtles live in all kinds o
freshwater habitats, from stil
shallow waters to rushing rivers
This soft-shelled turtle uses its lon
snout like a snorkel, poking it out o
the water to breathe as it swim
along or rests beneath the surface

Hard exoskeleton divided into segments

Broad tail shaped like a fan to push water aside

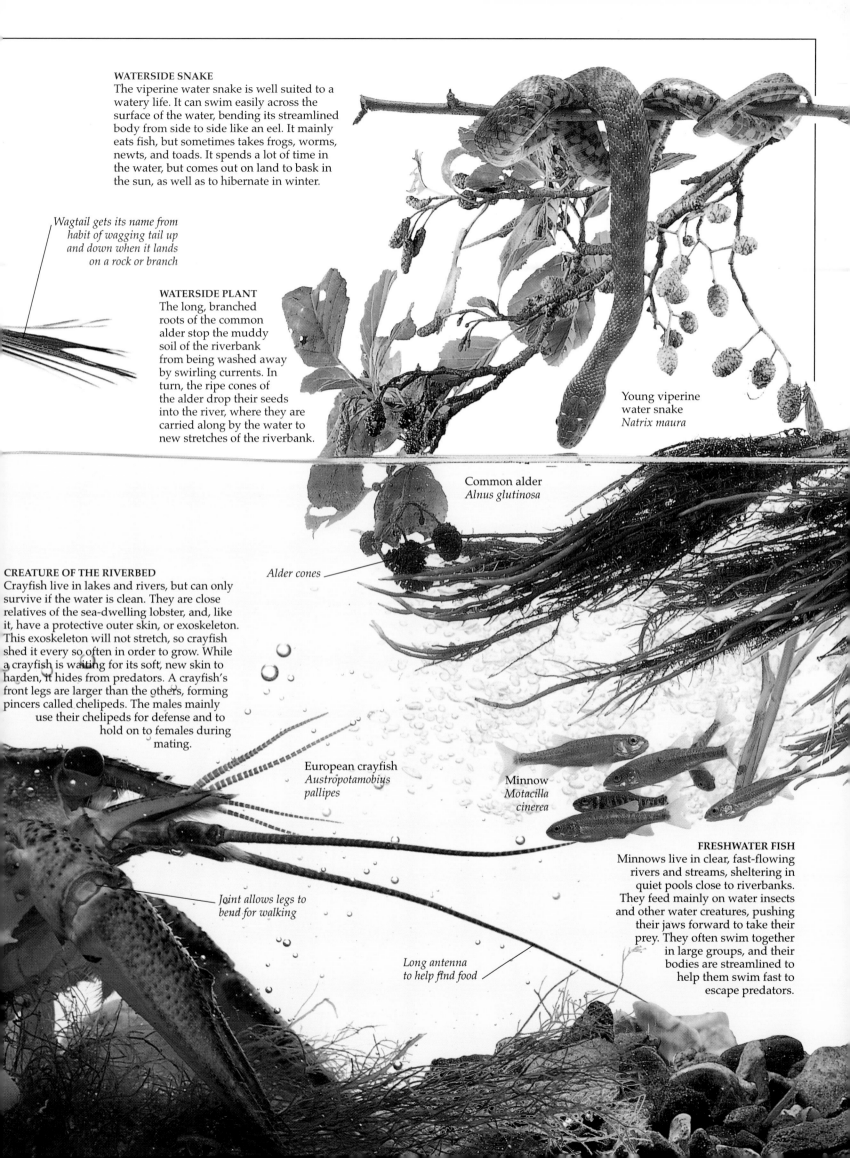

WATERSIDE SNAKE
The viperine water snake is well suited to a watery life. It can swim easily across the surface of the water, bending its streamlined body from side to side like an eel. It mainly eats fish, but sometimes takes frogs, worms, newts, and toads. It spends a lot of time in the water, but comes out on land to bask in the sun, as well as to hibernate in winter.

Wagtail gets its name from habit of wagging tail up and down when it lands on a rock or branch

WATERSIDE PLANT
The long, branched roots of the common alder stop the muddy soil of the riverbank from being washed away by swirling currents. In turn, the ripe cones of the alder drop their seeds into the river, where they are carried along by the water to new stretches of the riverbank.

Young viperine
water snake
Natrix maura

Common alder
Alnus glutinosa

CREATURE OF THE RIVERBED
Crayfish live in lakes and rivers, but can only survive if the water is clean. They are close relatives of the sea-dwelling lobster, and, like it, have a protective outer skin, or exoskeleton. This exoskeleton will not stretch, so crayfish shed it every so often in order to grow. While a crayfish is waiting for its soft, new skin to harden, it hides from predators. A crayfish's front legs are larger than the others, forming pincers called chelipeds. The males mainly use their chelipeds for defense and to hold on to females during mating.

Alder cones

European crayfish
Austropotamobius pallipes

Minnow
Motacilla cinerea

Joint allows legs to bend for walking

Long antenna to help find food

FRESHWATER FISH
Minnows live in clear, fast-flowing rivers and streams, sheltering in quiet pools close to riverbanks. They feed mainly on water insects and other water creatures, pushing their jaws forward to take their prey. They often swim together in large groups, and their bodies are streamlined to help them swim fast to escape predators.

The salt marsh

Mᴀɴʏ ᴇꜱᴛᴜᴀʀɪᴇꜱ ᴛʜʀᴏᴜɢʜᴏᴜᴛ ᴛʜᴇ ᴡᴏʀʟᴅ are flanked by a broad expanse of land and riddled with creeks and channels. This is the salt marsh, and it is a forbidding habitat for plants. Twice each day, seawater soaks into the soil and mud. As the tide retreats, evaporation leaves behind a salty residue. Spring tides flood the entire marsh with seawater. Yet a few hours later, at low tide, heavy rain may have turned the surface into an almost freshwater habitat. The plants growing in a salt marsh have evolved special adaptations for such fluctuating conditions.

PINKS AND PURPLES
Many marsh plants have pink, lavender, or purple flowers, coloring the whole marsh when in bloom. They tend to flower in late summer or fall.

Flower head

MARSH GRASS
The flower heads of couch grass show in this clump of grasses from the higher, drier part of the marsh.

Sea aster
*Aster
tripolium*

Flower spike

PLAIN PLANTAIN
The inconspicuous sea plantain populates the flat expanses of the salt marshes.

SEA ASTER
In late summer and early fall, the distinctive purple and yellow flowers of sea aster carpet large areas of the salt marsh.

*Flower stalk
rising out of
clump of
fleshy leaves*

Sea plantain
*Plantago
maritima*

*Flower
spike*

SEA-LAVENDER
In late summer, the flowers of the sea-lavender turn the salt marsh lilac.

Couch
grass
*Agropyron
repens*

*Leaves have
a bluish
tinge*

Sea-lavender
*Limonium
vulgare*

Sea arrow
grass
family
Gramineae

**SEA
ARROW
GRASS**
Among the dry, grassy stems of the marsh, there are the fleshy stems of sea arrow grass. Despite its name, it is not a true grass.

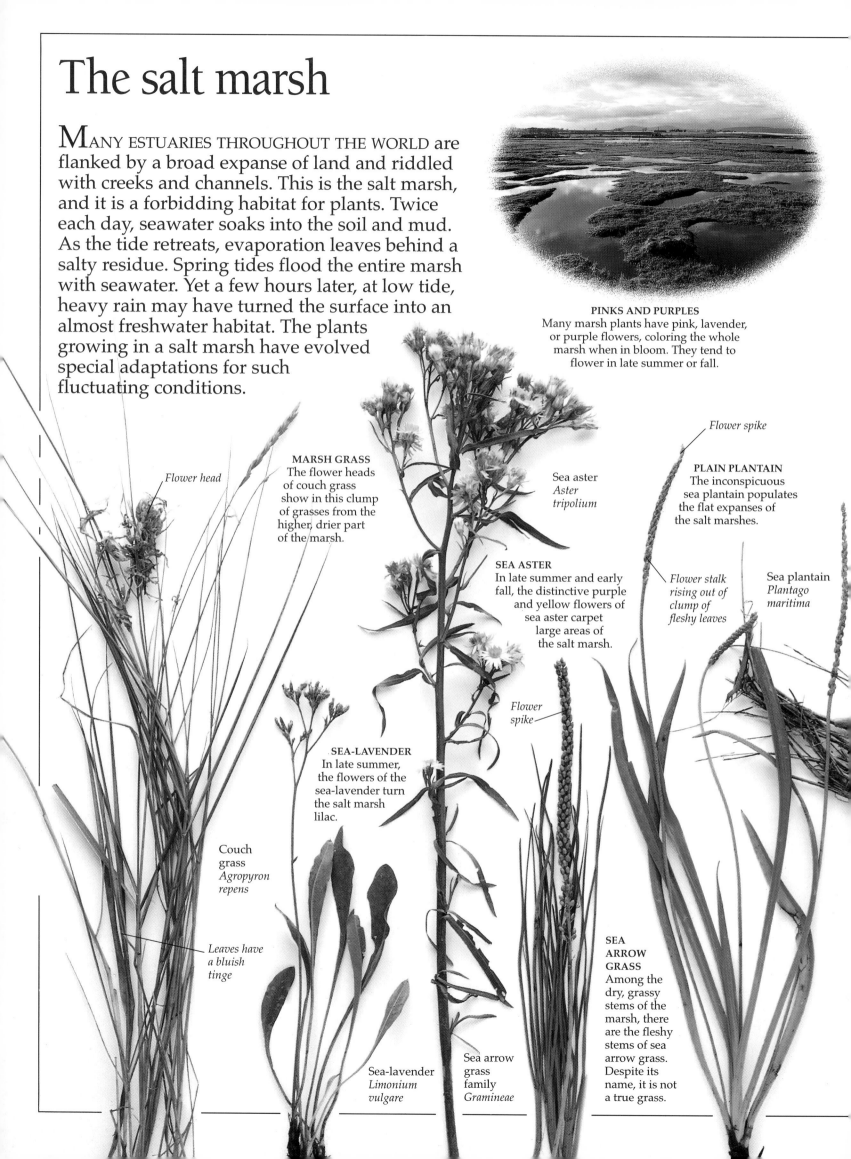

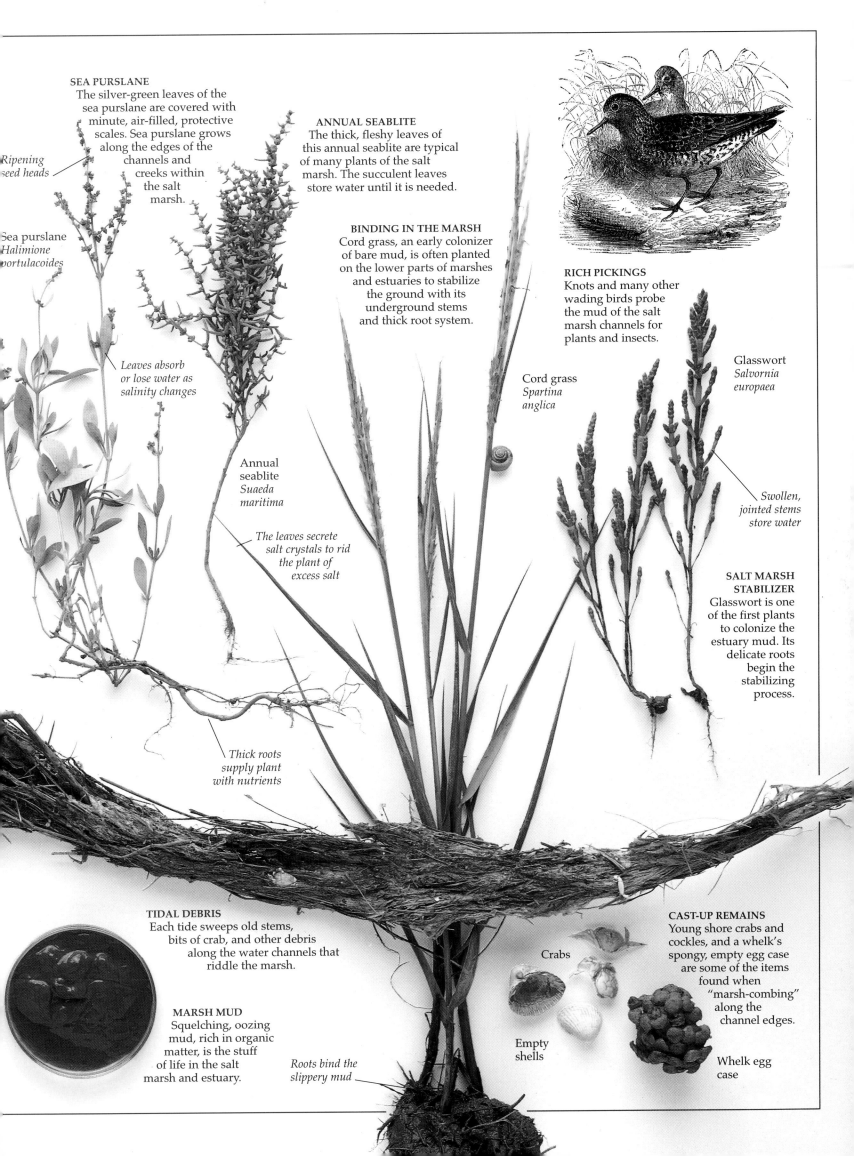

SEA PURSLANE
The silver-green leaves of the sea purslane are covered with minute, air-filled, protective scales. Sea purslane grows along the edges of the channels and creeks within the salt marsh.

Ripening seed heads

Sea purslane
Halimione portulacoides

Leaves absorb or lose water as salinity changes

ANNUAL SEABLITE
The thick, fleshy leaves of this annual seablite are typical of many plants of the salt marsh. The succulent leaves store water until it is needed.

BINDING IN THE MARSH
Cord grass, an early colonizer of bare mud, is often planted on the lower parts of marshes and estuaries to stabilize the ground with its underground stems and thick root system.

Annual seablite
Suaeda maritima

The leaves secrete salt crystals to rid the plant of excess salt

Thick roots supply plant with nutrients

RICH PICKINGS
Knots and many other wading birds probe the mud of the salt marsh channels for plants and insects.

Cord grass
Spartina anglica

Glasswort
Salvornia europaea

Swollen, jointed stems store water

SALT MARSH STABILIZER
Glasswort is one of the first plants to colonize the estuary mud. Its delicate roots begin the stabilizing process.

TIDAL DEBRIS
Each tide sweeps old stems, bits of crab, and other debris along the water channels that riddle the marsh.

CAST-UP REMAINS
Young shore crabs and cockles, and a whelk's spongy, empty egg case are some of the items found when "marsh-combing" along the channel edges.

Crabs

MARSH MUD
Squelching, oozing mud, rich in organic matter, is the stuff of life in the salt marsh and estuary.

Empty shells

Roots bind the slippery mud

Whelk egg case

Swamp life

DEEP LAYERS of mud and silt accumulate along sheltered tropical coastlines and in river estuaries. A number of different kinds of trees colonize these areas of still or slow-moving water. They are collectively known as mangroves and form swampy forests. Mangroves are the only trees that can live in the saltwater that is carried in and out of swamps by the tide twice a day. Among the mangroves' tangled roots live an amazing variety of animals that have adapted to the tidal ebb and flow of these thick jungles. Snapping turtles feed on water plants and carrion, while fiddler crabs emerge from muddy burrows to gather food. Water lettuces and water hyacinths provide food for the hungry herbivores, while overhead, iguanas and mangrove snakes sun themselves in the leafy branches.

IN THE TREES
The leafy canopy above the still waters of a swamp is home to many different animals. This agile green iguana is only 6 in (15 cm) long and lives in the swamps of Central America, South America, and the Caribbean. It is active during the day, sunbathing in leafy mangrove branches and leaping into the water if threatened. This fruit- and leaf-eating reptile has long, well-spread toes with sharp claws for gripping branches and twigs. Its scaly skin protects it and also stops it from drying out.

No teeth, but hard, sharp edge to mouth

Water lettuce
Pistia stratiotes

FIERCE SNAPPER
The snapping turtle lives in the still, warm waters of swamps and creeks. It is slow-moving, but well protected by its 3-in (8-cm) long shell and its fierce bite. The turtle spends most of its time in shallow water, well camouflaged among the floating plants, waiting for fish or other prey to swim past. Its feet are adapted for moving both underwater and on land. To get around in the water, it usually walks on the bottom, using its claws to grip the mud or rocks.

FLOATING PLANT
Water lettuces float on the swamp surface, their roots in the water. The waterproof leaves have air-filled floats that keep them the right way up. The leaves are broad and flat to absorb the sunlight the plant uses to produce its food.

Trailing roots absorb nutrients from the water

Strong legs with webbed toes and long claws

FIDDLER CRABS
As the tide recedes and the tangle of roots and mud is revealed, fiddler crabs pop out of their burrows and scuttle around looking for particles of food, such as algae, on the surface of the mud. Fiddlers have one giant pincer that they use to signal to females and to scare away other males. They are fiercely territorial, and usually simply threaten another male by waving the claw in the air. However, they will, on occasion, lock claws until one fiddler gains dominance and the other retreats. When the crabs are startled, they can run sideways very fast.

Seychelles palm
Verschaffeltia splendida

ADAPTED ROOTS
Many trees have specially adapted root systems to exist in difficult terrain. The palm *Verschaffeltia splendida* is found naturally only in the rain forests of the Seychelles Islands. It either grows in the wet conditions of river valley bottoms or on steep hillsides. Thick stilt roots grow out from the lower part of the trunk to give it firm anchorage in watery ground with only a thin layer of soil.

Fine hairs help protect trunk

New stilt root grows out from trunk

Splayed out stilt roots improve anchorage in mud

MANGROVES
The mud and the warm, shallow seawater on tropical coastlines are very low in oxygen. So that their roots can breathe, mangroves have pneumatophores, roots that stick up above the mud and take in air through large pores called lenticels. The roots of this mangrove, *Rhizophora*, grow in a tangle of arches.

Crab's eyes on long stalks so they can watch for danger

Fiddler crab
Uca vocans

Inside a tide pool

A TIDE POOL IS A miniature natural world – a specialized habitat shared by plants and animals. There is usually a wide range of plants, ranging from the film of microscopic algae coating almost any bare surface to wracks and other large seaweeds. These plants capture light energy from the Sun (pp. 12–13) and obtain nutrients from seawater. The plants in turn provide food for winkles, limpets, and other marine plant eaters. Flesh-eating animals – sea stars, small fish, whelks, and other creatures – eat the plant eaters. Tide pool scavengers such as crabs and prawns eat both plants and animals.

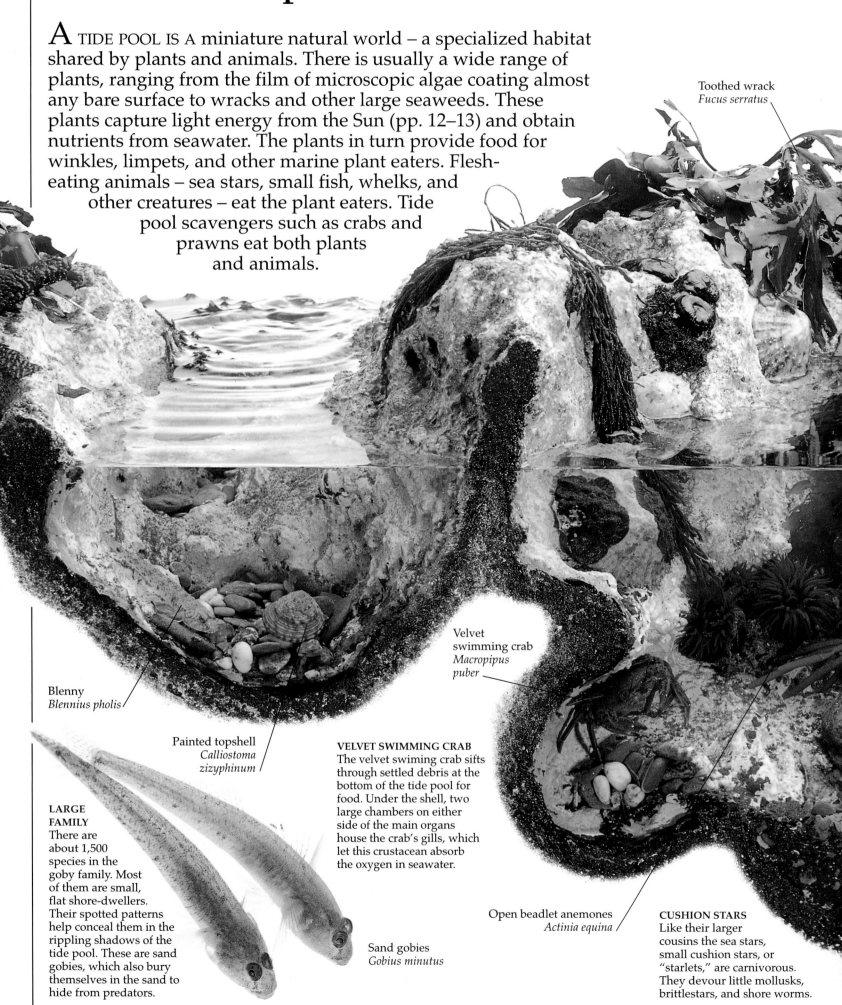

Toothed wrack
Fucus serratus

Velvet swimming crab
Macropipus puber

Blenny
Blennius pholis

Painted topshell
Calliostoma zizyphinum

VELVET SWIMMING CRAB
The velvet swiming crab sifts through settled debris at the bottom of the tide pool for food. Under the shell, two large chambers on either side of the main organs house the crab's gills, which let this crustacean absorb the oxygen in seawater.

LARGE FAMILY
There are about 1,500 species in the goby family. Most of them are small, flat shore-dwellers. Their spotted patterns help conceal them in the rippling shadows of the tide pool. These are sand gobies, which also bury themselves in the sand to hide from predators.

Sand gobies
Gobius minutus

Open beadlet anemones
Actinia equina

CUSHION STARS
Like their larger cousins the sea stars, small cushion stars, or "starlets," are carnivorous. They devour little mollusks, brittlestars, and shore worms.

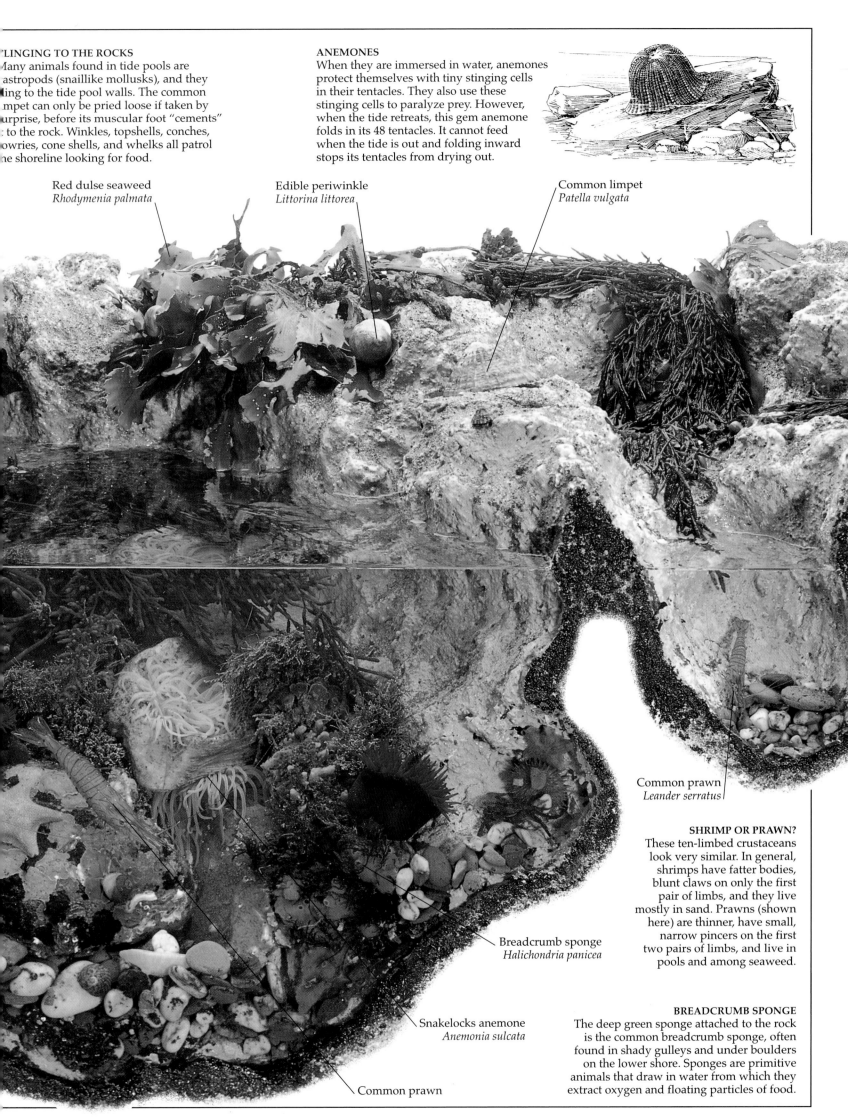

CLINGING TO THE ROCKS
Many animals found in tide pools are gastropods (snaillike mollusks), and they cling to the tide pool walls. The common limpet can only be pried loose if taken by surprise, before its muscular foot "cements" it to the rock. Winkles, topshells, conches, cowries, cone shells, and whelks all patrol the shoreline looking for food.

ANEMONES
When they are immersed in water, anemones protect themselves with tiny stinging cells in their tentacles. They also use these stinging cells to paralyze prey. However, when the tide retreats, this gem anemone folds in its 48 tentacles. It cannot feed when the tide is out and folding inward stops its tentacles from drying out.

Red dulse seaweed
Rhodymenia palmata

Edible periwinkle
Littorina littorea

Common limpet
Patella vulgata

Common prawn
Leander serratus

Breadcrumb sponge
Halichondria panicea

Snakelocks anemone
Anemonia sulcata

Common prawn

SHRIMP OR PRAWN?
These ten-limbed crustaceans look very similar. In general, shrimps have fatter bodies, blunt claws on only the first pair of limbs, and they live mostly in sand. Prawns (shown here) are thinner, have small, narrow pincers on the first two pairs of limbs, and live in pools and among seaweed.

BREADCRUMB SPONGE
The deep green sponge attached to the rock is the common breadcrumb sponge, often found in shady gulleys and under boulders on the lower shore. Sponges are primitive animals that draw in water from which they extract oxygen and floating particles of food.

Waders

In the soda lakes of Africa's Great Rift Valley, flamingos flock in hundreds of thousands, forming a sea of deep pink. They owe their color to the pink pigment in the small shrimps that they sift and eat from the lake-bottom mud. Flamingos nest on the ground in large colonies. Adults fly away every day to find more food and water. Flamingos' long legs allow them to wade in deep water as they search for food. Where rivers meet the sea, the shallow, muddy waters of estuaries teem with a wealth of food, and these are rich waters for other long-legged wading birds, too, such as stilts, dunlins, and oystercatchers.

Large bill

Flamingos feed their young on a rich "milk" produced in the crop, part of the esophagus

Lesser flamingo
Phoenicopterus minor

The more shrimps the flamingo eats the pinker the feathers become

Long neck

Slender bill

Long legs to wade through deep water while feeding

ESTUARY BIRD
The black-necked stilt lives in North America and northern South America, breeding in colonies on marshy ground or on the bare mud of the salt pans. In flight, their legs stick out 7 in (18 cm) beyond their tail to counterbalance the long neck and the weight of the head. The very long legs allow the stilt to feed on small creatures that it takes from the mud in deep water on shores and estuaries.

Black-necked stilt
Himantopus mexicanus

LONG LEGS
The long legs of the flamingo enable it to reach deep water, helping it avoid competition for the available food from other, shorter-legged birds. Like ducks and geese, flamingos have webs of skin between their toes. The webs work like paddles when the bird is in water. They are also useful when the flamingo is walking on soft, marshy ground, as they spread the flamingo's weight evenly over the boggy surface.

148

Marabou stork
*Leptoptilos
crumerniferus*

Characteristic
hunched shoulders

Long bill for
seizing prey

Adult has
large throat
pouch for inflation
in courtship rituals

Flexible
neck

Lesser flamingos
are the smallest of the
six species of flamingo

Marabou has
longest legs
of any stork

Sievelike edges
on top bill to
filter food

LARGE SCAVENGER
The Marabou stork of East
Africa scavenges on the
carcasses of large grazing
animals and human garbage
dumps. It also feeds on fish
and frogs, which it finds
while wading in the shallow
waters of riverbeds, and
sometimes eats sick or injured
birds, and flamingo eggs and
chicks. The Marabou stork is
also called the "adjutant" or
"adjutant stork" because of its
hunched military bearing.
It is the largest species
of stork, growing to a
height of 5 ft (1.5 m).

FILTER FEEDING
The flamingo has a unique method
of feeding. Sievelike edges on its
top bill filter out tiny plants and
invertebrates from the surface of
the water. The bottom bill and
tongue move up and down to
pump water through comb-like
fringes on the sides of the top bill.

Large,
splayed
feet

Weather by the sea

THE PRESENCE OF SO MUCH WATER gives weather by the sea its own particular characteristics. Winds blowing in off the sea naturally carry more moisture than those blowing off the land, so coastal areas tend to be noticeably wetter than inland areas – especially if they face into the wind. They can be cloudier, too. Cumulus clouds, for instance, usually form inland only during the day, but on coasts facing the wind, they drift overhead at night as well, when cold winds blow in over the warm sea. Sometimes these clouds bring localized showers to coastal areas. Fogs can form at sea in the same way, and creep slightly inland. At daybreak the sea is often shrouded in a thick mist that disperses only as the wind changes or as the Sun's heat begins to dry the atmosphere. The overall effect of all this water is to make weather in coastal areas generally less extreme than it is farther inland. Because the sea retains heat well, nights tend to be warmer on the coast, and winters are generally milder, summers slightly cooler.

CLEAR COAST
This picture shows the coast of Oregon, but it is typical of west coasts everywhere in the midlatitudes. Deep depressions are common at this latitude, and here a cold front has just passed over, moving inland. An overhang of cloud lingers in the upper air from the front itself, and cumulus clouds are still growing in its wake. More showers are clearly on the way. As the front moves inland, it may produce progressively less rain, because there is less moisture available to feed its progress.

OUT FOR A BLOW
Seaside resorts are often very windy, as depicted by this early 20th-century postcard. The open sea provides no obstacle to winds blowing off it, and temperature differences between land and sea can generate stiff breezes as well.

COASTAL FOG
Sea fog is an advection fog, which means that it occurs where a warm, moist wind blows over a cooler surface. Sea fog often happens off the coast of Newfoundland, in Canada (left), where warm westerly winds blow over a sea cooled by currents flowing down from the Arctic. Sometimes thick fogs linger there for days on end.

1000 mb

A little
cloud
cover

Strong
wind

WIND AND WAVES

The winds that help windsurfers skim across the
surface of the sea are often locally generated sea
breezes. But the waves they ride may be created
by winds thousands of miles away. Waves are
whipped up by the wind when air turbulence
over the water creates little pockets of low and
high pressure that suck and push on the water.
Just how big the waves are depends on the
strength of the wind, how long it blows, and
the "fetch," or how far it blows over the water.

Nighttime land breeze

*Warmer air from over sea pushes
cool air over land downward*

Land cools quickly

*Sinking air over land
drives air seaward,
creating land breeze*

Sea cools slowly

*Air rising over warm sea pushes
air at high altitude toward land*

Daytime sea breeze

*Air sinks over
the cool sea*

*Air pushed out to sea at
high altitude increases
air pressure over cool sea*

*Air rises over warm
land about 0.6 mile
(1 km) over ground*

Land and sea breezes

A marked characteristic of coastal areas
is the frequent occurrence of land and sea
breezes. Both occur because land and water
absorb and lose heat from the Sun at different
rates. During the day, the land heats up far
more quickly than the sea, and air begins to
rise. As warm air rises above the land, cool
air from the sea is drawn in underneath,
creating a stiff sea breeze blowing inland. At
night, the situation is reversed. The land
cools more quickly, and air begins to sink.
The cool air pushes out under the warm air
over the sea. This is called a land breeze.

*Land warms up quickly
in the warmth of the Sun*

*Sea warms
up very slowly*

*Sea air driven shoreward
creates stiff sea breeze at surface*

Turtles and tortoises

REPTILES WITH SHELLS are found in most warm areas of the world. There are more than 250 species, and they live in saltwater, freshwater, and on land. Turtles, also known as chelonians, make up most of the species. All chelonians lay eggs on land – some in sand, some in leaf litter, and some in the burrows of other animals. These reptiles have short, broad bodies enclosed in a bony shell. The bone of the shell is usually covered by horny plates or, less commonly, by leathery skin. Chelonians are divided into two main groups according to the way the neck bends when the head retreats into the shell. Hidden-necked chelonians include terrapins, sea turtles, softshell turtles, and tortoises. Side-necked chelonians include the matamata and African mud turtles.

ALLIGATOR SNAPPING TURTLE
This turtle is ferocious both in appearance and its habits. It spends nearly all its time in water, lying motionless on the riverbed, its mouth wide open, its knifelike jaws ready to scythe through its prey.

MIGRATING TURTLE
Some marine turtles have developed incredible migratory habits, traveling hundreds of miles from their feeding grounds to lay their eggs on the beaches where they were born. The green turtle travels to its nesting ground every two or three years.

Green turtle
Chelonia mydas

LEATHER SHELLED
The largest of all turtles, this giant leatherback has a leathery, ridged skin above and below its body, instead of the usual horny plates. It usually lives in the mid-depths of ocean waters, breeding in the warm waters of the Caribbean.

Turtles are air breathers, so must come to the surface regularly

RED-EARED TERRAPIN
This chelonian gets its name from the broad, red stripe that runs along the side of its head. Because they are gentle and attractive creatures, these terrapins are very popular as pets. Found in North America, they live in ponds and rivers, but frequently climb out of the water to bask.

Red-eared terrapin
Pseudemys scripta elegans

HERMANN'S TORTOISE
Different lifestyles lead to alterations in shell structure. Very few land tortoises have the speed or agility to escape a predator, so they usually have high-domed or knobby shells as a defense against predators' strong jaws. Turtles tend to have flatter shells that are streamlined for easy movement through the water. Soft-shelled tortoises have the flattest shells, allowing them to hide easily beneath sand and mud.

Hermann's tortoise
Testudo hermanni

High-domed shell

Swimming sequence
of green turtle

*Front flippers
help turtle "fly"
through water*

*Color of shell is
green, brown,
or black*

Painted
turtle

Stinkpot
turtle

Red-eared
slider

BASKING TERRAPINS
Terrapins live in freshwater habitats
and can often be seen basking in the
sun on rocks or riverbanks. Usually
smaller than either tortoises or
turtles, they are often kept as
pets in freshwater tanks.

*Back pair of
flippers used
as rudders
to steer*

*Smooth sections
do not overlap*

Streamlined shell

GREEN TURTLE
Green turtles live in
the warm waters of the
Atlantic, Pacific, and Indian
Oceans. Like all chelonians, they
come ashore to lay their eggs. First,
the females mate in shallow water
with the waiting males. Later, under
cover of darkness, the females crawl
up the beach to lay their eggs in the
sand before heading back to the water.
They may return several times in one
breeding season to lay more batches.

Life on the rocks

ROCKY SHORES provide a diverse and complex environment for many types of marine creatures. The types of rocks from which a beach is made, its position relative to the sea, and the range of tide levels it receives all play a part in determining the variety of creatures that live there. The tide may expose a rocky shore for several hours each day, and some creatures can tolerate living without water for extended periods. Those that cannot, and fail to reach deeper waters or find tidal pools when the water recedes, will dry out and die from exposure to the air and Sun. The pounding of powerful waves erodes the rocks themselves. Many animals have evolved very strong shells to withstand the force of the waves and have also developed ways of anchoring themselves firmly to the surface of rocks so they are not washed away.

TIDE POOLS
Life can be hard in the shallow water pools left by receding tides. Many creatures that prefer less light and warmth are left stranded and must try their best to find shelter.

New Zealand mussel

Bearded ark shell

BOUVIER'S CRAB
Like many small crabs, this one lives between or under rocks, and only emerges to scavenge for food at night.

BEARDED ARK SHELL
This bivalve gets its name from the tiny hairs that cover it. It lives in rock crevices and attaches itself by means of a broad byssus (see left). The shell often gets distorted as it grows to fit snugly into its rocky niche.

Mussel with byssal threads

Tail fan

Common blue mussels

ANCHORED
Mussels are common inhabitants of many rocky shores, often living in massive clusters high on the shore. Mussels anchor themselves to rocks and other surfaces by means of byssal threads – strong, thin filaments secreted by a gland in their feet.

JEWEL IN A SHELL
This rough star-shell lives on the rocky shores of the Mediterranean, but is found below tide level. The shell is often encrusted with marine growths. The bright red operculum, or gill cover, is sometimes used to make jewelry.

Operculum

WINKLES ON THE WEEDS
Tiny periwinkles are among the most common inhabitants of rocky shores. They tend to live high up on the shore, where they cling to rocks and clumps of seaweed.

Rough periwinkles

Antenna

Left large pincer, or cheliped, is larger and stronger than right

Common shore crab

Antennule

Eyes tucked in under carapace

ELUSIVE LOBSTER
The common lobster is highly prized as a food and is a favorite catch for divers. Lobsters can be difficult to find as they blend in well with their surroundings and often hide in crevices during the day, with only their claws and antennae exposed.

One of four pairs of walking legs

SHORE CRAB
The shore crab is one of the most common European crabs and is often found lurking under rocks and seaweed on the seashore.

STONY-SHELLED CRAB
The Mediterranean stone crab is so-called because of its heavy-looking, irregular shell.

Clever disguises

A CASUAL GLANCE into a tide pool may reveal only a few strands of seaweed and some dead-looking shells. But wait patiently, sitting still to avoid being seen, and watch carefully. A dark patch of rock may suddenly glide forward: it is a blenny, on the lookout for food. A slightly hazy-looking area of sand may walk away: it is a prawn, adjusting the spots and lines on its body to blend perfectly with the background. A small pebble may slip: it is a winkle grazing on algae. A patch of gravelly bottom ripples and two eyes may appear: a flatfish is wafting small pebbles and shell fragments over its body to hide its outline. All these creatures use camouflage to help conceal themselves from voracious predators – and to catch prey themselves.

PALE UNDERSIDE
Flatfish are well camouflaged when viewed from the surface of the water. The underside, flat against the seabed, has no need of special coloring, so it is white or pale in many flatfish species.

WEED LOOKALIKE
The leafy sea dragon, from the coastal waters of southern Australia, is a type of sea horse. Its loose lobes of skin resemble the seaweed fronds in which it hides.

Urchins graze on the rocks and weeds, eating small algal growths and animals

URCHIN COVER-UP
Several species of sea urchins grasp pebbles, shells, and pieces of seaweed with their long "tube feet" and hold them over their bodies. A well-draped urchin can be difficult to spot. These are green sea urchins, which are found on the lower shore and in inshore waters.

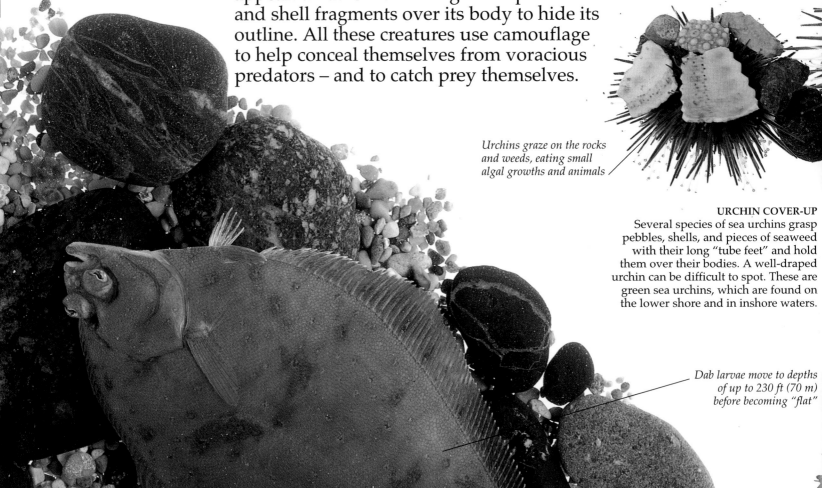

Dab larvae move to depths of up to 230 ft (70 m) before becoming "flat"

A DAB WILL DO
Many flatfish can change color to match the surface on which they are resting. A few minutes earlier, this young dab was a light sandy color. It became several shades darker when placed on selected dark pebbles, and the marks on its upper side became almost black. The largest dabs reach about 16 in (40 cm) in length.

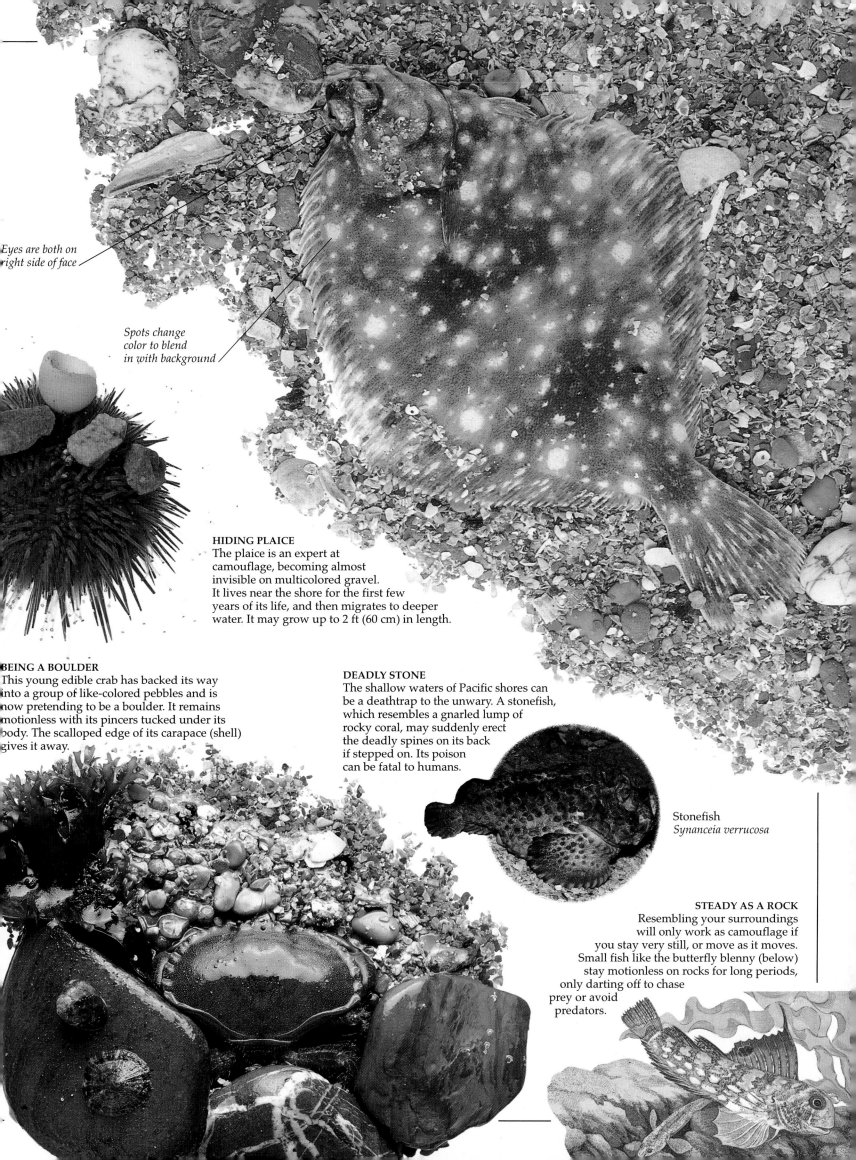

Eyes are both on right side of face

Spots change color to blend in with background

HIDING PLAICE
The plaice is an expert at camouflage, becoming almost invisible on multicolored gravel. It lives near the shore for the first few years of its life, and then migrates to deeper water. It may grow up to 2 ft (60 cm) in length.

BEING A BOULDER
This young edible crab has backed its way into a group of like-colored pebbles and is now pretending to be a boulder. It remains motionless with its pincers tucked under its body. The scalloped edge of its carapace (shell) gives it away.

DEADLY STONE
The shallow waters of Pacific shores can be a deathtrap to the unwary. A stonefish, which resembles a gnarled lump of rocky coral, may suddenly erect the deadly spines on its back if stepped on. Its poison can be fatal to humans.

Stonefish
Synanceia verrucosa

STEADY AS A ROCK
Resembling your surroundings will only work as camouflage if you stay very still, or move as it moves. Small fish like the butterfly blenny (below) stay motionless on rocks for long periods, only darting off to chase prey or avoid predators.

Many-colored seaweeds

THE MOST OBVIOUS seaweeds on the shore are usually the large brown seaweeds known as wracks and kelps. Wracks are leathery, straplike seaweeds that grow in bands between the high and low tide marks. Some species have air bladders that keep the main body (the thallus) of the weed afloat as waves come and go. Kelps have broader, bladelike fronds and usually live below the low-water mark. Less obvious red seaweeds are generally smaller and prefer tide pools and deeper water beyond the kelp zone. They contain a red pigment that masks out the green pigment chlorophyll, present in all plants. Red pigment uses the dim light that filters through seawater much more efficiently than the dark pigment of brown seaweeds, so red seaweeds are able to grow at greater depths.

FROM HIGH TO LOW
On rocky shores, seaweeds are found in horizontal bands or zones. These bands of bright green seaweeds, greenish brown wracks, red seaweeds, and brown kelps at the low-tide mark form a basic pattern that is repeated, with variations in the species, all over the world.

Mature bladder wrack

Air pocket

Toothed wrack

Immature bladder wrack

Sea lettuce

POCKETS OF AIR
Some specimens of bladder wrack develop large air pockets in pairs along the central midribs of fronds (above right). Yet other specimens, especially on exposed coasts, have few or even no bladders. No one knows why this is so. A mature bladder wrack (as in the engraving above) has swollen tips that contain its reproductive organs.

FROM HIGH TO LOW
Sea lettuce (left and above), which looks a lot like the plant we eat in salads, can grow in many different habitats – in the slightly salty water of estuaries, in seawater, and even in mildly polluted waters. This green seaweed is very common. It can be found attached to rocks, floating freely, or washed up on shore.

WEED WITH TEETH
Toothed, or serrated, wrack is named after the sawlike teeth along the edges of its fronds. It is a member of the *Fucus* group, but unlike its close relatives, it has no air bladders.

A TASTY DISH
The two red seaweeds carragheen (right) and dulse (far right) are both harvested commercially. Carragheen provides a gel for making aspic and ice cream, while dulse can be eaten raw, cooked as a vegetable, or added to a stew or soup.

SUGAR IN THE SALT

The sugar kelp, or sugar wrack, is a big brown seaweed of the low-water level and below. Its crinkly fronds and wavy edges are distinctive, as is the sweet taste of the white powder that forms on its drying surface. It is eaten as a delicacy in the Far East.

LONG THONGS

Thongweed is a leathery, strap-like brown seaweed found near the low-water level. Its narrow fronds may grow more than 10 ft (3 m) long. Like many seaweeds, its tough and rubbery texture protects it from the pounding of waves on rocks.

Thongweed

Sugar kelp

BUTTON-SHAPED BASE

The button-, or mushroom-, shaped base is one stage in the life cycle of the thongweed. In the plant's second year of growth, the thongs develop from this base. They contain the reproductive structures.

Nutrients are absorbed through the whole surface of the seaweed

Holdfasts (root-like structures) anchor brown seaweeds to rocks

Carragheen

Dulse

Oceans of the world

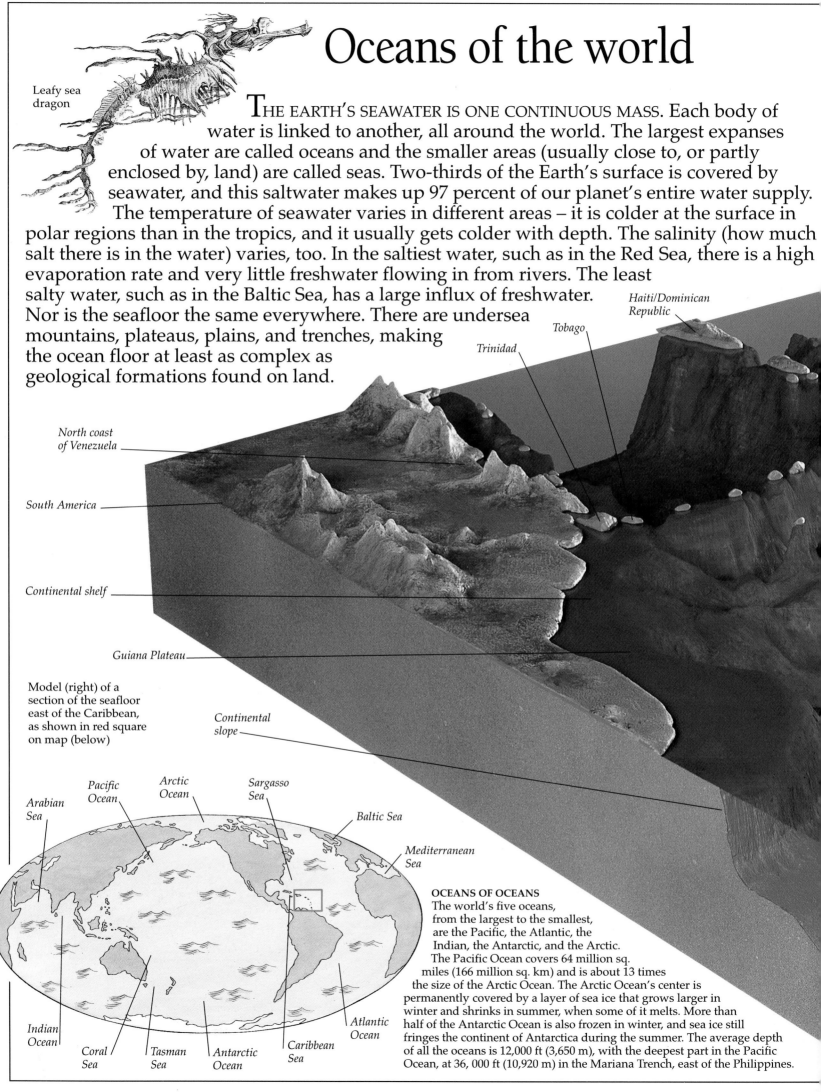

Leafy sea dragon

THE EARTH'S SEAWATER IS ONE CONTINUOUS MASS. Each body of water is linked to another, all around the world. The largest expanses of water are called oceans and the smaller areas (usually close to, or partly enclosed by, land) are called seas. Two-thirds of the Earth's surface is covered by seawater, and this saltwater makes up 97 percent of our planet's entire water supply. The temperature of seawater varies in different areas – it is colder at the surface in polar regions than in the tropics, and it usually gets colder with depth. The salinity (how much salt there is in the water) varies, too. In the saltiest water, such as in the Red Sea, there is a high evaporation rate and very little freshwater flowing in from rivers. The least salty water, such as in the Baltic Sea, has a large influx of freshwater. Nor is the seafloor the same everywhere. There are undersea mountains, plateaus, plains, and trenches, making the ocean floor at least as complex as geological formations found on land.

Haiti/Dominican Republic

Tobago

Trinidad

North coast of Venezuela

South America

Continental shelf

Guiana Plateau

Model (right) of a section of the seafloor east of the Caribbean, as shown in red square on map (below)

Continental slope

Arctic Ocean

Pacific Ocean

Sargasso Sea

Arabian Sea

Baltic Sea

Mediterranean Sea

Indian Ocean

Coral Sea

Tasman Sea

Antarctic Ocean

Caribbean Sea

Atlantic Ocean

OCEANS OF OCEANS
The world's five oceans, from the largest to the smallest, are the Pacific, the Atlantic, the Indian, the Antarctic, and the Arctic. The Pacific Ocean covers 64 million sq. miles (166 million sq. km) and is about 13 times the size of the Arctic Ocean. The Arctic Ocean's center is permanently covered by a layer of sea ice that grows larger in winter and shrinks in summer, when some of it melts. More than half of the Antarctic Ocean is also frozen in winter, and sea ice still fringes the continent of Antarctica during the summer. The average depth of all the oceans is 12,000 ft (3,650 m), with the deepest part in the Pacific Ocean, at 36, 000 ft (10,920 m) in the Mariana Trench, east of the Philippines.

GOD OF THE SEA

Neptune, the Roman god of the sea, seen here with a sea nymph, is usually depicted carrying a pronged trident or spear and riding a dolphin. He was also thought to control freshwater supplies, so offerings were made to him during the driest months of the year.

FLOATING MEAL
The sea otter will float on its back in the calm of a kelp bed by the coasts of the Pacific Ocean rather than come ashore. It feeds on sea urchins and crustaceans floating in this position, crushing the hard shells with a stone.

FORMING A TRENCH
The gigantic plates on the Earth's crust move like a conveyor belt. As new areas of ocean floor form, old areas disappear into the molten heart of the planet. This diagram shows one oceanic plate being forced under another to form the Mariana Trench. This process is called subduction, and here it creates an island arc.

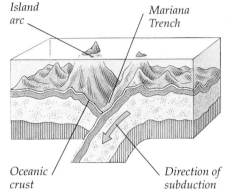

Island arc

Mariana Trench

Oceanic crust

Direction of subduction

Formation of Mariana Trench

Hatteras Abyssal Plain

Puerto Rico Trench

Nares Abyssal Plain

Mid-Atlantic Ridge

Kane Fracture Zone

Vema Fracture Zone

Demerara Abyssal Plain

OCEAN LANDSCAPE
This model shows the features on the bottom of the Atlantic Ocean off the northeastern coast of South America, from Guyana to Venezuela. Off this coast is the continental shelf, a region of relatively shallow water about 660 ft (200 m) deep. Here the continental shelf is about 125 miles (200 km) wide, but off the coast of northern Asia it is as much as 1,000 miles (1,600 km) wide. At the outer edge of the continental shelf, the ocean floor drops steeply away to form the continental slope. Sediments eroded from the land and carried by rivers like the Orinoco accumulate at the bottom of the slope. The ocean floor then opens out in almost flat areas called abyssal plains, which are covered with a deep layer of soft sediments. The Puerto Rico Trench formed where one of the Earth's plates, the North American Plate, is sliding past another, the Caribbean Plate. An arc of volcanic islands has also been created where the North American Plate is forced under the Caribbean Plate.

The coral kingdom

IN THE CRYSTAL-CLEAR, WARM WATERS of the tropics, coral reefs flourish, covering vast areas. The largest stony coral structure, Australia's Great Barrier Reef, stretches for 1,260 miles (2,027 km). Made of the skeletons of stony corals, coral reefs are cemented together by chalky algae. Most stony corals are colonies of many tiny, anemonelike individuals called polyps. Each polyp makes its own hard limestone cup (skeleton), which protects its soft body. To make their skeletons, the coral polyps need the help of microscopic, single-celled algae that live inside them. The algae need sunlight to grow, which is why coral reefs are found only in sunny surface waters. In return for giving the algae a home, corals get some food from them, but they also capture plankton with their tentacles. Only the upper layer of a reef is made of living corals, which build upon skeletons of dead polyps. Coral reefs are also home to soft corals and sea fans, which do not have stony skeletons.

Tentacle's stings catch food

Mouth also expels waste

Hard plates of stony skeleton

Baglike stomach

INSIDE A CORAL ANIMAL
In a stony coral, a layer of tissue joins each polyp to its neighbor. To reproduce, they divide in two or release eggs and sperm into the water.

Black coral's horny skeleton looks like a bunch of twigs

Orange sea fan, Indian and Pacific Oceans

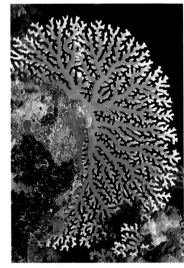

STINGING CORAL
Colorful hydrocorals are related to sea firs and, unlike horny and stony corals, produce jellyfishlike forms that carry their sex organs. Known as fire corals, they have potent stings on their polyps.

BLACK CORAL
In living black corals, the skeleton provides support for the living tissues and the branches bear rows of anemonelike polyps. Black corals are mainly found in tropical waters, growing in the deep part of coral reefs. Although they take a long time to grow, the black skeleton is sometimes used to make jewelry.

Intricate mesh developed to withstand strong currents

Stem of sea fan

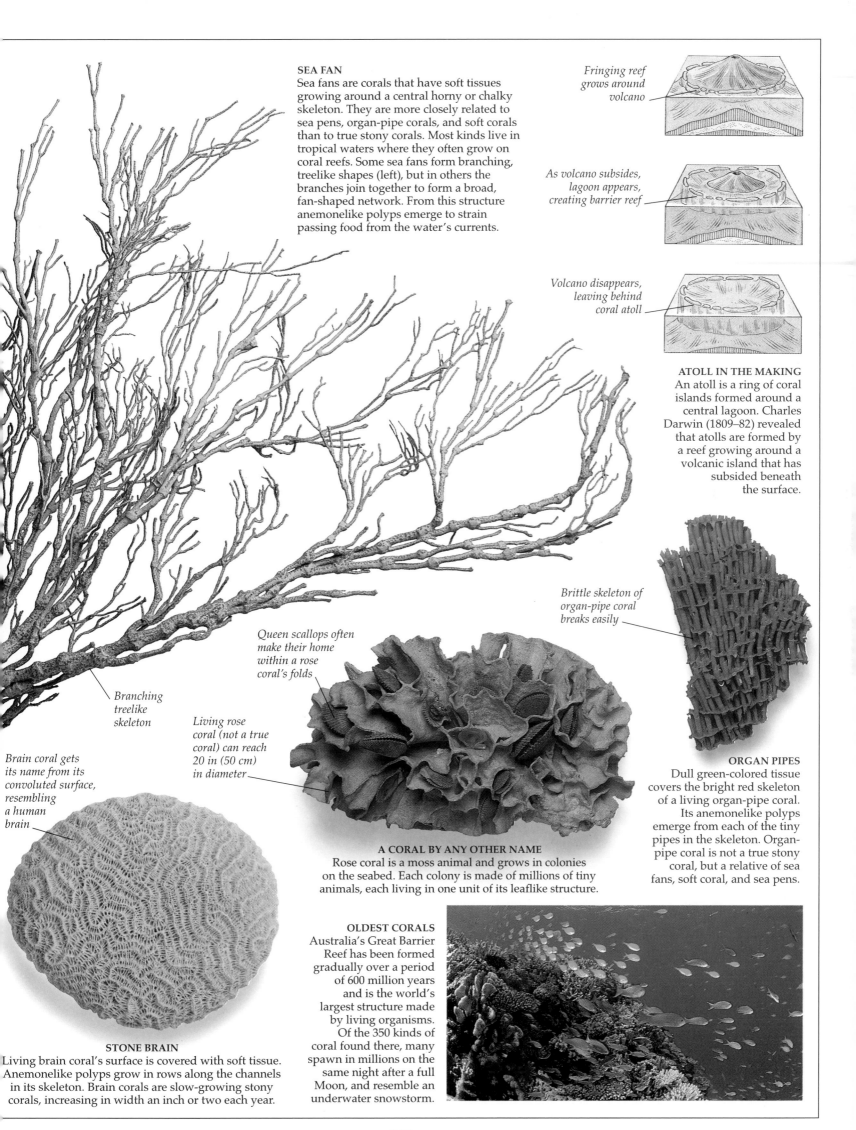

SEA FAN

Sea fans are corals that have soft tissues growing around a central horny or chalky skeleton. They are more closely related to sea pens, organ-pipe corals, and soft corals than to true stony corals. Most kinds live in tropical waters where they often grow on coral reefs. Some sea fans form branching, treelike shapes (left), but in others the branches join together to form a broad, fan-shaped network. From this structure anemonelike polyps emerge to strain passing food from the water's currents.

Fringing reef grows around volcano

As volcano subsides, lagoon appears, creating barrier reef

Volcano disappears, leaving behind coral atoll

ATOLL IN THE MAKING

An atoll is a ring of coral islands formed around a central lagoon. Charles Darwin (1809–82) revealed that atolls are formed by a reef growing around a volcanic island that has subsided beneath the surface.

Branching treelike skeleton

Queen scallops often make their home within a rose coral's folds

Living rose coral (not a true coral) can reach 20 in (50 cm) in diameter

Brittle skeleton of organ-pipe coral breaks easily

Brain coral gets its name from its convoluted surface, resembling a human brain

A CORAL BY ANY OTHER NAME

Rose coral is a moss animal and grows in colonies on the seabed. Each colony is made of millions of tiny animals, each living in one unit of its leaflike structure.

ORGAN PIPES

Dull green-colored tissue covers the bright red skeleton of a living organ-pipe coral. Its anemonelike polyps emerge from each of the tiny pipes in the skeleton. Organ-pipe coral is not a true stony coral, but a relative of sea fans, soft coral, and sea pens.

OLDEST CORALS

Australia's Great Barrier Reef has been formed gradually over a period of 600 million years and is the world's largest structure made by living organisms.

Of the 350 kinds of coral found there, many spawn in millions on the same night after a full Moon, and resemble an underwater snowstorm.

STONE BRAIN

Living brain coral's surface is covered with soft tissue. Anemonelike polyps grow in rows along the channels in its skeleton. Brain corals are slow-growing stony corals, increasing in width an inch or two each year.

Dangers of the reef

Clown fish
Amphiprion
species

Yellow
anemone

Clown anemone

CORAL REEFS TEEM WITH LIFE. Bright fish and sea slugs dart in and out of the jagged landscape, shrimps hide in the coral's natural crevices, and sea horses cling to the seaweeds and sponges of the reef. Yet a coral reef is a dangerous place. Its changing surfaces provide shelter and opportunity for prey and predator alike. Most of the hunted sea creatures, like small wrasse, must feed out in the open. However, at a second's notice, they can dart out of harm's way by digging themselves into loose sand or mud or diving into a narrow cleft in the rocks. Hunters like the mandarin fish and the common octopus (pp. 78–79) are content to lurk inside coral caves, watching for unsuspecting victims. And there are other dangers – many sea creatures have to avoid the deadly embrace of poisonous sea anemones and carnivorous corals. Sometimes, however, a dangerous situation can be advantageous, too. The clown fish lays its eggs and even rears its young safely among the tentacles of the clown anemone, which catches, poisons, and eats other small fish.

CLOWNING AROUND
On many tropical reefs, bright-colored clown fish dart among the tentacles of a sea anemone whose venomous sting would paralyze other small fish in seconds. Clown fish have an especially thick body covering that lacks the usual substances that stimulate the anemone to sting. The anemone absorbs pieces of food dropped by its colorful visitors.

Eyespots give impression of huge "face"

Loose gravel for wrasse to dive into

1 SELF-PROTECTION
The twinspot wrasse has two large eyespots on its dorsal fin. If this huge false "face" fails to frighten predators, the twinspot uses alternative means to avoid danger. A threatening sound, worrying scent, or an actual sighting of a predator makes the twinspot tilt its head down. As it dives, it searches out a bare patch of shell fragments and gravel for refuge.

2 TESTING THE BED
As the twinspot reaches the seabed, it swerves up to a horizontal position and thrusts its sensitive snout and chest into the gravel. Sometimes this turns out to be only a shallow layer on top of solid rock – no use for hiding.

Sea horse
*Hippocampus
kuda*

Ray of dorsal fin

*Sea horse's eyes
move independently*

*Long, hollow
snout to suck
up shrimps*

Mandarin fish
*Synchiropus
splendidus*

FOUL FINERY
The brilliant colors of its skin warn other sea
creatures that the mandarin fish tastes foul. Its skin
produces a slimy mucus that smells and tastes unpleasant.
The mucus helps protect the fish from attack by bacteria and
fungi, as well as larger fish. The mandarin fish lives near the
seabed and feeds on smaller fish and other creatures that
float past. It also nibbles at the algae on the coral reef.

CHANGING COLOR
Sea horses cannot swim quickly to escape danger, but
they can change color to match their background and
hide from enemies. They anchor themselves with their
strong, supple tail, to coral or seaweeds and wait for
food, such as prawns, to swim past. The
sea horse straightens its tail to rise up,
and curls it to sink. The fin on its back
bends backward and forward to push
it through the water.

*Loose gravel
flung upward
by wrasse's
activity*

3 DIGGING IN
Hurling its body into S-shaped curves, and
digging down in a diagonal direction, the twinspot
"swims" headfirst into the loose gravel and stones.
Its fins and tail fling the gravel up and out of the way.
Within seconds, the fish settles into the surface layer of
stones, and the falling gravel rains back down to add
to its covering. The twinspot stays still until it senses
that things above are back to normal. Many species of
wrasse, especially near the Pacific coral islands, bury
themselves in the gravel each night and "sleep" there.

Strawberry
shrimp
*Lysmata
debelius*

SHY SHRIMP
The strawberry shrimp hides
in natural crevices in coral or
digs a burrow in the sand with its
chelipeds (claws). The shrimp grows
in spurts, increasing in size each
time it molts. It has to hide
from enemies, such as fish
and crabs, while the
soft, new exoskeleton
stretches and hardens.

*Complete layer of
gravel hides wrasse
from predators*

Tropical storms

Hurricane force winds
often damage buildings

KNOWN AS TYPHOONS IN THE PACIFIC and as tropical cyclones by meteorologists, hurricanes claim more lives each year than any other storms. When a full-blown hurricane strikes, trees are uprooted and buildings flattened by raging winds that gust at up to 220 mph (360 km/h). Vast areas are swamped by torrential rain, and coastal regions can be overwhelmed by the "storm surge." This is a wall of water up to 26 ft (8 m) high sucked up by the storm's "eye" – the ring of low pressure at the storm's center – and topped by giant waves whipped up by the winds. Hurricanes begin as small thunderstorms over warm, tropical oceans. If the water is warm enough (over 75°F or 24°C), several storms may whirl around as one, encouraged by strong winds high in the atmosphere. Soon they drift westward across the ocean, drawing in warm, moist air and spinning in tighter circles. At first, the center of the storm may be more than 200 miles (330 km) across and the winds at gale force. As it moves west, it gains energy from the warm air it sucks in. By the time the storm reaches the far side of the ocean, the eye may have shrunk to 30 miles (50 km) across, pressure may have dropped, and the winds may be howling around at hurricane force.

ANATOMY OF A HURRICANE
The air in the eye of the hurricane is at low pressure. As the eye passes over, the winds may drop altogether, and a small circle of clear sky become visible for a while. The lull is short-lived as torrential rains fall around the eye, and raging winds, drawn in from hot air that spirals up its wall, circulate at speeds of 30 mph (50 km/h). Spiraling bands of rain and wind can occur up to 240 miles (400 km) away. It can be 18 hours or more before the storm passes over.

MIXED BLESSING
The vegetation and agriculture on many tropical islands depend on the torrential rains brought by hurricanes. But the terrible winds can also ravage crops, and only a few – like bananas – recover quickly.

Winds of more than 100 mph (165 km/h) occur over a large area beneath the storm

HURRICANE WATCH
Thanks to satellite images, meteorologists can detect hurricanes when they are far from land and track them as they approach. Special aircraft repeatedly fly through the storm to obtain accurate measurements that help predict its violence and likely path. Since 1954, names have been given to all tropical storms to prevent confusion when issuing forecasts and evacuation warnings.

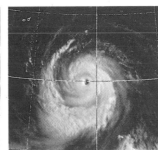

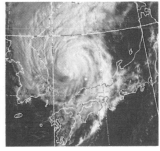

1 Day 1: Thunderstorms develop over the sea.

2 Day 2: Storms group to form a swirl of cloud.

3 Day 4: Winds grow; center forms in cloud swirl.

4 Day 7: Eye forms; typhoon is at its most dangerous.

5 Day 11: Eye passes over land; typhoon starts to die.

PACIFIC HURRICANE

The sequence above shows satellite images of a typhoon passing over the Pacific Ocean. It begins when water evaporates in the tropical sun over vast areas of the ocean to produce huge cumulonimbus clouds and bands of thunderstorms (1). A swirl of clouds develops and the growing storm looks like a vigorous, ordinary depression (2). The winds become even stronger and rotate around a single center (3). Eventually, an eye develops just inside the ring of the most destructive and violent winds (4). When such a storm passes over land – in this case, Japan – or over cold seas, it loses its source of energy and the winds drop rapidly (5).

Warm, moist air spirals up around the eye inside the hurricane

Hurricanes are enormous; some may be as much as 480 miles (800 km) across

The heat contained by the warm sea provides the energy needed to drive the whole system

Air descends in the eye, leaving it clear of cloud

The strongest winds, with gusts up to 220 mph (360 km/h), are found beneath the eye wall, immediately outside the eye

ALBANY HURRICANE

Hurricanes were far more dangerous before the strength of their approach could be predicted. In 1940, the fringes of a hurricane struck Albany, Georgia, without adequate warning, killing several people and wrecking large numbers of buildings, including big hotels. Two years before, 600 people were killed in New England by a sudden, fast-moving storm.

Ocean giants

THE BIGGEST WHALE – and the biggest animal that has ever lived – is the blue whale. Only other baleen whales and sperm whales come anywhere near its enormous size. The largest living land animal, the bull elephant, could stand on a blue whale's tongue! Even the biggest dinosaur weighed less than a quarter of a large blue whale. Such size has its benefits – big animals are less likely to be attacked by predators and it is easier for them to keep warm. Their main problem is to find enough food to nourish their awesome bulk.

Pectoral fin

Tail flukes

WHALE LICE
A number of animals make their homes on the great expanse of a whale's skin. Some are harmless hangers-on, but others, like this whale louse, probably irritate the skin.

TALL TAIL
Unlike some baleen whales, blue whales raise their tails in the air when they dive.

Stubby dorsal fin

A WHALE OF AN APPETITE
It is no coincidence that whale sharks, the world's largest fish, are also filter feeders. Because animals that feed on plankton do not need to chase individual prey, they do not have to be agile. This has allowed some to grow to great sizes. Whale sharks do not have baleen plates. Instead, they filter food from the water with their gills.

THE WORLD'S BIGGEST BABY
The day it is born, a baby blue whale is already as big as an elephant. It has no baleen plates, and relies entirely on its giant mother's milk. Like seal milk, this is very high in fat. Every day the growing whale drinks about 175 pints (100 liters) of milk and puts on another 200 lb (90 kg). By the time it is weaned, at the age of six or seven months, the young blue whale is already 52 ft (16 m) long.

Baby blue whales often breach when only a few weeks old

Adult blue whales can weigh 200 tons

WHALE OUT OF WATER
Whales can only reach such incredible sizes because
their weight is supported by the water. When a
large whale like this sperm whale is stranded,
it cannot support its own weight and
its internal organs are crushed.

BLUE SPLASH
No one knows why whales breach, or leap out of the
water. Adults often breach in the company of other
whales, and this suggests that the big splash is a way
of communicating. Young animals like this baby blue
whale may start breaching when they are only a few
weeks old. Perhaps by playing they are learning
skills that will be important to them as adults.

Paired blowholes

THE BIG BLUE
Blue whales grow to more than 104 ft (32 m) and
can weigh up to 220 tons (200 tonnes). They have
been hunted mercilessly in the southern oceans,
and most information about them comes from
the whaling industry, which estimated
weights by measuring chopped-off chunks
and adding a few tons to make up for lost
blood. Lengths may be incorrect as
well, since the whales could have
been stretched by towing. Blue
whales theoretically received
complete protection from
whalers in 1966. But there are
no signs that numbers have
increased, and there may
be only a few hundred
left in the entire
southern oceans.

*Throat
grooves allow
baleen whales to
gulp down huge
amounts of water*

PILOT STUDY
Measuring a stranded
whale is easy. But how do you
measure a live whale at sea? One way
is to take a series of photos as the whale
surfaces. By lining them end to end, scientists
can piece together the animal's entire length.

Vents and smokers

IN PARTS OF THE OCEAN FLOOR, there are deep cracks that let very hot, mineral-rich water gush into the ocean. These dramatic vents, or hot springs, exist at the spreading centers where the gigantic plates that make up the Earth's crust are moving apart. Cold seawater sinks deep into cracks in the crust where it is heated, and, in the process, collects dissolved minerals. At temperatures of up to 752°F (400°C), hot water spews out. Some of the minerals form chimneys known as black or white smokers. Water heated by the vents helps bacteria grow, and they create food from the hydrogen sulfide in the water. Extraordinary animals crowd around the cracks and rely on these microbes for food. The vents are independent of energy from the Sun, relying instead on chemosynthesis from sulfur-fixing bacteria. As recently as the late 1970s, scientists using submersibles found the first vent communities in the Pacific. Since then, vents have been found in other spreading centers in the Pacific Ocean and the Mid-Atlantic Ridge.

A CHANGING OCEAN
New areas of ocean floor are continually being created at spreading centers between two crustal plates. When hot, molten lava (rock) emerges from within the crust, it cools and solidifies along the edge of each adjoining plate.

Spreading center

Solidified lava

Magma

Crustal plate

SEEPING LAVA
Under the huge pressure of the ocean water, lava from vents or hot springs erupts constantly and gently, like toothpaste squeeze from a tube, and cools to form rounded shape known as pillow lava (above). Where there is a spreading ridge, the water is hot, acidic, and dark, with sulfides of copper, lead, and zinc. These valuable metals come from the new oceanic plate that is formed at the ridges. The minerals are dissolved out by seawater that percolates through the cooling rock.

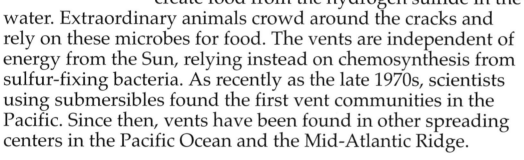

DEEP SEA PRAWNS
Animal life abounds at an active vent site. If the vent stops producing sulfur-rich water, the community is doomed. This new species of prawn was found at the Galápagos Rift in the Pacific Ocean in 1979.

Model of hydrothermal vents found in the eastern Pacific

VENT COMMUNITIES
This model shows the vent communities that have been found in the eastern Pacific, where giant clams and tube worms are the most distinctive animals. Vents in other parts of the world have different groups of animals, such as the hairy snails from the Mariana Trench, and eyeless shrimps from vents along the Mid-Atlantic Ridge.

Giant clams in the eastern Pacific can grow to 12 in (30 cm) long

Some animals graze on mats of bacteria covering rocks near a vent

Fis predato nibble to off tub worm

Plumes of hot water
rich in sulfides and
poisonous to most
animals

Black smoker
chimney can
reach 33 ft
(10 m)

Chimney made
from mineral
deposits

Dense
collection of
animals crowds
around a vent

THE MID-ATLANTIC RIDGE
The rocks that make up the ocean
floor are all relatively young –
nowhere older than 200 million
years – because new ocean plates are
constantly being made by volcanic
eruptions deep below the ocean
waters. A long range of mountains
snakes through the oceans, cut at its
heart by a rift valley. The volcanoes
in this valley erupt constantly,
producing new volcanic rock.
The new rock fills in the widening
rift as the plates pull apart. The
Mid-Atlantic Ridge (above), running
the length of the Atlantic Ocean
between Europe and Africa on the
east and the Americas on the
west, is part of the largest
mountain range in the world.

Tube worms, Riftia
pachyptila, can
grow to 10 ft
(3 m) long

Giant tube worm has
bacteria inside its
body to provide the
worm with food

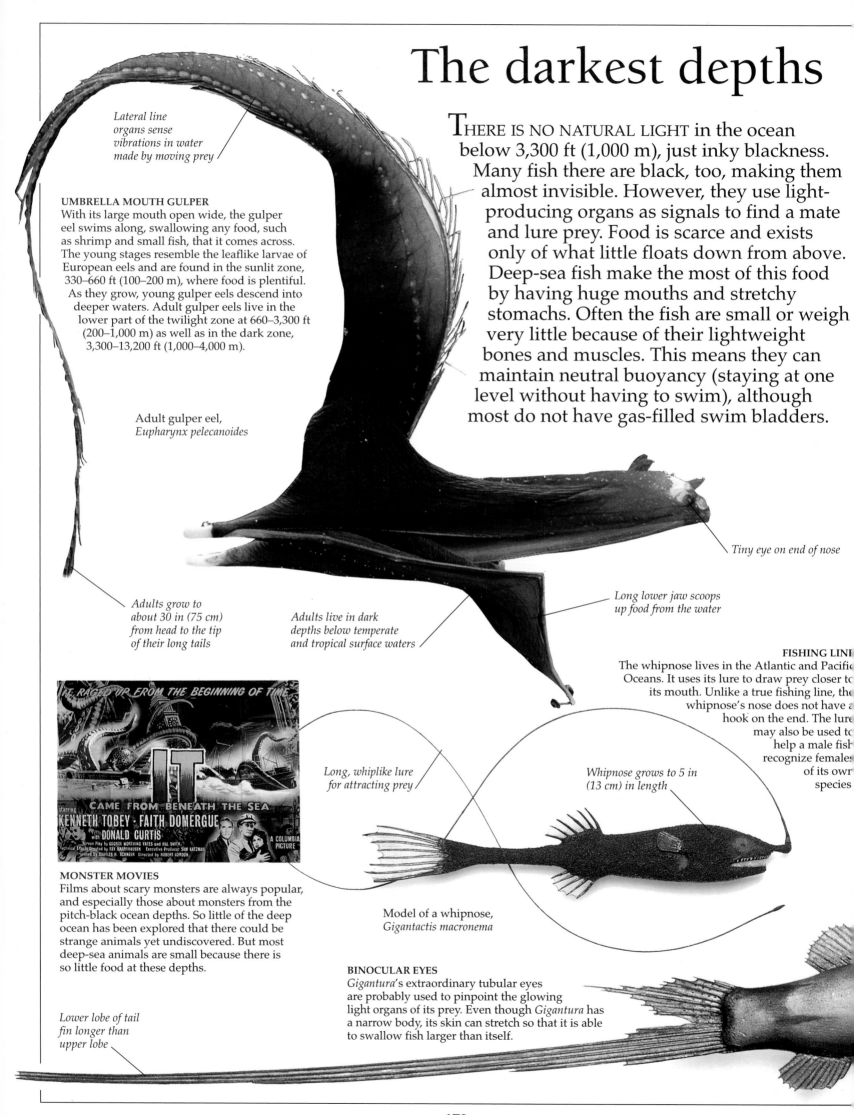

The darkest depths

THERE IS NO NATURAL LIGHT in the ocean below 3,300 ft (1,000 m), just inky blackness. Many fish there are black, too, making them almost invisible. However, they use light-producing organs as signals to find a mate and lure prey. Food is scarce and exists only of what little floats down from above. Deep-sea fish make the most of this food by having huge mouths and stretchy stomachs. Often the fish are small or weigh very little because of their lightweight bones and muscles. This means they can maintain neutral buoyancy (staying at one level without having to swim), although most do not have gas-filled swim bladders.

Lateral line organs sense vibrations in water made by moving prey

UMBRELLA MOUTH GULPER
With its large mouth open wide, the gulper eel swims along, swallowing any food, such as shrimp and small fish, that it comes across. The young stages resemble the leaflike larvae of European eels and are found in the sunlit zone, 330–660 ft (100–200 m), where food is plentiful. As they grow, young gulper eels descend into deeper waters. Adult gulper eels live in the lower part of the twilight zone at 660–3,300 ft (200–1,000 m) as well as in the dark zone, 3,300–13,200 ft (1,000–4,000 m).

Adult gulper eel,
Eupharynx pelecanoides

Tiny eye on end of nose

Long lower jaw scoops up food from the water

Adults grow to about 30 in (75 cm) from head to the tip of their long tails

Adults live in dark depths below temperate and tropical surface waters

FISHING LINE
The whipnose lives in the Atlantic and Pacific Oceans. It uses its lure to draw prey closer to its mouth. Unlike a true fishing line, the whipnose's nose does not have a hook on the end. The lure may also be used to help a male fish recognize females of its own species

Long, whiplike lure for attracting prey

Whipnose grows to 5 in (13 cm) in length

MONSTER MOVIES
Films about scary monsters are always popular, and especially those about monsters from the pitch-black ocean depths. So little of the deep ocean has been explored that there could be strange animals yet undiscovered. But most deep-sea animals are small because there is so little food at these depths.

Model of a whipnose,
Gigantactis macronema

BINOCULAR EYES
Gigantura's extraordinary tubular eyes are probably used to pinpoint the glowing light organs of its prey. Even though *Gigantura* has a narrow body, its skin can stretch so that it is able to swallow fish larger than itself.

Lower lobe of tail fin longer than upper lobe

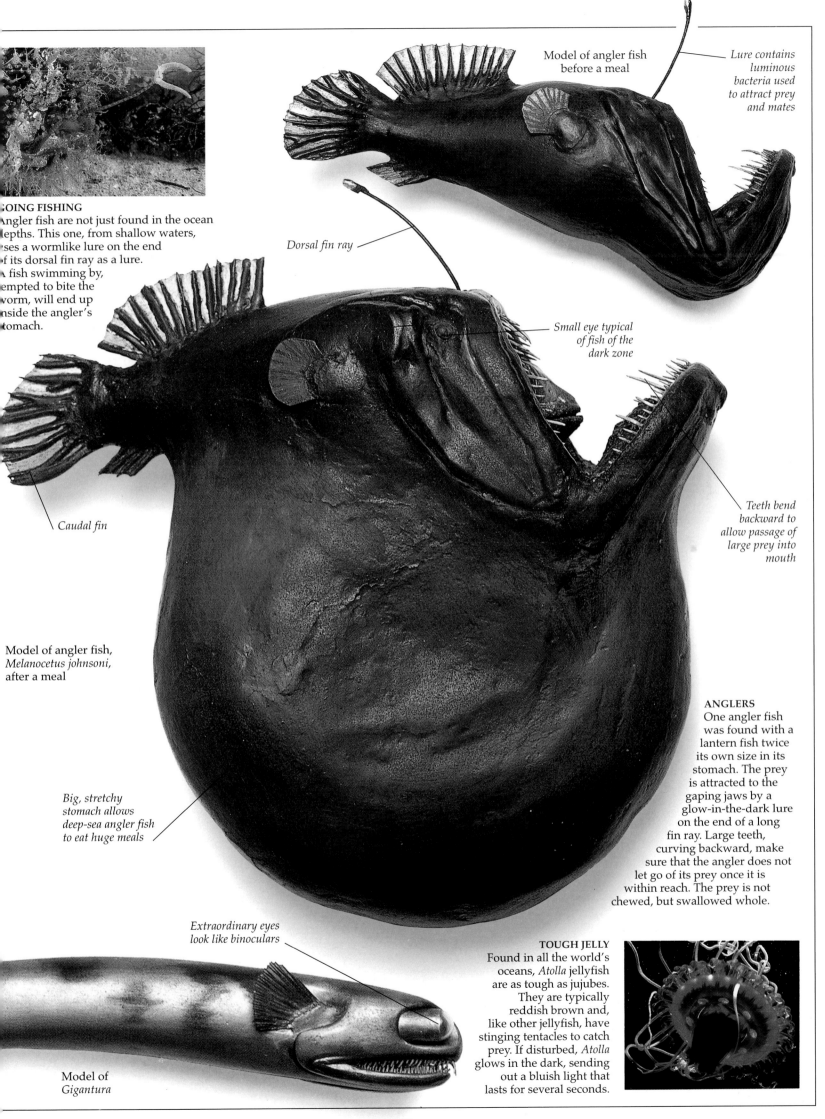

GOING FISHING

Angler fish are not just found in the ocean depths. This one, from shallow waters, uses a wormlike lure on the end of its dorsal fin ray as a lure. A fish swimming by, tempted to bite the worm, will end up inside the angler's stomach.

Model of angler fish before a meal

Lure contains luminous bacteria used to attract prey and mates

Dorsal fin ray

Small eye typical of fish of the dark zone

Caudal fin

Teeth bend backward to allow passage of large prey into mouth

Model of angler fish, *Melanocetus johnsoni*, after a meal

Big, stretchy stomach allows deep-sea angler fish to eat huge meals

ANGLERS
One angler fish was found with a lantern fish twice its own size in its stomach. The prey is attracted to the gaping jaws by a glow-in-the-dark lure on the end of a long fin ray. Large teeth, curving backward, make sure that the angler does not let go of its prey once it is within reach. The prey is not chewed, but swallowed whole.

Extraordinary eyes look like binoculars

TOUGH JELLY
Found in all the world's oceans, *Atolla* jellyfish are as tough as jujubes. They are typically reddish brown and, like other jellyfish, have stinging tentacles to catch prey. If disturbed, *Atolla* glows in the dark, sending out a bluish light that lasts for several seconds.

Model of *Gigantura*

Ocean wanderers

THE HUGE, GENTLE ALBATROSS of the Antarctic seas come ashore only to breed. They do not breed on the Antarctic land mass itself but on islands such as South Georgia, just north of the pack ice, the main advantage of these isolated locations being safety from predators. There are six species of albatross breeding in the Antarctic: black-browed, gray-headed, wandering, yellow-nosed, sooty, and light-mantled sooty. Probably about 750,000 pairs of birds breed each year. Albatross raise only one chick at a time and the chick takes a long time to mature, sometimes remaining in the nest for up to a year. Chicks are protected from the intense cold by thick down feathers and an insulating layer of fat or blubber. When winter sets in, most albatross set off over the southern oceans once more.

A man weighed down by more than grief: albatross can weigh up to 25 lb (12 kg)

DEAD WEIGHT
Sailors believed that albatross brought them bad luck. In Coleridge's *The Rime of the Ancient Mariner,* the unlucky mariner is forced to wear an albatross he has killed.

Wings very long and slender, for effortless gliding above the ocean

Black-browed albatross
Diomedea melanophris

BUMPY LANDING
Landing is a difficult task for a bird so well adapted to flying over the sea. When albatross approach their nest site, they circle around several times before putting their legs down like the landing gear on an aircraft. They often land with a bump.

Webbed feet held wide to push against the air and act as brakes

Gray-headed albatross
Diomedea chrysostoma

Large eyes indicate sharp eyesight needed for spotting food in the sea

BIRD MAN
People have always wanted to fly like birds, but this design for an early flying machine was no challenge to the albatross's mastery of the air. For birds, as with planes, takeoff and landing are the most dangerous parts of flying. Like planes, albatross need a runway to gather enough speed for takeoff. Without this, their enormous wingspan and body weight ensure that they remain earthbound.

Tube-shaped nostrils have glands at the base that excrete excess salt

Bill has razor-shar edges to cat fish and squi

LIVING THE HIGH LIFE
Gray-headed albatross live on the sides of steep cliffs because they need the strong winds rising up over the cliffs to help them take off. Although gray-headed albatross weigh half as much as wandering albatross, only half of their chicks survive because many of the parent birds cannot find and bring back enough food to keep the young alive.

*During courtship
the bird points its beak to
the sky and moos like a cow*

FAITHFUL FLYING ACE

The wandering albatross has the greatest wingspan of any living bird. Its wing power enables the bird to cover as much as 300 miles (500 km) a day, landing on the sea in calm weather and to feed. Like all albatross, it comes ashore only to breed. The breeding cycle is exceptionally long, taking a year to complete. It therefore breeds only every two years.

It precedes breeding with an elaborate courtship display in which the two birds dance face to face making a variety of sounds and clapping their beaks together loudly. Wandering albatross usually pair for life. The most elaborate displays take place among newly formed pairs; old, established partners are more discreet.

*Wingspan may
be 8 ft 4 in–
11 ft 10 in
(254–360 cm)*

SECONDHAND FOOD

Parent albatross feed their young by regurgitating (bringing up) the seafood they eat in the form of a sticky, oily mixture. This takes place when they return to the nest after many hours, or even days, fishing out at sea. Both adults and young can use this smelly and sticky oil in defense, ejecting it with reasonable accuracy over a 6-ft (2-m) range. Predators, such as skuas, may be repelled by the foul smell or immobilized if the sticky oil saturates their feathers.

*Mother feeds
regurgitated
food to
chick*

*Nest is lined with
grass and feathers*

*Nest is about 12 in
(30 cm) high*

Wandering albatross
Diomedea exulans

*Strong legs and wide feet help
in landing and swimming*

BARREL NEST

The black-browed albatross makes a raised nest of mud and straw among tussock grass.

GENTLE GIANT
The largest of all the land mammals, the elephant has the longest of all pregnancies – 22 months – and gives birth to only one calf at a time. Like many other large mammals, elephants spend considerable energy and time in nurturing their young, a strategy that helps ensure that the calf survives to breed. Unfortunately, the continued existence of the African elephant is threatened because elephants and people are often competing for the same territory.

CHAPTER 6
PRESERVING LIFE

Over millions of years, fluctuations in the Earth's climate have changed the conditions in which animals and plants live. Some of these changes have been minor, and nature has adapted. Some have been devastating, and whole species have disappeared forever. Today, there is justifiable fear that human activity is changing the climate – and threatening life as we know it on Earth.

UNIQUE EVOLUTION
The golden mantella is threatened by the destruction of its habitat, as are many other species of animals. Many brightly colored mantellas live on the island of Madagascar off the eastern coast of Africa. The island has a high level of "endemism"– that is, most of the species found there are found nowhere else in the world. The bright colors of the mantellas help them defend their territories and warn predators that they have poisonous chemicals in their skin.

Swallow-tailed manakin *Chiroxiphia caudata*

In danger

EVERY MINUTE OF THE DAY, 100 acres (40 hectares) of tropical rain forest are destroyed. The trees are felled for wood, burned to make way for farming, and damaged by pollution. If the clearance continues, 15 percent of plant species and 12 percent of bird species in the American rain forests alone could become extinct by the year 2000. This alarming pattern is being repeated all over the world, and not only in the rain forests. Scientists believe that humans are affecting the atmosphere so much that the world is steadily warming up (global warming). By releasing gases such as methane, CFCs, and carbon dioxide into the air, we have upset the balance in the atmosphere. In the right quantities, these gases are beneficial, trapping heat and keeping the Earth warm. But too many may make the Earth too warm, with terrible repercussions.

VULNERABLE
Manakins live in the thickest forests and are not endangered at present. However, they eat small, soft fruits, and, like many other creatures, are vulnerable to any disturbance of their forest habitat.

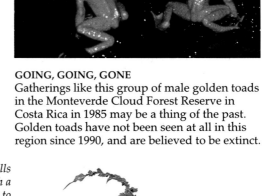

GOING, GOING, GONE
Gatherings like this group of male golden toads in the Monteverde Cloud Forest Reserve in Costa Rica in 1985 may be a thing of the past. Golden toads have not been seen at all in this region since 1990, and are believed to be extinct.

A leopard kills quickly, with a swift bite to the neck

KILLER CAT
The most versatile of the big cats, leopards occupy woodland habitats in places from west Africa to Korea and Southeast Asia. Leopards often relax under shady rocks or lie on branches high in the trees – exactly the places frequented by monkeys and the occasional young ape. Like other soft-footed members of the cat family, leopards are stealthy and deadly predators, as this unlucky vervet found out.

Diplazium proliferum

UNDER THREAT

There are many species of plants under threat, including the shade-loving aroid *Alocasia thibautiana*, which grows in the gloomiest parts of the jungles of Southeast Asia. The fern *Diplazium proliferum* thrives best on the jungle floor, where it is warm and damp. This fern produces bulbils on its fronds. Bulbils sprout and take root either when they are knocked off the fern, or when the frond dies.

Alocasia thibautiana

WALLS OF DEATH

Drift nets are like invisible curtains. In the open ocean, big fishing boats use drift nets up to 30 miles (50 km) long. If the nets get tangled, the fishermen often just cut them and let them drift off. Huge numbers of whales, dolphins, and seals are killed when they swim into these free-floating traps. The United Nations has banned long drift nets, but some countries are not members of the UN, and the laws are impossible to enforce in the open ocean.

Dense, waterproof coat turns gray-white in winter

Velvet contains blood vessels to nourish the growing antlers

Reindeer or caribou
Rangifer tarandus

Sensitive nose helps reindeer find food, even under snow

IN THE SNOW

Many animals and plants live in difficult habitats, where food and water are hard to find. Reindeer feed mainly on lichens, one of the few foods available throughout the Arctic winter. Some reindeer will also eat seaweed. Calves are born in June and grow fast on their mothers' rich milk, which is four times as nutritious as cow's milk. Although their thick coats insulate reindeer from the Arctic cold, they still migrate south in the winter to find food.

Sharp hooves grip ice and dig through snow for food

Studying populations

T HE WAYS IN WHICH animal and plant populations change tell scientists a lot about specific species and their methods of survival. Lemmings provide a vivid example. These small rodents inhabit the coldest regions of the northern hemisphere. Every three to four years, the lemming population grows so large scientists believe it outstrips its food supplies. The lemmings then migrate in large numbers. The result is a form of population control – lemmings swim across rivers in search of food, so on migration, when they reach the sea, they attempt to swim across it, and drown. This kind of natural population control affects other animals as well; in this case, the snowy owl.

White feathers for winter camouflage

Snowy owl
Nyctea scandiaca

PREDATOR AND PREY
The snowy owl, seen here swooping down on a vole, lives mainly in the tundra of North America and Eurasia, where it is normally a rare sight. However, every three or four years, snowy owls suddenly appear in large numbers and invade towns across the United States, going as far south as Georgia. This strange phenomenon appears to be linked to the population changes of the lemming, on which the snowy owl feeds. As the lemmings reach plague proportions, the snowy owls, provided with a plentiful food supply, increase rapidly in numbers. When the lemmings migrate, the owls also migrate, searching for food, and disperse over a wide area. Their numbers drop to low levels over the next few years.

Owl looks for movement of prey before swooping

Powerful claw with long talons for gripping

MIGRATION PATTERNS
Voles in northern latitudes (left) have a similar population cycle to the lemming, perhaps based on the cycle of plant growth. As the size of the population increases, more and more of the vital nutrients in the environment become locked up in the form of droppings. In the cold conditions of the Arctic, where decomposition takes a long time, these nutrients are released slowly. Plant growth suffers, and the rodents must leave the area to look for food. The vegetation can only begin to recover when the voles migrate.

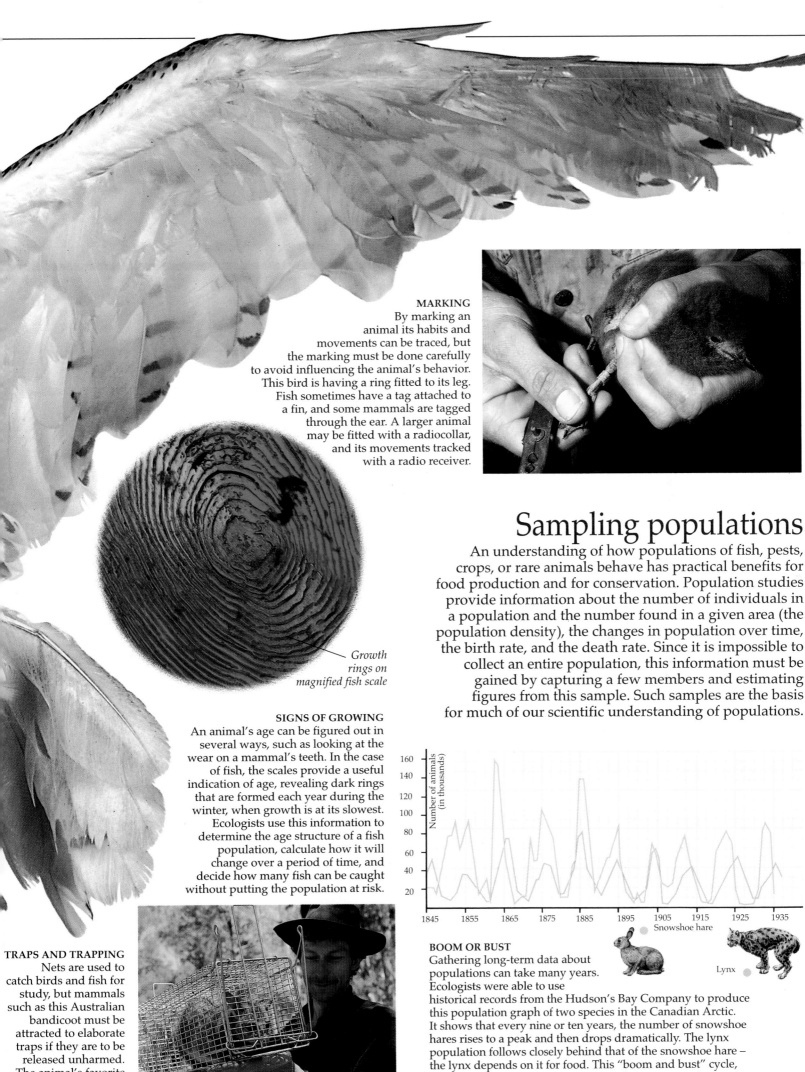

MARKING
By marking an animal its habits and movements can be traced, but the marking must be done carefully to avoid influencing the animal's behavior. This bird is having a ring fitted to its leg. Fish sometimes have a tag attached to a fin, and some mammals are tagged through the ear. A larger animal may be fitted with a radiocollar, and its movements tracked with a radio receiver.

Growth rings on magnified fish scale

Sampling populations
An understanding of how populations of fish, pests, crops, or rare animals behave has practical benefits for food production and for conservation. Population studies provide information about the number of individuals in a population and the number found in a given area (the population density), the changes in population over time, the birth rate, and the death rate. Since it is impossible to collect an entire population, this information must be gained by capturing a few members and estimating figures from this sample. Such samples are the basis for much of our scientific understanding of populations.

SIGNS OF GROWING
An animal's age can be figured out in several ways, such as looking at the wear on a mammal's teeth. In the case of fish, the scales provide a useful indication of age, revealing dark rings that are formed each year during the winter, when growth is at its slowest. Ecologists use this information to determine the age structure of a fish population, calculate how it will change over a period of time, and decide how many fish can be caught without putting the population at risk.

TRAPS AND TRAPPING
Nets are used to catch birds and fish for study, but mammals such as this Australian bandicoot must be attracted to elaborate traps if they are to be released unharmed. The animal's favorite food is usually placed in the trap as bait.

Number of animals (in thousands)

160
140
120
100
80
60
40
20

1845 1855 1865 1875 1885 1895 1905 1915 1925 1935

Snowshoe hare

Lynx

BOOM OR BUST
Gathering long-term data about populations can take many years. Ecologists were able to use historical records from the Hudson's Bay Company to produce this population graph of two species in the Canadian Arctic. It shows that every nine or ten years, the number of snowshoe hares rises to a peak and then drops dramatically. The lynx population follows closely behind that of the snowshoe hare – the lynx depends on it for food. This "boom and bust" cycle, which is still not fully understood, is characteristic of several animal species living in extreme environmental conditions.

Surviving

SPECIAL ADAPTATIONS

A camel is well suited to desert conditions because it can go for days without water. Its body temperature can rise many degrees before the animal starts to sweat, conserving moisture. It also uses the fat stores in its hump. The fat is gradually used up if it does not eat enough, and as the fat is depleted, the hump shrinks.

Nᴀᴛᴜʀᴇ ɪꜱ ᴀ finely tuned balancing act and no one living thing can survive without some dependence on, or ability to affect, another. All animals and plants need energy and materials from the environment, and they survive despite the precarious nature of food chains and difficult environments, even coping with the additional problems of bad weather, disease, and pollution. The adaptability of life on Earth is endlessly ingenious. For example, in cold places where there are few insects to pollinate, many plants reproduce from small pieces of themselves, such as runners or bulbils. Some animals, such as the polar bear and the fox, have even benefited from the creation of towns and cities, changing their diets and scavenging on human refuse.

Northen fleabane
Erigeron borealis

LIVING FOSSIL

Some species survive for millions of years. The coelacanth is a fish that was thought to be extinct; all the known fossils were more than 200 million years old. Then, in 1938, a live coelacanth was fished out of the ocean. If such a creature can survive for 200 million years without leaving any fossils, it is not surprising that some steps in the evolution of life on Earth are not recorded.

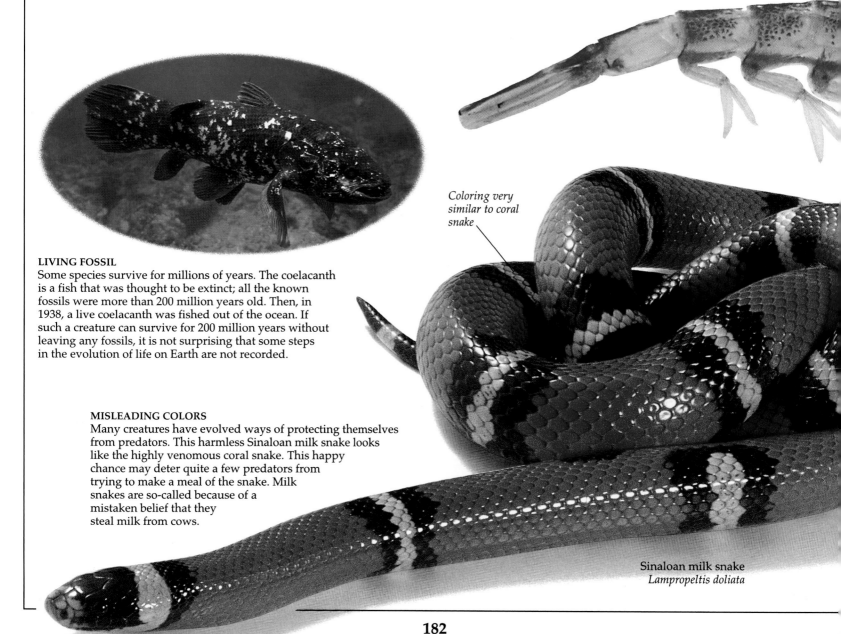

Coloring very similar to coral snake

MISLEADING COLORS

Many creatures have evolved ways of protecting themselves from predators. This harmless Sinaloan milk snake looks like the highly venomous coral snake. This happy chance may deter quite a few predators from trying to make a meal of the snake. Milk snakes are so-called because of a mistaken belief that they steal milk from cows.

Sinaloan milk snake
Lampropeltis doliata

HARDY PLANTS
In order to survive, many plants have evolved in special ways. Low cushions of northern fleabane flower in the Arctic summer when the tundra lands become waterlogged. The plant grows in a low, compact tussock to keep out of the freezing, drying wind, to trap available moisture, and to avoid being crushed by snow and ice.

Krill are omnivores, eating phytoplankton, other crustaceans, and other krill

Krill sieve food from water with their feathery feeding apparatus

At night, the luminescent organs of krill shimmer in the darkness

Bulbous eyes

Female krill spawn twice a year, laying 2,000–3,000 eggs, which sink into deep water

Krill are just 2 in (5 cm) long, but sometimes occur in such vast numbers they turn the sea red

CAREFUL PARENTING
Survival of a species is dependent on the species' ability to produce young. This female leaf beetle, guarding her family, produces relatively few young, but by protecting them in early life, she increases their chances of survival. Some animals produce very few young and invest considerable time and energy in raising them. Others produce huge numbers of offspring, but do nothing to look after them. A female cod, for example, lays more than a million eggs, but nearly all are eaten before they have a chance to grow into adults.

FOOD SOURCES
The shrimplike crustacean krill is the basis of most of the Antarctic food chains, forming a vital food source for whales and seals, as well as penguins and seabirds. A blue whale needs more than 0.9 tons (900 kg) of krill to feel full! The reduction in whale numbers caused by human hunting in the past has made krill numbers increase. Other krill-eating species such as penguins and fur seals have increased in number to exploit the extra food source. This has upset the balance of existing food webs. The long-term repercussions of this kind of change are as yet unknown.

Glossary

ALGAE Simple plants that do not have true stems, roots, or leaves, but contain chlorophyll. Most are found in water.
See also CHLOROPHYLL.

AMOEBA A tiny, simple animal that has no fixed shape and lives in water.

AMPHIBIAN Cold-blooded and smooth-skinned vertebrate that begins life in the water, but can live on land when it is adult; for example, a frog, toad, or salamander.
See also VERTEBRATE.

ANTENNA One of a pair of flexible feelers on the head of some animals, such as insects or crustaceans.
See also CRUSTACEAN.

ANTHER The upper part of the stamen of a flowering plant.
See also STAMEN.

ARTHROPOD Creature with segmented covering and jointed limbs, such as an insect, crustacean, arachnid, and centipede.
See also CRUSTACEAN.

BACTERIUM (pl. bacteria) Microorganism that brings about decomposition; or a parasite, many of which cause disease.

BAROMETER Instrument for measuring atmospheric pressure, used in weather forecasting.

BIOSPHERE Regions of the Earth and its atmosphere in which living things are found.

BIVALVE A mollusk with a shell consisting of two hinged parts. Bivalves include oysters, cockles, clams, scallops, and mussels.
See also MOLLUSK.

BYSSAL THREADS Mass of threads that bivalves use to attach themselves to rocks.
See also BIVALVE.

CAECILIAN Legless, burrowing amphibian found in tropical regions.
See also AMPHIBIAN.

CAMOUFLAGE Color, marking, or shape of an animal or plant that enables it to hide in its surroundings.

CARNIVOROUS Meat eating.

CARPEL The central, female part of a flower, consisting of an ovary, style, and stigma.

CELL The smallest unit of an organism that can exist on its own.

CEPHALOPOD Mollusk with a beaked head and tentacles. Cephalopods include the octopus and nautilus.
See also MOLLUSK.

CHELONIAN Belonging to the Chelonia, a group of reptiles that includes turtles.

CHLOROPHYLL Green pigment found in plants that traps energy from sunlight.
See also PIGMENT.

CHLOROPLAST Tiny body in some plant cells that contains chlorophyll.
See also CHLOROPHYLL.

CHRYSALIS The stage of life between caterpillar and adult butterfly or moth.

CILIA Hairlike growths from the surface of a cell or organism.
See also CELL.

COCOON Covering of silk spun by the larvae of moths and other insects to protect them in their pupa stage.
See also LARVA.

COELENTERATE Invertebrate animal with sacklike internal cavity, such as jellyfish, sea anemone, and cord.

COMPOUND EYE Eye of most insects, made up of separate lenses that work as individual eyes, each forming a part of the image.

CROSS-POLLINATION The transfer of pollen from the stamens of one plant to the stigma of another.
See also STAMEN.

CRUSTACEAN Any of a usually aquatic group of animals with a segmented body and paired, jointed limbs. Includes lobsters, crabs, shrimps, and sow bugs.

DECOMPOSER Something that breaks down dead organic matter, such as a bacterium or fungus.
See also BACTERIUM, FUNGUS.

DIAPAUSE A period during which certain insects do not grow or develop.

DIATOM Minute, single-celled algae.
See also ALGAE.

ECHOLOCATION A way of finding objects by sending out sounds, then listening for the echo. Bats use echolocation to navigate.

ECOSYSTEM A complete area in the biosphere that contains living things, such as a forest.

ELEMENT A substance that cannot be broken down into more simple substances by chemical reactions.

ENDOSPERM The tissue that surrounds and feeds the embryo of a flowering plant.

ENVIRONMENT The surroundings of plants or animals – the environment affects the way they live.

EPIDERMIS The outer layer of the skin.

EVAPORATION The changing of a liquid into a vapor by the escape of molecules from its surface.

EXOSKELETON The hard, outer skin of arthropods.
See also ARTHROPOD.

FOSSIL The ancient remains of a plant or animal, usually found in rocks. A fossil may be the actual bones of an animal or the shape left by the animal's body in the rock.

FOSSIL FUEL Flammable material that comes from the remains of animals and plants that lived millions of years ago. Includes coal and oil.

FUNGUS One of a group of organisms that lack chlorophyll and are usually parasitic.
See also CHLOROPHYLL.

GASTROPOD A mollusk with a coiled shell and a large, muscular foot that it uses to move.
See also MOLLUSK.

GERMINATION In plants, when seeds or spores sprout.

GILLS Parts of a fish used for breathing underwater.

HABITAT A place where an animal or plant usually lives; woodlands, grasslands, and mountains are examples of different habitats.

HERBIVOROUS Plant eating.

HIBERNATE To sleep deeply or remain still through the winter in order to conserve energy and survive the winter.

INCUBATION The warming of eggs by bodily heat or other means to encourage the growth and hatching of young.

INVERTEBRATE An animal with no backbone.

LARVA The second stage in the life of an insect, which occurs between the egg and the emergence of the adult. Tadpoles and caterpillars are larvae.

LAVA Hot, liquid rock that flows from deep inside the Earth. The lava cools and hardens when it reaches the surface.

MAGMA Melted rock beneath the Earth's crust.

MAMMAL Warm-blooded animal that gives birth to live young that feed on the mother's milk.

MANDIBLE Jaw or sharp, hard part of an insect's mouthparts. Most insects have two mandibles.

MANTLE The layer of the Earth that lies beneath the surface and the center.

MARSUPIAL A mammal that has a pouch on the outside of its body in which its young develop.

METAMORPHOSIS The transformation of an animal during growth. Includes the emergence of an adult fly from a maggot, a butterfly from a caterpillar, and a frog from a tadpole.

METEOROLOGIST Scientist who studies weather and weather conditions.

MICROBE Tiny, living organism that can only be seen with a microscope.
See also ORGANISM.

MIGRATION Moving from one place to another. Animals migrate to find food, produce young, or escape from cold weather.

MOLLUSK An animal with a soft body that usually lives in a shell. Snails, limpets, and slugs are mollusks.

MONOTREME One of a group of egg-laying animals that lives in Australia and New Guinea. Includes the platypus and the echidna.

MUTUALISM Relationship between two or more animals in which all benefit.

NECTARY Glandlike organ at the base of a flower in which nectar is stored.

NEMATOCYST Stinging organ in coelenterates such as jellyfish.
See also COELENTERATE.

NUCLEUS The center of an atom, a nucleus is made up of electrically charged protons and of neutrons.

NYMPH A young insect. A nymph looks like its parents, but does not have any wings.

OCELLUS A small, simple eye found in many vertebrates.
See also VERTEBRATE.

ORGANISM Any living plant or animal.

PALEONTOLOGIST Scientist who studies fossils and ancient life forms.
See also FOSSIL.

PARASITE An organism that grows and feeds on or in another organism, but does not contribute to the survival of the host.
See also ORGANISM.

PHOTOSYNTHESIS The way that plants make food, using energy from sunlight and turning carbon dioxide and water into sugars.

PHYTOPLANKTON Minute, floating aquatic plants.

PIGMENT A substance, such as chlorophyll, that produces a particular color in plant or animal tissue.
See also CHLOROPHYLL.

PLACENTAL Having a placenta, the organ that develops in female mammals during pregnancy to provide the fetus with the nutrients that it needs.

PNEUMATOPHORE A gas-filled sac that serves as a float for colonies such as the jellyfish Portuguese man-of-war.

POLLINATOR The animal that carries pollen from one flower to another to help make seeds. Insects are the most common pollinators.

POLYP A coelenterate with a cylindrical body and tentacles, such as coral.

PREDATOR An animal that lives by hunting and eating other animals.

PREY An animal that is hunted and eaten by another animal.

PRIMATE A member of the mammal group that includes gorillas, monkeys, chimpanzees, and human beings.
See also MAMMAL.

PROBOSCIS A tube in some insects used for feeding and sucking.

PROMINENCE A bright spout of gas reaching out from the Sun's surface into space.

PUPA The last stage in the life of some young insects. The pupa is the resting stage during which the adult takes shape.

RADICLE The part of the plant that develops into the primary root.

REPTILE One of a group of animals with dry, scaly skin that usually lay eggs with shells. The group includes snakes, turtles, and crocodiles.

RESPIRATION The process of inhaling and exhaling; the process by which an organism takes in oxygen, releasing carbon dioxide and energy.
See also ORGANISM.

RODENT An animal with long, front teeth that are used for gnawing, such as a mouse, rat, and squirrel.

STAMEN The pollen-producing part of the plant.

SUCCULENT A thick-leaved plant such as a cactus that stores water in its stems and leaves.

SWIM BLADDER Part of the body of a fish that can be filled with air. It stops the fish from sinking.

THERMAL Hot air current that blows upward.

THORAX The central part of an insect's body. The wings and legs are fixed to the thorax, which contains all the muscles that the insect uses to move them.

TUBER Swollen, usually underground stem or root, such as the potato.

TUNDRA Frozen treeless plain found close to the Arctic.

ULTRAVIOLET Color or light with a short wavelength that the human eye cannot see. To insects, it is a pale shade of blue.

VERTEBRATE Animal with a bony skeleton and a backbone. Fish, amphibians, reptiles, birds, and mammals are all vertebrates.
See also MAMMAL, REPTILE.

ZOOPLANKTON Microscopic crustaceans, fish larvae, and other aquatic animals.

Index

A

Acknowledgments

DK would like to thank

Susila Baybars and Marion Dent for editorial
assistance; Ivan Finnegan, Cormac Jordan,
Sailesh Patel, and Susan St. Louis for design
assistance; and Alex Arthur, David Burnie,
David Carter, Jack Challoner, Dr. Barry Clarke,
Brian Cosgrove, John Farndon, Theresa
Greenaway, William Lindsay, Dr. Miranda
MacQuitty, Colin McCarthy, Laurence Mound,
Vassili Papastavrou, Steve Parker, Steve Pollock,
Ian Redmond, Scott Steadman, Barbara Taylor,
Dr. Paul D. Taylor, Susanna van Rose, and
Paul Whalley for contributing to the book

Special Photography
Peter Anderson, Geoff Brightling, Jane Burton,
Peter Chadwick, Andy Crawford, Geoff Dann,
Philip Dowell, John Downes, Neil Fletcher,
Steve Gorton, Frank Greenaway, Colin Keates,
Dave King, Cyril Laubscher, Mike Linley,
Andrew McRobb, Karl Shone, James Stevenson,
Clive Streeter, Harold Taylor, Kim Taylor,
Andreas von Einsiedel, Spike Walker,
Jerry Young

Illustrators
Simone End, Andrew Macdonald, Richard Orr,
Sallie Alane Reason, Colin Salmon,
Richard Ward, John Woodcock, Dan Wright

Model makers
David Donkin, John Downes, Peter Griffiths,
Graham High and Jeremy Hunt/Centaur
Studios, John Holmes

Index
Marion Dent

Picture research
Lorna Ainger, Katie Bradshaw, Liz Cooney,
John Stevenson

Picture credits
t=top b=bottom c=center l=left r=right

**DK would like to thank the following
for their kind permission to
reproduce the photographs**

Aldus Archive 33ca
Alison Anholt-White 102cb
Bryan & Cherry Alexander 94bl, 111br
American Museum of Natural History 168-9c
Ardea 62bc, 63br, 67cr, 126c, 152c
Biofotos/Heather Angel 62bl, 137tr, 154tr
Bridgeman Art Library 111tl/Prado, Madrid
  161tr/Uffizi Gallery, Florence 68tl
A. Buckland 150cl
Caroline Cartwright 118tl, 119br
©Casterman 84tr
John Clegg 135tl
Bruce Coleman Ltd. 102tr, 102-3c, 103tl, 104cla,
  112bc/Jane Burton 28tl, 91bl/Bob & Clara
  Calhoun 73c/J. Cancalosi 97tr/A. Compost
  98bl/Eric Crichton 158tl/G.Dove 142tr/
  Michael Fogden 178c/Jeff Foott 17c,
  181tr/ L. C. Marigo 136bl/Carl Roessler
  162c/Rod Williams 121tl/G. Zeisler 85clb
Brian Cosgrove 102cl, c, 103tr, cra, cr, crb, br
E. T. Archive 60tl
Mary Evans Picture Library 14bl, 32tl, 72tl, c,
  84cl, 106tl, 113tr, 132tl, 158c, 166tl, 167br
Forschungsinstitut und Naturmuseum
  Senckenberg, Frankfurt 34-5c
Geological Survey of Greenland,
  Copenhagen/A. A. Garde 21br
Ronald Grant Archive 172bl
Greenpeace/Rowlands 179t
Sonia Halliday 64cl
Robert Harding Picture Library 20c, 107tr, cr
Bruce C. Heezen & Marie Tharp, 1977/
  ©MarieTharp: 171tr
Illustrated London News 174cr
The Image Bank 150-1c, 151tr
Jacana/F. Gohier 168cl
Japan Meterological Agency/
  Meterological Office 167t
Frank Lane Picture Agency 20tr, 166bl/
  Hannu Hautala 129tc/Silvestris 98tr/
  Tony Wharton 129tl/Roger Wilmshurst 139tr, cra
Mike Linley 81tr, 87tc
Barbara Lofthouse 59tr
Mansell Collection 64tl, bl
Simon Conway Morris 24tr
Musée Nationale, Paris/
  Gallimard-Jeunesse 169bl
NASA 12tl
NHPA 166cl/Anthony Bannister 118cl/
  G. I. Bernard 41tr/Stephen Dalton 48tr/
  D. Frazier 156tr/Pavel German 157crb/
  Peter Johnson 86cra, 175c/Jany Sauvanet
  83cr/Lady Phillipa Scott 175bl/John Shaw 38tr
Natural History Museum 35bl
Oxford Scientific Films 17br, 181cl, bl/Doug
  Allan 126tl, 128bl/Kathie Atkinson 81tl,
  tc/Anthony Bannister 119cr/Fred Bavendam
  173tl/Mike Birkhead 33bc/Jim Fraser 81cr/
  Z. Leszczynski 85c/Ben Osbourne 174bl, 175cl/
  S. Osolinski 178bl/Partridge Films, C. Farneti 99tr
K. Pilsbury 104cr, crb
Planet Earth Pictures 105cl, 113tr, 150b,
  170tr/Gary Bell 95tl, 163br/Steve Bloom 77c/
  Conlin 76br/Larry Madin 173br/
  Peter Scoones 145tl, 161tl/Seaphot 122bl/
  M.Snyderman 168cr/D.Weisel 107br

Roger-viollet 169t
Royal Meterological Society 102tl
Science Photo Library 39tr/John Walsh 41tl
Frank Spooner Pictures 106cr, 107tl, 112-3c
Tony Stone Images/R.Everts 108cr
Wildlife Matters 104tr, 105tr
ZEFA 76cla, 174cla.

Every effort has been made to trace the
copyright holders and we apologize in
advance for any unintentional omissions.
We would be pleased to insert the
appropriate acknowledgment in any
subsequent edition of this publication.

PART TWO
NATURAL EARTH

CONTENTS OF PART TWO

FOREWORD

LIFE EXISTS IN MANY FORMS. There are about 4,000,000 known species of plants and animals living today, and most people encounter only a few of them. But through photographs in books, and films on television, we all have an opportunity to study the incredible array of living things with which we share ou planet. Often, we are surprised: some animals appear bizarre, while others seem extravagant in their use of colors and decorations. But Nature does not view them that way. Their extraordinary looks and vivid colors are functional as well. The tiger's striped coat was not designed by chance, but evolved as camouflage. The pattern enables this hunter to blend in with its forest home and ambush its unsuspecting victims. Isolate the tiger from its natural surroundings and place it in a world of white, and at once its beautiful coat and powerful frame are revealed. The animal seems to leap right off the page in the celebrated style of Eyewitness.

PHOTOGRAPHIC TECHNIQUES

Specialized close-up lenses provide us with a new view of the familiar, revealing such detail that we can learn more about each plant and animal subject and so appreciate it all the more. High-speed photography freezes rapid movement, while time-lapse techniques enable us to experience the passage of time. Together these remarkable methods bring to us the action and drama in the living world. Photography is also a means by which new discoveries can be recorded. Discoveries need no longer be suspected as figments of an explorer's imagination. We can now have photographic proof of genuine scientific bombshells. We may not have believable pictures of the Loch Ness monster or the yeti, but we do have photographs of the okapi, discovered for science in 1901, the megamouth shark, lifted accidentally from the deep Pacific in 1976, and a whole lot more.

MAKING NEW DISCOVERIES

Photographers and filmmakers can make new discoveries themselves. A team in Borneo, for example, once chanced upon a small, nondescript frog which, quite unexpectedly, waved a bright blue foot in the air. A photographer was there to record the event and in doing so presented the scientific community with a brand-new species of frog. It lives beside a waterfall where normal frog sounds are drowned by the roar of the water, so the curious creature communicates with its fellow frogs by shaking a leg. Scientists chance upon previously undiscovered species of plants and animals almost daily – in rainforests, grasslands, deserts, on the top of mountains, and in the depths of the sea. It is disturbing to realize that by destroying rainforests and polluting the seas we are losing plants and animals without even knowing that they are there. Films and photographs help us to keep a permanent record of the plants and animals we know, and Eyewitness is contributing to this audit of life on Earth.

Michael Bright

Managing Editor
Wildvision
BBC Natural History Unit

CHAPTER 1

FORM & FUNCTION

AN ANIMAL'S SIZE, shape, and design
provide many clues about its food,
habits, way of life, and the group
to which it belongs. The form and
structure of the millions of different
creatures in the animal kingdom,
which range from tiny ants
to enormous elephants, are
invariably adapted to their
particular functions
and lifestyle.

MANY SLIMY ARMS
Unlike human limbs, the
tentacles of the common octopus
have no stiff bones in them. Its
rubbery, flexible flesh suits its shy
and stealthy lifestyle. The octopus
spends much of its time squeezed
into caves or crevices, where it
lurks in wait to grab crabs, fish,
and shellfish as they pass by.

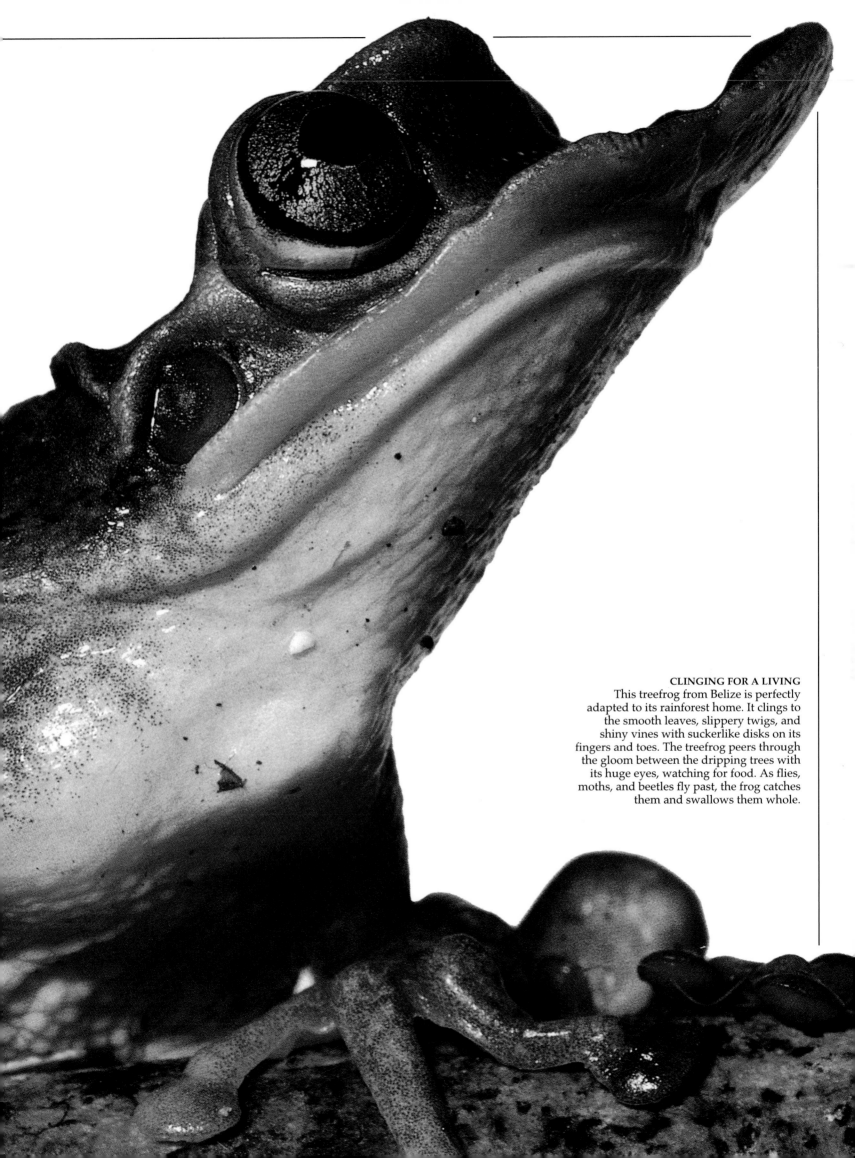

CLINGING FOR A LIVING
This treefrog from Belize is perfectly adapted to its rainforest home. It clings to the smooth leaves, slippery twigs, and shiny vines with suckerlike disks on its fingers and toes. The treefrog peers through the gloom between the dripping trees with its huge eyes, watching for food. As flies, moths, and beetles fly past, the frog catches them and swallows them whole.

Hard-wearing parts

MOST ANIMALS have hard parts somewhere in or on their body. Some, such as mammals, birds, reptiles, fish, and amphibians, have a bony internal skeleton, called an endoskeleton, as support; others, such as insects, spiders, shellfish, and other invertebrates have an outside skeleton, or exoskeleton. Some animals, such as lobsters, tortoises, and turtles, have a hard shell. The type and design of shell depends on the animal group from which the creature comes. These shells are from very different kinds of animals.

A RIGID CASE
The tortoise above and the turtle below are both reptiles. Their shells are made of plates of bone. Inside the shell, and fused to it at various sites, are the usual skeleton bones.

Special hairs called setae help the crab find its way around. They also detect the movements of predators or food in the water

Upper carapace covers back of turtle

Lower plastron covers belly

A STIFF BAG
The land tortoise and the river turtle have the same basic shell, but the differing details indicate their contrasting habitats and lifestyles. The river turtle's shell is not quite as hard, heavy, and rigid as that of the tortoise. Its curved plates of bone have large air spaces in them, for lightness. This helps the turtle to swim near the surface and at middle depths, rather than sinking like a stone to the bottom. The horny outer plates that cover the tortoise's shell are absent, and the whole shell has a more streamlined shape for faster movement. Tortoises are not noted for their speed. But the river turtle can swim quite swiftly using its powerful, paddle-shaped limbs.

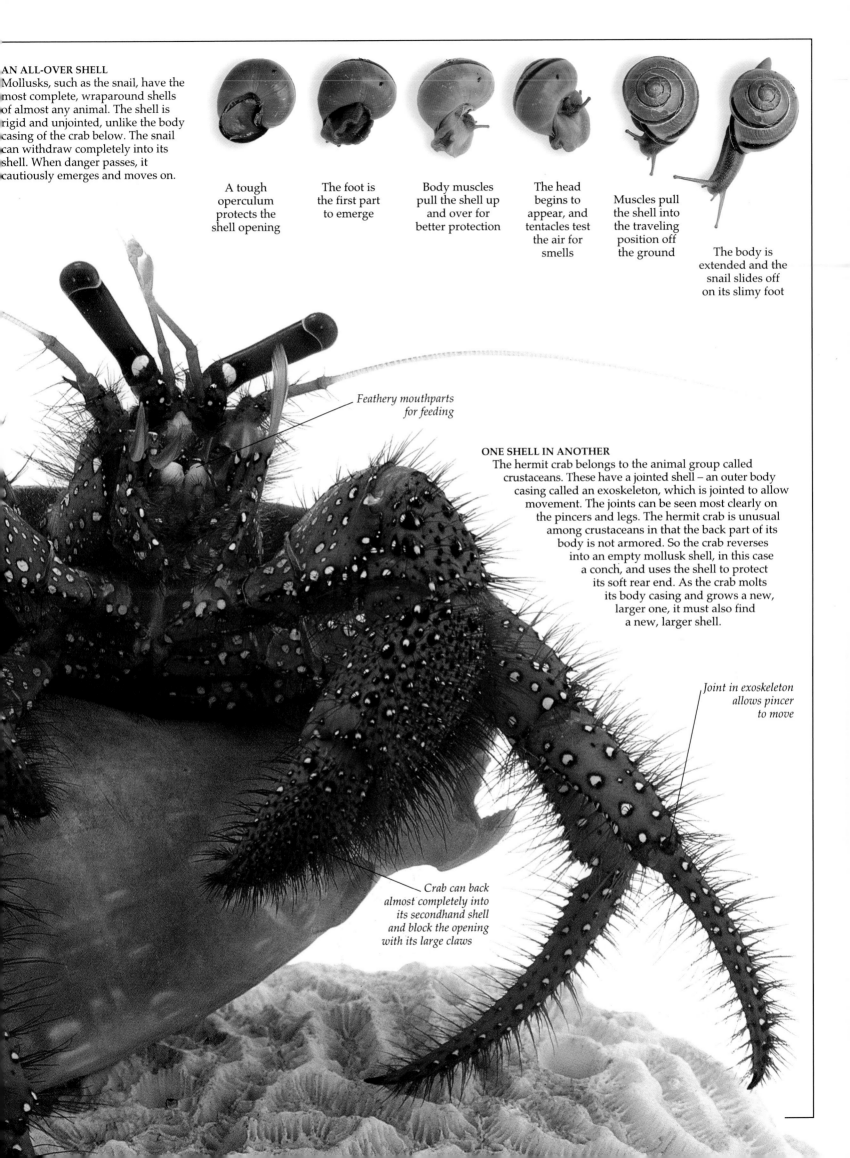

AN ALL-OVER SHELL

Mollusks, such as the snail, have the most complete, wraparound shells of almost any animal. The shell is rigid and unjointed, unlike the body casing of the crab below. The snail can withdraw completely into its shell. When danger passes, it cautiously emerges and moves on.

A tough operculum protects the shell opening

The foot is the first part to emerge

Body muscles pull the shell up and over for better protection

The head begins to appear, and tentacles test the air for smells

Muscles pull the shell into the traveling position off the ground

The body is extended and the snail slides off on its slimy foot

Feathery mouthparts for feeding

ONE SHELL IN ANOTHER

The hermit crab belongs to the animal group called crustaceans. These have a jointed shell – an outer body casing called an exoskeleton, which is jointed to allow movement. The joints can be seen most clearly on the pincers and legs. The hermit crab is unusual among crustaceans in that the back part of its body is not armored. So the crab reverses into an empty mollusk shell, in this case a conch, and uses the shell to protect its soft rear end. As the crab molts its body casing and grows a new, larger one, it must also find a new, larger shell.

Joint in exoskeleton allows pincer to move

Crab can back almost completely into its secondhand shell and block the opening with its large claws

Under the skin

UNDER AN ANIMAL'S FUR, feathers, scales, skin, or shell, are the soft, fleshy bits – such as muscles, guts, nerves, and blood vessels. Apart from a few very simple animals, such as sponges and jellyfish, most creatures have the same basic set of main internal parts, called organs. There is a digestive tube incorporating a stomach and intestines; muscles for movement; a blood system to transport food and oxygen around the body; a waste-disposal system; sense organs such as eyes, to detect what is going on; and nerves and a brain to make sure everything works together.

This siphon squirts out waste products; a small siphon at the other end allows water to pass into the body

MUSCLE POWER
Most animal movements are based on muscles. The dog leaps using more than 500 body muscles. Each shortens, or contracts, for a precise time to give a smooth, coordinated jump. The clam clamps closed using fewer than 10 muscles. Yet these can hold the two valves of its shell shut together for many hours.

LOVELY LIPS
The "lips" of the giant blue clam are its mantle, the fleshy wraparound part that covers its body and lines its shell. The mantle is sensitive to touch and chemicals. It also has rows of simple eyes. The green patches are algae (microscopic plants). They grow naturally in the clam's flesh.

When the clam closes, the ridges and lumps on its shell disguise it as an old rock

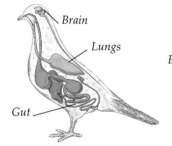

Brain

Lungs

Gut

Brain

Lungs

Gut

INTERNAL DESIGN
Despite the different shapes and layouts, the rabbit and the pigeon have the same basic set of internal organs. The brain is in the head, the lungs are in the chest, and the long gut squiggles through the rear part of the body. Similarity in internal design shows an evolutionary relationship.

At each stage of the dog's leap, dozens of
muscles are making sure that the animal
is well balanced. The strong muscles of
the hips and back legs push hard on takeoff. The head and tail shift position for
control and balance in midair. The front
legs extend to take the force of the landing.
Even as it curves through the air, the dog
is alert and keeps looking and listening.
The leap is the natural movement when
a dog pounces on its prey.

*Simple eyes are all
the clam needs*

*Algae catch
sunlight for
energy and
make nutrients,
which the clam
uses. In return,
the clam gives
these tiny plants
a safe home*

The parts of an insect

INSECTS MAKE UP by far the largest group of animals, with more than one million different species. A typical insect has three main body sections: the head with mouthparts and antennae; the thorax with six legs and (usually) wings; and the abdomen. These are encased in a hard external skeleton composed largely of a tough, horny substance called chitin. This "exoskeleton" covers all parts of the body including the legs, feet, eyes, antennae, and even the internal breathing tubes, or tracheae. Young insects have to shed their exoskeleton, or molt, several times during their lives in order to grow to adult size.

Tarsus

Tibia

Femur

Claw

Folding point

Front, or leading edge of wing

Tip, or apex of wing

Base of wing fold underneath

HIND WING FOLDED
In order to fit beneath the wing cases, the larger hind wings, with which the beetle flies, must be folded. The wing tip, or apex, is folded back at a special break in the front, known as the folding point. The base of the wing is also folded underneath.

JEWEL BEETLE
This adult jewel beetle, shown here at over three times life size, comes from South America. Beetles are the largest subgroup of insects, with more than 250,000 species. They have the typical jointed legs possessed by all insects.

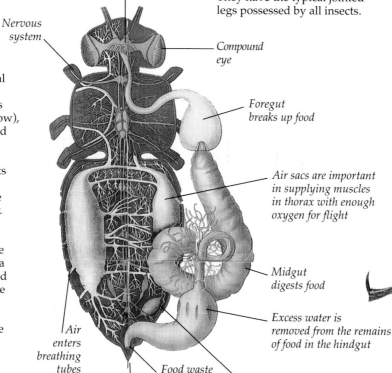

Ganglion (brain) in head

Nervous system

Compound eye

Foregut breaks up food

Air sacs are important in supplying muscles in thorax with enough oxygen for flight

Midgut digests food

Excess water is removed from the remains of food in the hindgut

Air enters breathing tubes through spiracles

Food waste is ejected through anus

Poison store for sting

Sting

INTERNAL ANATOMY
This illustration shows the internal anatomy of a typical insect – a worker bee. Along the center of its body is the digestive system (yellow), which is a continuous tube divided into the foregut, midgut, and hindgut. The breathing, or respiratory, system (white) consists of a network of branched tubes, through which air passes from the spiracles to every part of the body. The two large air sacs in the abdomen are important for supplying the flight muscles in the thorax with air. The bee's heart is a long thin tube, which pumps blood along most of the upper part of the body. There are no other blood vessels. Blood leaves the heart to carry food to the other organs. The simple nervous system (blue) is formed by one main nerve, which has knots of massed nerve cells, or ganglia, along its length. The ganglion in the head is the insect's brain. The female sexual organs and store of poison leading to the sting are shown in green.

ABDOMEN
The abdomen of an insect contains most of its "maintenance equipment" – the digestive system, heart, and sexual organs. Like the other parts of the body it is protected by the rigid exoskeleton, or cuticle, which is composed mainly of horny chitin. But between the segments the body is flexible. The whole surface is covered by a thin layer of wax, which prevents the insect from losing too much water.

FRONT WING
In beetles, the front pair of wings is adapted as a pair of hard wing cases called elytra. These protect the delicate flying wings and the body, and are often brightly colored. When the beetle flies, they are held forward.

LEGS

Insects have three pairs of jointed legs, which are used for walking, running, or jumping – depending on the species. Each leg has four main parts. The coxa joins the leg to the thorax. The femur, or thigh, is the most muscular section of the leg. The tibia, or lower leg, often carries a number of spines for self-defense. The tarsus, the equivalent of a human foot, consists of between one and five segments and two claws between which is sometimes a small pad for gripping smooth surfaces.

ARMOR PLATING

A tank is like a large beetle, with its hard outer skin protecting the important inner workings from being damaged by enemies.

Tarsus has between one and five segments

Tibia

Femur

Coxa

Second and third segments of the thorax each bear a pair of wings and a pair of legs

Coxa

Each foot bears two claws for climbing on rough surfaces

FEEDING IN INFORMATION

The head carries the feeding apparatus as well as important sense organs such as the compound eyes, antennae, and the palps, or feelers. These are attached to the mouthparts and help give the insect information about the taste and smell of its food.

Compound eye

ANTENNAE

The antennae, or "feelers," of insects vary in size and shape from long and thin, as in crickets, to short and hairlike, as in some flies. But whatever their shape, the antennae bear sensory structures that are able to detect air movements, vibrations, and smells.

COMPOUND EYES

Insect eyes are called compound because each is made up of hundreds of tiny, simple eyes. These eyes enable an insect to detect movement around it in almost every direction at once.

First segment of thorax bears front pair of legs

THORAX

The thorax is made up of three segments. The first bears the first pair of legs and is often clearly separated from the second and third segments, each of which has a pair of wings and a pair of legs. The second and third segments are closely joined to the abdomen.

Segmented antenna detects vibrations and smells

Claw

Leading edge of hind wing

A spiracle can be closed to prevent the entry of air and control water loss

HIND WING OUTSTRETCHED

The wings have no muscles in them. As the wing cases are lifted, muscles inside the thorax pull on the leading edge of the hind wings, making them open automatically and then flick up and down.

Wing case, or elytron

A BREATH OF FRESH AIR

Insects breathe air through a network of tubes (tracheae), that extend into the body from pairs of openings in the cuticle called spiracles. Some insects, like this caterpillar, have a pair of spiracles on each segment. More active insects often have fewer spiracles, as they can force air out of the tracheae.

Life in a shell

THE MOLLUSKS ARE ONE OF THE LARGEST of all animal groups, with about 100,000 species. They include the two-shelled bivalves, commonly called shellfish, such as oysters, mussels, and cockles. Also in the mollusk group are gastropods such as slugs, snails, limpets, and conches, and the cephalopods – nautilus, cuttlefish, squid, and octopus. Most mollusks live in the sea, and most have a hard, lime-rich shell to protect their soft body. The shell is produced by the fleshy mantle, which encloses the body organs on the inside.

ROCOCO DECORATION
The beautiful forms of mollusk shells have inspired countless artists and architects throughout the centuries. Here, the radiating shape of a clam shell has been used to decorate an arched recess.

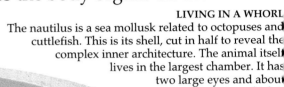

LIVING IN A WHORL
The nautilus is a sea mollusk related to octopuses and cuttlefish. This is its shell, cut in half to reveal the complex inner architecture. The animal itself lives in the largest chamber. It has two large eyes and about 30 tentacles which it uses to seize its prey

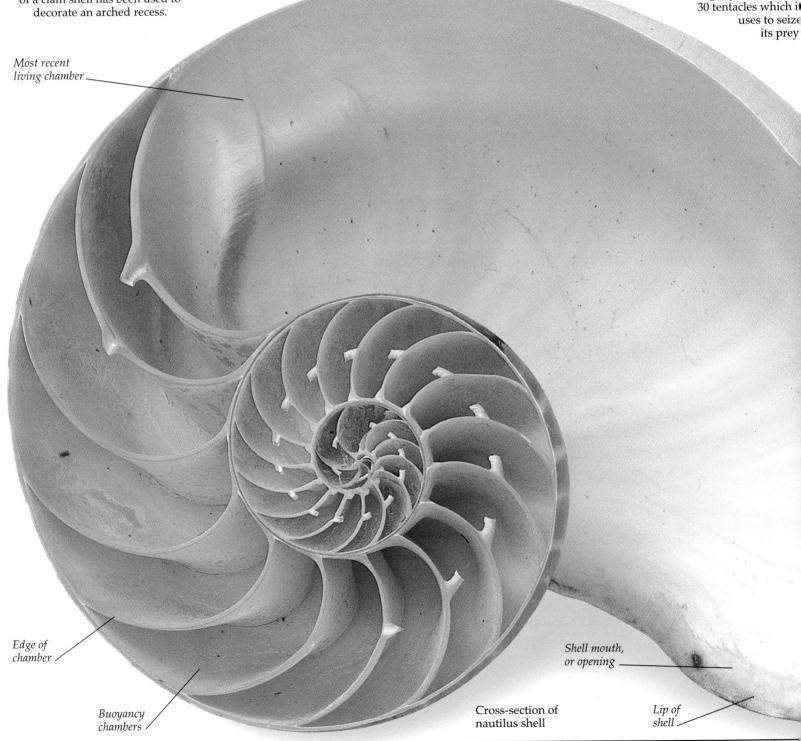

Most recent living chamber

Edge of chamber

Buoyancy chambers

Cross-section of nautilus shell

Shell mouth, or opening

Lip of shell

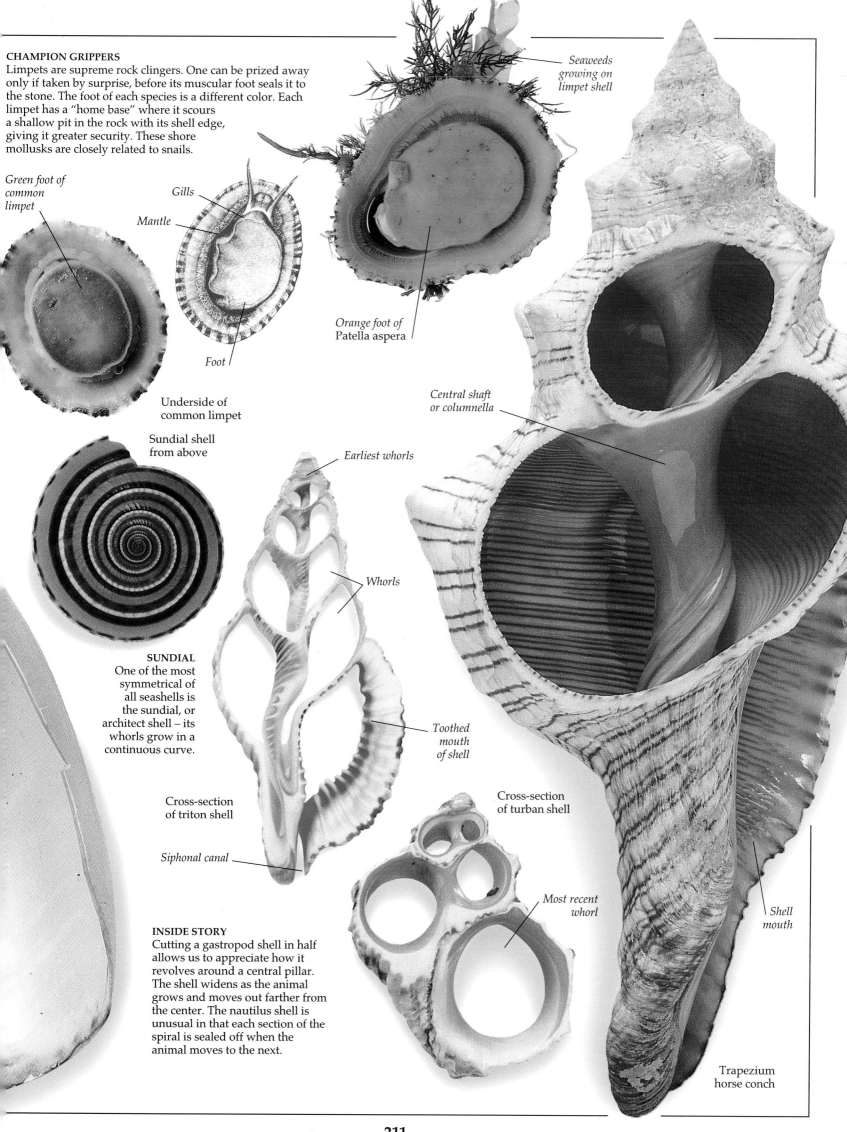

CHAMPION GRIPPERS

Limpets are supreme rock clingers. One can be prized away only if taken by surprise, before its muscular foot seals it to the stone. The foot of each species is a different color. Each limpet has a "home base" where it scours a shallow pit in the rock with its shell edge, giving it greater security. These shore mollusks are closely related to snails.

Green foot of common limpet

Gills

Mantle

Foot

Underside of common limpet

Seaweeds growing on limpet shell

Orange foot of Patella aspera

Sundial shell from above

Earliest whorls

Whorls

Central shaft or columnella

SUNDIAL

One of the most symmetrical of all seashells is the sundial, or architect shell – its whorls grow in a continuous curve.

Cross-section of triton shell

Siphonal canal

Toothed mouth of shell

Cross-section of turban shell

Most recent whorl

INSIDE STORY

Cutting a gastropod shell in half allows us to appreciate how it revolves around a central pillar. The shell widens as the animal grows and moves out farther from the center. The nautilus shell is unusual in that each section of the spiral is sealed off when the animal moves to the next.

Shell mouth

Trapezium horse conch

Circular animals

IN NEARLY ALL the major animal groups, from worms to mammals, the basic body plan is bilateral symmetry – that is, one side of their body is a mirror image of the other. The glaring exception is the echinoderms, or "spiny skins." This animal group has radial symmetry – a circular body plan. Echinoderms include the many kinds of starfish, brittlestars, and sea urchins, and the less familiar forms such as sea cucumbers, sea lilies, and feather stars. All the 6,000-plus species of echinoderms live only in the oceans, many of them in deep water. The closest most people get to them is on the seashore.

GETTING A GRIP
When handled, starfish are rigid and resistant. However, the flexibility of their arms is shown when a wave flips them over: the arm tips curl under, the tiny tube feet get a grip on the rock, and slowly the animal rights itself.

Starfish have suckers on their tube feet which help them to grip onto rocks

A BALL WITH FIVE ARMS
The sea urchin, like the starfish, has five rays or "arms," as this underside view shows. An urchin is like a starfish whose arms have curled up and come together over its center, making a ball. The long tilting spines give protection. The thin tube feet grip the rock, seize food, and throw off debris.

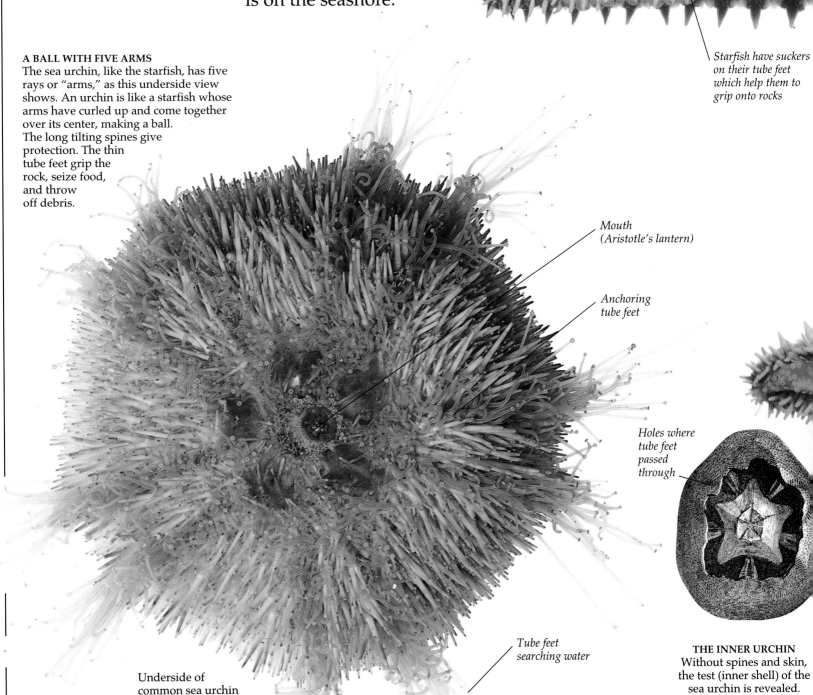

Mouth (Aristotle's lantern)

Anchoring tube feet

Holes where tube feet passed through

Tube feet searching water

Underside of common sea urchin

THE INNER URCHIN
Without spines and skin, the test (inner shell) of the sea urchin is revealed.

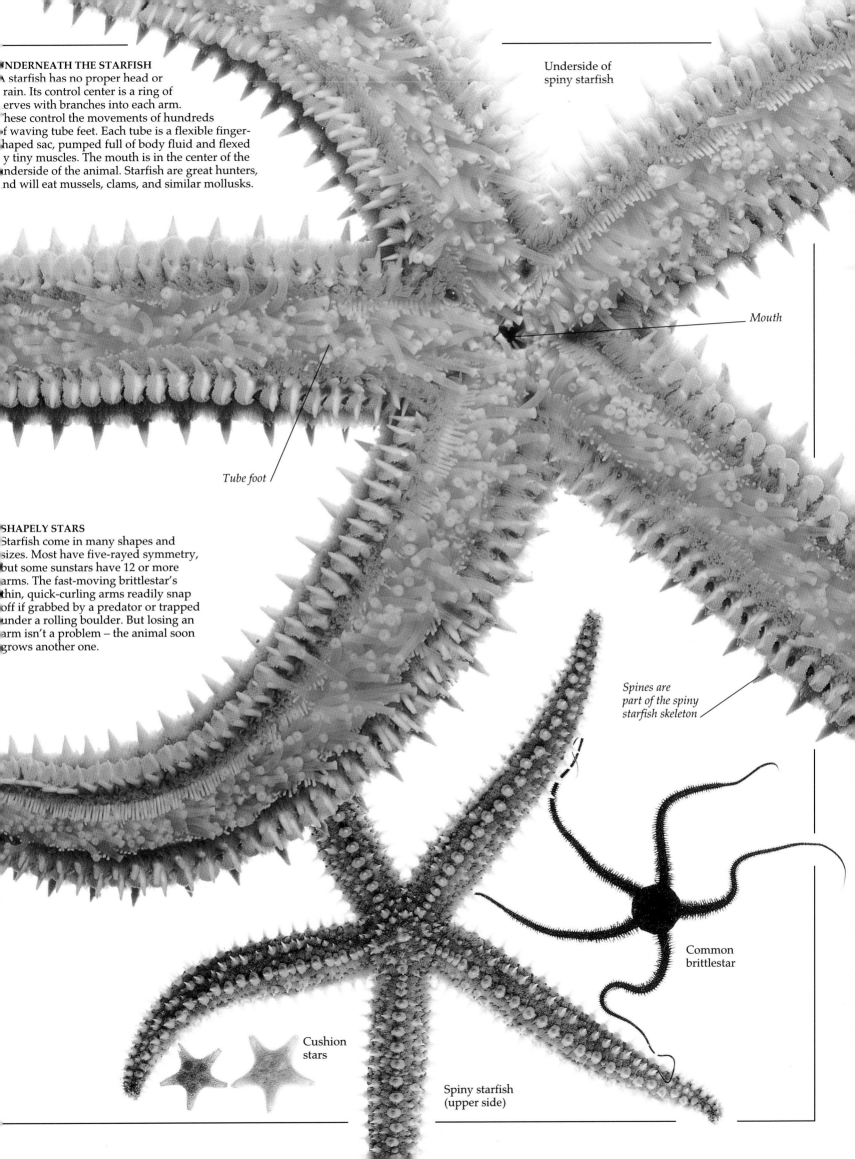

UNDERNEATH THE STARFISH
A starfish has no proper head or brain. Its control center is a ring of nerves with branches into each arm. These control the movements of hundreds of waving tube feet. Each tube is a flexible finger-shaped sac, pumped full of body fluid and flexed by tiny muscles. The mouth is in the center of the underside of the animal. Starfish are great hunters, and will eat mussels, clams, and similar mollusks.

SHAPELY STARS
Starfish come in many shapes and sizes. Most have five-rayed symmetry, but some sunstars have 12 or more arms. The fast-moving brittlestar's thin, quick-curling arms readily snap off if grabbed by a predator or trapped under a rolling boulder. But losing an arm isn't a problem – the animal soon grows another one.

Underside of
spiny starfish

Mouth

Tube foot

*Spines are
part of the spiny
starfish skeleton*

Cushion
stars

Common
brittlestar

Spiny starfish
(upper side)

Crusty crustaceans

OFTEN CALLED SHELLFISH, crustaceans are neither true fish, nor do they have true shells, like mollusks. The hard outer body casing of a crustacean is jointed and gives overall protection. This exoskeleton, similar to the hard outer casing of an insect's body, is made mainly of a limy substance and the protein chitin. There are many other similarities between crustaceans and insects, including segmented bodies and jointed limbs, and the shedding of its exoskeleton to allow the animal to grow. There are more than 30,000 species of crustaceans, and the vast majority live in the sea. They range from tiny daphnias and sowbugs to sandhoppers, barnacles, krill, shrimps, prawns, and spindly spider crabs with legs almost ten feet long. The massive armored lobster, here shown slightly larger than life-size, is also a crustacean.

Still Life with Lobster by Joris Van Son

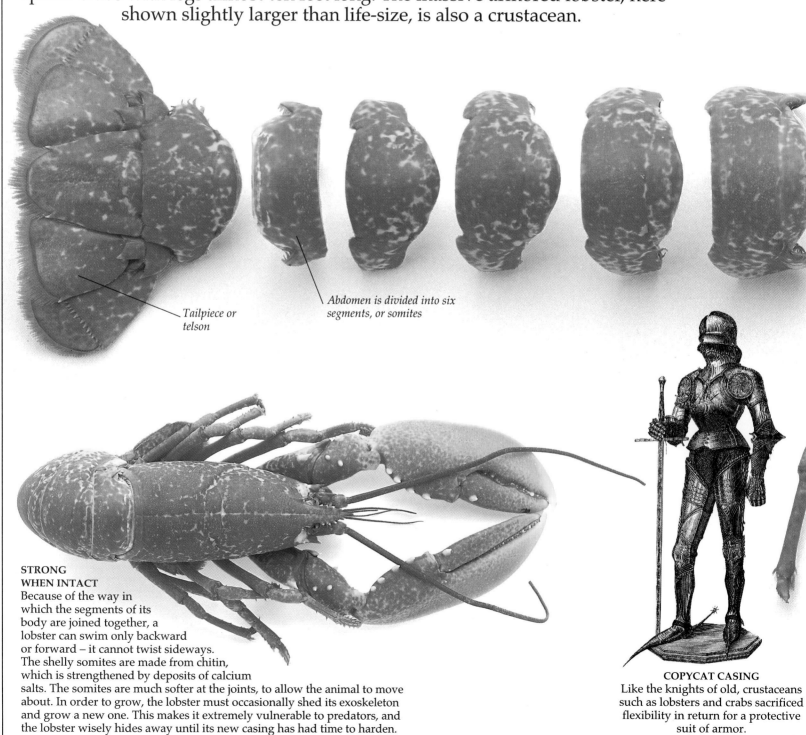

Tailpiece or telson

Abdomen is divided into six segments, or somites

STRONG WHEN INTACT
Because of the way in which the segments of its body are joined together, a lobster can swim only backward or forward – it cannot twist sideways. The shelly somites are made from chitin, which is strengthened by deposits of calcium salts. The somites are much softer at the joints, to allow the animal to move about. In order to grow, the lobster must occasionally shed its exoskeleton and grow a new one. This makes it extremely vulnerable to predators, and the lobster wisely hides away until its new casing has had time to harden.

COPYCAT CASING
Like the knights of old, crustaceans such as lobsters and crabs sacrificed flexibility in return for a protective suit of armor.

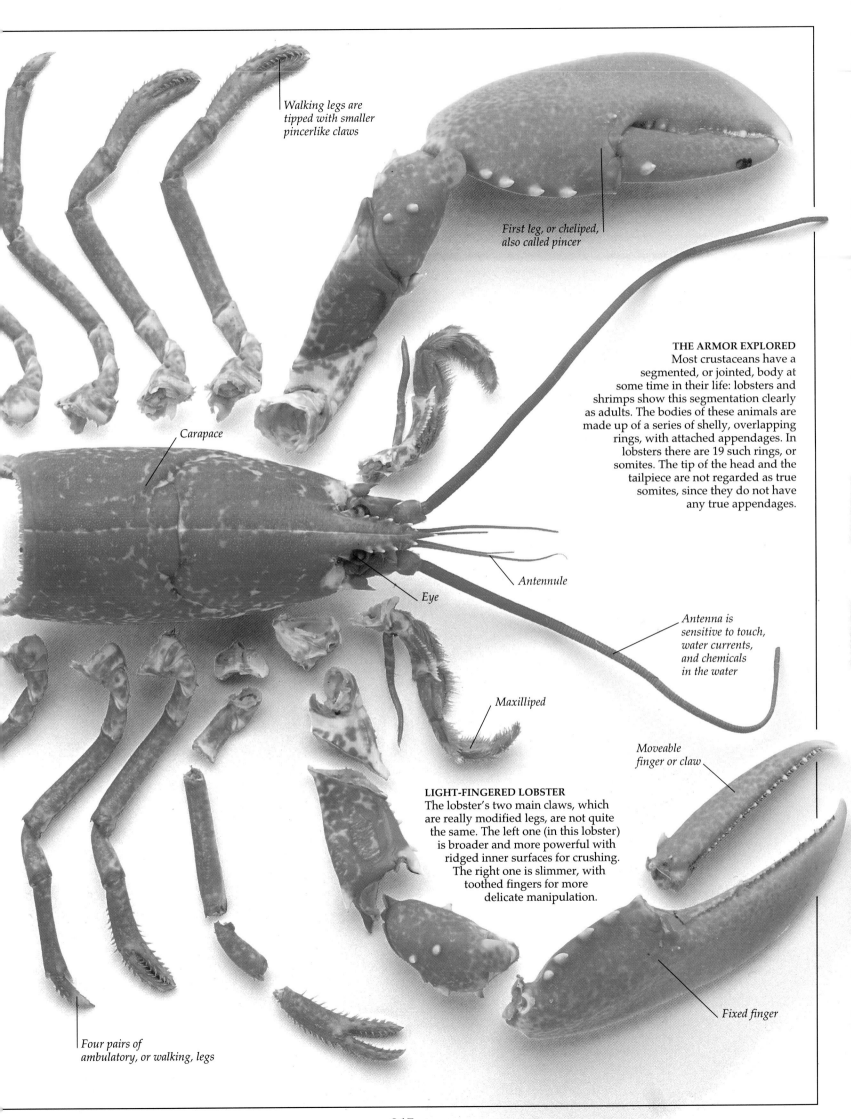

Walking legs are tipped with smaller pincerlike claws

First leg, or cheliped, also called pincer

Carapace

THE ARMOR EXPLORED
Most crustaceans have a segmented, or jointed, body at some time in their life: lobsters and shrimps show this segmentation clearly as adults. The bodies of these animals are made up of a series of shelly, overlapping rings, with attached appendages. In lobsters there are 19 such rings, or somites. The tip of the head and the tailpiece are not regarded as true somites, since they do not have any true appendages.

Antennule

Eye

Antenna is sensitive to touch, water currents, and chemicals in the water

Maxilliped

Moveable finger or claw

LIGHT-FINGERED LOBSTER
The lobster's two main claws, which are really modified legs, are not quite the same. The left one (in this lobster) is broader and more powerful with ridged inner surfaces for crushing. The right one is slimmer, with toothed fingers for more delicate manipulation.

Fixed finger

Four pairs of ambulatory, or walking, legs

Masters of the watery world

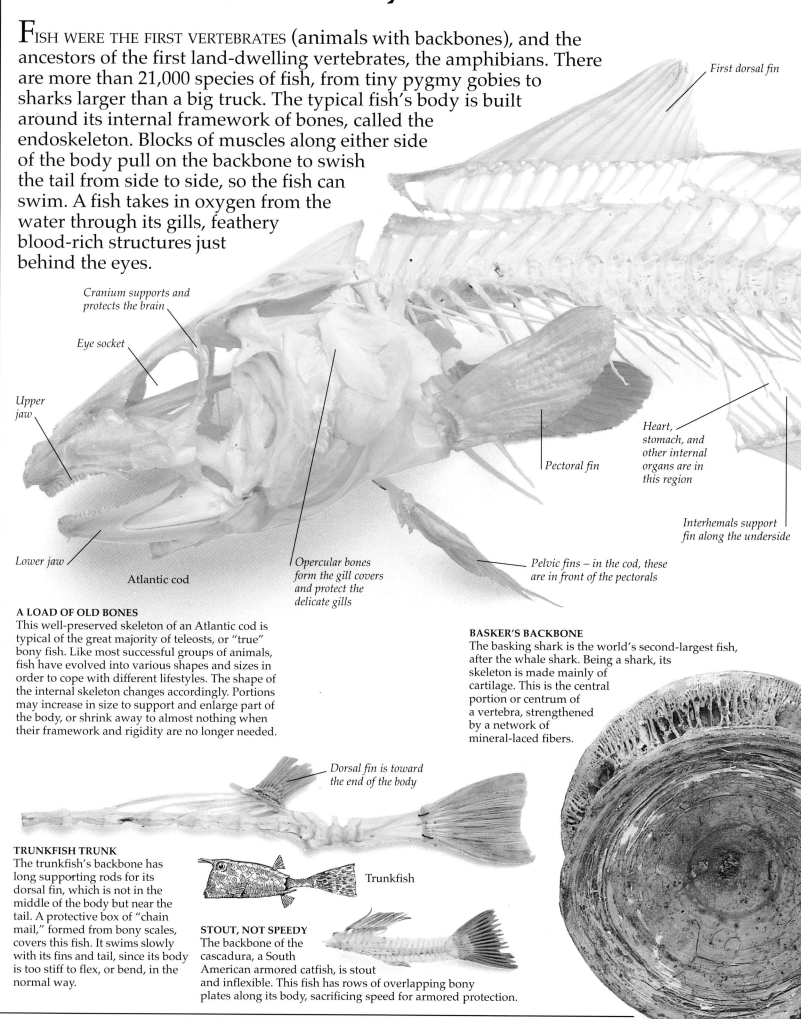

FISH WERE THE FIRST VERTEBRATES (animals with backbones), and the ancestors of the first land-dwelling vertebrates, the amphibians. There are more than 21,000 species of fish, from tiny pygmy gobies to sharks larger than a big truck. The typical fish's body is built around its internal framework of bones, called the endoskeleton. Blocks of muscles along either side of the body pull on the backbone to swish the tail from side to side, so the fish can swim. A fish takes in oxygen from the water through its gills, feathery blood-rich structures just behind the eyes.

First dorsal fin

Cranium supports and protects the brain

Eye socket

Upper jaw

Lower jaw

Atlantic cod

Opercular bones form the gill covers and protect the delicate gills

Pectoral fin

Heart, stomach, and other internal organs are in this region

Interhemals support fin along the underside

Pelvic fins – in the cod, these are in front of the pectorals

A LOAD OF OLD BONES
This well-preserved skeleton of an Atlantic cod is typical of the great majority of teleosts, or "true" bony fish. Like most successful groups of animals, fish have evolved into various shapes and sizes in order to cope with different lifestyles. The shape of the internal skeleton changes accordingly. Portions may increase in size to support and enlarge part of the body, or shrink away to almost nothing when their framework and rigidity are no longer needed.

BASKER'S BACKBONE
The basking shark is the world's second-largest fish, after the whale shark. Being a shark, its skeleton is made mainly of cartilage. This is the central portion or centrum of a vertebra, strengthened by a network of mineral-laced fibers.

Dorsal fin is toward the end of the body

Trunkfish

TRUNKFISH TRUNK
The trunkfish's backbone has long supporting rods for its dorsal fin, which is not in the middle of the body but near the tail. A protective box of "chain mail," formed from bony scales, covers this fish. It swims slowly with its fins and tail, since its body is too stiff to flex, or bend, in the normal way.

STOUT, NOT SPEEDY
The backbone of the cascadura, a South American armored catfish, is stout and inflexible. This fish has rows of overlapping bony plates along its body, sacrificing speed for armored protection.

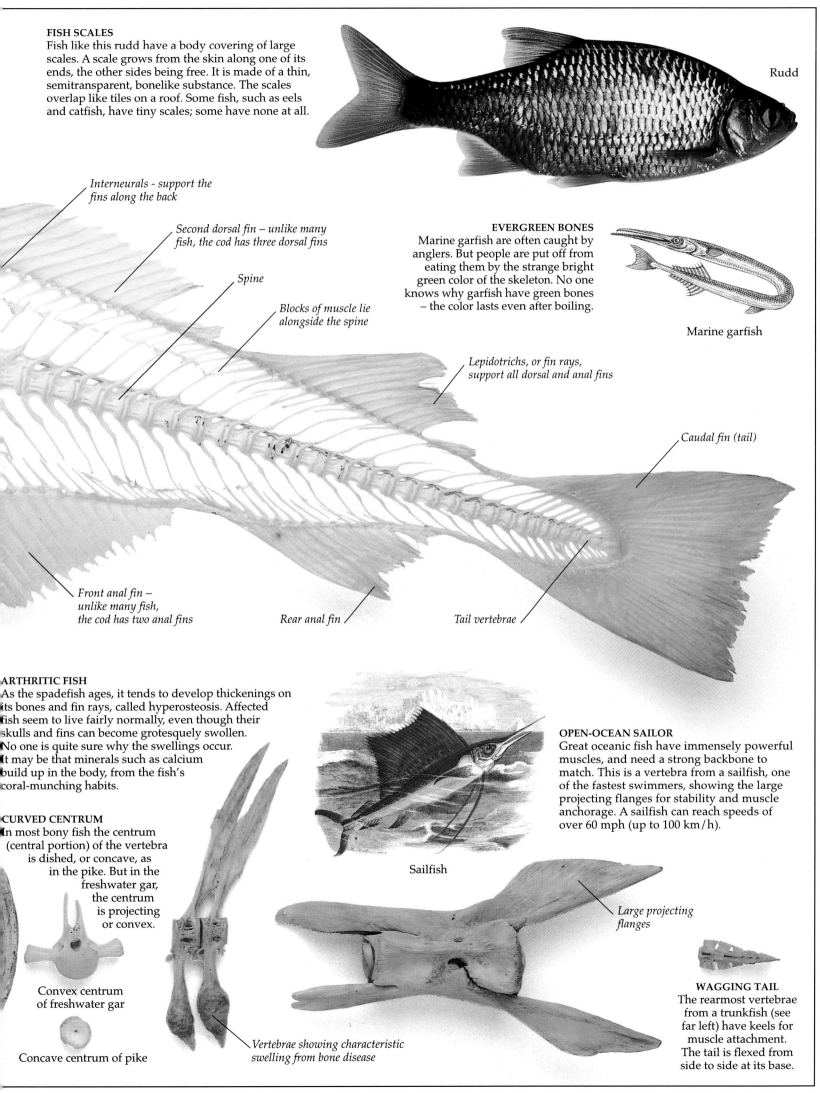

FISH SCALES
Fish like this rudd have a body covering of large scales. A scale grows from the skin along one of its ends, the other sides being free. It is made of a thin, semitransparent, bonelike substance. The scales overlap like tiles on a roof. Some fish, such as eels and catfish, have tiny scales; some have none at all.

Rudd

Interneurals - support the fins along the back

Second dorsal fin – unlike many fish, the cod has three dorsal fins

Spine

Blocks of muscle lie alongside the spine

EVERGREEN BONES
Marine garfish are often caught by anglers. But people are put off from eating them by the strange bright green color of the skeleton. No one knows why garfish have green bones – the color lasts even after boiling.

Marine garfish

Lepidotrichs, or fin rays, support all dorsal and anal fins

Caudal fin (tail)

Front anal fin – unlike many fish, the cod has two anal fins

Rear anal fin

Tail vertebrae

ARTHRITIC FISH
As the spadefish ages, it tends to develop thickenings on its bones and fin rays, called hyperosteosis. Affected fish seem to live fairly normally, even though their skulls and fins can become grotesquely swollen. No one is quite sure why the swellings occur. It may be that minerals such as calcium build up in the body, from the fish's coral-munching habits.

CURVED CENTRUM
In most bony fish the centrum (central portion) of the vertebra is dished, or concave, as in the pike. But in the freshwater gar, the centrum is projecting or convex.

Convex centrum of freshwater gar

Concave centrum of pike

Vertebrae showing characteristic swelling from bone disease

Sailfish

OPEN-OCEAN SAILOR
Great oceanic fish have immensely powerful muscles, and need a strong backbone to match. This is a vertebra from a sailfish, one of the fastest swimmers, showing the large projecting flanges for stability and muscle anchorage. A sailfish can reach speeds of over 60 mph (up to 100 km/h).

Large projecting flanges

WAGGING TAIL
The rearmost vertebrae from a trunkfish (see far left) have keels for muscle attachment. The tail is flexed from side to side at its base.

Inside a shark

SHARKS, SKATES, AND RAYS make up a distinct group of fish called chondrichthyes, or cartilaginous fish. Their skeleton is made not of bone, but of the slightly flexible rubbery cartilage. There are about 715 species in the group. Apart from the skeletal difference, packaged neatly inside a shark's body are all the usual vertebrate organs which keep it alive. The heart pumps the blood around the body, delivering oxygen and nutrients while taking away carbon dioxide and other wastes. Food passes into the digestive system, which is like a large tube. From the mouth the food goes down the esophagus into the stomach, where digestion begins, and then into the intestine where digested food is absorbed. Indigestible wastes collect in the rectum to be passed out of the body. Digested food is further processed in the large liver, which also increases the shark's buoyancy. Unlike most bony fish, sharks do not have a swim bladder. Kidneys remove wastes from the blood and regulate its concentration. Large muscles in the body wall keep the shark swimming, while the skeleton and skin provide support. Like all vertebrates, the brain coordinates the shark's actions with signals or instructions passed back and forth along the spinal cord.

DANGER BELOW
Sharks have been known to attack people coming down into the water, as this Australian parachutist will soon discover.

Paired kidneys regulate waste products to keep concentration of body fluids just above that of seawater, or sharks will dehydrate

As in other fish, the segmented swimming muscles contract alternately, sending a wave motion from head to tail

Model of a female spinner shark, showing internal anatomy

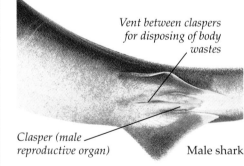

Vent between claspers for disposing of body wastes

Clasper (male reproductive organ)

Male shark

Female shark

Cloaca (opening for reproduction, and vent for waste disposal)

MALE OR FEMALE
All male sharks have a pair of claspers which are formed from the inner edge of their pelvic fins. During mating, one of the claspers is rotated forward and inserted into the female's body opening, or cloaca. Sperm is pumped down a groove in the clasper into the female, so fertilization of her eggs takes place inside her body. This is another feature that distinguishes sharks from bony fish.

Rectal gland (third kidney) passes excess salt out of the body through the vent

ALL IN THE TAIL
Sharks have a backbone, or vertebral column, which extends into the upper lobe of their tail, or caudal fin. This type of caudal fin is called a heterocercal tail, as opposed to those in most bony fish where the upper lobe does not contain an extension of the vertebral column. Cartilaginous rods and dermal filaments help to strengthen the shark's tail.

Scroll valve in intestine, or gut – other sharks have spiral or ring valves

Left lobe of large liver

Caudal fin

Vertebral column

Cartilaginous rod

Dermal filament

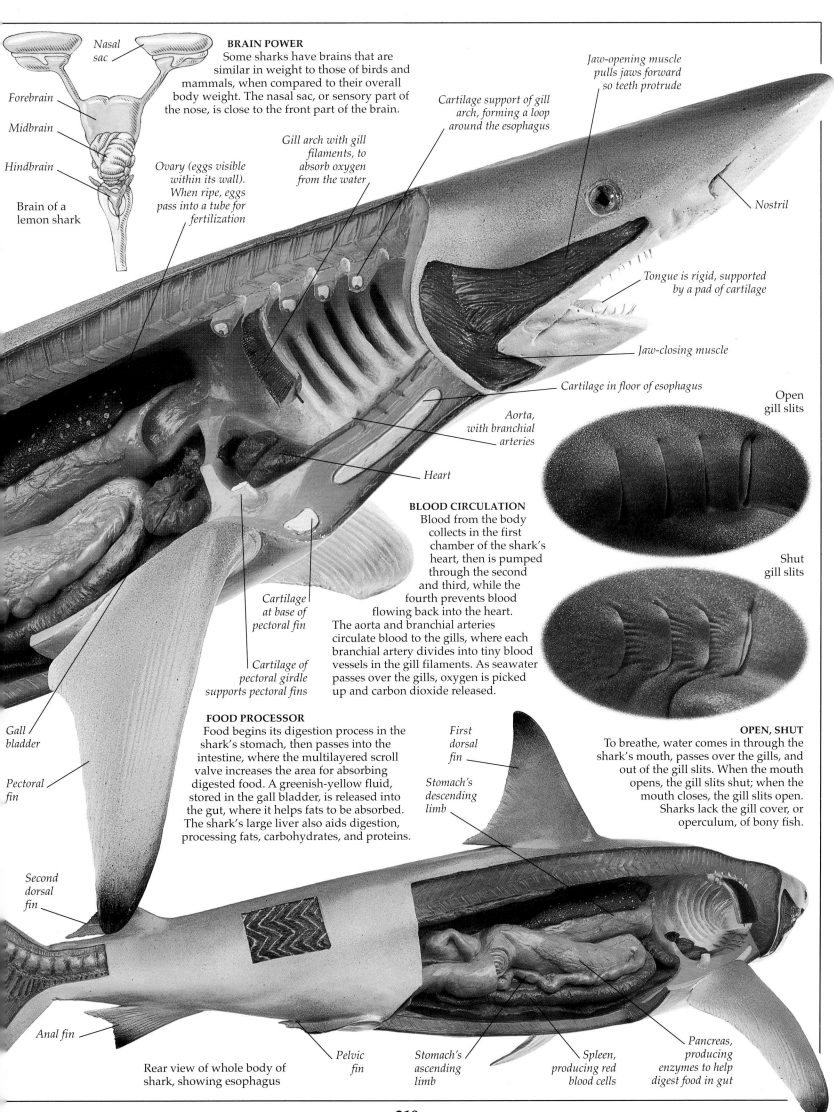

BRAIN POWER
Some sharks have brains that are similar in weight to those of birds and mammals, when compared to their overall body weight. The nasal sac, or sensory part of the nose, is close to the front part of the brain.

Nasal sac

Forebrain

Midbrain

Hindbrain

Brain of a lemon shark

Ovary (eggs visible within its wall). When ripe, eggs pass into a tube for fertilization

Gill arch with gill filaments, to absorb oxygen from the water

Cartilage support of gill arch, forming a loop around the esophagus

Jaw-opening muscle pulls jaws forward so teeth protrude

Nostril

Tongue is rigid, supported by a pad of cartilage

Jaw-closing muscle

Cartilage in floor of esophagus

Aorta, with branchial arteries

Heart

Open gill slits

Shut gill slits

BLOOD CIRCULATION
Blood from the body collects in the first chamber of the shark's heart, then is pumped through the second and third, while the fourth prevents blood flowing back into the heart. The aorta and branchial arteries circulate blood to the gills, where each branchial artery divides into tiny blood vessels in the gill filaments. As seawater passes over the gills, oxygen is picked up and carbon dioxide released.

Cartilage at base of pectoral fin

Cartilage of pectoral girdle supports pectoral fins

Gall bladder

Pectoral fin

FOOD PROCESSOR
Food begins its digestion process in the shark's stomach, then passes into the intestine, where the multilayered scroll valve increases the area for absorbing digested food. A greenish-yellow fluid, stored in the gall bladder, is released into the gut, where it helps fats to be absorbed. The shark's large liver also aids digestion, processing fats, carbohydrates, and proteins.

First dorsal fin

Stomach's descending limb

OPEN, SHUT
To breathe, water comes in through the shark's mouth, passes over the gills, and out of the gill slits. When the mouth opens, the gill slits shut; when the mouth closes, the gill slits open. Sharks lack the gill cover, or operculum, of bony fish.

Second dorsal fin

Anal fin

Pelvic fin

Rear view of whole body of shark, showing esophagus

Stomach's ascending limb

Spleen, producing red blood cells

Pancreas, producing enzymes to help digest food in gut

The bare bones

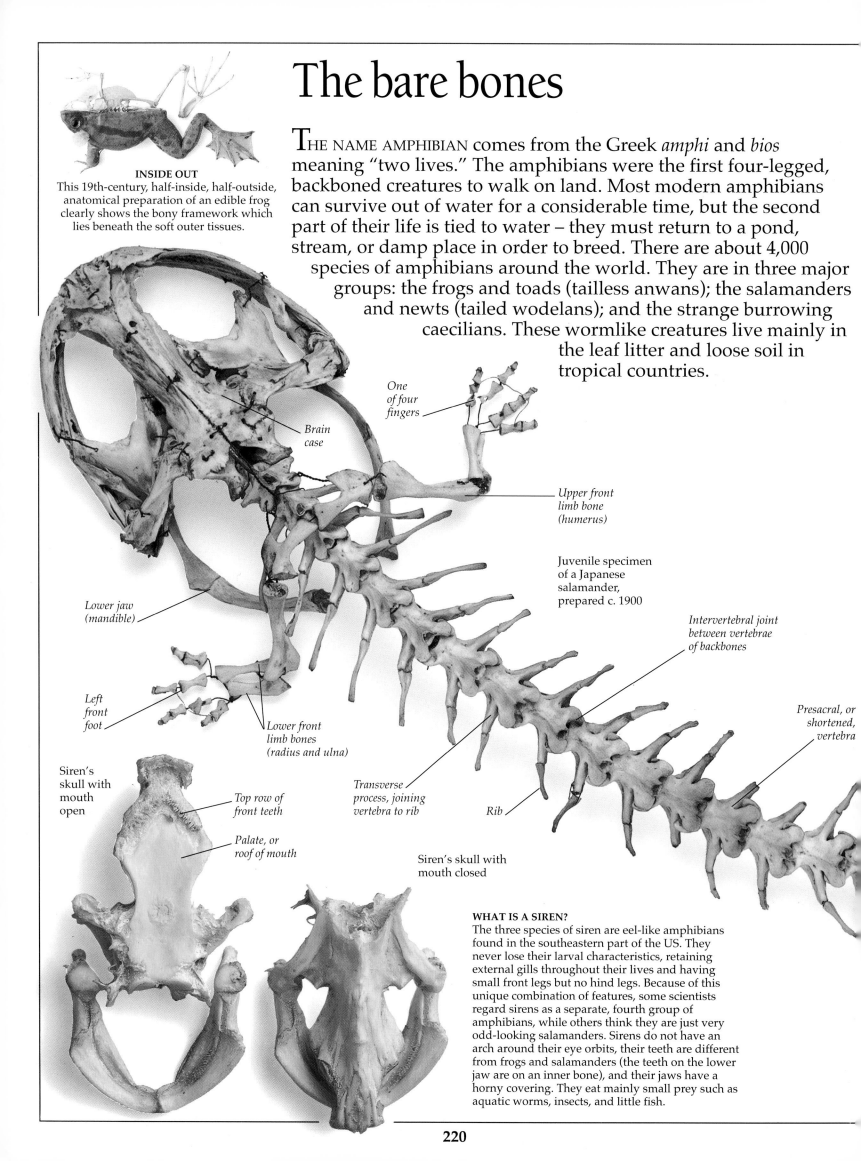

THE NAME AMPHIBIAN comes from the Greek *amphi* and *bios* meaning "two lives." The amphibians were the first four-legged, backboned creatures to walk on land. Most modern amphibians can survive out of water for a considerable time, but the second part of their life is tied to water – they must return to a pond, stream, or damp place in order to breed. There are about 4,000 species of amphibians around the world. They are in three major groups: the frogs and toads (tailless anwans); the salamanders and newts (tailed wodelans); and the strange burrowing caecilians. These wormlike creatures live mainly in the leaf litter and loose soil in tropical countries.

One of four fingers

Brain case

Upper front limb bone (humerus)

Juvenile specimen of a Japanese salamander, prepared c. 1900

Intervertebral joint between vertebrae of backbones

Lower jaw (mandible)

Presacral, or shortened, vertebra

Left front foot

Lower front limb bones (radius and ulna)

Siren's skull with mouth open

Top row of front teeth

Transverse process, joining vertebra to rib

Rib

Palate, or roof of mouth

Siren's skull with mouth closed

WHAT IS A SIREN?
The three species of siren are eel-like amphibians found in the southeastern part of the US. They never lose their larval characteristics, retaining external gills throughout their lives and having small front legs but no hind legs. Because of this unique combination of features, some scientists regard sirens as a separate, fourth group of amphibians, while others think they are just very odd-looking salamanders. Sirens do not have an arch around their eye orbits, their teeth are different from frogs and salamanders (the teeth on the lower jaw are on an inner bone), and their jaws have a horny covering. They eat mainly small prey such as aquatic worms, insects, and little fish.

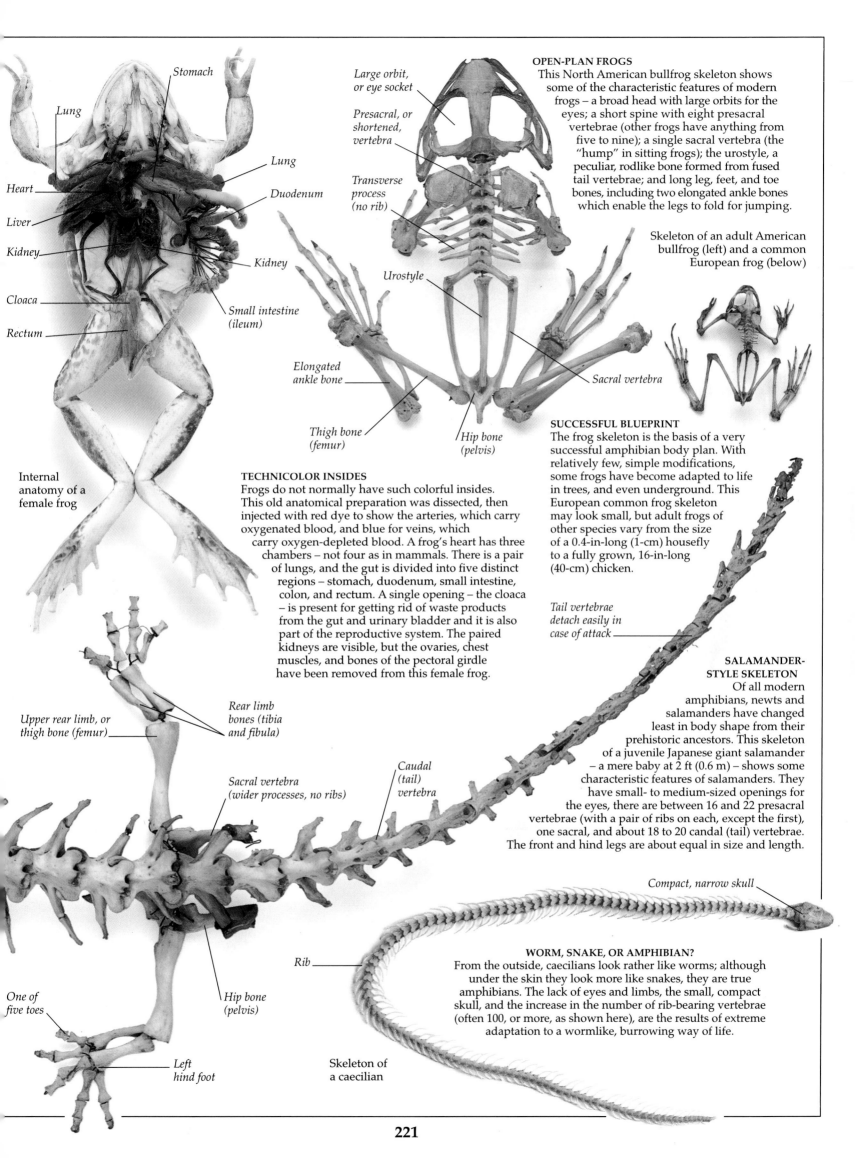

Stomach

Lung

Heart

Liver

Kidney

Cloaca

Rectum

Lung

Duodenum

Kidney

Small intestine (ileum)

Internal anatomy of a female frog

OPEN-PLAN FROGS
This North American bullfrog skeleton shows some of the characteristic features of modern frogs – a broad head with large orbits for the eyes; a short spine with eight presacral vertebrae (other frogs have anything from five to nine); a single sacral vertebra (the "hump" in sitting frogs); the urostyle, a peculiar, rodlike bone formed from fused tail vertebrae; and long leg, feet, and toe bones, including two elongated ankle bones which enable the legs to fold for jumping.

Large orbit, or eye socket

Presacral, or shortened, vertebra

Transverse process (no rib)

Urostyle

Elongated ankle bone

Thigh bone (femur)

Hip bone (pelvis)

Sacral vertebra

Skeleton of an adult American bullfrog (left) and a common European frog (below)

TECHNICOLOR INSIDES
Frogs do not normally have such colorful insides. This old anatomical preparation was dissected, then injected with red dye to show the arteries, which carry oxygenated blood, and blue for veins, which carry oxygen-depleted blood. A frog's heart has three chambers – not four as in mammals. There is a pair of lungs, and the gut is divided into five distinct regions – stomach, duodenum, small intestine, colon, and rectum. A single opening – the cloaca – is present for getting rid of waste products from the gut and urinary bladder and it is also part of the reproductive system. The paired kidneys are visible, but the ovaries, chest muscles, and bones of the pectoral girdle have been removed from this female frog.

SUCCESSFUL BLUEPRINT
The frog skeleton is the basis of a very successful amphibian body plan. With relatively few, simple modifications, some frogs have become adapted to life in trees, and even underground. This European common frog skeleton may look small, but adult frogs of other species vary from the size of a 0.4-in-long (1-cm) housefly to a fully grown, 16-in-long (40-cm) chicken.

Tail vertebrae detach easily in case of attack

SALAMANDER-STYLE SKELETON
Of all modern amphibians, newts and salamanders have changed least in body shape from their prehistoric ancestors. This skeleton of a juvenile Japanese giant salamander – a mere baby at 2 ft (0.6 m) – shows some characteristic features of salamanders. They have small- to medium-sized openings for the eyes, there are between 16 and 22 presacral vertebrae (with a pair of ribs on each, except the first), one sacral, and about 18 to 20 candal (tail) vertebrae. The front and hind legs are about equal in size and length.

Upper rear limb, or thigh bone (femur)

Rear limb bones (tibia and fibula)

Sacral vertebra (wider processes, no ribs)

Caudal (tail) vertebra

Compact, narrow skull

One of five toes

Hip bone (pelvis)

Rib

Left hind foot

Skeleton of a caecilian

WORM, SNAKE, OR AMPHIBIAN?
From the outside, caecilians look rather like worms; although under the skin they look more like snakes, they are true amphibians. The lack of eyes and limbs, the small, compact skull, and the increase in the number of rib-bearing vertebrae (often 100, or more, as shown here), are the results of extreme adaptation to a wormlike, burrowing way of life.

Legs or legless?

Rᴇᴘᴛɪʟᴇs ʜᴀᴠᴇ ᴛʜᴇ sᴀᴍᴇ basic skeleton and main internal organs as other four-limbed (quadruped) vertebrates such as amphibians, birds, and mammals. But in many reptiles, bone growth does not stop at maturity, which means that some reptiles keep growing throughout their lives. If a reptile survives the everyday dangers of life, it may eventually become giant-sized. This is particularly true of pythons, crocodiles, and giant tortoises. Snakes are unusual in that they have lost almost all traces of their limbs during evolution to become the main group of legless vertebrates.

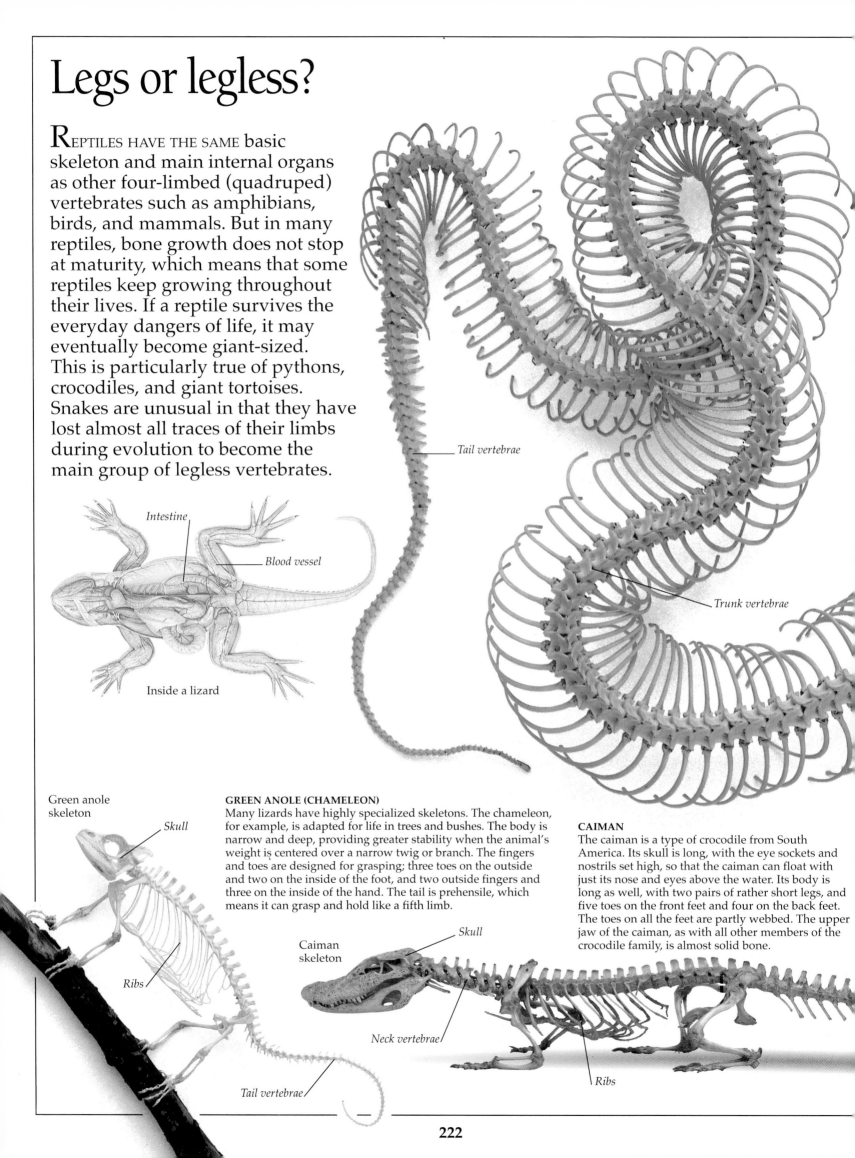

Tail vertebrae

Intestine

Blood vessel

Inside a lizard

Trunk vertebrae

Green anole skeleton

Skull

Ribs

GREEN ANOLE (CHAMELEON)
Many lizards have highly specialized skeletons. The chameleon, for example, is adapted for life in trees and bushes. The body is narrow and deep, providing greater stability when the animal's weight is centered over a narrow twig or branch. The fingers and toes are designed for grasping; three toes on the outside and two on the inside of the foot, and two outside fingers and three on the inside of the hand. The tail is prehensile, which means it can grasp and hold like a fifth limb.

CAIMAN
The caiman is a type of crocodile from South America. Its skull is long, with the eye sockets and nostrils set high, so that the caiman can float with just its nose and eyes above the water. Its body is long as well, with two pairs of rather short legs, and five toes on the front feet and four on the back feet. The toes on all the feet are partly webbed. The upper jaw of the caiman, as with all other members of the crocodile family, is almost solid bone.

Caiman skeleton

Skull

Neck vertebrae

Ribs

Tail vertebrae

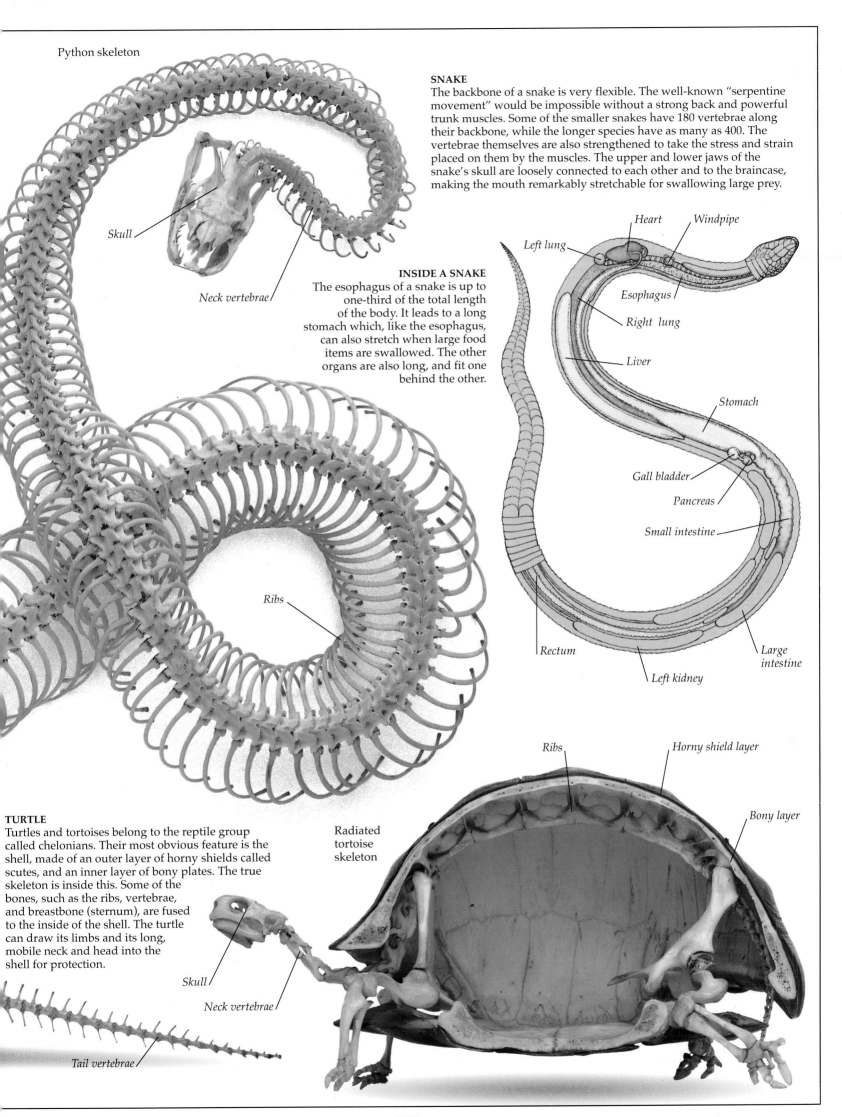

Python skeleton

Skull

Neck vertebrae

Ribs

SNAKE
The backbone of a snake is very flexible. The well-known "serpentine movement" would be impossible without a strong back and powerful trunk muscles. Some of the smaller snakes have 180 vertebrae along their backbone, while the longer species have as many as 400. The vertebrae themselves are also strengthened to take the stress and strain placed on them by the muscles. The upper and lower jaws of the snake's skull are loosely connected to each other and to the braincase, making the mouth remarkably stretchable for swallowing large prey.

INSIDE A SNAKE
The esophagus of a snake is up to one-third of the total length of the body. It leads to a long stomach which, like the esophagus, can also stretch when large food items are swallowed. The other organs are also long, and fit one behind the other.

Heart

Windpipe

Left lung

Esophagus

Right lung

Liver

Stomach

Gall bladder

Pancreas

Small intestine

Large intestine

Rectum

Left kidney

Ribs

Horny shield layer

Bony layer

TURTLE
Turtles and tortoises belong to the reptile group called chelonians. Their most obvious feature is the shell, made of an outer layer of horny shields called scutes, and an inner layer of bony plates. The true skeleton is inside this. Some of the bones, such as the ribs, vertebrae, and breastbone (sternum), are fused to the inside of the shell. The turtle can draw its limbs and its long, mobile neck and head into the shell for protection.

Radiated tortoise skeleton

Skull

Neck vertebrae

Tail vertebrae

Taking to the air

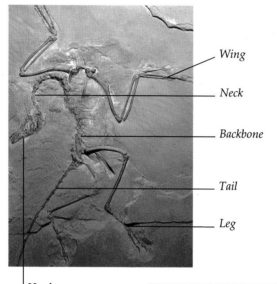

*Archaeopteryx –
the primeval bird*

IN THE LONG HISTORY OF EVOLUTION, birds were not the first creatures to fly. That achievement belongs to insects. Neither were they the first large flying animals. This honor belongs to the winged reptiles called pterosaurs, which appeared during the Age of Dinosaurs, around 200 million years ago. But today, birds are the dominant form of life in the air. There are about 9,000 species of birds, and they occupy virtually every habitat on Earth, from the terns, geese, and albatrosses soaring near the frozen poles, to the parrots and hummingbirds of steamy tropical forests. Penguins, loons, and similar seabirds are completely at home even in the water of the oceans. The earliest known bird is preserved as one of the world's most famous fossils, called *Archaeopteryx*, or ancient wing. Although this creature lived over 150 million years ago, when the pterosaurs were still in their heyday, the fossils show that this crow-sized animal was thickly feathered, and therefore was a bird. For it is the possession of feathers that makes a bird a bird.

THE FIRST LINK
The first *Archaeopteryx* fossil was found in Germany in 1861, in an area that was once flooded by sea. When the animal died, its body was covered by fine silt which preserved not only the outlines of bones, but also those of the feathers. Over millions of years, this compressed silt gradually became limestone, and when it was quarried, the stone yielded up the fossils. In this specimen, the birdlike wings and legs are clearly visible, as are the reptilian teeth and tail. It is likely that *Archaeopteryx* evolved from small dinosaurs that ran upright instead of walking on all fours. Seven *Archaeopteryx* fossils have been found, all from the same area in Bavaria.

Wing

Neck

Backbone

Tail

Leg

Head

STAYING BALANCED
Compared to many animals, birds are compact creatures. A bird's legs, wings, and neck are all lightweight structures. The heavy parts, particularly the wing and leg muscles, are packed closely around the ribcage and backbone. This allows a bird to stay balanced both in the air and on the ground.

Front view of a crow's skeleton

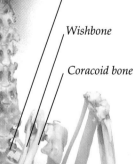

Skull

Neck

Backbone

Wishbone

Coracoid bone

Ribcage

Breastbone

Leg bones

EVOLUTIONARY EXPERIMENT
Although fossils show that pterosaurs were highly successful in their time, they died out with the dinosaurs 65 million years ago. They were not ancestors of modern birds.

AS DEAD AS THE DODO
The dodo was a flightless bird of Madagascar and neighboring islands in the Indian Ocean, and was driven to extinction by humans in the late 17th century. When Lewis Carroll described the encounter between the dodo and Alice in his book *Through the Looking Glass*, the species was already "as dead as a dodo." Flying birds have also suffered from human hunting and persecution. The last passenger pigeon died in 1914, whereas 100 years earlier, the species formed flocks in North America over a *billion* strong.

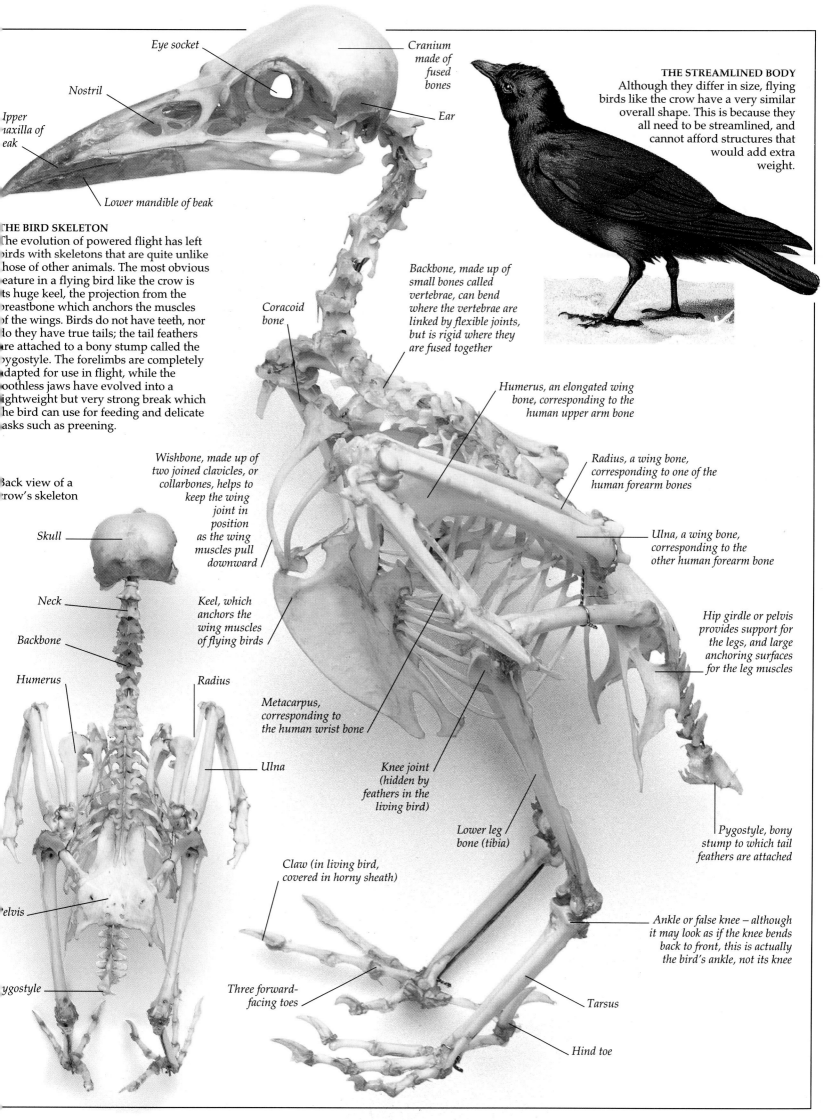

Eye socket

Nostril

Ipper
maxilla of
eak

Lower mandible of beak

Cranium made of fused bones

Ear

THE STREAMLINED BODY
Although they differ in size, flying birds like the crow have a very similar overall shape. This is because they all need to be streamlined, and cannot afford structures that would add extra weight.

THE BIRD SKELETON
The evolution of powered flight has left birds with skeletons that are quite unlike those of other animals. The most obvious feature in a flying bird like the crow is its huge keel, the projection from the breastbone which anchors the muscles of the wings. Birds do not have teeth, nor do they have true tails; the tail feathers are attached to a bony stump called the pygostyle. The forelimbs are completely adapted for use in flight, while the toothless jaws have evolved into a lightweight but very strong break which the bird can use for feeding and delicate tasks such as preening.

Back view of a crow's skeleton

Backbone, made up of small bones called vertebrae, can bend where the vertebrae are linked by flexible joints, but is rigid where they are fused together

Coracoid bone

Humerus, an elongated wing bone, corresponding to the human upper arm bone

Radius, a wing bone, corresponding to one of the human forearm bones

Ulna, a wing bone, corresponding to the other human forearm bone

Wishbone, made up of two joined clavicles, or collarbones, helps to keep the wing joint in position as the wing muscles pull downward

Skull

Neck

Backbone

Humerus

Radius

Keel, which anchors the wing muscles of flying birds

Ulna

Hip girdle or pelvis provides support for the legs, and large anchoring surfaces for the leg muscles

Metacarpus, corresponding to the human wrist bone

Knee joint (hidden by feathers in the living bird)

Lower leg bone (tibia)

Pygostyle, bony stump to which tail feathers are attached

Claw (in living bird, covered in horny sheath)

Pelvis

Pygostyle

Three forward-facing toes

Ankle or false knee – although it may look as if the knee bends back to front, this is actually the bird's ankle, not its knee

Tarsus

Hind toe

225

Wing power

THREE GROUPS OF ANIMALS – insects, bats, and birds – are capable of powered flight. Of these, birds are by far the largest, fastest, and most powerful fliers. The secret of their success lies in the design of their wings. A bird's wing is light, strong, and flexible. It is also slightly curved like an aircraft wing, producing an airfoil profile which literally pulls the bird upward as it flaps through the air. Although wing size and shape vary according to each bird's lifestyle, they all share the same basic pattern, shown here in the wing of an owl.

OVER THE LIMIT
A bird's wings can bear its weight, plus light luggage such as food and nesting materials. Heavier loads, like human passengers, are strictly out of the question.

FLIGHT OF FANCY
Legend describes how Icarus flew from Crete to Greece. He climbed too near to the Sun and the wax that held his feathers melted. But birds flying at high altitude have to cope with quite different and much more real problems – thin air, scarce oxygen, and intense cold.

ALULA
This group of feathers, also called the bastard wing, is held open in slow flight to prevent stalling.

MECHANICAL MIMICRY
A brilliant artist, inventor, and anatomist, Leonardo da Vinci drew on his knowledge of bird wings to design machines that would imitate their flight. He replaced bones with wood, tendons with ropes, and feathers with sailcloth. As far as is known, none of these devices ever got beyond his drawing board. They would have been far too heavy to fly.

FLAPPING FAILURES
The heroic birdmen of bygone days did not realize that flapping flight would always be beyond the power of human muscles. True human-powered flight has only been achieved through the later invention of the propeller, and using leg muscles, not arms.

PRIMARY FLIGHT FEATHERS
The primaries make the power for flight as the bird brings its wings downward. The outermost primaries can be used for steering, like the flaps on a plane's wing.

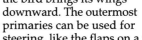

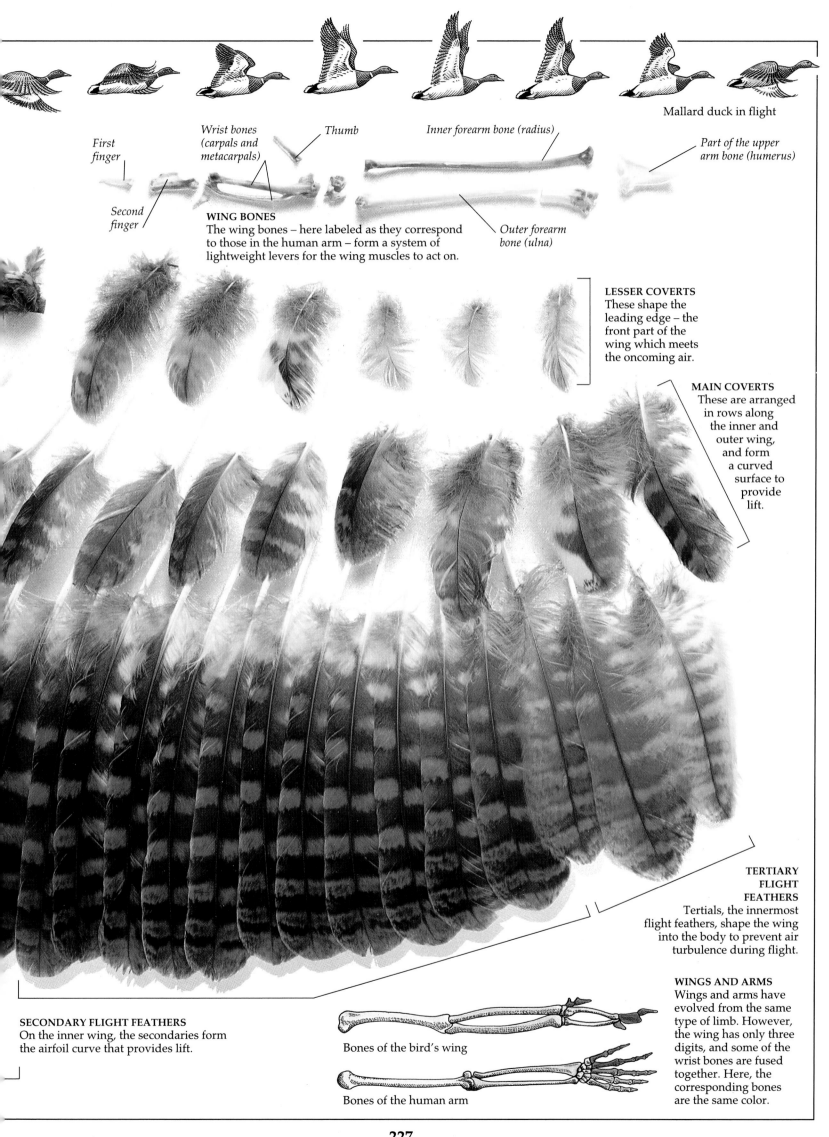

Mallard duck in flight

First finger

Second finger

Wrist bones (carpals and metacarpals)

Thumb

Inner forearm bone (radius)

Part of the upper arm bone (humerus)

WING BONES
The wing bones – here labeled as they correspond to those in the human arm – form a system of lightweight levers for the wing muscles to act on.

Outer forearm bone (ulna)

LESSER COVERTS
These shape the leading edge – the front part of the wing which meets the oncoming air.

MAIN COVERTS
These are arranged in rows along the inner and outer wing, and form a curved surface to provide lift.

TERTIARY FLIGHT FEATHERS
Tertials, the innermost flight feathers, shape the wing into the body to prevent air turbulence during flight.

WINGS AND ARMS
Wings and arms have evolved from the same type of limb. However, the wing has only three digits, and some of the wrist bones are fused together. Here, the corresponding bones are the same color.

SECONDARY FLIGHT FEATHERS
On the inner wing, the secondaries form the airfoil curve that provides lift.

Bones of the bird's wing

Bones of the human arm

The feather phenomenon

FEATHERS ARE THE UNIQUE evolutionary innovation that separates birds from all other animals. The plumage of a hummingbird may number less than 1,000 feathers, while a large bird like a swan may have over 25,000, with nearly four-fifths of these covering the head and neck alone. Like hair, claws, and horns, feathers are made from a protein called keratin, which gives feathers their great strength and flexibility. But for all their intricate structure, fully grown feathers are quite dead. As each feather develops, it divides to form a complex mesh of interlocking filaments. Once this has happened, its blood supply is cut off. The feathers then serve their time, unless lost by accident, and are shed during molting when they are worn out.

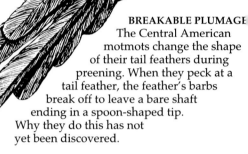

BREAKABLE PLUMAGE
The Central American motmots change the shape of their tail feathers during preening. When they peck at a tail feather, the feather's barbs break off to leave a bare shaft ending in a spoon-shaped tip. Why they do this has not yet been discovered.

Feather sheaths

Emerging feather tufts

Growing feathers within sheaths

Fully grown feathers after the protective sheaths have fallen away

HOW FEATHERS GROW
Feathers start their growth as fleshy lumps inside tubes known as feather sheaths. The tip of a feather gradually begins to emerge from the growing sheath, unrolling and splitting apart to form a flat blade. Eventually the feather sheath falls away, leaving the fully formed feather.

FEATHER SHAFT
The hollow shaft contains the dried remains of the fleshy pulp.

Hollow interior

Pulp from interior of shaft

Quill tip embedded in skin and attached to muscles

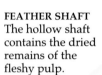

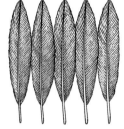

WEARING FEATHERS
Feathers have long been used by people for adornment and for more practical purposes. Headdresses and quill pens both made use of flight feathers. The down feathers of ducks and geese are still collected for bedding, while the brilliantly colored plumes of some tropical birds find their way into objects such as fishing flies.

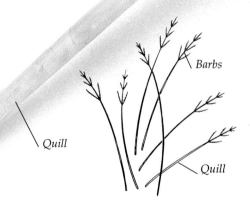

Quill

FILOPLUMES
These hairlike growths are found between the feathers on a bird's body. They help the bird to detect how its feathers are lying.

Barbs

Quill

Aftershaft, second shaft from a single quill

SPLIT FEATHERS
Some feathers are split to form two different halves attached to the same shaft. This enables a single feather to perform two different functions.

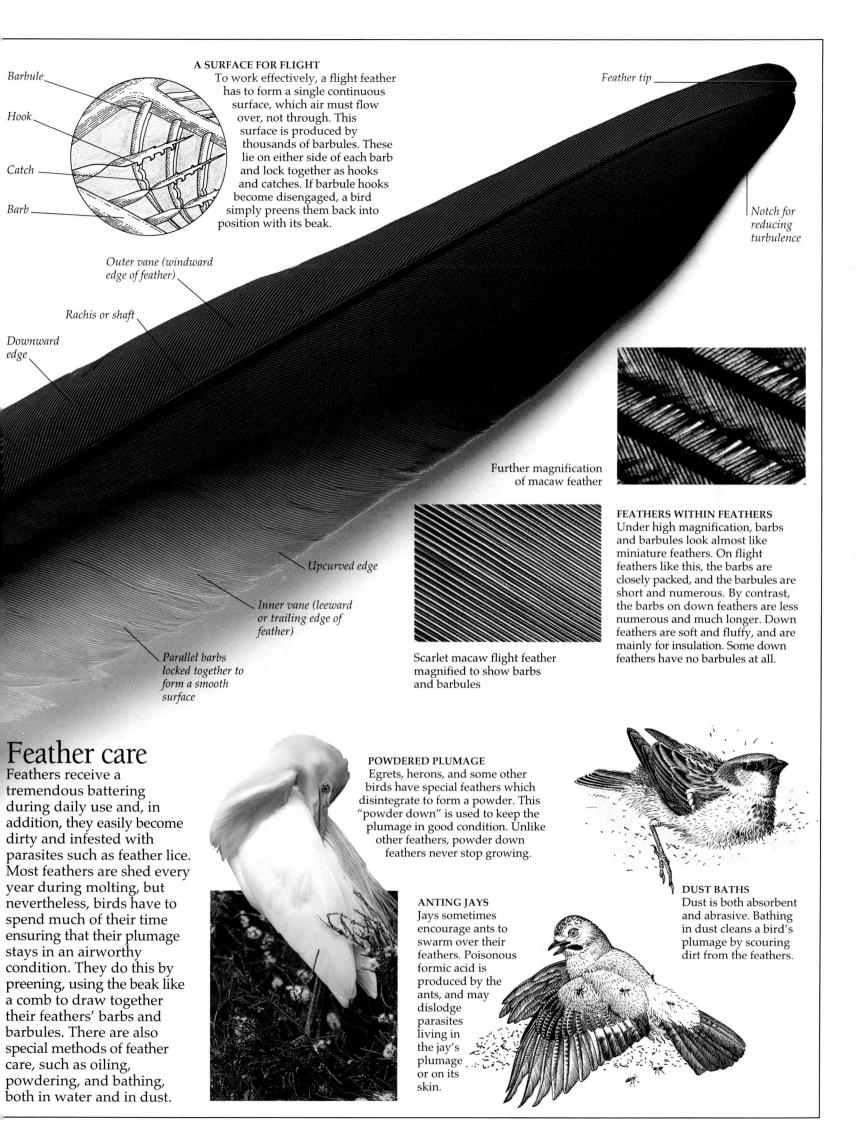

A SURFACE FOR FLIGHT
To work effectively, a flight feather has to form a single continuous surface, which air must flow over, not through. This surface is produced by thousands of barbules. These lie on either side of each barb and lock together as hooks and catches. If barbule hooks become disengaged, a bird simply preens them back into position with its beak.

Barbule

Hook

Catch

Barb

Outer vane (windward edge of feather)

Rachis or shaft

Downward edge

Feather tip

Notch for reducing turbulence

Further magnification of macaw feather

FEATHERS WITHIN FEATHERS
Under high magnification, barbs and barbules look almost like miniature feathers. On flight feathers like this, the barbs are closely packed, and the barbules are short and numerous. By contrast, the barbs on down feathers are less numerous and much longer. Down feathers are soft and fluffy, and are mainly for insulation. Some down feathers have no barbules at all.

Upcurved edge

Inner vane (leeward or trailing edge of feather)

Parallel barbs locked together to form a smooth surface

Scarlet macaw flight feather magnified to show barbs and barbules

Feather care
Feathers receive a tremendous battering during daily use and, in addition, they easily become dirty and infested with parasites such as feather lice. Most feathers are shed every year during molting, but nevertheless, birds have to spend much of their time ensuring that their plumage stays in an airworthy condition. They do this by preening, using the beak like a comb to draw together their feathers' barbs and barbules. There are also special methods of feather care, such as oiling, powdering, and bathing, both in water and in dust.

POWDERED PLUMAGE
Egrets, herons, and some other birds have special feathers which disintegrate to form a powder. This "powder down" is used to keep the plumage in good condition. Unlike other feathers, powder down feathers never stop growing.

ANTING JAYS
Jays sometimes encourage ants to swarm over their feathers. Poisonous formic acid is produced by the ants, and may dislodge parasites living in the jay's plumage or on its skin.

DUST BATHS
Dust is both absorbent and abrasive. Bathing in dust cleans a bird's plumage by scouring dirt from the feathers.

Mammal skeletons

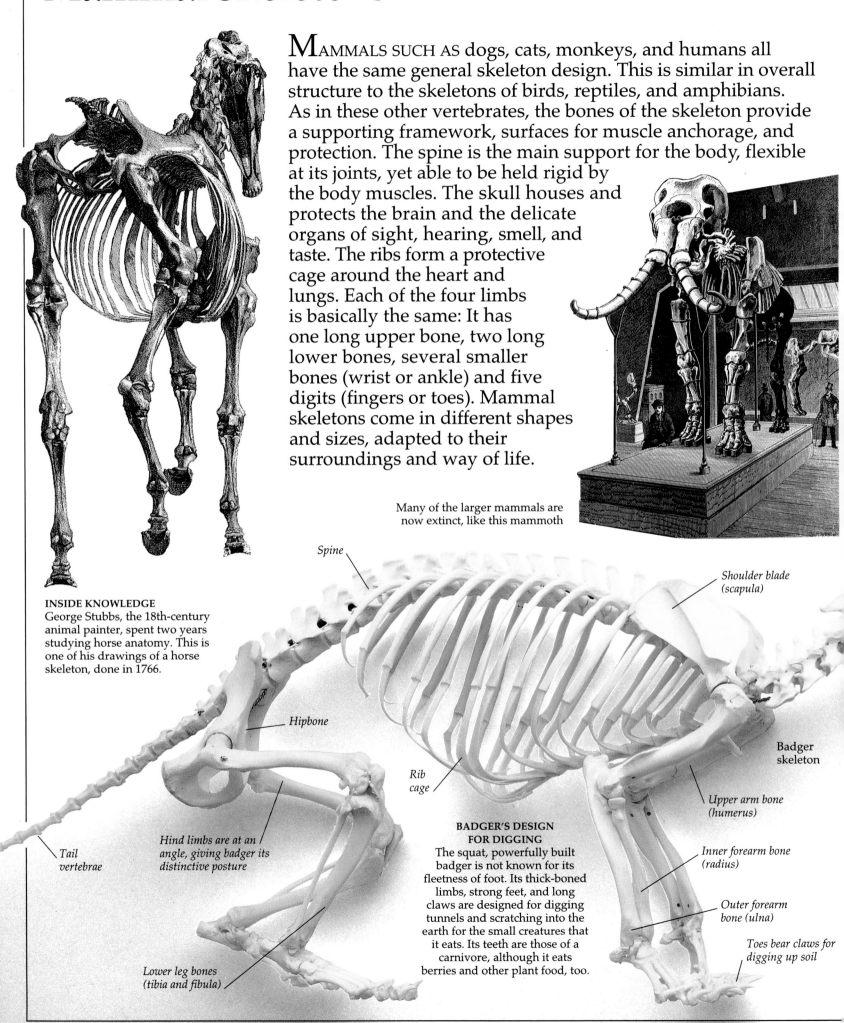

MAMMALS SUCH AS dogs, cats, monkeys, and humans all have the same general skeleton design. This is similar in overall structure to the skeletons of birds, reptiles, and amphibians. As in these other vertebrates, the bones of the skeleton provide a supporting framework, surfaces for muscle anchorage, and protection. The spine is the main support for the body, flexible at its joints, yet able to be held rigid by the body muscles. The skull houses and protects the brain and the delicate organs of sight, hearing, smell, and taste. The ribs form a protective cage around the heart and lungs. Each of the four limbs is basically the same: It has one long upper bone, two long lower bones, several smaller bones (wrist or ankle) and five digits (fingers or toes). Mammal skeletons come in different shapes and sizes, adapted to their surroundings and way of life.

Many of the larger mammals are now extinct, like this mammoth

INSIDE KNOWLEDGE
George Stubbs, the 18th-century animal painter, spent two years studying horse anatomy. This is one of his drawings of a horse skeleton, done in 1766.

Spine

Shoulder blade (scapula)

Hipbone

Badger skeleton

Rib cage

Tail vertebrae

Hind limbs are at an angle, giving badger its distinctive posture

Upper arm bone (humerus)

BADGER'S DESIGN FOR DIGGING
The squat, powerfully built badger is not known for its fleetness of foot. Its thick-boned limbs, strong feet, and long claws are designed for digging tunnels and scratching into the earth for the small creatures that it eats. Its teeth are those of a carnivore, although it eats berries and other plant food, too.

Inner forearm bone (radius)

Outer forearm bone (ulna)

Toes bear claws for digging up soil

Lower leg bones (tibia and fibula)

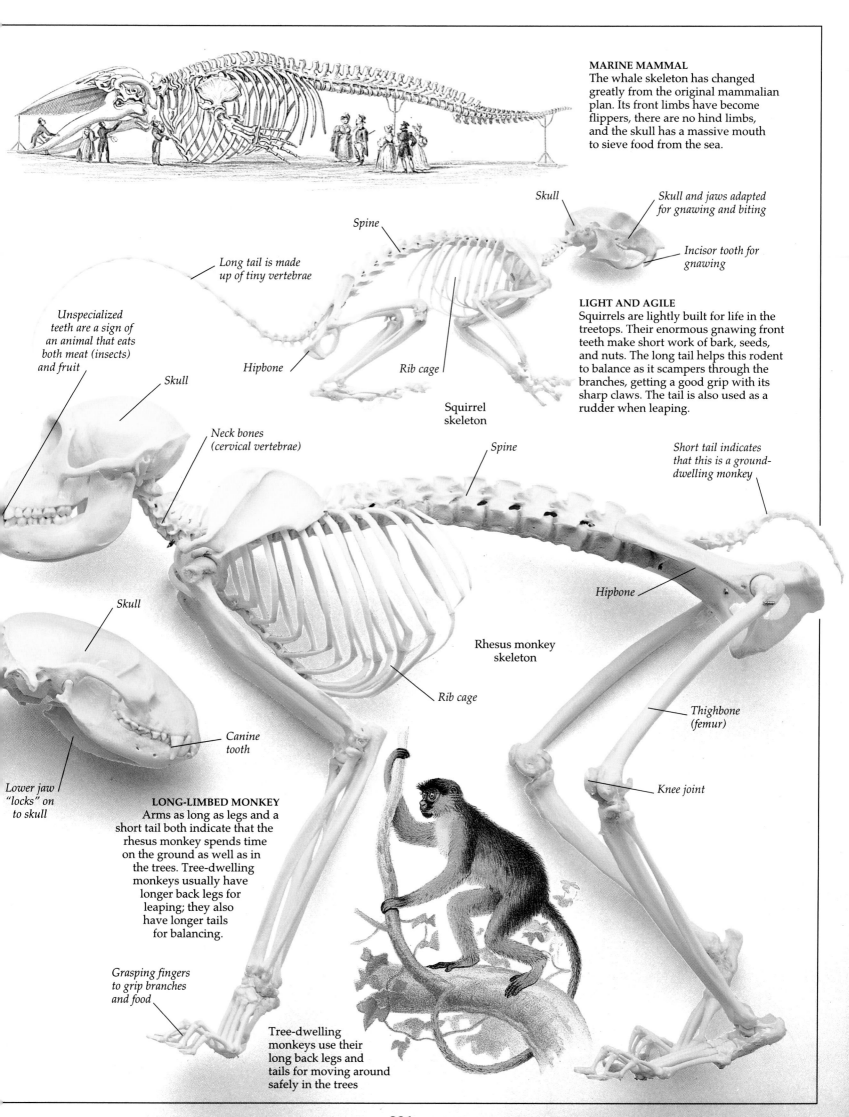

MARINE MAMMAL
The whale skeleton has changed greatly from the original mammalian plan. Its front limbs have become flippers, there are no hind limbs, and the skull has a massive mouth to sieve food from the sea.

Skull

Skull and jaws adapted for gnawing and biting

Incisor tooth for gnawing

Spine

LIGHT AND AGILE
Squirrels are lightly built for life in the treetops. Their enormous gnawing front teeth make short work of bark, seeds, and nuts. The long tail helps this rodent to balance as it scampers through the branches, getting a good grip with its sharp claws. The tail is also used as a rudder when leaping.

Long tail is made up of tiny vertebrae

Unspecialized teeth are a sign of an animal that eats both meat (insects) and fruit

Skull

Hipbone

Rib cage

Squirrel skeleton

Neck bones (cervical vertebrae)

Spine

Short tail indicates that this is a ground-dwelling monkey

Hipbone

Rhesus monkey skeleton

Skull

Rib cage

Thighbone (femur)

Canine tooth

Knee joint

Lower jaw "locks" on to skull

LONG-LIMBED MONKEY
Arms as long as legs and a short tail both indicate that the rhesus monkey spends time on the ground as well as in the trees. Tree-dwelling monkeys usually have longer back legs for leaping; they also have longer tails for balancing.

Grasping fingers to grip branches and food

Tree-dwelling monkeys use their long back legs and tails for moving around safely in the trees

Largest on land

THE ELEPHANT is the largest living land mammal. During its evolution, the skeleton has greatly altered from the usual mammal design for two main reasons. One is to cope with the great weight of huge grinding cheek teeth and elongated tusk teeth, making the skull particularly massive. The other is to support the enormous bulk of such a huge body. The elephant has all the usual internal parts of any mammal such as muscles, nerves, and internal organs including a heart, lungs, and intestines. But these have become proportionally gigantic – the heart alone is the weight of a 9-year-old child. When an elephant stands at rest, the bones in each leg stack one above the other to form a sturdy pillar. This is how an elephant can relax, and even fall asleep while standing up – and not fall over. There are slight differences between the two species of elephants, African and Asian, as shown here.

ASIAN ROUNDHEADS
An Asian elephant's skull rises to two domes, side by side, on the top of the head. In the male, shown here, the upper jaw juts out much farther than the short lower jaw because it contains the roots of the massive tusks.

Tusk sockets

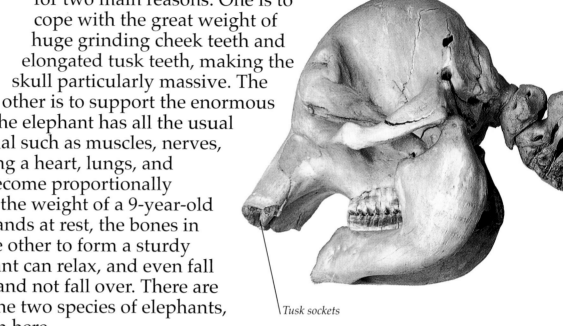

An Asian elephant has a concave forehead

ASIAN ELEPHANT SKELETON
An Asian elephant normally holds its neck up at an angle of about 45 degrees, so the top of the head is the highest point of the body. The muscles that hold it up are attached to the back of the skull and to the long spines sticking up from each vertebra. The presence of tusks in this young Asian elephant means that it must be a male, because female Asian elephants seldom grow tusks as long as this, even when fully mature.

Long spines

Hipbone (pelvis)

Skeleton of male baby Asian elephant

Elbow joint

Knee joint

Large, flat toe bones splay out to spread body weight

Convex, or hump-shaped, back

Head has two domes

HUMPBACKED ELEPHANTS
The body of the Asian elephant is shorter and more barrel-shaped than that of the African. By comparing this picture with the skeleton (left), you can see how the length of the spinous processes determines the shape of the back.

Asian elephant

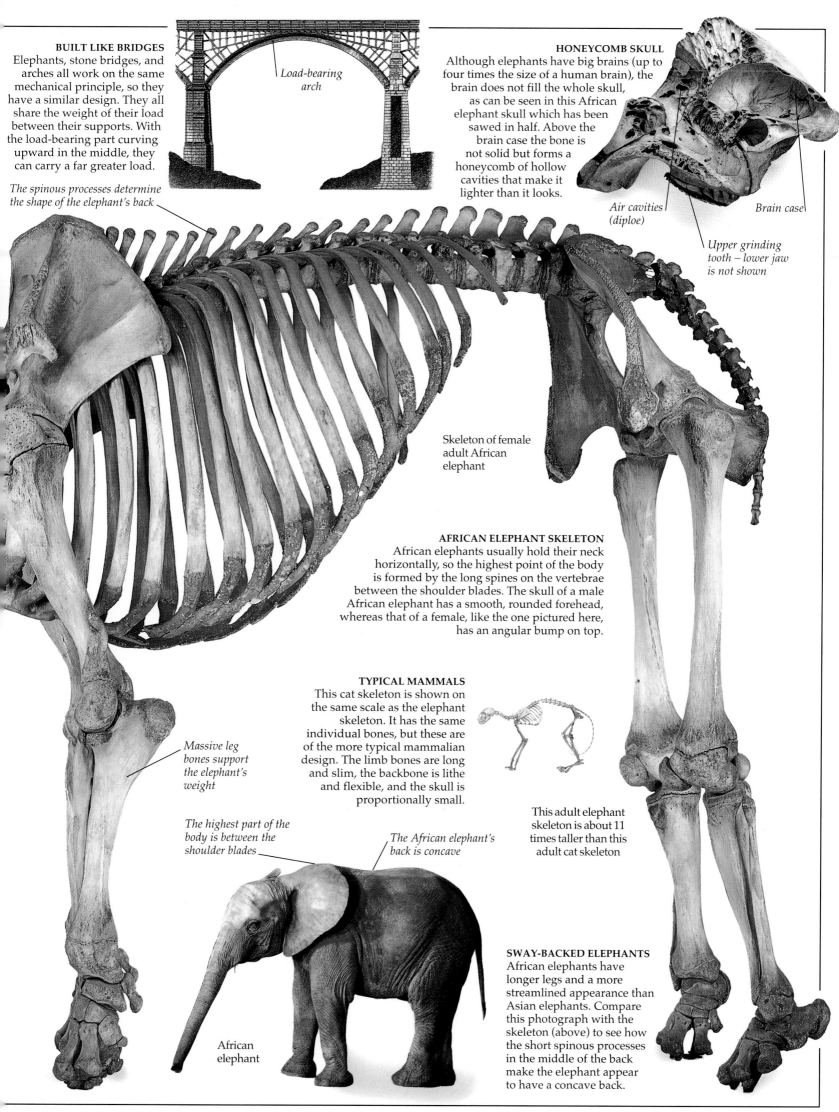

BUILT LIKE BRIDGES
Elephants, stone bridges, and arches all work on the same mechanical principle, so they have a similar design. They all share the weight of their load between their supports. With the load-bearing part curving upward in the middle, they can carry a far greater load.

Load-bearing arch

HONEYCOMB SKULL
Although elephants have big brains (up to four times the size of a human brain), the brain does not fill the whole skull, as can be seen in this African elephant skull which has been sawed in half. Above the brain case the bone is not solid but forms a honeycomb of hollow cavities that make it lighter than it looks.

Air cavities (diploe)

Brain case

Upper grinding tooth – lower jaw is not shown

The spinous processes determine the shape of the elephant's back

Skeleton of female adult African elephant

AFRICAN ELEPHANT SKELETON
African elephants usually hold their neck horizontally, so the highest point of the body is formed by the long spines on the vertebrae between the shoulder blades. The skull of a male African elephant has a smooth, rounded forehead, whereas that of a female, like the one pictured here, has an angular bump on top.

TYPICAL MAMMALS
This cat skeleton is shown on the same scale as the elephant skeleton. It has the same individual bones, but these are of the more typical mammalian design. The limb bones are long and slim, the backbone is lithe and flexible, and the skull is proportionally small.

Massive leg bones support the elephant's weight

The highest part of the body is between the shoulder blades

The African elephant's back is concave

This adult elephant skeleton is about 11 times taller than this adult cat skeleton

African elephant

SWAY-BACKED ELEPHANTS
African elephants have longer legs and a more streamlined appearance than Asian elephants. Compare this photograph with the skeleton (above) to see how the short spinous processes in the middle of the back make the elephant appear to have a concave back.

Coats and claws

THE NATURAL WORLD is full of hairy creatures, from "woolly bear" caterpillars to tarantula spiders. But mammals are the only animals with true fur. Fur is made from the substance keratin, which is the same material that makes up the outer layer of mammalian skin, as well as your fingernails and toenails. Fur is very versatile. It can be thick or thin, long or short, according to the mammal's habitat and needs. It keeps its owner warm and protected, and its patterning acts as camouflage, or as a breeding or warning signal.

CURLY AND STRAIGHT
This domestic cat has been bred for its unusual curly fur. The fur of most mammals is much straighter, so that water runs off more easily, and the fur is less likely to trap dirt and pests. But the "fur" on humans – the hair on our heads – can be straight, wavy, or curly.

Close-up fur

Close up, mammals reveal the delicate shading and patterning on their fur. This young lioness still has the spotty coloration from her time as a young cub, although the spots are gradually fading.

SPOT ME
The colors and patterns of some mammals, such as this leopard, have evolved to give camouflage in the animal's natural habitat. They may stand out in a zoo in broad daylight, but in the light conditions at dusk, when the leopard is normally active, its spotted coat merges in with the wooded grasslands.

FUR COATS
All the colors and patterns in mammal fur are produced by melanin – a pigment, or coloring substance. It exists as tiny dark brown particles inside the microscopic cells that make up skin and hair. The coloring effect comes from the amount of melanin in each hair, and its precise position in the hair shaft. Here are the coats of six cats, showing their intricate and characteristic markings.

Tiger

Leopard

Panther

Jaguar

Ocelot

Serval

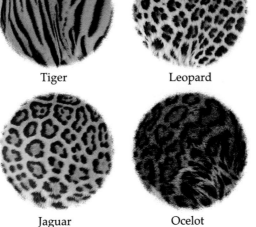

Cat claws

A cat can unsheath its claws by a muscle in each leg and foot. As the muscle contracts, it pulls the claw down and forward. Normally the muscle is relaxed, and the claw retracted.

Relaxed, with claw withdrawn into toe

Muscle and ligament tightened to expose claw

PAINFUL PETS
Many mammals rub and sharpen their claws, as a natural habit to keep them smooth and in working order. With pets, this can lead to painful problems!

ADJUSTABLE DUVET
A tiny muscle at the base of each hair, embedded in the skin, can tighten to make the hair stand up straight, or relax to let it lie flat. Fluffed up fur traps more air between the hairs, to improve heat-retaining abilities. It may also stand on end so the owner looks bigger and fiercer when confronting danger. These cats are warm and comfortable, so their fur lies fairly flat.

HOOVES
Keratin is light, strong, and durable, and also makes the hooves of the hoofed mammals, or ungulates. The horse has only one large toe in each foot and stands on the toe tip. In human terms, the horse runs on the nail of its middle fingers and toes.

CLAWS
Keratin makes up the claws of various mammals. Cat claws can be withdrawn into the flesh and muscles of the toes to keep them sharp (see top). The claws of this lioness are almost hidden in the fleshy folds and fur of her toes. The leathery pads on her soles are yet another form of the ever-useful keratin. They give good grip and are very hard-wearing, and also allow silent stalking.

HIDDEN CURVES
Fluffy fur gives a false impression of the real shape and curves of a mammal's body. With its fur and skin gone, and the outer layer of muscles exposed, this cat looks strangely thin, long-necked, and small-headed.

BIG HUNTER
The great white shark is a
top carnivore (meat eater). It
does little except feed and breed.
With an ultra-sharp sense of smell, a
mouth full of triangular-bladed teeth,
and a powerful swishing tail, the shark
is a complete hunting machine.

CHAPTER 2

HUNTING & FEEDING

Food is the fuel and raw material for life. Every animal must eat to live, and there are almost as many different foods, and ways of obtaining them, as there are different kinds of hungry animal.

SMALL HUNTERS
Piranhas play the role of freshwater minisharks. They have razor-sharp teeth and gather around a wounded animal to tear flesh from the body. What piranhas lack in size, they make up for in numbers. The ecological balance of nature allows smaller predators to be more numerous, since the same amount of food can fuel one large body or several smaller ones.

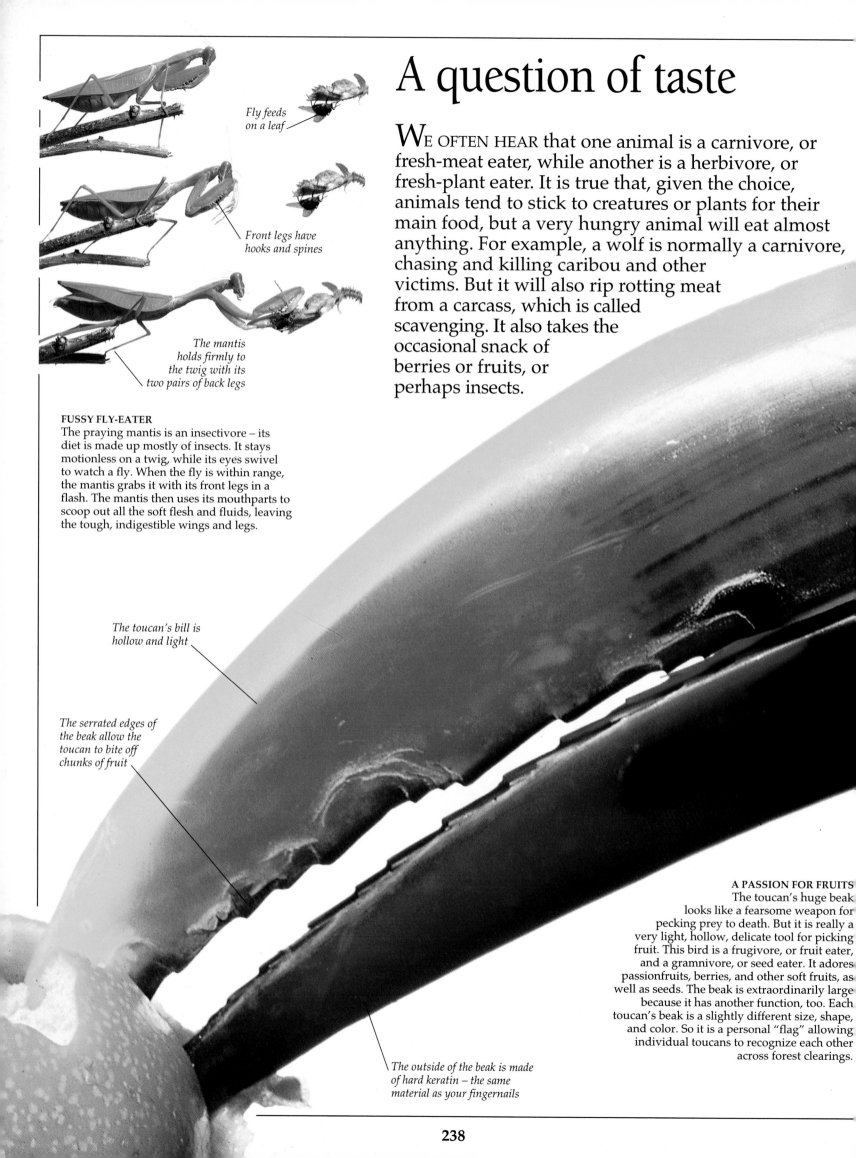

A question of taste

WE OFTEN HEAR that one animal is a carnivore, or fresh-meat eater, while another is a herbivore, or fresh-plant eater. It is true that, given the choice, animals tend to stick to creatures or plants for their main food, but a very hungry animal will eat almost anything. For example, a wolf is normally a carnivore, chasing and killing caribou and other victims. But it will also rip rotting meat from a carcass, which is called scavenging. It also takes the occasional snack of berries or fruits, or perhaps insects.

Fly feeds on a leaf

Front legs have hooks and spines

The mantis holds firmly to the twig with its two pairs of back legs

FUSSY FLY-EATER
The praying mantis is an insectivore – its diet is made up mostly of insects. It stays motionless on a twig, while its eyes swivel to watch a fly. When the fly is within range, the mantis grabs it with its front legs in a flash. The mantis then uses its mouthparts to scoop out all the soft flesh and fluids, leaving the tough, indigestible wings and legs.

The toucan's bill is hollow and light

The serrated edges of the beak allow the toucan to bite off chunks of fruit

A PASSION FOR FRUITS
The toucan's huge beak looks like a fearsome weapon for pecking prey to death. But it is really a very light, hollow, delicate tool for picking fruit. This bird is a frugivore, or fruit eater, and a gramnivore, or seed eater. It adores passionfruits, berries, and other soft fruits, as well as seeds. The beak is extraordinarily large because it has another function, too. Each toucan's beak is a slightly different size, shape, and color. So it is a personal "flag" allowing individual toucans to recognize each other across forest clearings.

The outside of the beak is made of hard keratin – the same material as your fingernails

Toucans have sharp eyesight for seeing food, friends, and enemies in the tropical woodlands where they live

A FONDNESS FOR FISH
The caiman is a close relative of crocodiles and alligators, and comes from South America. It is a true carnivore – it eats fresh meat. The meat may be frogs or small fish, or mammals such as the pig-sized peccary.

Strong sharp teeth for tearing meat

Hunters' weapons

DURING MILLIONS of years of evolution, almost every part of the body of various hunting animals has become adapted to the pursuit and capture of prey. In many creatures, from cats and dogs to crocodiles and dinosaurs, the teeth and perhaps claws are the primary weapons. All spiders and centipedes, and some snakes, have combined physical and chemical weapons – poison-injecting fangs. In carnivorous insects such as mantises, the front legs help grasp and subdue victims. Some bats catch their airborne prey in a "scoop" formed by the legs and tail membrane. Even apparently slow, simple, ill-equipped animals can be successful predators. The starfish has muscular arms to prize open its prey of mussels and other shellfish.

CLOSE-QUARTER WEAPONS
These curved claws, as big as your hand, are over 100 million years old. They are fossilized dinosaur remains. The left one is a foot claw from *Albertosaurus*, a fearsome meat-eater resembling *Tyrannosaurus*. The right one is a hand claw from *Chirostenotes*, a small predatory dinosaur.

DETECTION
Most bats use a sound radar system called echolocation. They emit high-pitched sounds and, from the pattern of returning echoes, work out the shape and position of nearby objects. This horseshoe bat has detected an oak beauty moth (right).

Between the scales, the snake's skin is gray-blue

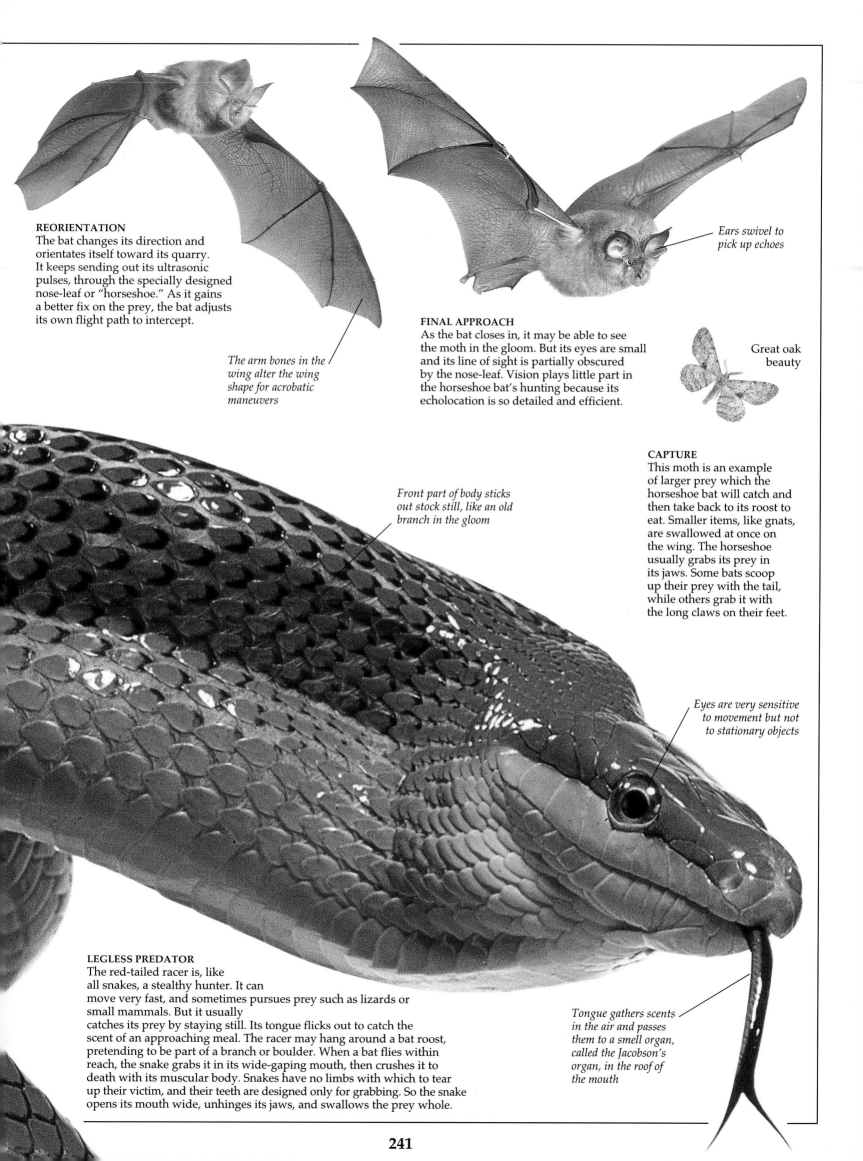

REORIENTATION
The bat changes its direction and orientates itself toward its quarry. It keeps sending out its ultrasonic pulses, through the specially designed nose-leaf or "horseshoe." As it gains a better fix on the prey, the bat adjusts its own flight path to intercept.

The arm bones in the wing alter the wing shape for acrobatic maneuvers

Ears swivel to pick up echoes

FINAL APPROACH
As the bat closes in, it may be able to see the moth in the gloom. But its eyes are small and its line of sight is partially obscured by the nose-leaf. Vision plays little part in the horseshoe bat's hunting because its echolocation is so detailed and efficient.

Great oak beauty

CAPTURE
This moth is an example of larger prey which the horseshoe bat will catch and then take back to its roost to eat. Smaller items, like gnats, are swallowed at once on the wing. The horseshoe usually grabs its prey in its jaws. Some bats scoop up their prey with the tail, while others grab it with the long claws on their feet.

Front part of body sticks out stock still, like an old branch in the gloom

Eyes are very sensitive to movement but not to stationary objects

LEGLESS PREDATOR
The red-tailed racer is, like all snakes, a stealthy hunter. It can move very fast, and sometimes pursues prey such as lizards or small mammals. But it usually catches its prey by staying still. Its tongue flicks out to catch the scent of an approaching meal. The racer may hang around a bat roost, pretending to be part of a branch or boulder. When a bat flies within reach, the snake grabs it in its wide-gaping mouth, then crushes it to death with its muscular body. Snakes have no limbs with which to tear up their victim, and their teeth are designed only for grabbing. So the snake opens its mouth wide, unhinges its jaws, and swallows the prey whole.

Tongue gathers scents in the air and passes them to a smell organ, called the Jacobson's organ, in the roof of the mouth

Tentacles and stings

Gray
snakelocks
anemone

KRAKEN AHOY
The Kraken, a sea monster of Norse legend, made short work of ships and their crews. As is often the case, the fable has some basis in fact. The Kraken bears more than a passing resemblance to the squid, a member of the mollusk group. Atlantic giant squid have been recorded at 50 ft (15 m) long, including tentacles. However, unlike jellyfish tentacles, those of the squid do not possess stings. The squid hunts by grabbing and grasping its prey.

THE CNIDARIAN, or coelenterate, animals include the jellyfish, sea anemones, and corals. There are about 9,400 species and the vast majority live in the sea. They are relatively simple creatures which lack a brain and sophisticated sense organs such as eyes and ears. But they are still deadly predators. Their method of attack, and defense, is the tiny stinging cells contained in their tentacles. Inside each cell is a capsule called a nematocyst, which contains a long, coiled thread. In some species these are barbed, in others they contain venom. Stimulated by touch or by certain chemicals, the threads flick out and then either the barbs hold onto the prey, or venom is injected into it. The animal then drags its victim into the digestive cavity, or stomach, within its body, to feast on the flesh. Some jellyfish have exceedingly powerful venom that can cause great pain if swimmers brush against them. Nematocysts remain active for a time even after the animal is washed up and dies on the shore.

Common prawn

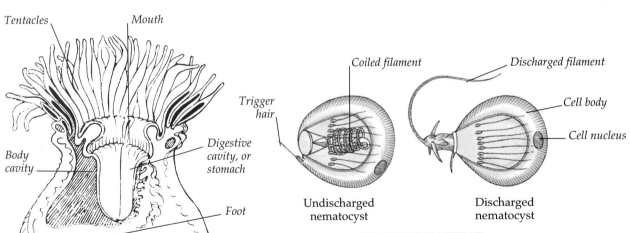

Tentacles

Mouth

Body cavity

Digestive cavity, or stomach

Foot

INSIDE AN ANEMONE
Anemones and their cnidarian relatives are simply constructed creatures. A ring of tentacles surrounds the mouth which leads to a digestive cavity inside the body. Prey is pushed into the cavity, digested and absorbed, and any remains excreted through the mouth.

Coiled filament

Trigger hair

Discharged filament

Cell body

Cell nucleus

Undischarged nematocyst

Discharged nematocyst

THE STINGING THREAD
Under the microscope it is possible to see tiny sting-containing cells (nematocysts) on the tentacles of cnidarians. When the cell is triggered by touch or certain chemicals, its internal fluid pressure quickly increases. This forces the threadlike filament to shoot out. Some filaments are barbed; some contain the stinging venom; and some are both barbed and venomous.

PRAWN SNACK
This snakelocks anemone is in the process of capturing a common prawn and pulling it toward its mouth. The barbed stinging cells in the tentacles help subdue the prey and paralyze it. When the prawn is drawn into the anemone's stomach, more stings will finish it off.

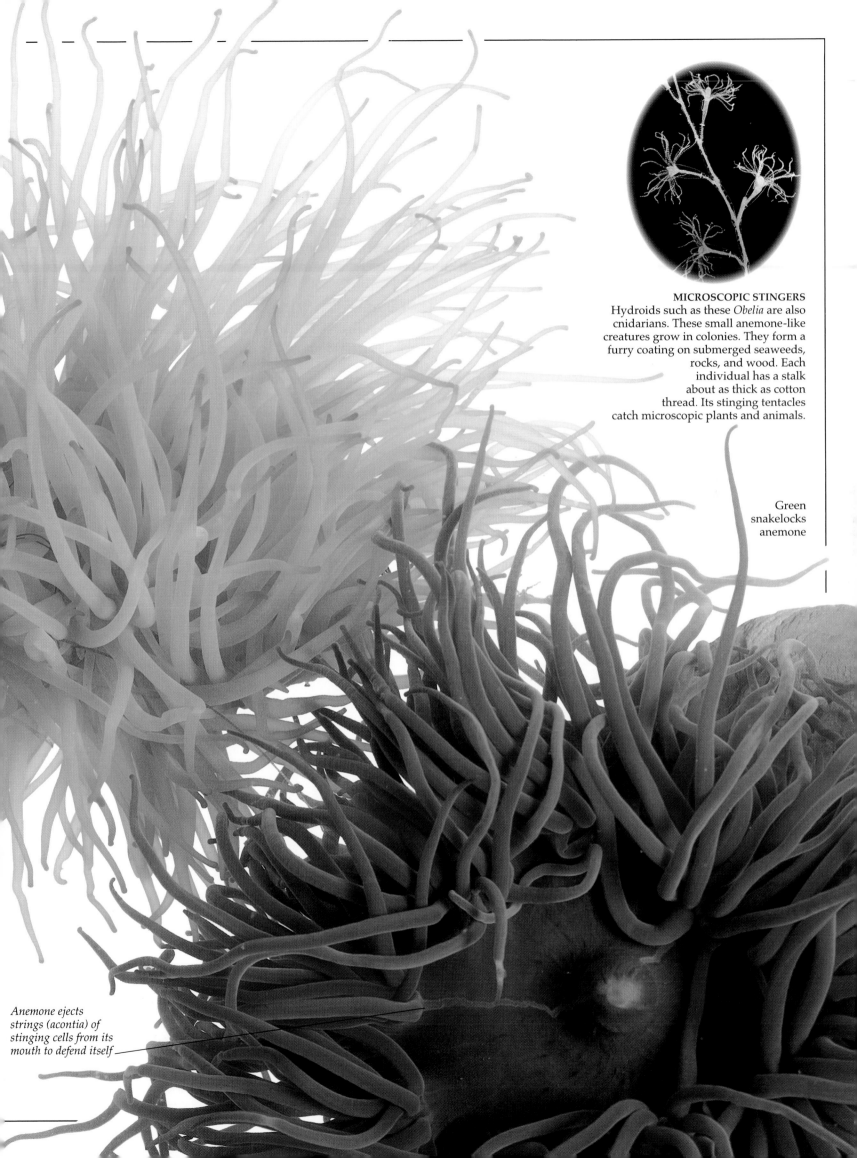

MICROSCOPIC STINGERS

Hydroids such as these *Obelia* are also cnidarians. These small anemone-like creatures grow in colonies. They form a furry coating on submerged seaweeds, rocks, and wood. Each individual has a stalk about as thick as cotton thread. Its stinging tentacles catch microscopic plants and animals.

Green
snakelocks
anemone

Anemone ejects strings (acontia) of stinging cells from its mouth to defend itself

A feeding machine

As BEFITS their number and variety, insects have an amazing range of hunting and feeding methods. A typical insect has three sets of mouthparts: the large biting and chewing mandibles or "jaws"; the smaller, manipulative maxillae; and the liplike labia. These are modified according to diet into piercing needles, long sucking tubes, absorbent sponges, and crushing pincers. The larval stages of many insects, such as caterpillars and grubs, spend virtually all their time eating – they are living "eating machines."

BUSH CRICKET
This bush cricket is feeding on part of a flower. It is holding the plant with its front legs while the large and powerful sawlike mandibles chew it up. Crickets also eat other insects – even their own young.

FLEA BITES
This old engraving is not accurate, but it shows that fleas have a strong sucking tube surrounded by two pairs of palps, or sensory organs.

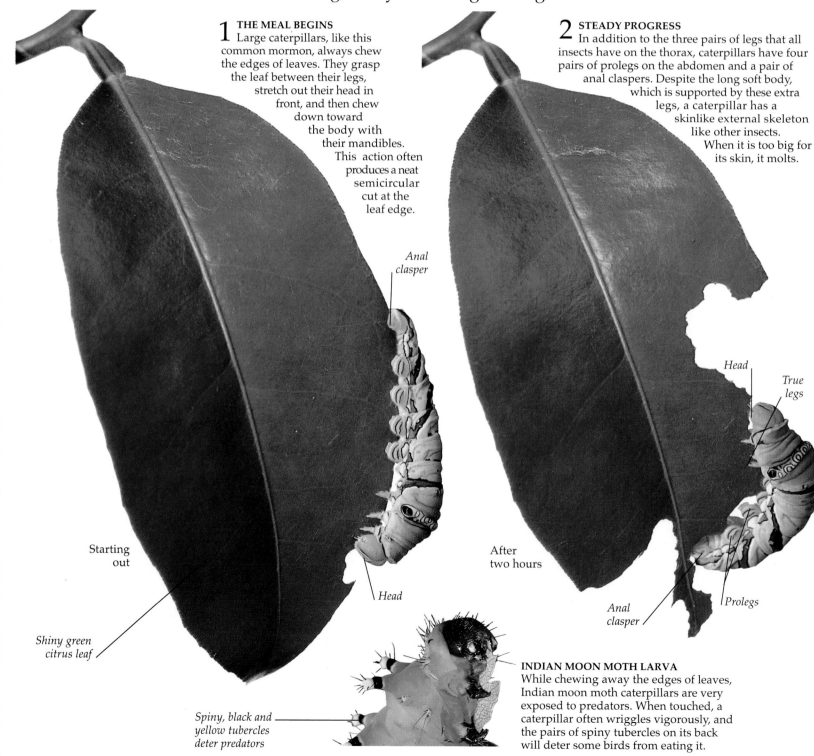

1 THE MEAL BEGINS
Large caterpillars, like this common mormon, always chew the edges of leaves. They grasp the leaf between their legs, stretch out their head in front, and then chew down toward the body with their mandibles. This action often produces a neat semicircular cut at the leaf edge.

Anal clasper

Starting out

Shiny green citrus leaf

Head

2 STEADY PROGRESS
In addition to the three pairs of legs that all insects have on the thorax, caterpillars have four pairs of prolegs on the abdomen and a pair of anal claspers. Despite the long soft body, which is supported by these extra legs, a caterpillar has a skinlike external skeleton like other insects. When it is too big for its skin, it molts.

Head

True legs

After two hours

Anal clasper

Prolegs

INDIAN MOON MOTH LARVA
While chewing away the edges of leaves, Indian moon moth caterpillars are very exposed to predators. When touched, a caterpillar often wriggles vigorously, and the pairs of spiny tubercles on its back will deter some birds from eating it.

Spiny, black and yellow tubercles deter predators

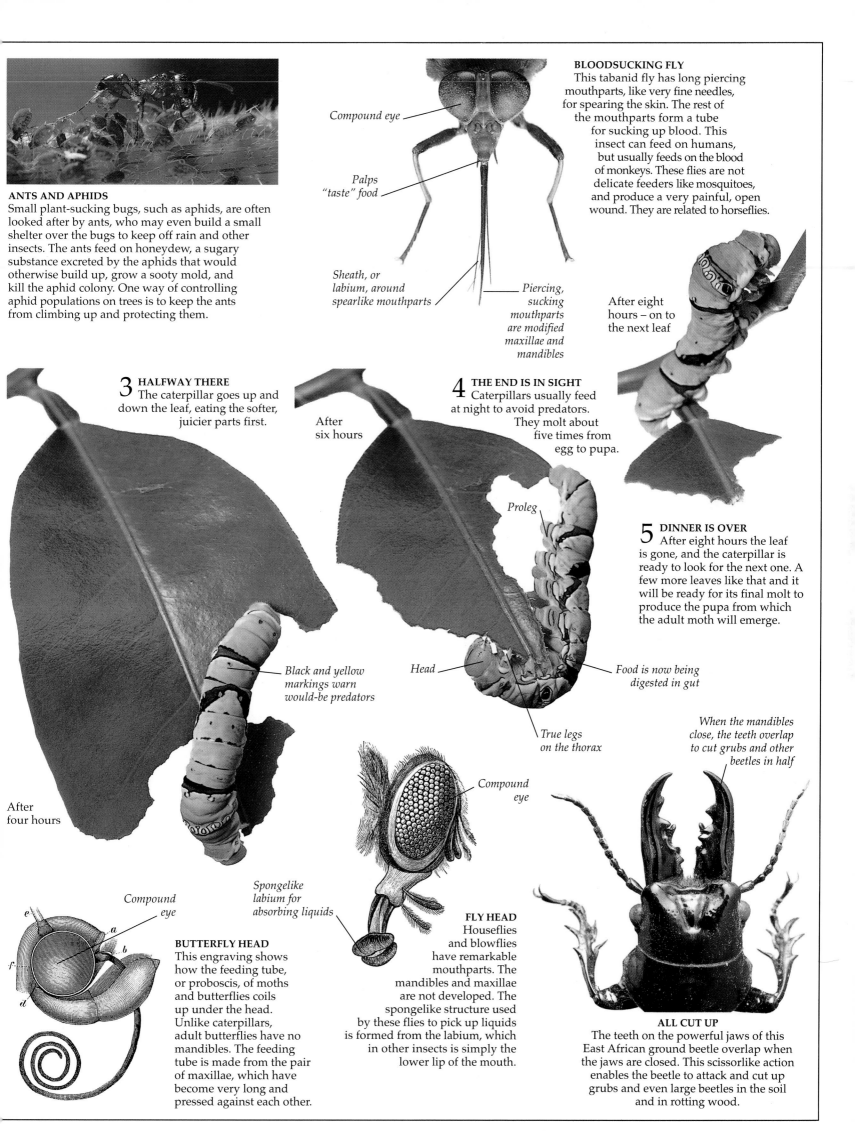

ANTS AND APHIDS
Small plant-sucking bugs, such as aphids, are often looked after by ants, who may even build a small shelter over the bugs to keep off rain and other insects. The ants feed on honeydew, a sugary substance excreted by the aphids that would otherwise build up, grow a sooty mold, and kill the aphid colony. One way of controlling aphid populations on trees is to keep the ants from climbing up and protecting them.

Compound eye

Palps "taste" food

Sheath, or labium, around spearlike mouthparts

Piercing, sucking mouthparts are modified maxillae and mandibles

BLOODSUCKING FLY
This tabanid fly has long piercing mouthparts, like very fine needles, for spearing the skin. The rest of the mouthparts form a tube for sucking up blood. This insect can feed on humans, but usually feeds on the blood of monkeys. These flies are not delicate feeders like mosquitoes, and produce a very painful, open wound. They are related to horseflies.

After eight hours – on to the next leaf

3 HALFWAY THERE
The caterpillar goes up and down the leaf, eating the softer, juicier parts first.

After six hours

4 THE END IS IN SIGHT
Caterpillars usually feed at night to avoid predators. They molt about five times from egg to pupa.

Proleg

5 DINNER IS OVER
After eight hours the leaf is gone, and the caterpillar is ready to look for the next one. A few more leaves like that and it will be ready for its final molt to produce the pupa from which the adult moth will emerge.

Black and yellow markings warn would-be predators

Head

Food is now being digested in gut

True legs on the thorax

When the mandibles close, the teeth overlap to cut grubs and other beetles in half

After four hours

Compound eye

Compound eye

Spongelike labium for absorbing liquids

BUTTERFLY HEAD
This engraving shows how the feeding tube, or proboscis, of moths and butterflies coils up under the head. Unlike caterpillars, adult butterflies have no mandibles. The feeding tube is made from the pair of maxillae, which have become very long and pressed against each other.

FLY HEAD
Houseflies and blowflies have remarkable mouthparts. The mandibles and maxillae are not developed. The spongelike structure used by these flies to pick up liquids is formed from the labium, which in other insects is simply the lower lip of the mouth.

ALL CUT UP
The teeth on the powerful jaws of this East African ground beetle overlap when the jaws are closed. This scissorlike action enables the beetle to attack and cut up grubs and even large beetles in the soil and in rotting wood.

Fishy food

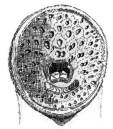

THE BLOODSUCKER
The jawless lamprey feeds by attaching itself to its prey with a sucker, then rasping away at the flesh with its teeth, and sucking the blood.

ALMOST 500 MILLION years ago, fish were the first animals with a backbone. The earliest fish were jawless, with sucking mouthparts. About 440 million years ago, the group evolved the first true jaws. Invertebrates such as insects have jawlike mouthparts (mandibles), but these usually work in a side-to-side fashion. True jaws are hinged and move up and down, worked by powerful muscles on the side of the head. Today, fish have adapted to an incredible array of foods and feeding methods. Large, crushing teeth indicate meals of shellfish, corals, or tough plant matter; sharp, pointed teeth indicate a hunting lifestyle; while a wide, gaping mouth shows a gulping method of feeding.

SKEWERED FISH
The popular notion of a swordfish with an unfortunate victim impaled on its sword is shown in this fanciful engraving. In reality, the sword may be used to jab or swipe sideways at prey.

Elephant-snout fish skull

Tiny jaws at end of "nose"

POKING ITS NOSE IN
The elephant-snout fish from Africa has a long, curved "nose" with tiny jaws at the end. It pokes these between stones, into cracks, and down into the mud, to find its food of small water creatures.

Pouting mouth for sucking in food

European bream skull

SURPRISING JAWS
Deep-bodied but extremely thin, the European John Dory creeps up on smaller fish and prawns. Its great jaws suddenly lever forward and engulf the prey.

John Dory skull

CHEWING THROAT
The common or European bream, a silvery-olive freshwater fish, has a "pouting" mouth which it uses to sift and churn through the mud, sucking up small bottom-dwelling worms, shellfish, and insect larvae. These are then ground up by pharyngeal, or throat, teeth.

Pharyngeal teeth of bream

Lever mechanism thrusts jaws forward

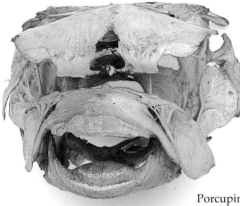

Porcupine fish skull

PRICKLES NO PROBLEM
The porcupine fish is well known for the ability to puff itself up and erect its spines when threatened. Lesser known is its diet, which consists of hard-shelled mussels and other shellfish, corals lurking in their stony homes, and even sea urchins hiding beneath their own spines. In each jaw, the teeth are fused to form a hard-edged biting ridge at the front, with a flat crushing plate behind.

The porcupine fish can crack hard-shelled mussels with its jaws

FRUIT AND NUT CASE
The pacu, from the Amazon of Brazil, eats fruits and nuts that fall into the river. Its strong, crushing teeth are at the front of its mouth.

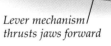

Prawn

Trumpetfish skull

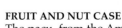

Strong, crushing teeth

Brazil nuts

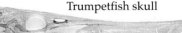

Seed of the piranha tree

TRUMPETFISH TWEEZERS
A long, rigid "beak" extends between the trumpetfish's small mouth and its eyes. The snout and the tiny teeth at the end are used like tweezers, to tease small aquatic animals out of their holes.

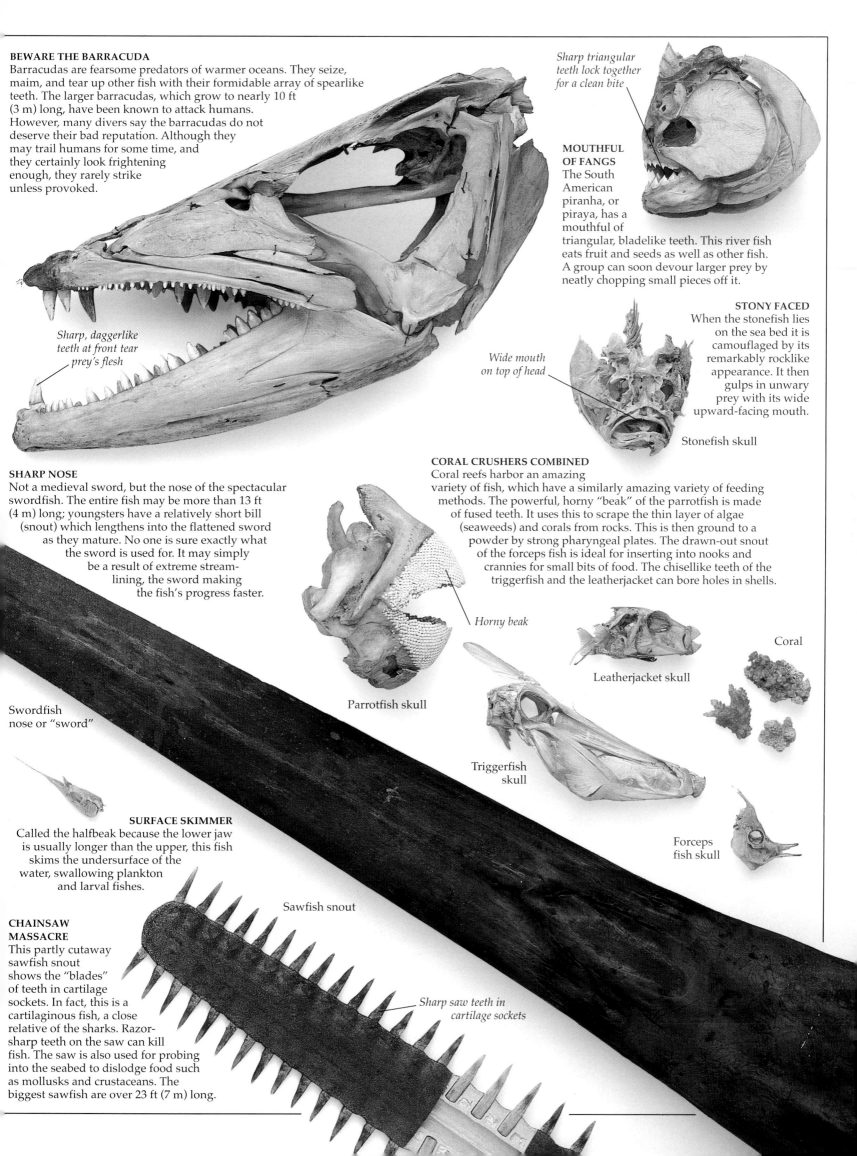

BEWARE THE BARRACUDA
Barracudas are fearsome predators of warmer oceans. They seize, maim, and tear up other fish with their formidable array of spearlike teeth. The larger barracudas, which grow to nearly 10 ft (3 m) long, have been known to attack humans. However, many divers say the barracudas do not deserve their bad reputation. Although they may trail humans for some time, and they certainly look frightening enough, they rarely strike unless provoked.

Sharp triangular teeth lock together for a clean bite

Sharp, daggerlike teeth at front tear prey's flesh

MOUTHFUL OF FANGS
The South American piranha, or piraya, has a mouthful of triangular, bladelike teeth. This river fish eats fruit and seeds as well as other fish. A group can soon devour larger prey by neatly chopping small pieces off it.

STONY FACED
When the stonefish lies on the sea bed it is camouflaged by its remarkably rocklike appearance. It then gulps in unwary prey with its wide upward-facing mouth.

Wide mouth on top of head

Stonefish skull

SHARP NOSE
Not a medieval sword, but the nose of the spectacular swordfish. The entire fish may be more than 13 ft (4 m) long; youngsters have a relatively short bill (snout) which lengthens into the flattened sword as they mature. No one is sure exactly what the sword is used for. It may simply be a result of extreme stream-lining, the sword making the fish's progress faster.

CORAL CRUSHERS COMBINED
Coral reefs harbor an amazing variety of fish, which have a similarly amazing variety of feeding methods. The powerful, horny "beak" of the parrotfish is made of fused teeth. It uses this to scrape the thin layer of algae (seaweeds) and corals from rocks. This is then ground to a powder by strong pharyngeal plates. The drawn-out snout of the forceps fish is ideal for inserting into nooks and crannies for small bits of food. The chisellike teeth of the triggerfish and the leatherjacket can bore holes in shells.

Horny beak

Coral

Leatherjacket skull

Swordfish nose or "sword"

Parrotfish skull

Triggerfish skull

Forceps fish skull

SURFACE SKIMMER
Called the halfbeak because the lower jaw is usually longer than the upper, this fish skims the undersurface of the water, swallowing plankton and larval fishes.

Sawfish snout

CHAINSAW MASSACRE
This partly cutaway sawfish snout shows the "blades" of teeth in cartilage sockets. In fact, this is a cartilaginous fish, a close relative of the sharks. Razor-sharp teeth on the saw can kill fish. The saw is also used for probing into the seabed to dislodge food such as mollusks and crustaceans. The biggest sawfish are over 23 ft (7 m) long.

Sharp saw teeth in cartilage sockets

Jaws of death

LIKE BONY FISH, the cartilaginous fish, such as sharks, continually lose their old teeth and grow new ones. In bony fish, new teeth develop below the old ones. But in sharks, when the front teeth wear out they are replaced by new ones growing in another row behind them. An individual shark can go through thousands of teeth in a lifetime. As the shark grows, its new teeth are larger than the ones they replace. Sharks' teeth come in many shapes according to the food they eat. Teeth shaped like small spikes are used for gripping small prey. Serrated teeth are used for cutting. Long, curved teeth can hold slippery fish. Blunt teeth crunch up shellfish. A few species of shark, such as basking and whale sharks, have tiny teeth compared to their great size. They do not use their teeth to feed, but instead filter food out of the water.

Tiny teeth of basking shark

Gill rakers

MOUTH WIDE OPEN
Basking sharks swim along with their mouths open to catch shrimps and other small creatures, called plankton, that drift in the sea. The food is trapped on rows of bristles called gill rakers as the water flows through the mouth and out through the gill slits. The gill rakers are shed each year during the winter months when there is little food to eat. A new set of rakers grows in the spring and then the basking sharks can start to feed again.

EPAULETTE EATING
Epaulette sharks live on coral reefs in the southwest Pacific Ocean around Australia and Papua New Guinea. They grow to about 3.3 ft (1 m) long and can crawl along the bottom using their pectoral fins. These sharks search among the shallows and tidepools for small fish, crabs, shrimps, and other small creatures to eat.

Epaulette eating

SMILE PLEASE
Swell sharks (top right) from the eastern Pacific Ocean have big mouths for their 3.3 ft (1 m) length. Armed with rows of tiny teeth, these sharks eat bony fish that they ambush at night while the fish rest on the sea bed. Only the rows of small front teeth of the Port Jackson (bottom right) are visible when its mouth is open. At the back of its jaws are strong, flat teeth for crushing shelled prey.

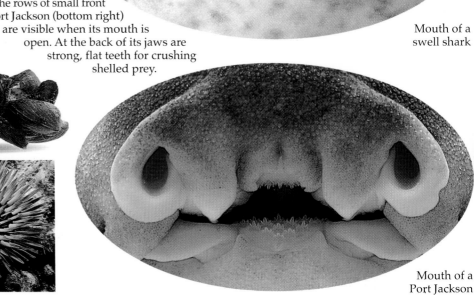

Mouth of a swell shark

CRUNCHY DIET
Port Jackson sharks have small, pointed front teeth to grasp their prey. The strong, flat back teeth can crunch through hard-shelled crabs, mussels (right), and sea urchins (below right).

Section through a Port Jackson's jaws

Mouth of a Port Jackson

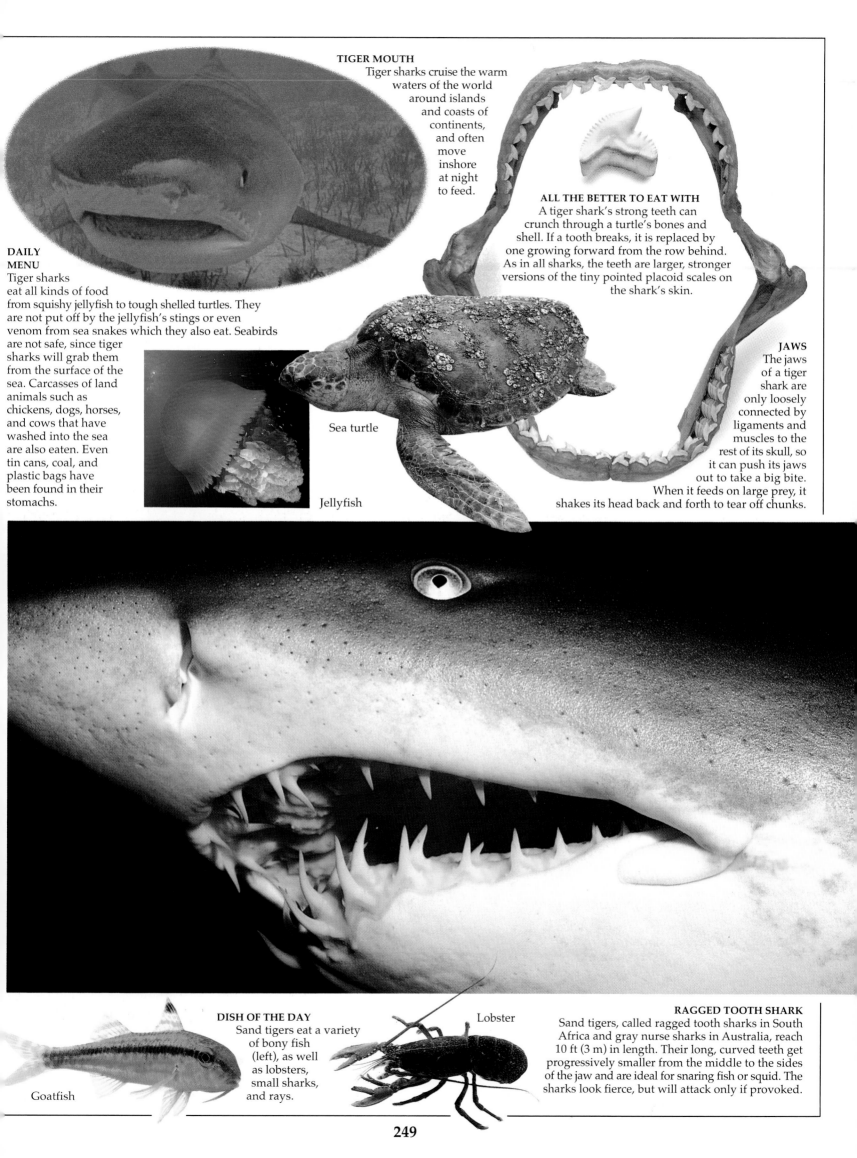

TIGER MOUTH
Tiger sharks cruise the warm waters of the world around islands and coasts of continents, and often move inshore at night to feed.

ALL THE BETTER TO EAT WITH
A tiger shark's strong teeth can crunch through a turtle's bones and shell. If a tooth breaks, it is replaced by one growing forward from the row behind. As in all sharks, the teeth are larger, stronger versions of the tiny pointed placoid scales on the shark's skin.

DAILY MENU
Tiger sharks eat all kinds of food from squishy jellyfish to tough shelled turtles. They are not put off by the jellyfish's stings or even venom from sea snakes which they also eat. Seabirds are not safe, since tiger sharks will grab them from the surface of the sea. Carcasses of land animals such as chickens, dogs, horses, and cows that have washed into the sea are also eaten. Even tin cans, coal, and plastic bags have been found in their stomachs.

Sea turtle

Jellyfish

JAWS
The jaws of a tiger shark are only loosely connected by ligaments and muscles to the rest of its skull, so it can push its jaws out to take a big bite. When it feeds on large prey, it shakes its head back and forth to tear off chunks.

DISH OF THE DAY
Sand tigers eat a variety of bony fish (left), as well as lobsters, small sharks, and rays.

Goatfish

Lobster

RAGGED TOOTH SHARK
Sand tigers, called ragged tooth sharks in South Africa and gray nurse sharks in Australia, reach 10 ft (3 m) in length. Their long, curved teeth get progressively smaller from the middle to the sides of the jaw and are ideal for snaring fish or squid. The sharks look fierce, but will attack only if provoked.

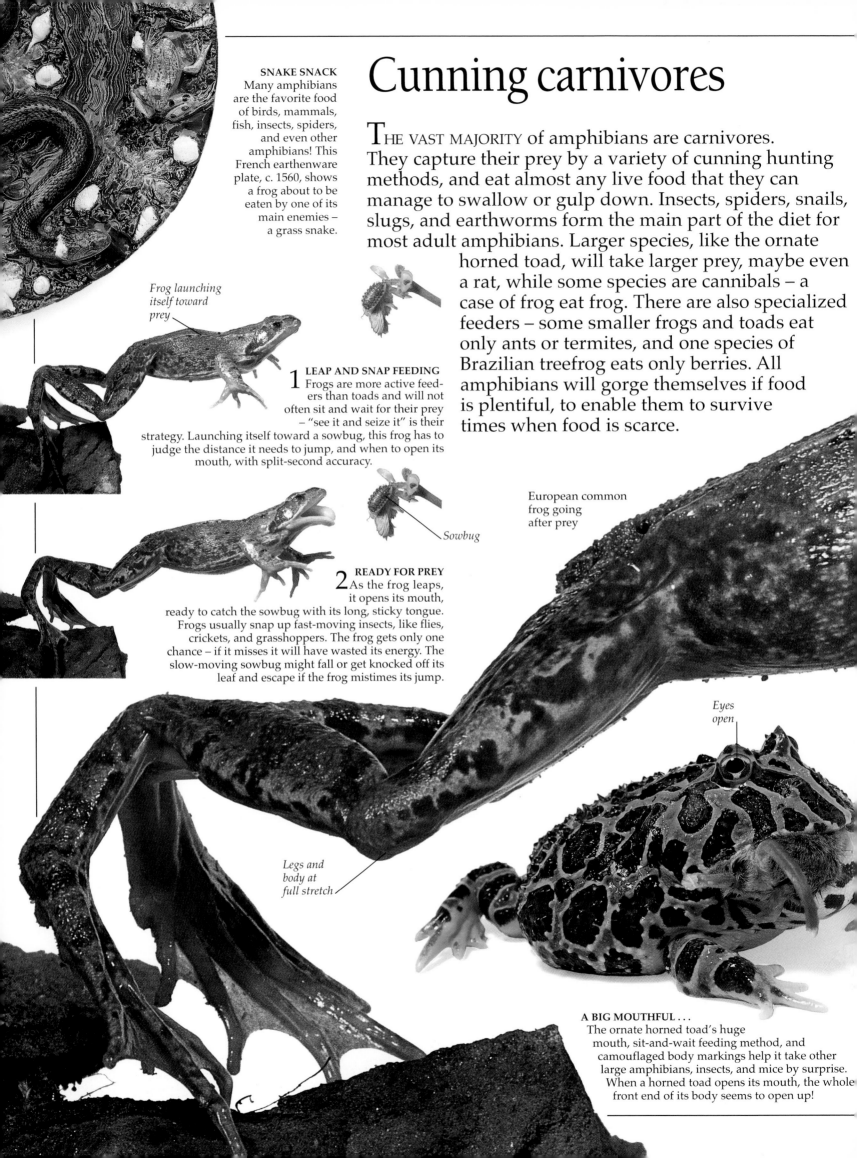

Cunning carnivores

THE VAST MAJORITY of amphibians are carnivores. They capture their prey by a variety of cunning hunting methods, and eat almost any live food that they can manage to swallow or gulp down. Insects, spiders, snails, slugs, and earthworms form the main part of the diet for most adult amphibians. Larger species, like the ornate horned toad, will take larger prey, maybe even a rat, while some species are cannibals – a case of frog eat frog. There are also specialized feeders – some smaller frogs and toads eat only ants or termites, and one species of Brazilian treefrog eats only berries. All amphibians will gorge themselves if food is plentiful, to enable them to survive times when food is scarce.

SNAKE SNACK
Many amphibians are the favorite food of birds, mammals, fish, insects, spiders, and even other amphibians! This French earthenware plate, c. 1560, shows a frog about to be eaten by one of its main enemies – a grass snake.

Frog launching itself toward prey

1 LEAP AND SNAP FEEDING
Frogs are more active feeders than toads and will not often sit and wait for their prey – "see it and seize it" is their strategy. Launching itself toward a sowbug, this frog has to judge the distance it needs to jump, and when to open its mouth, with split-second accuracy.

Sowbug

2 READY FOR PREY
As the frog leaps, it opens its mouth, ready to catch the sowbug with its long, sticky tongue. Frogs usually snap up fast-moving insects, like flies, crickets, and grasshoppers. The frog gets only one chance – if it misses it will have wasted its energy. The slow-moving sowbug might fall or get knocked off its leaf and escape if the frog mistimes its jump.

European common frog going after prey

Eyes open

Legs and body at full stretch

A BIG MOUTHFUL . . .
The ornate horned toad's huge mouth, sit-and-wait feeding method, and camouflaged body markings help it take other large amphibians, insects, and mice by surprise. When a horned toad opens its mouth, the whole front end of its body seems to open up!

SLOW, SLOW, QUICK . . .
Newts, salamanders, and caecilians tend to eat slow-moving, soft-bodied animals, like this earthworm. They approach their prey slowly, then make a quick, last-minute grab, often turning their head on one side. They grip the food using teeth in their upper and lower jaws.

Eyelid starting to close

Mandarin salamander eating an earthworm

Sowbug

Tongue flips out from front of mouth

Sticky tip of tongue

3 SUCCESSFUL STRIKE
With the precision of a guided missile homing in on its target, the frog's tongue flips out of the open mouth and strikes the sowbug.

Making a meal of a mealworm

Watching its prey

TONGUE FLIPS
The boy's party whistle flips open and forward because air is blown into it. The tongue of a frog or toad flips out and over, because muscles in the floor of the mouth push the tongue forward.

SEE IT, WATCH IT, EAT IT
Toads are careful, deliberate feeders. This common toad's attention has been attracted by a wriggling mealworm. It turns its head toward its prey, watching it intently. Some toads even stalk their prey using creeping, catlike movements. Suddenly, leaning over the mealworm, the toad gives a rapid tongue-flick, and the mealworm disappears.

Ready for action

Tongue flicks out

Eyes firmly shut as ornate horned toad swallows its prey

. . . TAKES SOME SWALLOWING
The blinking of the eye pushes the eyeball down, increases the pressure in the mouth, and helps the toad swallow its meal.

All but the tail has disappeared

. . . and mealworm disappears

Toad swallows, blinking its eyes

Reptilian repast

Most REPTILES EAT MEAT. Crocodiles and snakes are all carnivores, and have perfected methods of eating their food, but some snakes have specialized diets, including birds' eggs and fish eggs (eaten by some sea snakes). Many of the lizards are also predators, feeding on insects, mammals, birds, and other reptiles. The Komodo dragon has serrated teeth rather like a shark's, which it uses to cut flesh from prey as big as water buffalos. Among the lizards, large iguanas and some of the bigger skinks are mostly vegetarian. Tortoises eat a variety of plants, but even they occasionally eat meat. Freshwater turtles often eat worms, snails, fish, and other small animals. Sea turtles generally feed on jellyfish, crabs, mollusks, and fish, but they also eat plants.

SLOW BUT SURE
Very few tortoises or turtles have the speed or agility to catch fast-moving prey. As a result, most feed on vegetation, or on slow-moving animals, such as mollusks, worms, and insect larvae. They all make the most of food that is nearby and then move to the next feeding area. In addition to fleshy plants, the spur-thighed tortoise also enjoys the occasional morsel of any dead animal it finds.

HOOK MEETS HIS END
In J.M. Barrie's *Peter Pan*, Hook is haunted by the crocodile who has already eaten his hand – and is looking for more! Helped for a time by a clock that ticks in the creature's stomach, Hook is finally tricked and eaten.

CROCODILE LARDER
Nile crocodiles occasionally share the carcass of a large animal such as a wildebeest or a buffalo. Crocodiles cannot eat a big animal all at once because their stomachs are only the size of a basketball. Prey is often, therefore, hidden wedged under an old log or boulder to be finished off later. This has led to the mistaken belief that crocodiles like to eat meat that has rotted. In fact, they prefer fresh meat.

Armlets

Stones

Bracelets

Pieces of turtle shell

Porcupine quills

STOMACH STORE
Crocodiles often devour hard, heavy objects, such as stones and pieces of metal. One can only hope that no one was wearing the bracelet when it was swallowed! The objects may be eaten to weigh down the crocodile, so it floats low in the water, or perhaps to help the crocodile digest its food.

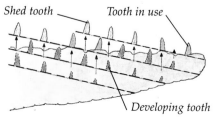

Shed tooth   Tooth in use

Developing tooth

DEVELOPING TEETH
Crocodiles and other reptiles shed their teeth throughout their lives, with new ones constantly replacing the old ones. The developing teeth grow up through the holes of those already in use.

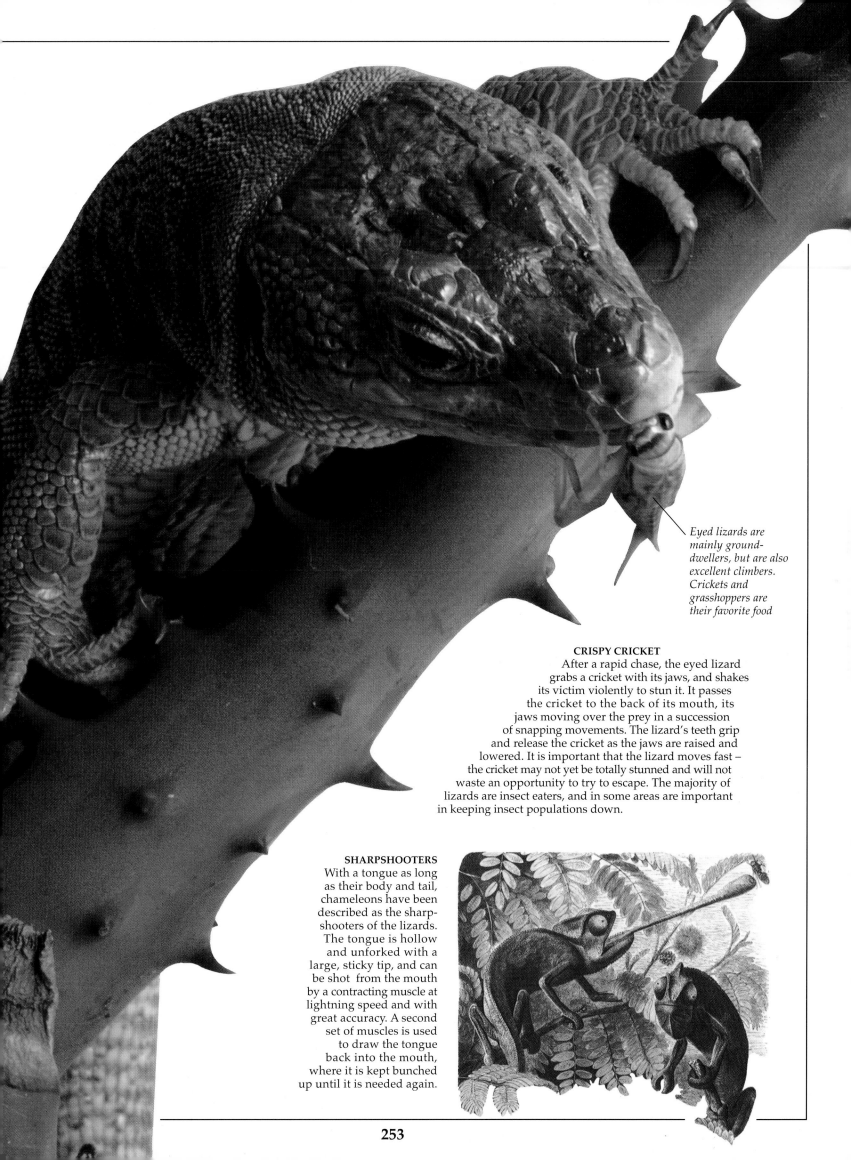

Eyed lizards are mainly ground-dwellers, but are also excellent climbers. Crickets and grasshoppers are their favorite food

CRISPY CRICKET

After a rapid chase, the eyed lizard grabs a cricket with its jaws, and shakes its victim violently to stun it. It passes the cricket to the back of its mouth, its jaws moving over the prey in a succession of snapping movements. The lizard's teeth grip and release the cricket as the jaws are raised and lowered. It is important that the lizard moves fast – the cricket may not yet be totally stunned and will not waste an opportunity to try to escape. The majority of lizards are insect eaters, and in some areas are important in keeping insect populations down.

SHARPSHOOTERS

With a tongue as long as their body and tail, chameleons have been described as the sharpshooters of the lizards. The tongue is hollow and unforked with a large, sticky tip, and can be shot from the mouth by a contracting muscle at lightning speed and with great accuracy. A second set of muscles is used to draw the tongue back into the mouth, where it is kept bunched up until it is needed again.

A specialized snake

MOST GROUPS of animals have their specialized feeders, adapted to a very limited type of food. Among the reptiles, perhaps the most extraordinary is the African egg-eating snake. Many snakes eat eggs as part of a varied diet, but the egg-eater eats exclusively eggs. Small eggs, especially the soft-shelled ones laid by lizards and some other snakes, are easy to eat, since they can be quickly slit open by the snake's teeth. Larger, hard-shelled eggs, such as those laid by birds, need special treatment. True egg-eating snakes eat only birds' eggs, which they swallow whole because they have few teeth. They have toothlike spines that stick down from the backbone and crack open the egg as it passes down to the snake's throat.

Diet of eggs

One problem with an egg diet is that food is not always available. In some parts of the world, birds lay their eggs only at certain times of the year, so an egg-eating snake may have to go for a long time without food. Fortunately, egg-eating snakes can bring up, or regurgitate, eggshell. This means that no space is wasted in the snake's stomach, and it can eat as many eggs as it finds. Nor does the snake waste vital energy in passing the shell through its digestive system.

2 SWALLOW HARD
The jaws "unhinge" so the egg can pass between them and down into the snake's throat. The skin on the side of the neck is very elastic, and at this stage the egg is still unbroken.

Head arched down, pushing egg against bony inner spines to puncture shell

Finely interlinked scales, which separate as skin stretches

3 SPINY BONES
The passage of the egg has now been stopped by the toothlike spines on the underside of the neck bones. These protrude into the esophagus (gullet) and crack or slice open the eggshell.

A valve at the entrance to the stomach accepts yolks and liquids, but rejects pieces of shell

The "bulge" is noticeably smaller

4 GOING DOWN....
Once the egg is punctured, the muscles of the snake's body work in waves to squeeze out the contents, which then continue on to the stomach. The snake now bends its body into S-shaped curves, forcing the collapsed shell back toward the mouth.

5 AND UP IT COMES.........
It may take from five minutes to an hour, depending on the size of the egg, for it to be completely swallowed. Finally, the snake gapes widely and the compacted cigar-shaped shell is brought up. The fragments of shell are still held together by the sticky egg membranes.

The jagged edges of the shell pieces are stuck together. All the nourishment in the egg has been drained and swallowed

Regurgitated shell

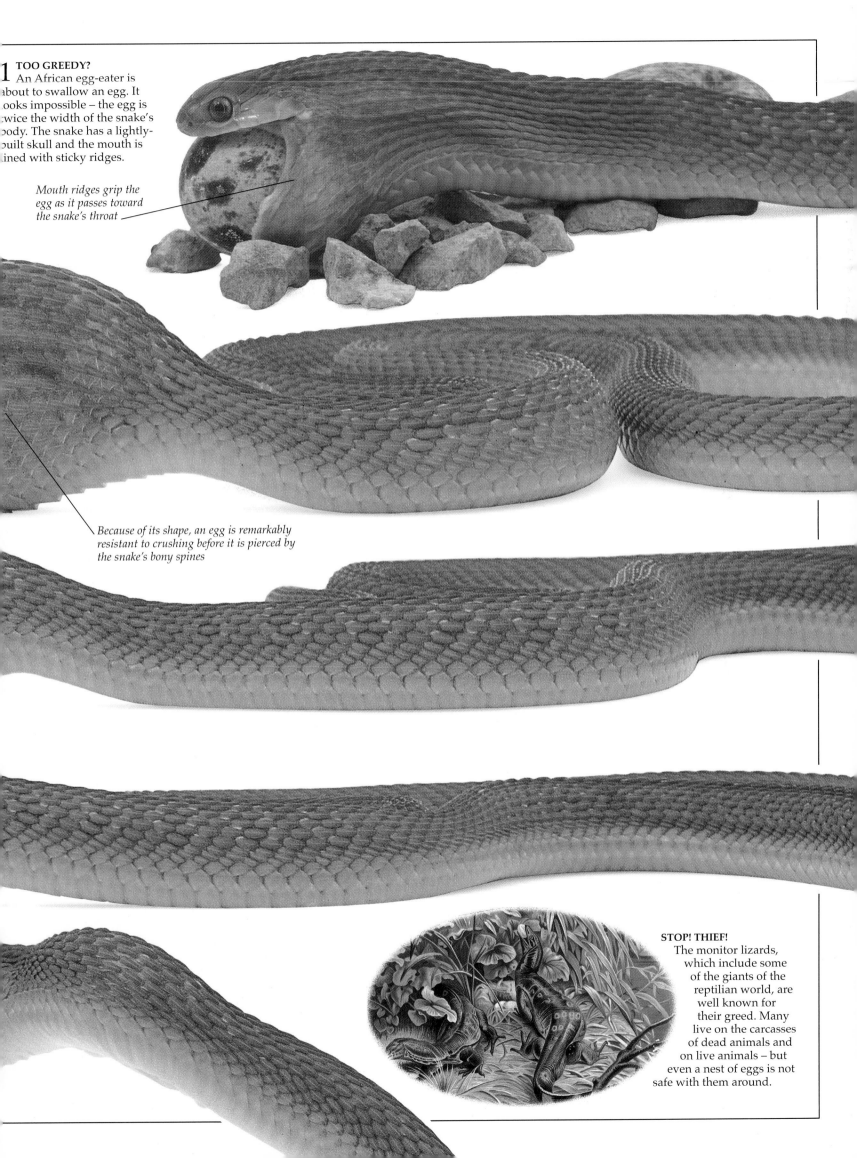

1 TOO GREEDY?
An African egg-eater is about to swallow an egg. It looks impossible – the egg is twice the width of the snake's body. The snake has a lightly-built skull and the mouth is lined with sticky ridges.

Mouth ridges grip the egg as it passes toward the snake's throat

Because of its shape, an egg is remarkably resistant to crushing before it is pierced by the snake's bony spines

STOP! THIEF!
The monitor lizards, which include some of the giants of the reptilian world, are well known for their greed. Many live on the carcasses of dead animals and on live animals – but even a nest of eggs is not safe with them around.

Bird beaks, big and small

MILLIONS OF YEARS AGO, birds lost their teeth. They were too heavy for their low-weight airborne lifestyle. The teeth have been replaced by the beak, or bill, made of the lightweight substance keratin, like your fingernails. The beak covers the jaw bones inside it. Bird beaks have evolved into an endless variety of shapes and sizes, adapted mainly to various food items, but also to other aspects of the bird's life, such as preening its feathers, defending itself against enemies, and displaying to mates at breeding time.

Thrush

Eating plants and seeds

Birds that eat plants and seeds have to crush their food before they can digest it. Since they have no teeth, they do this with powerful beaks and also with the gizzard – a muscular "grinding chamber" in the stomach.

Finch skull

Hard-cased seeds

SPECIALIZED SEED-EATERS
Finches, which number more than 150 species, have short, sharp bills for breaking open seeds and nuts. Some finches have bills which can exert much more crushing force than a human hand.

Goose skull

Leaf crops

Cultivated grain

Pigeon skull

FEEDING ON CROPS
Pigeons and doves originally ate the leaves and seeds of wild plants. Now they often feed on cultivated ones as well. They can also use their pointed bills like a straw when drinking – a unique ability among birds.

LIVING ON GRASS
Geese are among the few kinds of bird that can live on a diet of grass. But geese digest grass poorly, and it passes through their body in just two hours. Because they get so little out of their food, they must eat a lot of it, and so feed almost constantly.

Powerful hooked beak for grasping leaves from trees and crushing seeds

Capercaillie skull

Broad bill for tearing grass

ALL-ROUND PLANT-EATERS
Game birds – species such as pheasants, grouse, and this capercaillie from northern Europe – eat whatever plant food is available, although their preference is for seeds. In winter, the capercaillie lives on the leaves of coniferous trees, a source of food which few other animals can utilize. It pulls the leaves from branches with its powerful hooked beak.

The grass and waterplants on which geese feed

Seeds

Needle-shaped leaves of conifer trees

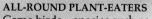

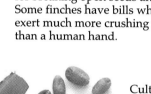

256

Invertebrate eaters

Every spring, the number of insects and other invertebrates (animals without backbones) increases dramatically. These animals form the food for many species of migratory birds. In winter, the supply is much smaller and food is harder to find, consisting mainly of worms and insect larvae (grubs) in wood or in the soil. These are sought out by specialized insect-eating birds.

Blackcap skull

Aphids

Caterpillar

PROBING WARBLERS
These small songsters use their probing beaks to pick insects from leaves and bark. When the supply dries up in early autumn, they migrate southward.

THE SNAIL-SMASHER
Thrushes eat a wide range of food – both plant and animal. Some feed on snails, which they smash open on stone "anvils."

Thrush skull

Snail shells broken open by thrush

Pecked apple

Woodpecker skull

Centipedes

Beetle larvae

Adult beetle

LARGE INSECT EATERS
Birds like woodpeckers and the mainly ground-feeding hoopoe use their beak to pick large insects out of crevices in trees. Woodpeckers also chisel into the wood to find concealed grubs. Their extremely long tongues have spearlike tips which are used for impaling their prey.

Hoopoe skull

A DIET OF WORMS
Earthworms are eaten not only by garden birds, but also by some owls and even hawks.

Ribbonworm, or ragworm

Silt-burrowing lugworm

Feeding on the shore

Although there are very few saltwater insects, the seashore contains a year-round supply of other invertebrates for birds to eat, from crabs and shellfish to burrowing worms.

Avocet feeding

Avocet skull

THE SWEEP-NET BEAK
The avocet catches worms and other prey by striding forward and sweeping its beak from side to side in the water on the surface of the sand or mud. It is one of the very few birds with an upturned beak.

Marine worms

Crab broken open and eaten; the hard skeleton is usually discarded

Cockle

Oystercatcher skull

A BUILT-IN HAMMER
The oystercatcher feeds on seashore animals with hard shells. It has a long beak like the avocet but, instead of ending in a fine point, its tip is blunt. This built-in hammer enables the oystercatcher to smash through the shells of its prey. This kind of feeding needs considerable skill, and some oystercatchers prize shells open instead. An experienced bird will know precisely where the weak points are on a mussel or cockle shell and, if it is lying on sand, the bird will carry the shell to a rock to break it open.

Tellins

Mussel

Beaks of hunting birds

FLIGHT ENABLES birds to cover long distances in search of food. This gives them a great advantage as predators, because few animals – on land or far out at sea – are beyond their reach. Flight also makes birds very effective feeders. A dead animal, an unprotected nest, or a field of ripening crops is quickly spotted by passing birds and turned into a satisfying meal.

Kingfishers

Meat and fish eaters

Birds that feed on larger animals and fish catch their prey in two different ways. Most fish eaters use their beak to catch their quarry while, on land, birds of prey use their talons for catching and their beak for tearing.

Strips of meat torn from prey with powerful, hooked beak

Tawny owl skull

Fur is swallowed and later regurgitated as pellets

NIGHT AND DAY HUNTERS
Most owls hunt at night, using their huge eyes and astonishingly sensitive ears to locate prey such as mice, voles, and insects. As dawn breaks, the owls retire to rest, and day-hunting birds of prey such as hawks and buzzards take over.

Buzzard skull

Large forward-pointing eyes enable the gannet to pinpoint fish below

Halves of the beak meet at a long straight line for holding fish before they are swallowed

Streamlined point for diving

Gannet skull

ABOVE AND BELOW WATER
Gannets dive-bomb shoals of fish such as mackerel by plunging, with their wings folded, from heights of up to 100 ft (30 m). They stay below the surface for only a few seconds. Cormorants pursue fish under water. Their feathers do not trap air like those of other waterbirds, and this enables them to dive swiftly and overtake their prey.

PATIENCE REWARDED
The heron fishes by stealth, staying motionless until its prey swims within reach of its long stabbing beak.

Hooked beak for grasping fish

Cormorant skull

Mackerel

A mixed diet

It doesn't take much intelligence to be a successful seed eater, but birds that survive on a mixed diet must live on their wits. These scavengers are quick to take a chance that might lead to a meal, where other birds would hesitate and miss out. They thrive on waste food and household garbage, as well as more natural food items.

METAL MEALS
Ostriches are famed for their scavenging. They have even been known to eat metal, sometimes with fatal results.

Magpie skull

Crow skull

Hinge joint of upper jaw (maxilla) and lower jaw (mandible)

Jay skull

EVER-ADAPTABLE CROWS
The three members of the crow family shown above are among the most successful general feeders in the bird world. There are few places where they cannot be found. One of the reasons for their success is their inquisitive nature, which is backed up by boldness and a strong, all-purpose beak. Insects, dead birds, live mammals, worms, and seeds are all featured on their menu, while anything that cannot be eaten may well be carried off for further inspection.

Crows eat all kinds of animal remains and are particularly adept at finding animal casualties on roads

Seeds from fields and farmyards

Ground beetle

Centipede

Insects and invertebrates are usually swallowed whole and the hard bits regurgitated as pellets

Egg broken open by magpie after being stolen from nest

Earthworm

Nuts eaten by birds have rough-edged holes from pecking; those eaten by rodents show small teeth marks

A FRESHWATER OPPORTUNIST
The coot is a small aggressive bird of lakes and rivers. It eats any water life that it can find – this can include not only waterweed, snails, tadpoles, and fish, but also young birds. Young ducklings are particularly at risk from the coot's attacks.

Coot skull

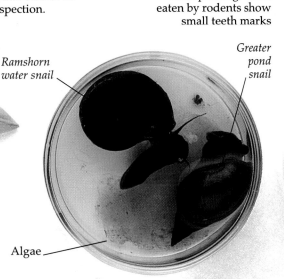

Ramshorn water snail

Greater pond snail

Algae

Water snails from slow-moving freshwater

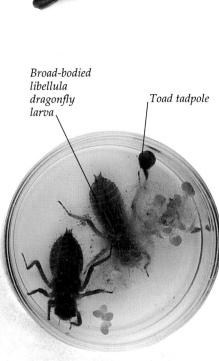

Broad-bodied libellula dragonfly larva

Toad tadpole

Animals and plants eaten by coots in shallow ponds

Teeth for the job

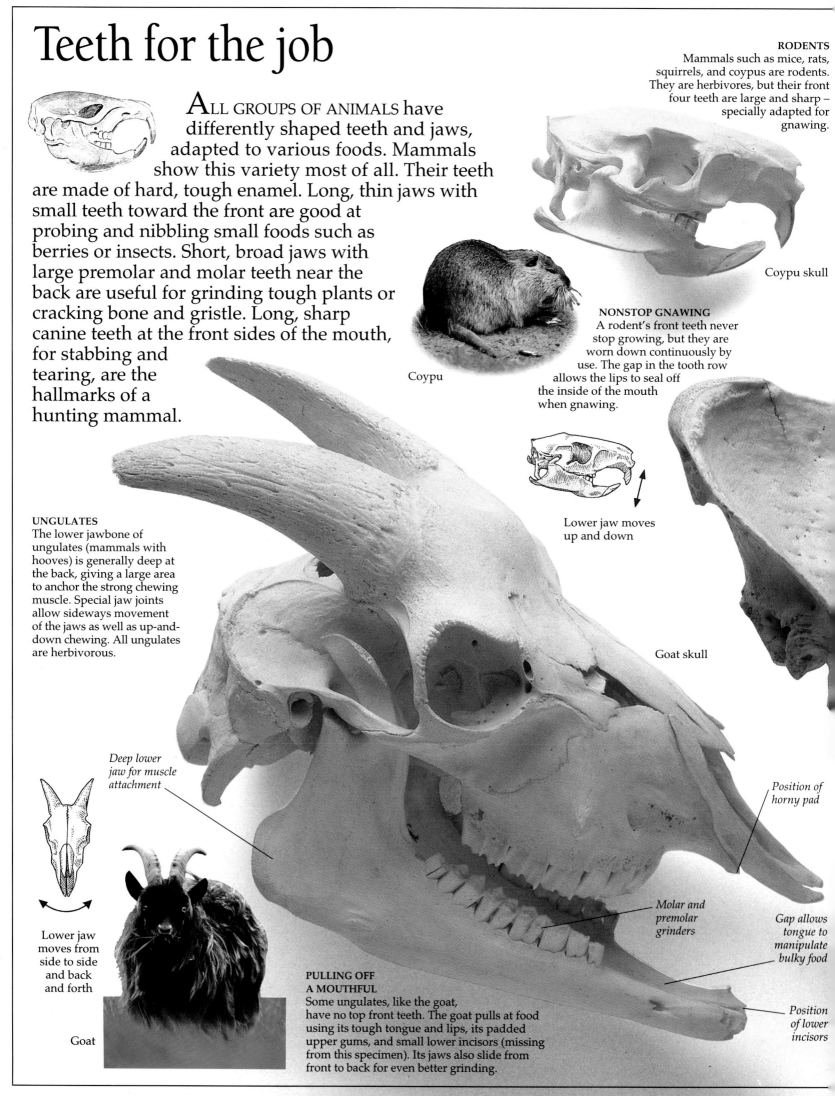

ALL GROUPS OF ANIMALS have differently shaped teeth and jaws, adapted to various foods. Mammals show this variety most of all. Their teeth are made of hard, tough enamel. Long, thin jaws with small teeth toward the front are good at probing and nibbling small foods such as berries or insects. Short, broad jaws with large premolar and molar teeth near the back are useful for grinding tough plants or cracking bone and gristle. Long, sharp canine teeth at the front sides of the mouth, for stabbing and tearing, are the hallmarks of a hunting mammal.

RODENTS
Mammals such as mice, rats, squirrels, and coypus are rodents. They are herbivores, but their front four teeth are large and sharp – specially adapted for gnawing.

Coypu skull

Coypu

NONSTOP GNAWING
A rodent's front teeth never stop growing, but they are worn down continuously by use. The gap in the tooth row allows the lips to seal off the inside of the mouth when gnawing.

Lower jaw moves up and down

UNGULATES
The lower jawbone of ungulates (mammals with hooves) is generally deep at the back, giving a large area to anchor the strong chewing muscle. Special jaw joints allow sideways movement of the jaws as well as up-and-down chewing. All ungulates are herbivorous.

Goat skull

Deep lower jaw for muscle attachment

Position of horny pad

Molar and premolar grinders

Gap allows tongue to manipulate bulky food

Lower jaw moves from side to side and back and forth

Goat

Position of lower incisors

PULLING OFF A MOUTHFUL
Some ungulates, like the goat, have no top front teeth. The goat pulls at food using its tough tongue and lips, its padded upper gums, and small lower incisors (missing from this specimen). Its jaws also slide from front to back for even better grinding.

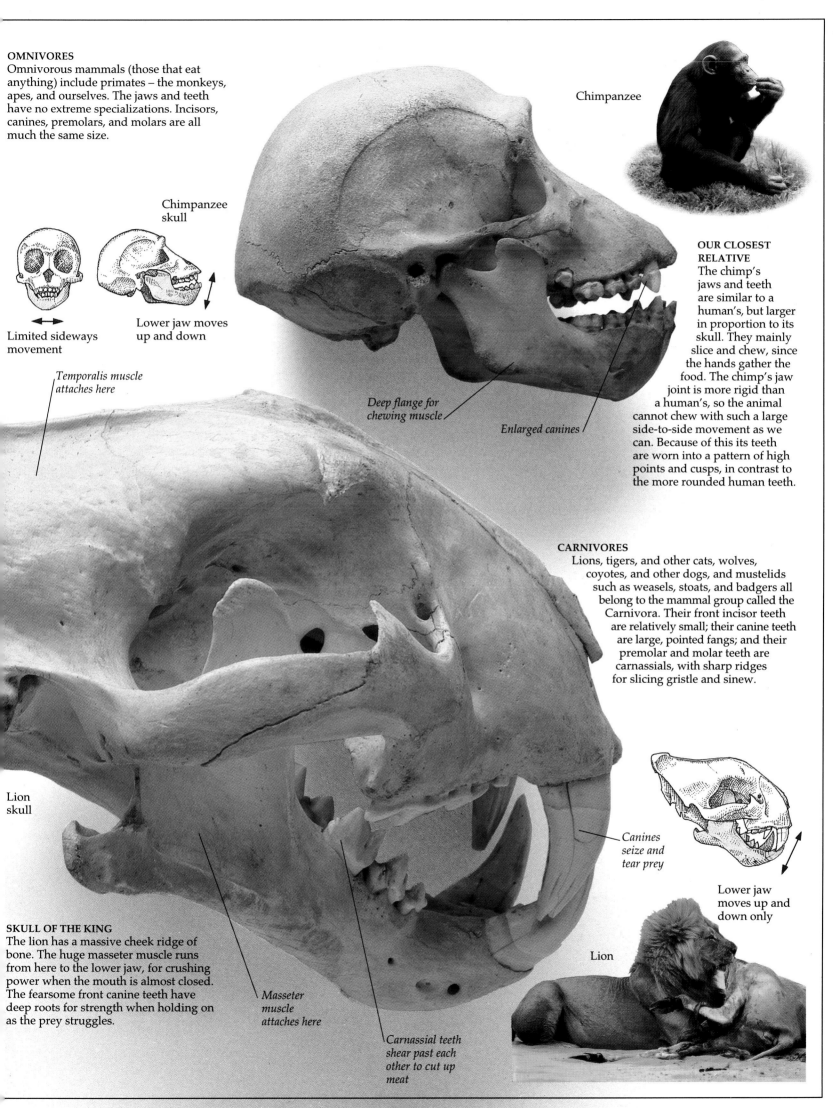

OMNIVORES
Omnivorous mammals (those that eat anything) include primates – the monkeys, apes, and ourselves. The jaws and teeth have no extreme specializations. Incisors, canines, premolars, and molars are all much the same size.

Chimpanzee skull

←→ Limited sideways movement

Lower jaw moves up and down

Temporalis muscle attaches here

Chimpanzee

Deep flange for chewing muscle

Enlarged canines

OUR CLOSEST RELATIVE
The chimp's jaws and teeth are similar to a human's, but larger in proportion to its skull. They mainly slice and chew, since the hands gather the food. The chimp's jaw joint is more rigid than a human's, so the animal cannot chew with such a large side-to-side movement as we can. Because of this its teeth are worn into a pattern of high points and cusps, in contrast to the more rounded human teeth.

CARNIVORES
Lions, tigers, and other cats, wolves, coyotes, and other dogs, and mustelids such as weasels, stoats, and badgers all belong to the mammal group called the Carnivora. Their front incisor teeth are relatively small; their canine teeth are large, pointed fangs; and their premolar and molar teeth are carnassials, with sharp ridges for slicing gristle and sinew.

Lion skull

Canines seize and tear prey

Lower jaw moves up and down only

Lion

SKULL OF THE KING
The lion has a massive cheek ridge of bone. The huge masseter muscle runs from here to the lower jaw, for crushing power when the mouth is almost closed. The fearsome front canine teeth have deep roots for strength when holding on as the prey struggles.

Masseter muscle attaches here

Carnassial teeth shear past each other to cut up meat

Champion herbivore

Most mammals, including humans, have two sets of teeth in their lifetime. By the time a human stops growing, at about 20 years of age, he or she will have a complete second set of teeth, although the last molars, or wisdom teeth, sometimes take longer. A 20-year-old elephant, on the other hand, will already be well into its fourth set of cheek teeth. There are six sets of four in total, but at any one time, only one set is functional. Each set consists of two cheek teeth in each jaw, one on each side. As the elephant grows, each new set of teeth moves into place, and is slightly bigger than the last set. The teeth do not erupt from above in the top jaw and from below in the bottom jaw, as in humans, but move along the jaw from the back toward the front. Each tooth gets more and more worn as it moves forward, but by the time the last bits drop out, it has been completely replaced by the tooth behind it, as if the teeth were on a very slow conveyor belt. These successive sets of teeth are responsible for chewing and grinding more food than any other animal – an adult elephant consumes up to 440 lb (200 kg) of grasses, leaves, twigs, fruits, and other plant food each day.

A THORNY PROBLEM
The sharp, finger-length thorns of acacia trees are no defense against an elephant. Carefully avoiding the thorns with her trunk, this African elephant has torn off a branch and is crushing off the bark with her molars.

JAWBONE
This left half of an African elephant's jawbone has had the bone chipped away to reveal the roots of the teeth. The big tooth is molar 5, but the last bit of molar 4 is still in use. The round lump in the angle of the jaw is the beginning of molar 6.

Molar 6

Molar 5 is good for about 20 years of chewing

Roots deep in jawbone

Molar 6

The last molar is bigger than a brick and appears when the elephant is about 40 years old

SET OF TEETH
When an elephant dies, the size of its teeth, and the amount of wear on them, enable scientists to work out how long it lived. These six teeth come from five different African elephants, ranging from a tiny calf to an adult of more than 50 years.

Molar 5

Molar 4

Molar 3

Molar 2

Molar 1

Only the first five ridges of molar 5 have come into use

Molar 4 is almost worn out. It comes from the same elephant as molar 5

Molar 3 usually lasts from about three and a half to about nine years of age

Molar 2 usually erupts before the age of 18 months

Molar 1 is present in newborn baby elephants

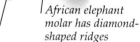

Human molar

African elephant molar has diamond-shaped ridges

Asian elephant molar has parallel ridges

TEETH RIDGES
An elephant molar is made up of several plates, or lamellae, stuck together. The enamel top of each molar wears down as it grinds on its opposite tooth, revealing a diamond shape in African elephants, and thin parallel ridges in Asian elephants.

Root of mammoth tooth

MAMMOTH TOOTH
Fossil mammoth teeth are sometimes dredged up from the bottom of the North Sea. The ridges on the grinding surface are more like those of an Asian elephant than an African.

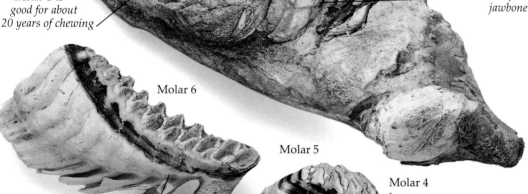

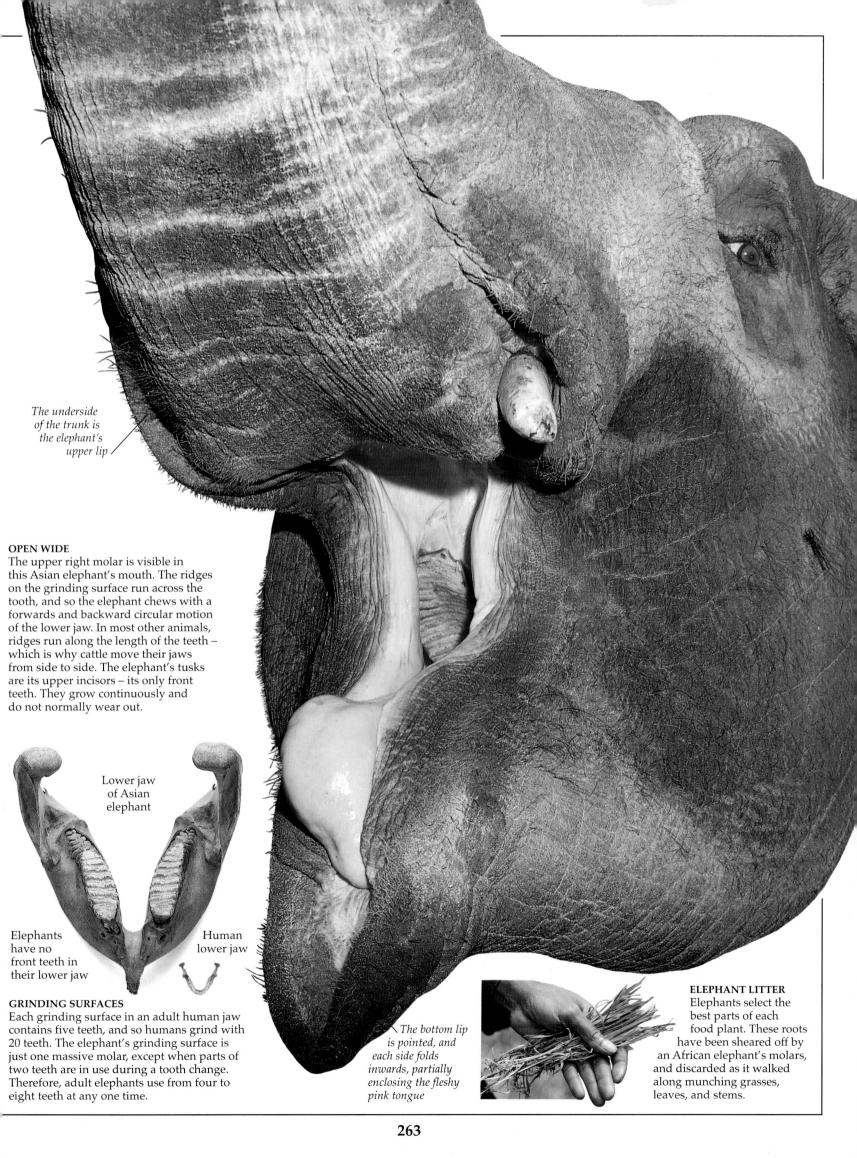

The underside of the trunk is the elephant's upper lip

OPEN WIDE

The upper right molar is visible in this Asian elephant's mouth. The ridges on the grinding surface run across the tooth, and so the elephant chews with a forwards and backward circular motion of the lower jaw. In most other animals, ridges run along the length of the teeth – which is why cattle move their jaws from side to side. The elephant's tusks are its upper incisors – its only front teeth. They grow continuously and do not normally wear out.

Lower jaw of Asian elephant

Elephants have no front teeth in their lower jaw

Human lower jaw

GRINDING SURFACES

Each grinding surface in an adult human jaw contains five teeth, and so humans grind with 20 teeth. The elephant's grinding surface is just one massive molar, except when parts of two teeth are in use during a tooth change. Therefore, adult elephants use from four to eight teeth at any one time.

The bottom lip is pointed, and each side folds inwards, partially enclosing the fleshy pink tongue

ELEPHANT LITTER

Elephants select the best parts of each food plant. These roots have been sheared off by an African elephant's molars, and discarded as it walked along munching grasses, leaves, and stems.

Dealing with a meal

THE FOOD OF SOME MAMMALS comes in convenient ready-to-eat form, for immediate consumption. Grass, leaves, and insects are instant prepackaged snacks. But other sources of food are more difficult to gather, or more awkward to manipulate. The mammals that rely on them need the bodily equivalent of shopping bags, can-openers, crowbars, and knives and forks to deal with their meal. For example, acorns and nuts are bursting with nutrients, but they are packaged in a strong, hard case which is tough to crack. The long, ever-growing, chisel-sharp incisor teeth of rodents are especially suited to gnawing, chipping, and levering open nuts. It's a successful approach – rodents make up one-quarter of all mammal species.

GRASPING TONGUE
The giraffe is an ungulate, or hoofed mammal. It is the tallest living land animal at more than 17 ft (5 m) tall, so it can reach high up in the trees for its food. It can reach 1 ft (30 cm) higher by sticking out its long black tongue, like a grabbing hand, to pull leaves into its mouth. Then the long canine teeth strip the leaves from the twigs.

CHISELING TEETH
In autumn and winter, the brown squirrel feeds mainly on nuts such as oak acorns, beech seeds, and hazelnuts. The squirrel rolls the nut in its forepaws until it is the right way up, then applies the tremendous levering force of its sharp front teeth to a certain weak spot. The nut case then splits open. Young squirrels are born with a certain amount of case-cracking knowledge, but they refine the technique with practice.

BULGING CHEEKS
The golden hamster is a well-known pet. Like the wild hamster and many other rodent relatives, it collects food when it is abundant and caches it – stores it in a hidden place. The hamster's cheek pouches work like shopping bags.

Cheek pouches are empty

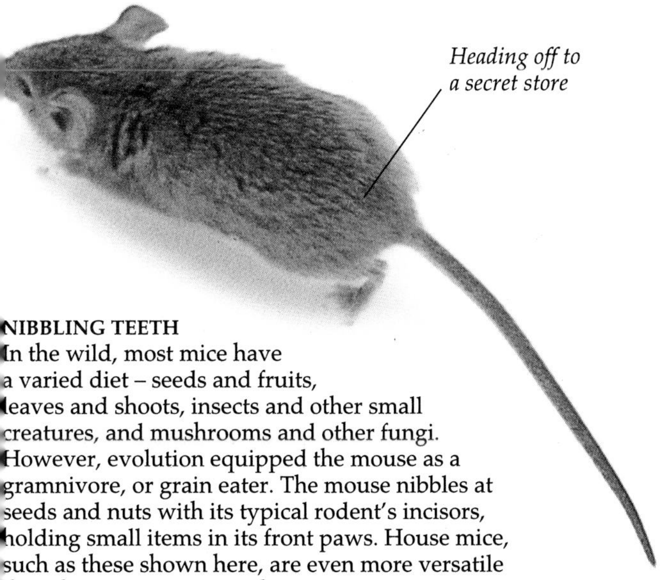

Heading off to a secret store

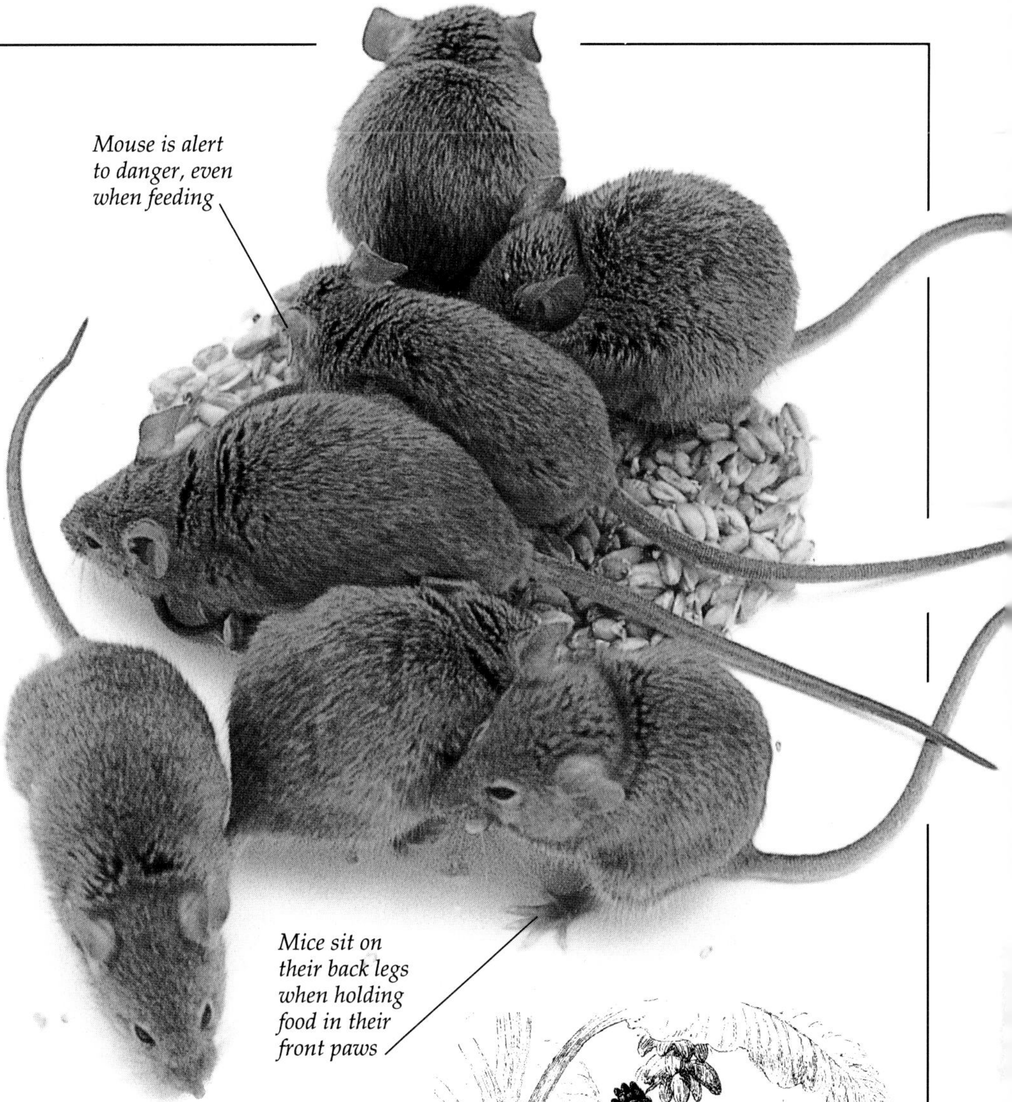

NIBBLING TEETH

In the wild, most mice have a varied diet – seeds and fruits, leaves and shoots, insects and other small creatures, and mushrooms and other fungi. However, evolution equipped the mouse as a gramnivore, or grain eater. The mouse nibbles at seeds and nuts with its typical rodent's incisors, holding small items in its front paws. House mice, such as these shown here, are even more versatile than their wild cousins. They gnaw paper, string, soap, candle wax, and many other household substances.

Mouse is alert to danger, even when feeding

Mice sit on their back legs when holding food in their front paws

HOLDING HANDS

The otter rarely eats its catch of fish in the water. It comes to the shore and holds down the slippery meal with its front feet, tearing the flesh with its sharp canine teeth. Otters also eat small mammals, birds, frogs, mollusks, and sea urchins.

HOOKING CLAWS

The Malayan sun bear is the smallest of the seven species of bear. Its long, curved claws are multipurpose tools. In addition to providing the grip for climbing, they can hook fruit from branches, tear bark off trunks to get at grubs, and rip open the nests of termites, ants, and bees to eat the occupants or steal the honey.

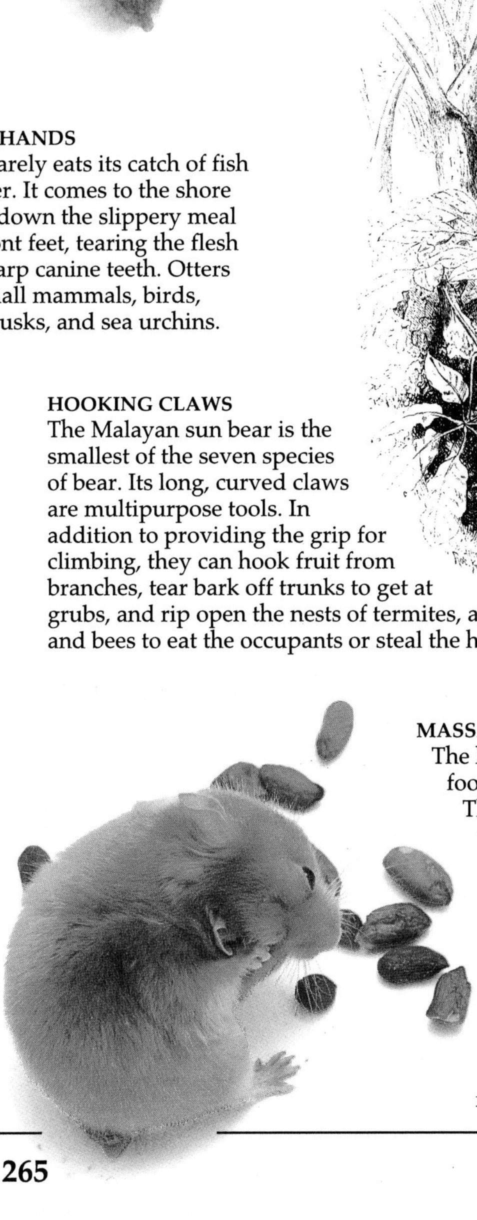

MASSAGING PAWS

The hamster quickly crams as much food as possible into its cheeks. Then it heads back to its burrow to unpack the pouches by massaging the items out with its front paws. This strategy reduces the time that this small, fairly defenseless animal would otherwise spend out in the open, chewing and swallowing the food. In the wild, a single hamster has been known to amass nuts and other food weighing more than an adult human.

Pouches beginning to extend

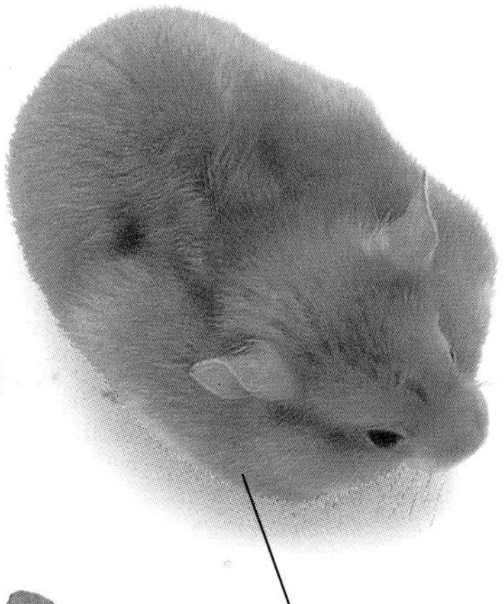

Full pouches

Supreme hunter

O F ALL THE MAMMALS, those that rely on fresh meat the most, and follow the hunting lifestyle most completely, are the felids – the 35 or so species in the cat family. They range from enormous tigers, weighing over 660 lb (350 kg), and with a body 10 ft (3 m) long, to the black-footed cat of southern Africa, smaller than most pet cats. All cats are solitary predators, except for the lion which hunts in a family group, or pride. Cats usually kill victims smaller than themselves. Motionless animals sometimes escape attack, but with practice, cats can recognize prey by sound and scent alone. They have an excellent memory for places and will return many times to a spot where they once had successful hunting. Most cats stalk their prey, sometimes for a long time, then with a sudden rush, leap on it and sink their sharp canine teeth into the neck. Small cats feed mostly on mice, birds, lizards, beetles, and any other small animals they can catch. Large cats, like the leopard, feed on bigger animals about the size of a goat, and often drag their prey up into trees to keep it away from other predators.

TOM AND JERRY
In the famous cartoon, quickwitted Jerry the mouse often gets the better of the swashbuckling but slightly stupid Tom – not often the case in real life.

A stalking cat holds its body close to the ground

The pads on a cat's paws help it to move silently

READY FOR ACTION
This black panther, a black form of the leopard species, is stalking and getting ready for the kill. Every part of its body is tensed and ready for action. A cat on the prowl moves very slowly and silently until it is near enough to make a quick and decisive pounce. All cats hunt in this way, from a lion killing a buffalo, to a domestic cat killing a house mouse.

MEDIEVAL MOUSERS
This medieval picture comes from a 13th-century book called *The Harleian Bestiary*. It is interesting because it is such an early illustration of cats with a rat. For centuries, cats were suspected of being in league with witches and the devil. Despite being hunted themselves, their superb senses and agility allowed cats to survive and prosper.

IN FOR THE KILL
Cats very often choose a vantage point from which they can see but not be seen. This domestic cat would have sat absolutely silently and still on the fence for some time, watching the happenings in the grass below, before leaping down with great accuracy on the unsuspecting prey.

Black panther

TELLING TAILS
The cat's tail is a
barometer of its moods.
It lashes its tail when angry
and twitches it gently to and fro
when concentrating or contented.

A FISHY BUSINESS
The fishing cat of India does not hunt for its food quite
like any other cat. It can flip fish out of the water
with its slightly webbed paws, and several
times has been seen diving under the surface
for fish that it catches in its mouth.

RUNNING DOWN
The cheetah and the
springboks are keeping a wary eye
on each other. The cheetah will not
begin to hunt unless there is a springbok
on its own in a vulnerable position. The
springboks know this and they will not be
disturbed unless the cheetah comes too close.
However, once the prey has been singled out, the
cheetah will pursue it at great speed. Even so, about
one or two pursuits in three are unsuccessful.

A PRACTICED KILLER
Many cats, both wild and domestic, play with their prey before
killing it. Mother cats teach their kittens how to hunt by
capturing prey, and releasing it, to allow the kittens
to watch their actions. It is not really known why
adult cats with no kittens still play with their prey.
It may be that some cats need to constantly
practice and hone their hunting skills.

*A cat playing with
a toy is reacting as
if it were prey*

Serval

BIG MEAL
With its massive teeth, this tiger can
snap a bone with one bite, and will
devour a whole carcass, skin and all.

CHICKEN DINNER
This serval of Africa, like the
other small cats, crouches
down to eat its food. When
big cats eat, they tend to lie
down with the food positioned
between their front paws. Small
cats begin by eating the head,
which is swallowed whole
with very little chewing.

COURTING COLORS
The eastern rosella is a type of parrot living in eastern Australia. In spring, the male grows splendid and colorful new feathers. He then puts on a dramatic performance to gain the attention of a female, by drooping his wings, fluffing up his breast feathers, and moving his fanned-out tail from side to side. This type of visual courtship is especially common in birds, which make much use of sight during their lives. Courting behavior such as this is the first stage of the breeding cycle.

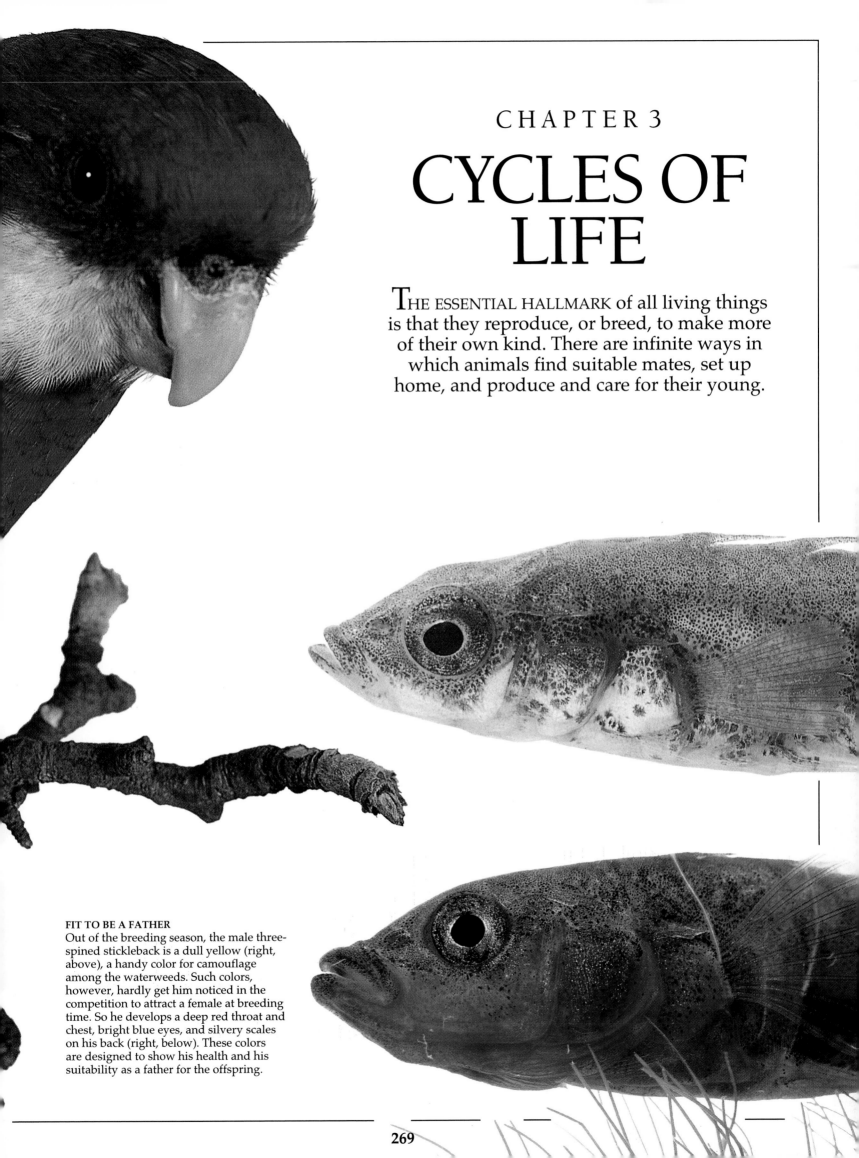

CHAPTER 3
CYCLES OF LIFE

The ESSENTIAL HALLMARK of all living things is that they reproduce, or breed, to make more of their own kind. There are infinite ways in which animals find suitable mates, set up home, and produce and care for their young.

FIT TO BE A FATHER
Out of the breeding season, the male three-spined stickleback is a dull yellow (right, above), a handy color for camouflage among the waterweeds. Such colors, however, hardly get him noticed in the competition to attract a female at breeding time. So he develops a deep red throat and chest, bright blue eyes, and silvery scales on his back (right, below). These colors are designed to show his health and his suitability as a father for the offspring.

Egg samples

Aᴌʟ ᴍᴀᴍᴍᴀʟs, including humans, are born as tiny versions of their parents. In nature, however, mammals and the way in which they give birth is unusual. Most animal mothers lay eggs. Some care for the eggs, and perhaps for the babies when they hatch. But the vast majority of animal species do not show any egg or parental care. They simply leave the eggs to hatch, protected by their shells. Some species bury the eggs in soft soil, or lay them in a crack or crevice for extra protection. And when these babies emerge, they must fend for themselves.

Whelk egg case bundle

MOLLUSK EGGS
The whelk, a type of sea snail, lays a mass of rubbery-cased eggs which it fixes to a stone. The tiny but fully formed babies crawl out of their case, and the empty egg case bundle is often dislodged and washed up on the shore.

Egg mass under body

Murre eggs

Quail egg

Swallow egg

Snake-necked turtle egg

African house snake egg

Javan bloodsucker lizard egg

Starling egg

Kittiwake egg

REPTILE EGGS
Most reptile eggs have slightly soft, flexible shells, like leather or parchment. Mother turtles make or dig a nest for their eggs. The African house snake lays her eggs in a rotting heap of manure, which provides extra warmth to speed the babies' development.

BIRD EGGS
The shell of bird eggs is hard and brittle, unlike the eggshells of most other animals. Shell color and patterning is important for camouflage when the nest site is relatively exposed, as with most of these examples. Eggs that are hidden away, like the swallow's, tend to be light or white.

Partridge chicks can run around a few hours after hatching

Pincers are held forward and ready for action

Partridge chicks

HATCHING
When a baby hatches from its egg, its stage of development is often linked to the amount of parental care it will receive and the dangers of its habitat. Newly hatched partridge chicks have a camouflaging striped pattern. It improves their chance of survival in their exposed ground-nesting site. Reptile hatchlings also need to be alert and active when they emerge, because their parents are long gone, apart from a few exceptions such as crocodiles. The newly hatched chicks of birds who nest in the relative safety of a tree or hole are often blind and helpless.

CRAB EGGS
The velvet crab is one of the fiercest animals on the shore, attacking and eating almost anything it can find. The female shows similar ferocity when protecting her eggs. This one is holding her pincers in the defense pose, partly because she is carrying thousands of eggs under her body. Her abdomen forms a special flap to hold the eggs in place. After about three months the eggs hatch into tiny larvae, called zoea. These swim off and become part of the plankton, the countless tiny plants and animals drifting in the sea.

Growing up

Animals make the transition from baby to adult in many different ways. Some hatch or are born as miniature versions of their parents, and hardly change at all except for increasing in size. More commonly, the youngsters resemble the adults, but they differ in certain body features or proportions. Still others look nothing like their parents, as in the damselfly and other insects. Their bodies change dramatically in shape, a process called metamorphosis. In addition to growing, the animal's bodily framework, be it bones on the inside (endoskeleton), or a hard casing on the outside (exoskeleton), becomes harder and tougher; its muscles develop greater strength and coordination; its sexual organs mature, ready for adulthood; and the behavior of the creature develops as it learns to survive in the world.

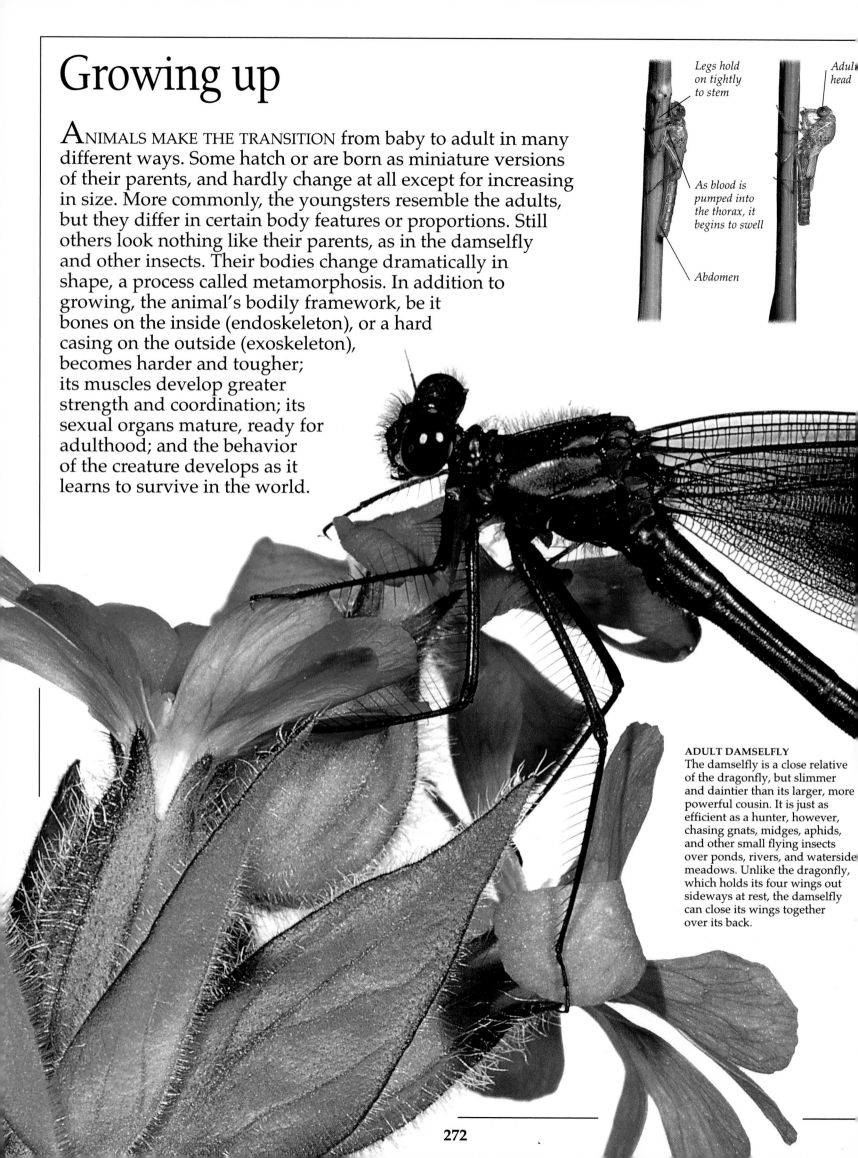

Legs hold on tightly to stem

Adult head

As blood is pumped into the thorax, it begins to swell

Abdomen

ADULT DAMSELFLY
The damselfly is a close relative of the dragonfly, but slimmer and daintier than its larger, more powerful cousin. It is just as efficient as a hunter, however, chasing gnats, midges, aphids, and other small flying insects over ponds, rivers, and waterside meadows. Unlike the dragonfly, which holds its four wings out sideways at rest, the damselfly can close its wings together over its back.

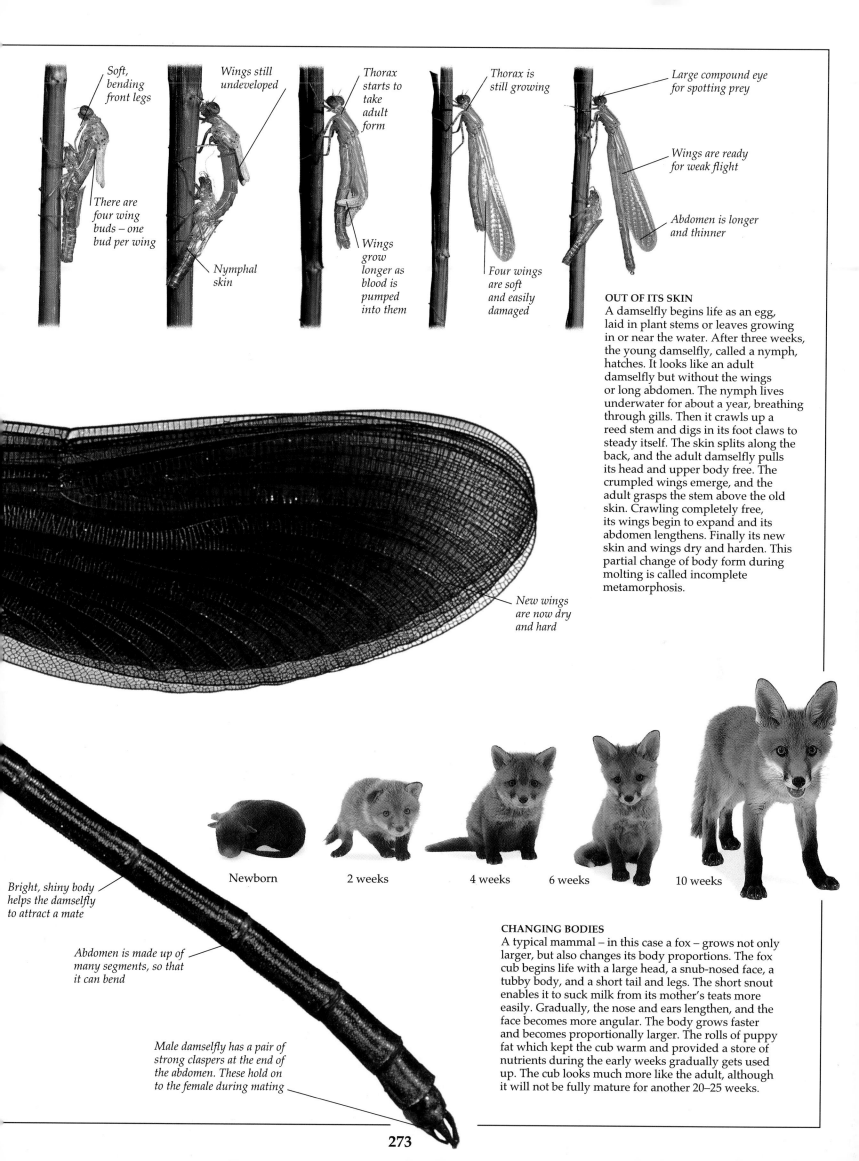

Soft, bending front legs

Wings still undeveloped

Thorax starts to take adult form

Thorax is still growing

Large compound eye for spotting prey

There are four wing buds – one bud per wing

Nymphal skin

Wings grow longer as blood is pumped into them

Four wings are soft and easily damaged

Wings are ready for weak flight

Abdomen is longer and thinner

New wings are now dry and hard

OUT OF ITS SKIN

A damselfly begins life as an egg, laid in plant stems or leaves growing in or near the water. After three weeks, the young damselfly, called a nymph, hatches. It looks like an adult damselfly but without the wings or long abdomen. The nymph lives underwater for about a year, breathing through gills. Then it crawls up a reed stem and digs in its foot claws to steady itself. The skin splits along the back, and the adult damselfly pulls its head and upper body free. The crumpled wings emerge, and the adult grasps the stem above the old skin. Crawling completely free, its wings begin to expand and its abdomen lengthens. Finally its new skin and wings dry and harden. This partial change of body form during molting is called incomplete metamorphosis.

Bright, shiny body helps the damselfly to attract a mate

Abdomen is made up of many segments, so that it can bend

Male damselfly has a pair of strong claspers at the end of the abdomen. These hold on to the female during mating

Newborn

2 weeks

4 weeks

6 weeks

10 weeks

CHANGING BODIES

A typical mammal – in this case a fox – grows not only larger, but also changes its body proportions. The fox cub begins life with a large head, a snub-nosed face, a tubby body, and a short tail and legs. The short snout enables it to suck milk from its mother's teats more easily. Gradually, the nose and ears lengthen, and the face becomes more angular. The body grows faster and becomes proportionally larger. The rolls of puppy fat which kept the cub warm and provided a store of nutrients during the early weeks gradually gets used up. The cub looks much more like the adult, although it will not be fully mature for another 20–25 weeks.

Animal parents

DIFFERENT ANIMALS invest time and energy into different stages of the breeding process. Some animals produce thousands or perhaps millions of eggs, but give no later care. This is because the number of eggs is so huge that the likelihood of one or two surviving is very great. Other animals produce only a few eggs, but protect them in eggshells or their own bodies. Some animals, including turtles, give their young no further care once they are born. Other animals, including most birds and mammals, will care for their few offspring over months and even years.

FATHER FISH
The seahorse is a fish, related to the perch, which shows unusual breeding behavior. The female releases her eggs into the water, and the male gathers them into a sacklike brood pouch on his belly. The babies grow, and he "gives birth" by releasing them through a hole in the pouch.

MOTHER MARSUPIAL
The wallaby is a marsupial, or pouched animal. The baby is born tiny and very underdeveloped, as small as a child's fingertip. It crawls through its mother's fur to the pouch, or marsupium, on her underside. Here it attaches itself to a teat with its mouth, and drinks milk in the usual mammal manner. Three months later it has grown large enough to leave the protection of the pouch.

Adult female red-necked wallaby

The green of the birch leaf helps camouflage the young parent bugs

Four-month-old male red-necked wallaby

Powerful back legs ready to propel the wallaby out of danger

PARENT BUG
The parent bug is unusual among insects in that it takes great care of its young. The female lays 30-40 tiny eggs on a leaf. She then guards them for about three weeks. They hatch into tiny nymphs, very similar to herself but much smaller and without wings. The nymphs stay clustered near their mother, and their green coloring helps them to blend in with the leaf. She continues to protect them from enemies such as birds for another few weeks, until they wander off to live by themselves.

The tiny, brightly colored nymph looks similar to the adult, except that it has no wings

Colors and scents

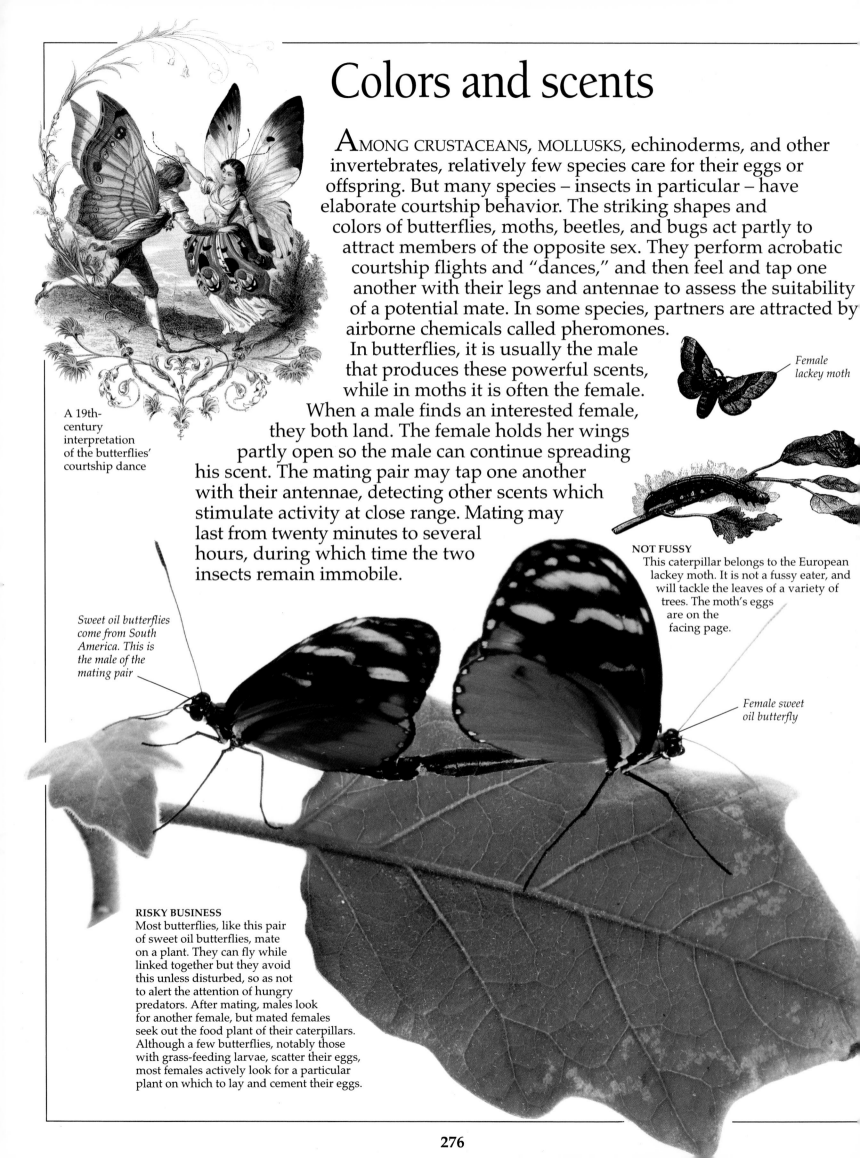

AMONG CRUSTACEANS, MOLLUSKS, echinoderms, and other invertebrates, relatively few species care for their eggs or offspring. But many species – insects in particular – have elaborate courtship behavior. The striking shapes and colors of butterflies, moths, beetles, and bugs act partly to attract members of the opposite sex. They perform acrobatic courtship flights and "dances," and then feel and tap one another with their legs and antennae to assess the suitability of a potential mate. In some species, partners are attracted by airborne chemicals called pheromones.

In butterflies, it is usually the male that produces these powerful scents, while in moths it is often the female. When a male finds an interested female, they both land. The female holds her wings partly open so the male can continue spreading his scent. The mating pair may tap one another with their antennae, detecting other scents which stimulate activity at close range. Mating may last from twenty minutes to several hours, during which time the two insects remain immobile.

A 19th-century interpretation of the butterflies' courtship dance

Female lackey moth

NOT FUSSY
This caterpillar belongs to the European lackey moth. It is not a fussy eater, and will tackle the leaves of a variety of trees. The moth's eggs are on the facing page.

Sweet oil butterflies come from South America. This is the male of the mating pair

Female sweet oil butterfly

RISKY BUSINESS
Most butterflies, like this pair of sweet oil butterflies, mate on a plant. They can fly while linked together but they avoid this unless disturbed, so as not to alert the attention of hungry predators. After mating, males look for another female, but mated females seek out the food plant of their caterpillars. Although a few butterflies, notably those with grass-feeding larvae, scatter their eggs, most females actively look for a particular plant on which to lay and cement their eggs.

A TWO-HEADED BUTTERFLY?
A mating pair, like these two Asian swallowtails, can look like a two-headed insect. The tail-to-tail position links the genitalia of male and female together while the male grips the female's abdomen with his clasper.

Female swallowtail

Male swallowtail

HIS AND HERS
The males and females of some invertebrate species look totally different. Several female butterflies are larger than the males of the same species, while some female moths are flightless. These two butterflies (right) look like different species but are in fact male and female orange-tip butterflies.

Male has bright-orange wing tips

Dark underside markings show through transparent wing

The female has black wing tips

Central spot on forewing is larger on the female

Laying eggs
After selecting the correct plant for her offspring to eat, the female butterfly walks over a leaf, carefully testing to make sure it belongs to the right plant species. Many insect species can detect chemicals from different plants. By putting traces of extract from cabbages on the surface of different leaves, cabbage-eating large and small white butterflies have even been persuaded to lay eggs on plants that their caterpillars will not eat.

SILK SUPPLIER
This female silkmoth has laid her batch of eggs on a mulberry leaf. For thousands of years, silkworms have been bred on special silk farms, where their silk is used to weave delicate fabrics. As a result of their domestication, silkmoths are no longer found in the wild.

DELICATE OPERATION
This Central American Pierid butterfly is laying her eggs on the upper surface of the leaf. She is very vulnerable here, since any disturbance, such as a heavy rainstorm, could disrupt her task.

Some Heliconius butterflies lay their eggs on passionflower tendrils

EGG SITES
The lackey moth lays its eggs in a ring around a twig, so that they look like part of the plant.

Eggs

Eggs are hidden under leaf

ABOUT TO HATCH
These blue mormon butterfly eggs have darkened and are about to hatch. Tiny caterpillars will soon emerge. A blue mormon lays its eggs in a random pattern rather than a cluster, so predatory bugs will overlook some of them.

A place to breed

THREE MAIN GROUPS of animals build special places for breeding, to shelter and protect their offspring. These are certain insects, such as wasps, bees, ants, and termites; birds, who construct nests in a wide range of shapes and sizes; and mammals, who dig burrows or prepare dens. A few fish, such as sticklebacks, show parental care by building a nest for the eggs and fry (baby fish). The male stickleback, shown here in his courting colors, puts great effort into fashioning a nest, impressing and luring the female there to breed, and guarding the young as they develop. This helps give his offspring a greater chance of survival. It is partly for this reason that sticklebacks are among the world's most widespread freshwater fish.

A goby, a common tide pool fish parent watches over its hatchlings. It will distract threats such as gulls and crabs.

SPRING BREEDERS
Every spring, male three-spined sticklebacks develop their bright red and blue breeding colors. Spring is a good time to breed because the weather is warm and the days are long. These conditions encourage the growth of plants, on which all animal life depends. The male stakes out his own patch of water, called a territory, where he can set up his nest and chase away rival males.

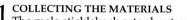

Piece of water plant in stickleback' mouth for the nest

Bright blue eye

Red throat

1 COLLECTING THE MATERIALS
The male stickleback sets about collecting little bits of water plants for the nest.

Beneath a small boulder is the ideal site on which to build a nest

Stickleback shovels gravel with his snout

2 DIGGING THE FOUNDATION
He pushes his snout into the stones and mud of the bottom, shoveling them aside to make a shallow hole. The nest is often found among water weeds or in the shelter of a small rock.

MULTIFAMILY FATHER
The male bowfin, a fish from eastern North America, has several breeding partners. Each spring he makes a rough scoop of gravel, roots, and other plant pieces, usually in a swampy part of his lake or river home. One or more females lay the eggs, which the male fertilizes and then guards until the larvae hatch. These stick themselves into the nest by glue-glands on their heads, feeding off the food reserves called yolk in their eggs, until they can swim freely.

3 A FIRM BASE
As the male begins to push plant pieces into place, he taps and prods them firmly to make a secure base. The large fanlike pectoral fins are useful for the precise maneuvering that this process requires.

Stickleback makes a firm base by prodding weeds into place with his snout

4 CEMENT STAGE
As the pile of nest material grows, the male cements it together with a sticky "glue," a secretion made by specialized parts of his kidneys. Gradually the nest grows, layer by layer.

Fanlike pectoral fins create a current of water to aerate the nest

5 ADDED VENTILATION
The collection of weeds and glue prevents a good flow of freshwater through the nest, which will be needed to keep the eggs well aerated. So the fish uses his large fins to fan a current of water through the nest.

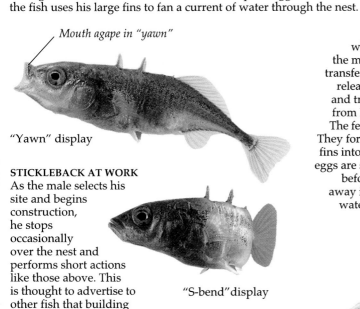

Mouth agape in "yawn"

"Yawn" display

STICKLEBACK AT WORK
As the male selects his site and begins construction, he stops occasionally over the nest and performs short actions like those above. This is thought to advertise to other fish that building is in progress, so keep away!

"S-bend" display

Dogfish egg cases

INDIVIDUAL PROTECTION
Instead of a communal nest and a guardian parent like the stickleback, the dogfish gives each of her babies its own leathery suit for protection. The female lays her egg cases in pairs, attached to seaweed by long, curly tendrils at each corner. The embryos grow inside, living on the stored food called yolk. After 6 to 9 months the young dogfish wriggle out around 4 in (10 cm) long. The empty egg cases are often washed up on the beach as "mermaid's purses."

COMPLICATED COURTING
Baby animals develop from the mother's eggs, which are fertilized by father's sperm. On land, the male and female usually get close together to transfer sperm. In water, many creatures simply release their eggs and sperm into the water, and trust to chance. The dragonet, a fish from Europe, improves on this method. The female lies under the colorful male. They form a channel with their anal fins into which the sperm and eggs are shed and mixed, before wafting away in the water.

Male and female dragonet pair, ready to release eggs and sperm

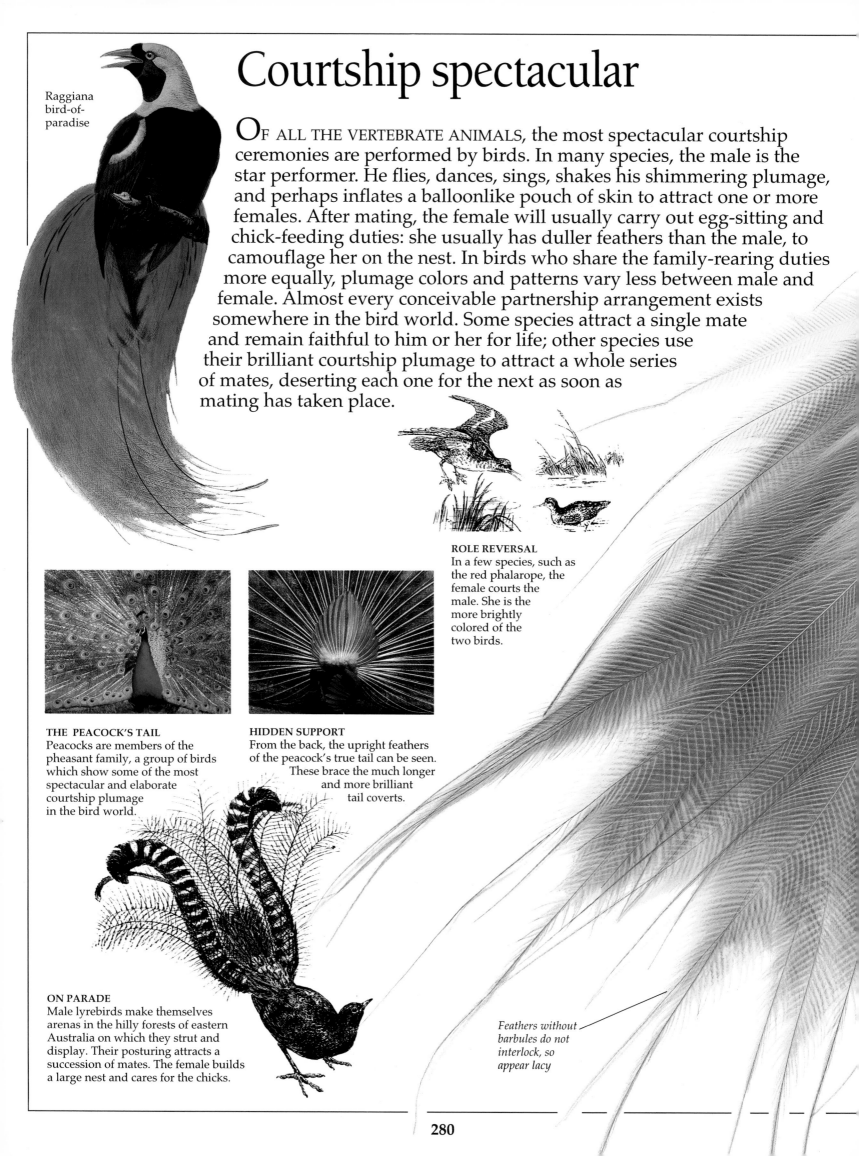

Courtship spectacular

Raggiana bird-of-paradise

OF ALL THE VERTEBRATE ANIMALS, the most spectacular courtship ceremonies are performed by birds. In many species, the male is the star performer. He flies, dances, sings, shakes his shimmering plumage, and perhaps inflates a balloonlike pouch of skin to attract one or more females. After mating, the female will usually carry out egg-sitting and chick-feeding duties: she usually has duller feathers than the male, to camouflage her on the nest. In birds who share the family-rearing duties more equally, plumage colors and patterns vary less between male and female. Almost every conceivable partnership arrangement exists somewhere in the bird world. Some species attract a single mate and remain faithful to him or her for life; other species use their brilliant courtship plumage to attract a whole series of mates, deserting each one for the next as soon as mating has taken place.

ROLE REVERSAL
In a few species, such as the red phalarope, the female courts the male. She is the more brightly colored of the two birds.

THE PEACOCK'S TAIL
Peacocks are members of the pheasant family, a group of birds which show some of the most spectacular and elaborate courtship plumage in the bird world.

HIDDEN SUPPORT
From the back, the upright feathers of the peacock's true tail can be seen. These brace the much longer and more brilliant tail coverts.

ON PARADE
Male lyrebirds make themselves arenas in the hilly forests of eastern Australia on which they strut and display. Their posturing attracts a succession of mates. The female builds a large nest and cares for the chicks.

Feathers without barbules do not interlock, so appear lacy

MYSTERY SOLVED

was only in the last century that naturalists
enetrated the New Guinea forests and saw
e raggiana bird-of-paradise using its
lumage. During courtship displays,
e male bird hangs upside
own and throws its
lumes open.

Body feathers

Streaked central feather

Hairlike golden plumes

Softer display feathers toward edge

During display, feathers open to produce a fountain of color as the male bird swings upside down from a branch

Many birds molt their colorful breeding feathers after mating is over and grow duller ones for camouflage during the rest of the year

INFLATABLE ATTRACTION
The male frigatebird has a brilliant
red throat pouch which he uses to
attract a mate. He keeps his pouch
inflated for many hours until a
female, lured by his irresistable
courtship device, joins him.

DEFUSING TENSION
Boobies and gannets nest
in densely packed colonies,
stabbing any neighbor
that dares to intrude on
another's private patch, or
territory. A lengthy courtship
is needed between pairs to
defuse this aggression. Here,
two blue-footed boobies join
in the "pelican" display,
pointing their beaks out of
each other's way.

IN STEP WITH THE SEASON
The brilliant colors on
puffins' beaks are at their
brightest during the
breeding season in early
summer. The color lies in
a horny sheath that covers the
outside of the beak. When the
puffins abandon their cliff-top
burrows and head out to sea
for the winter, this sheath
falls off. The beak is then
a much more subdued
color until the
following spring.

DANCING IN WATER
Great crested grebes perform
bizarre dances during their
courtship. They often begin
with a head-shaking dance,
in which the birds face each
other, jerking their heads.
Suddenly, they dive and
reappear with beakfuls
of waterweed. During the
courtship dance both birds
rear up out of the water,
paddling furiously
as they present the
weed to each other.
After repeating the
dance several times,
the birds mate.

MINIATURE RIVALS
A territory in which to nest and
collect food is a necessity for
successful pairing in many bird
species. These male hummingbirds,
though tiny, are pugnaciously
defending their territories.

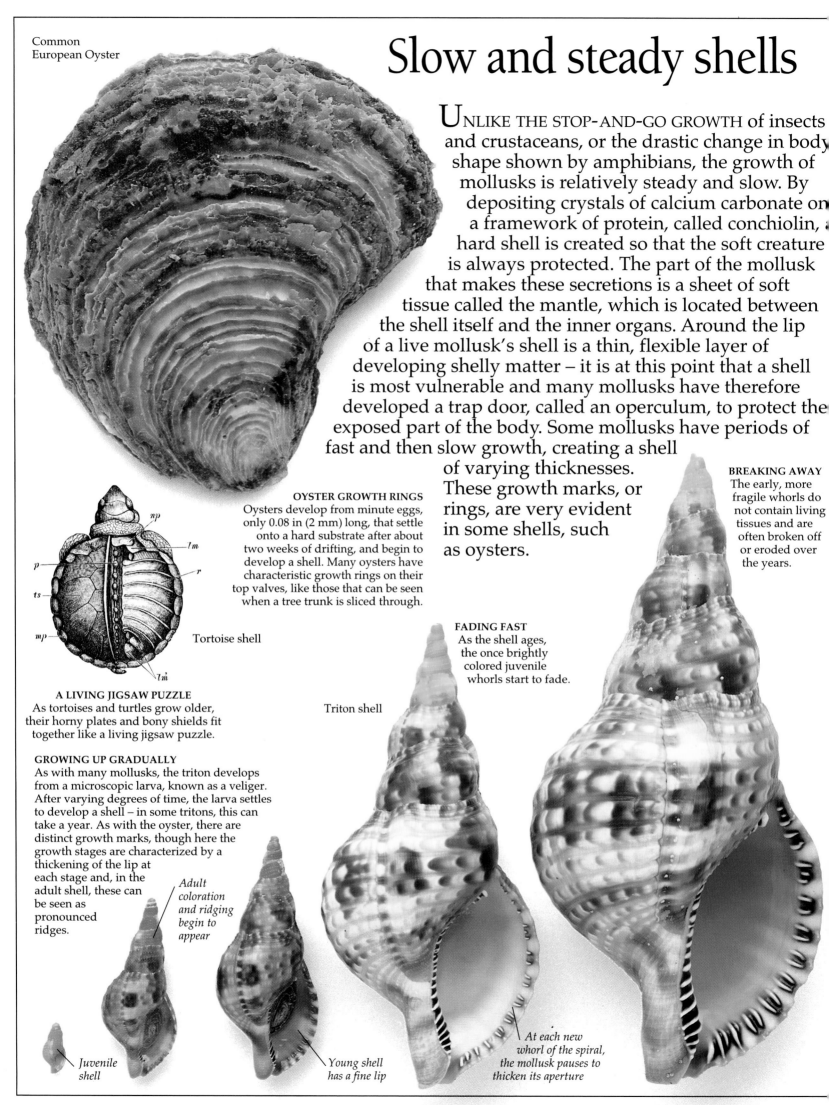

Common European Oyster

Slow and steady shells

UNLIKE THE STOP-AND-GO GROWTH of insects and crustaceans, or the drastic change in body shape shown by amphibians, the growth of mollusks is relatively steady and slow. By depositing crystals of calcium carbonate on a framework of protein, called conchiolin, a hard shell is created so that the soft creature is always protected. The part of the mollusk that makes these secretions is a sheet of soft tissue called the mantle, which is located between the shell itself and the inner organs. Around the lip of a live mollusk's shell is a thin, flexible layer of developing shelly matter – it is at this point that a shell is most vulnerable and many mollusks have therefore developed a trap door, called an operculum, to protect the exposed part of the body. Some mollusks have periods of fast and then slow growth, creating a shell of varying thicknesses. These growth marks, or rings, are very evident in some shells, such as oysters.

OYSTER GROWTH RINGS
Oysters develop from minute eggs, only 0.08 in (2 mm) long, that settle onto a hard substrate after about two weeks of drifting, and begin to develop a shell. Many oysters have characteristic growth rings on their top valves, like those that can be seen when a tree trunk is sliced through.

Tortoise shell

A LIVING JIGSAW PUZZLE
As tortoises and turtles grow older, their horny plates and bony shields fit together like a living jigsaw puzzle.

GROWING UP GRADUALLY
As with many mollusks, the triton develops from a microscopic larva, known as a veliger. After varying degrees of time, the larva settles to develop a shell – in some tritons, this can take a year. As with the oyster, there are distinct growth marks, though here the growth stages are characterized by a thickening of the lip at each stage and, in the adult shell, these can be seen as pronounced ridges.

Adult coloration and ridging begin to appear

Juvenile shell

Young shell has a fine lip

BREAKING AWAY
The early, more fragile whorls do not contain living tissues and are often broken off or eroded over the years.

FADING FAST
As the shell ages, the once brightly colored juvenile whorls start to fade.

Triton shell

At each new whorl of the spiral, the mollusk pauses to thicken its aperture

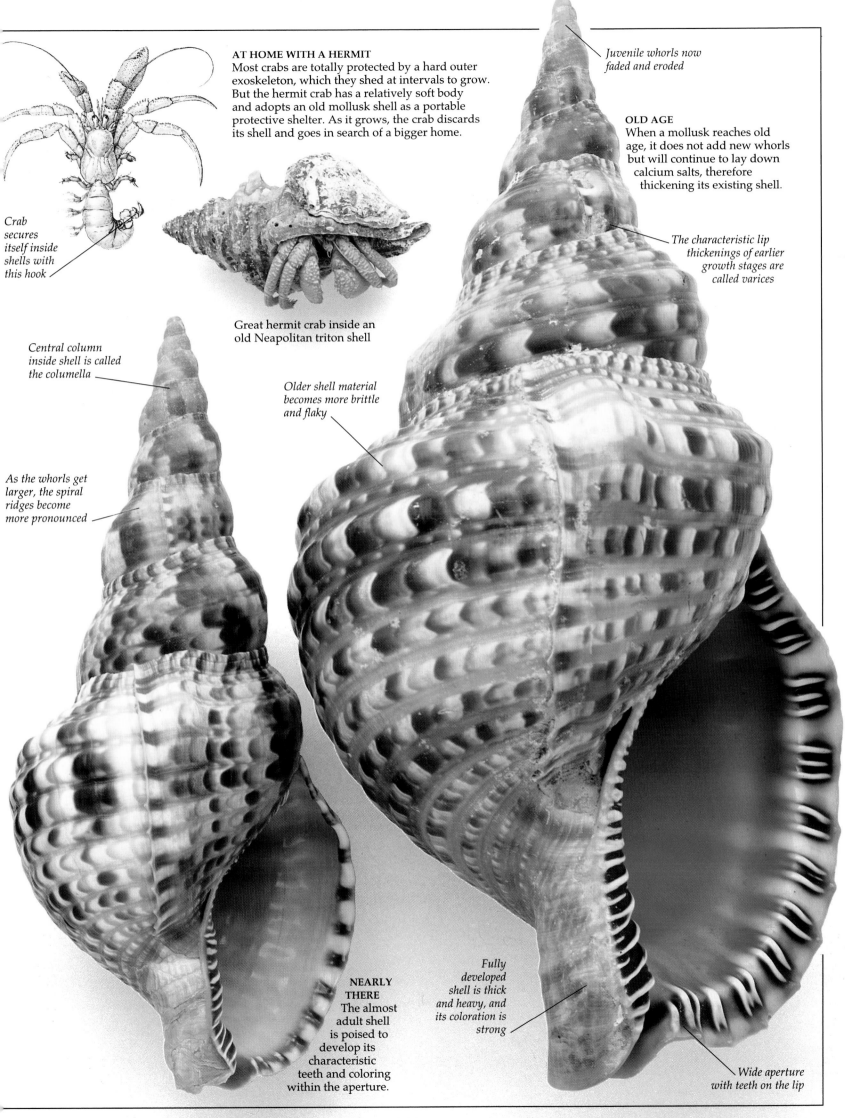

AT HOME WITH A HERMIT
Most crabs are totally protected by a hard outer exoskeleton, which they shed at intervals to grow. But the hermit crab has a relatively soft body and adopts an old mollusk shell as a portable protective shelter. As it grows, the crab discards its shell and goes in search of a bigger home.

Crab secures itself inside shells with this hook

Juvenile whorls now faded and eroded

OLD AGE
When a mollusk reaches old age, it does not add new whorls but will continue to lay down calcium salts, therefore thickening its existing shell.

The characteristic lip thickenings of earlier growth stages are called varices

Great hermit crab inside an old Neapolitan triton shell

Central column inside shell is called the columella

Older shell material becomes more brittle and flaky

As the whorls get larger, the spiral ridges become more pronounced

NEARLY THERE
The almost adult shell is poised to develop its characteristic teeth and coloring within the aperture.

Fully developed shell is thick and heavy, and its coloration is strong

Wide aperture with teeth on the lip

Eggs and hatching

Apart from the amphibians, most vertebrate animals are born or hatch as smaller versions of their parents. All birds and many reptiles hatch from tough-shelled eggs, although some mother snakes and lizards give birth to fully formed babies rather than laying eggs. All mammals except the platypus and echidna also give birth. The new babies then grow steadily by getting bigger all over, rather than changing their body shape or form. As the new babies grow, they alter their feeding habits according to the type and size of food items they can deal with. A young crocodile, for example, may be able to survive on insects, but, as it grows bigger, it will eat considerably larger prey, including mammals, birds, and fish.

Young caiman

LIKE MOTHER LIKE DAUGHTER
This young caiman meets the world fully formed and able to fend for itself. Like the young alligator, it will stay close to its mother for a few weeks, sometimes using her back as a basking platform. Despite the mother's care, unusual in reptiles, at the first sign of danger the young are able to dive under water for cover.

HATCHING OUT
Once they are laid, snake eggs often swell and get heavier as they absorb moisture from the surroundings, but the length of time needed before they hatch varies according to the temperature. The warmer it is, the faster the eggs develop, so the mother often chooses to lay them in a place that is both warm and slightly moist. Piles of vegetation produce heat as the plant material rots, so compost heaps are sometimes selected as nesting sites, particularly by snakes living in cooler areas. The hatchling is often much longer than the egg from which it hatched. This is possible because, as the embryo develops, the whole body is coiled into a tight spiral.

1 THE EGG
This is the egg of a rat snake, a common and rather large snake from North America. It mates from April to June and also in the autumn. Between June and August the female lays 5 to 30 soft-shelled, oblong eggs, often choosing rotten wood, leaf litter, or a spot under some rocks as her "nest."

4 MAKING A MOVE
The snake leaves the egg quite quickly. It is able to slither along in the normal snakelike way immediately. Interestingly, however, if a snake is removed from its egg a little too early, it will writhe about, unable to move along properly, although in every other way it looks quite normal. It therefore seems likely that the snake only becomes fully coordinated just before hatching.

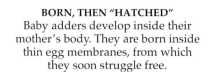

BORN, THEN "HATCHED"
Baby adders develop inside their mother's body. They are born inside thin egg membranes, from which they soon struggle free.

LOOKS CAN DECEIVE

Most geckos lay their eggs between pieces of bark or stuck to a wall. This sandstone gecko laid her eggs between the crevices of rocks. Their hard shells were necessary because they were exposed to the elements. Many lizards, snakes, and turtles have leathery-shelled eggs, while in tortoises and crocodiles the shell is harder and more brittle. Although many geckos lay their eggs in shared sites, they take no care of their young at all – in fact, it is unusual that mother and young should be as close to one another as this.

Female

Young

THE HAZARDS OF HATCHING

Among the reptiles, turtles lay the most eggs, but care for them the least. Abandoned to the earth or sand in which its egg was buried, from the start this little hatchling will have to fight alone to survive in a dangerous world.

The young snake checks its surroundings with its tongue

Slit made by egg tooth

The snake is in no hurry to leave the safety of its shell

2 BREAKING THE SHELL

While it is developing inside the egg, the young rat snake takes nourishment from the yolk. A day or two before hatching, the yolk sac is drawn into the body and the remaining yolk is absorbed into the young snake's intestine. A small scar, rather like a navel, shows the point where the embryo was joined to its food supply. As the young snake develops, a sharp but temporary "egg tooth" grows from the tip of its upper jaw, and the hatchling uses this to pierce the egg shell. The young snake gets its first view of the world through one of the slits it makes.

3 LEAVING THE EGG

Having tested its surroundings by flicking its tongue in and out to "taste" the air, the young snake cautiously peers from its shell. It will be in no hurry to leave, and may stay where it is, with only its head poking out, for a day or two. That way, if disturbed, it can always go back inside the egg. Rat snakes can be ready to leave their eggs anytime between 7 and 15 weeks after laying.

Adult color and pattern is already developed on scales

5 MINOR MIRACLE

Fully out of its shell now, it seems amazing that such a long snake could ever have been packed inside such a relatively small egg. The hatchlings may be as much as seven times longer than the egg, at 11–16 in (28–40 cm) in length.

Caring parents

TWO GROUPS OF ANIMALS develop and grow in a most remarkable way. These are the amphibians and the insects, and the life cycle feature they have in common is metamorphosis – change in body shape. In amphibians this happens as eggs hatch into tadpoles, which change into adults. Most amphibians return to water or a damp place to breed. The female lays her soft, jelly-covered eggs, or spawn, and the male fertilizes them with his sperm. In many species, the eggs are then left as the parents disperse. But some amphibians are dutiful parents and take care of their eggs and offspring. The kind of care ranges from choosing a sheltered egg-laying site, to enclosing eggs in a protective foam, to guarding the eggs. Some amphibians carry their eggs or tadpoles on their back, or in a skin pocket; others take their eggs inside the body, into vocal sacs, or even into their stomach.

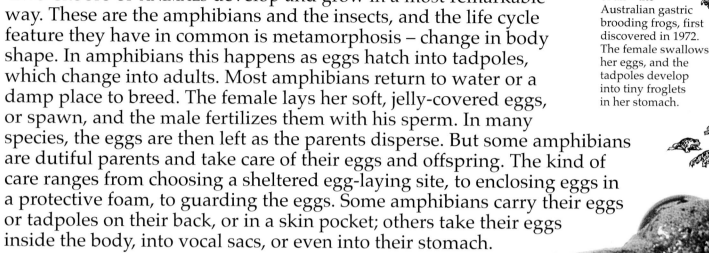

STOMACH UPSET
This fairy-tale character looks as though she is having a bad time. So are the most remarkable frogs of all – the Australian gastric brooding frogs, first discovered in 1972. The female swallows her eggs, and the tadpoles develop into tiny froglets in her stomach.

SAFETY DEPOSIT BOX
The back of this female marsupial, or pouched, frog from South America looks swollen. After she laid a hundred or more fertilized eggs, the male placed them in the brood pouch on her back. After incubation, the female makes her way to the water. She uses the toes on her back feet to open up the pouch, releasing the tadpoles into the water to complete their development.

EGG MIMIC
The patterns on the back of these two glass frogs from the rainforests of Costa Rica look very similar to the eggs they are guarding. The male's camouflage enables him to guard the eggs in safety for 24 hours a day. These frogs are so well camouflaged that they can avoid predators and feed on any insects that may alight on the leaf.

A LONG WAIT
This little lungless salamander, found in Costa Rica and Panama, is a devoted parent, guarding its egg clutch for some four to five months. The guarding parent, which may be either the male or the female, lies curled around the eggs, which it turns occasionally. This protects the eggs from both predators and fungal infection.

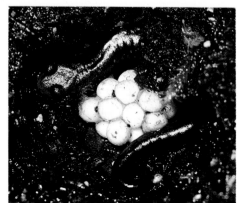

Male midwife toad, ranging from 1.25–2 in (3–5 cm) in length, carries a string of eggs

SAFE PLACE

The female Surinam toad from South America looks like dead leaves on the muddy bottom of the sluggish waters in which she lives. After mating, the male fertilizes the eggs released by the female, which stick onto a thick, spongy layer of skin on her back.

Skin of female Surinam toad swells up, almost covering her eggs

Some males take on two, or even three, egg clutches

POCKETS FULL OF TOADLETS

The eggs are placed on the female Surinam toad's back when the male and female perform an egg-laying roll, or loop movement, underwater. The pair are upside down when the female lays about five eggs which are fertilized and drop onto her back as the pair turn right way up in the water. In all, about 55 eggs are laid in this way. After four weeks they hatch as perfect, small toadlets.

HITCHING A LIFT

This little nonpoisonous frog from Trinidad is related to the more brightly colored poison-dart frogs from Central and South America. In this species, the male stays with his egg clutch. When they hatch, he carries the entire tadpole brood on his back to a nearby stream to complete their development. In other closely related species, the female is the tadpole carrier.

VOCAL SAC BROODING

The male Darwin's frog from Chile watches over his developing clutch of eggs. When the newly hatched tadpoles start to squirm, he takes them into his vocal sac, or "chin." The tadpoles remain there, apparently receiving some form of nourishment, until they are ejected as tiny froglets.

THE MALE MIDWIFE

The male midwife toad from western Europe shows a unique form of parental care – he carries his eggstring of some 35–50 eggs, wrapped around his hind legs. After the eggs are laid and fertilized, he keeps hold of the female and, moving his legs alternately back and forth through the eggs, fastens them securely around his legs. After about three weeks, he takes his egg load into the water where the tadpoles hatch and complete their development.

Tadpole to frog

M<small>ETAMORPHOSIS IS</small> the change in body shape as an animal grows from an immature larval form to its mature adult form. Amphibians are the only land vertebrates to develop in this way. Frog and toad larvae, or tadpoles, look completely different from their parents. The most notable difference is that a tadpole has an all-in-one head and body, as well as a long tail.

At first a tadpole lacks legs, which develop later, and it must live in water to survive. The time taken to develop from eggs hatching to a fully formed froglet varies from about 12 to 16 weeks, but this time span is greatly affected by water temperature and food supply. Tadpoles found in colder regions, at high altitudes, or from spawn laid late in the breeding season may hibernate in the tadpole state, and will not turn into frogs until the following spring. This is the life cycle of the common or European frog, from a tadpole with gills, tail, and no legs, to an adult with lungs, legs, and no tail.

Very short tail

NOW A FROGLET
At 12 weeks, the tail has reduced to a stump and will soon disappear. The froglets are ready to leave the water. Every generation reenacts the transition from water to land that occurred in the first amphibians.

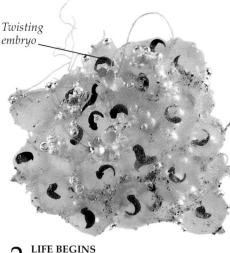

Twisting embryo

2 LIFE BEGINS
After fertilization, the single egg cell in the dark blob of yolk divides into two, then four, then eight, and so on. Gradually the developing embryo grows longer and takes on a comma shape, still enclosed in its protective jelly. It becomes a tadpole and hatches about six days after fertilization.

Female common frog

Frog's egg

A pair of common frogs in amplexus

Male common frog

1 A TIGHT SQUEEZE
The male frog is clasping the female underneath him, in a tight, mating embrace, called "amplexus." The male grasps the female behind her front legs – in other species, the grasp may be in front of her hind legs or around her head. Amplexus can last for several days. The male fertilizes the eggs, which in this species number about 2,000. In other species the eggs can vary from one to 20,000 or more. They may be laid singly, in clumps, or in strings.

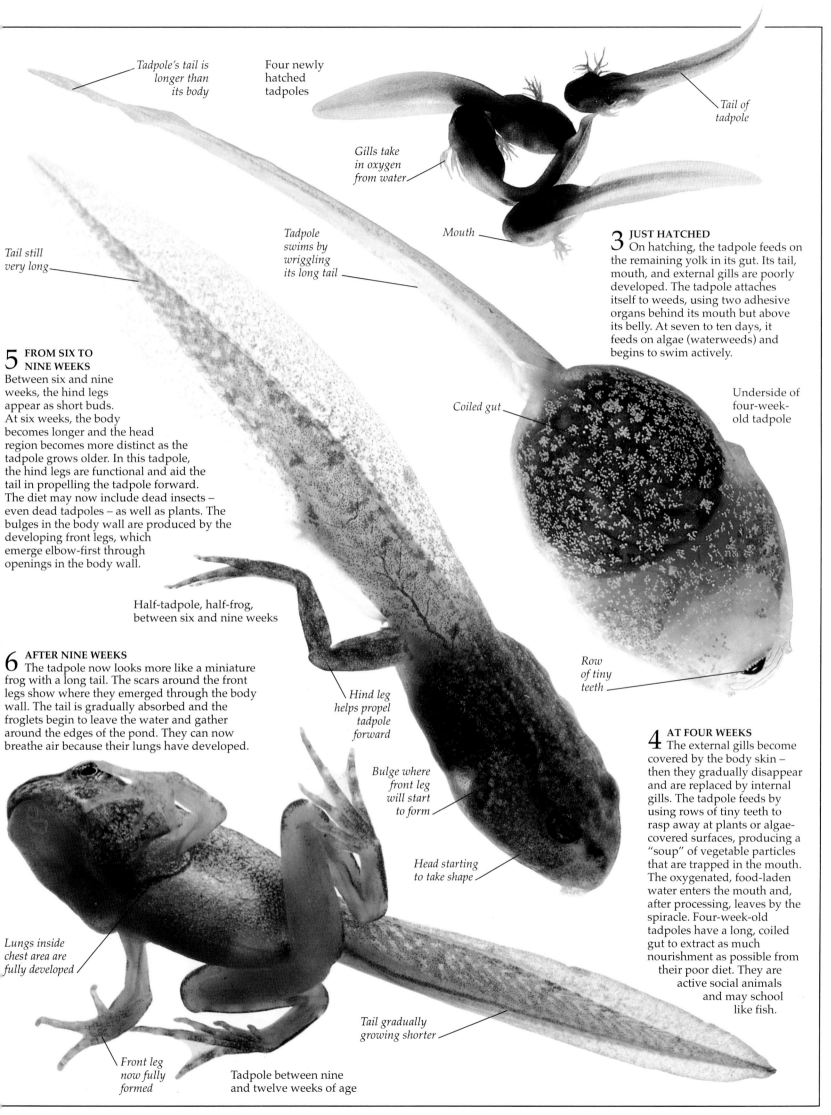

Tadpole's tail is longer than its body

Four newly hatched tadpoles

Tail of tadpole

Gills take in oxygen from water

Mouth

3 JUST HATCHED

On hatching, the tadpole feeds on the remaining yolk in its gut. Its tail, mouth, and external gills are poorly developed. The tadpole attaches itself to weeds, using two adhesive organs behind its mouth but above its belly. At seven to ten days, it feeds on algae (waterweeds) and begins to swim actively.

Tail still very long

Tadpole swims by wriggling its long tail

Coiled gut

Underside of four-week-old tadpole

5 FROM SIX TO NINE WEEKS

Between six and nine weeks, the hind legs appear as short buds. At six weeks, the body becomes longer and the head region becomes more distinct as the tadpole grows older. In this tadpole, the hind legs are functional and aid the tail in propelling the tadpole forward. The diet may now include dead insects – even dead tadpoles – as well as plants. The bulges in the body wall are produced by the developing front legs, which emerge elbow-first through openings in the body wall.

Half-tadpole, half-frog, between six and nine weeks

Row of tiny teeth

6 AFTER NINE WEEKS

The tadpole now looks more like a miniature frog with a long tail. The scars around the front legs show where they emerged through the body wall. The tail is gradually absorbed and the froglets begin to leave the water and gather around the edges of the pond. They can now breathe air because their lungs have developed.

Hind leg helps propel tadpole forward

Bulge where front leg will start to form

4 AT FOUR WEEKS

The external gills become covered by the body skin – then they gradually disappear and are replaced by internal gills. The tadpole feeds by using rows of tiny teeth to rasp away at plants or algae-covered surfaces, producing a "soup" of vegetable particles that are trapped in the mouth. The oxygenated, food-laden water enters the mouth and, after processing, leaves by the spiracle. Four-week-old tadpoles have a long, coiled gut to extract as much nourishment as possible from their poor diet. They are active social animals and may school like fish.

Head starting to take shape

Lungs inside chest area are fully developed

Front leg now fully formed

Tadpole between nine and twelve weeks of age

Tail gradually growing shorter

Caterpillar to chrysalis

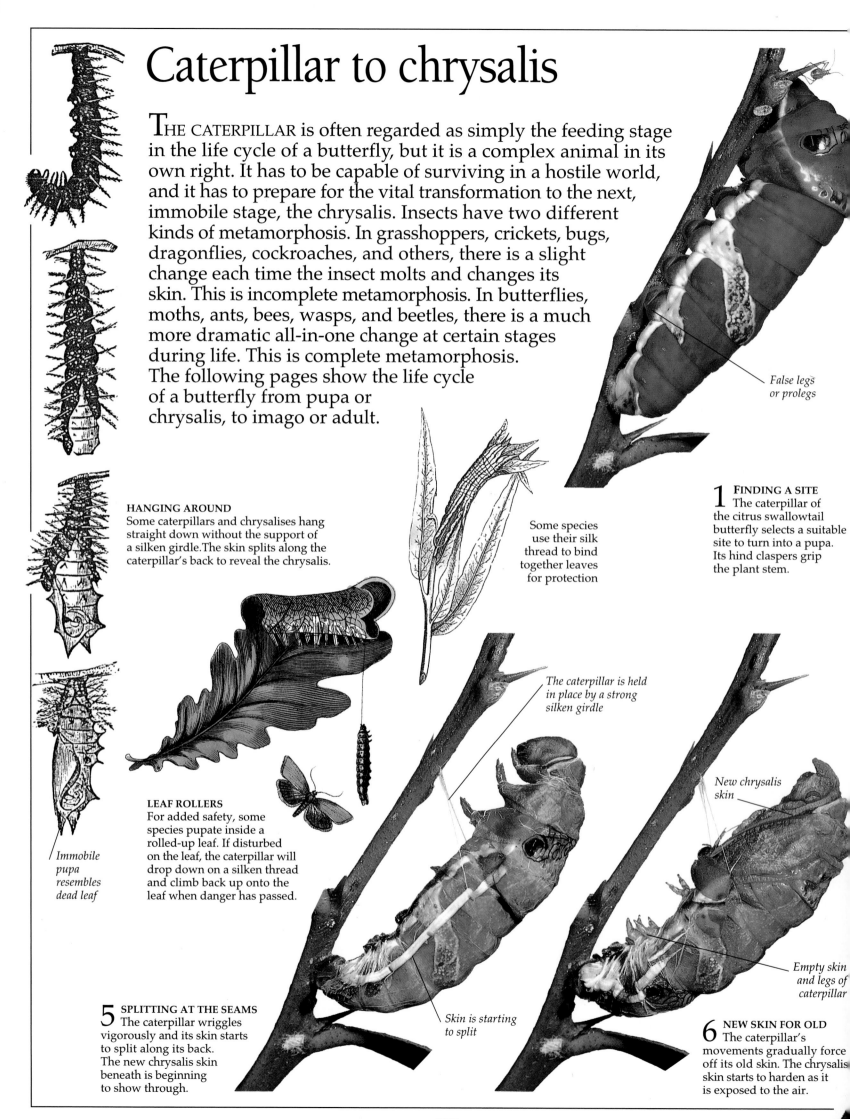

THE CATERPILLAR is often regarded as simply the feeding stage in the life cycle of a butterfly, but it is a complex animal in its own right. It has to be capable of surviving in a hostile world, and it has to prepare for the vital transformation to the next, immobile stage, the chrysalis. Insects have two different kinds of metamorphosis. In grasshoppers, crickets, bugs, dragonflies, cockroaches, and others, there is a slight change each time the insect molts and changes its skin. This is incomplete metamorphosis. In butterflies, moths, ants, bees, wasps, and beetles, there is a much more dramatic all-in-one change at certain stages during life. This is complete metamorphosis. The following pages show the life cycle of a butterfly from pupa or chrysalis, to imago or adult.

False legs or prolegs

HANGING AROUND
Some caterpillars and chrysalises hang straight down without the support of a silken girdle. The skin splits along the caterpillar's back to reveal the chrysalis.

Some species use their silk thread to bind together leaves for protection

1 FINDING A SITE
The caterpillar of the citrus swallowtail butterfly selects a suitable site to turn into a pupa. Its hind claspers grip the plant stem.

Immobile pupa resembles dead leaf

LEAF ROLLERS
For added safety, some species pupate inside a rolled-up leaf. If disturbed on the leaf, the caterpillar will drop down on a silken thread and climb back up onto the leaf when danger has passed.

The caterpillar is held in place by a strong silken girdle

New chrysalis skin

Empty skin and legs of caterpillar

5 SPLITTING AT THE SEAMS
The caterpillar wriggles vigorously and its skin starts to split along its back. The new chrysalis skin beneath is beginning to show through.

Skin is starting to split

6 NEW SKIN FOR OLD
The caterpillar's movements gradually force off its old skin. The chrysalis skin starts to harden as it is exposed to the air.

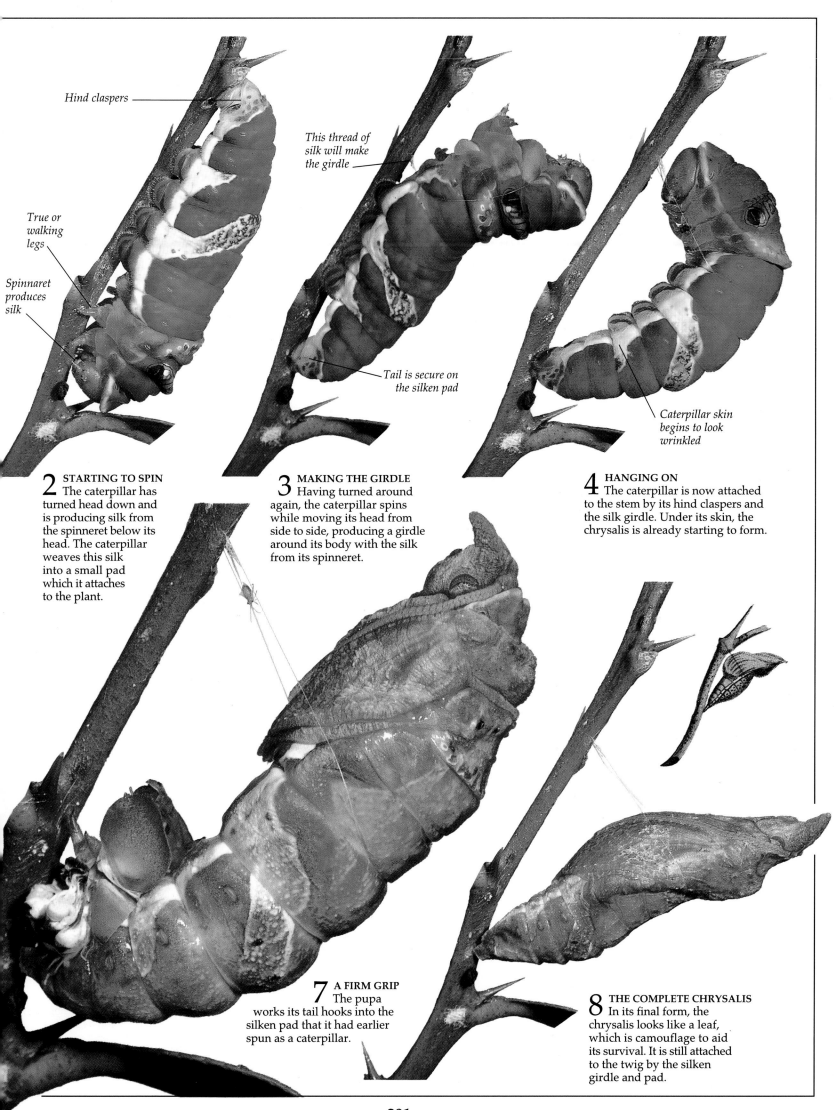

Hind claspers

This thread of silk will make the girdle

True or walking legs

Spinneret produces silk

Tail is secure on the silken pad

Caterpillar skin begins to look wrinkled

2 STARTING TO SPIN
The caterpillar has turned head down and is producing silk from the spinneret below its head. The caterpillar weaves this silk into a small pad which it attaches to the plant.

3 MAKING THE GIRDLE
Having turned around again, the caterpillar spins while moving its head from side to side, producing a girdle around its body with the silk from its spinneret.

4 HANGING ON
The caterpillar is now attached to the stem by its hind claspers and the silk girdle. Under its skin, the chrysalis is already starting to form.

7 A FIRM GRIP
The pupa works its tail hooks into the silken pad that it had earlier spun as a caterpillar.

8 THE COMPLETE CHRYSALIS
In its final form, the chrysalis looks like a leaf, which is camouflage to aid its survival. It is still attached to the twig by the silken girdle and pad.

Pupa to butterfly

A BUTTERFLY PUPA may hang quite still in its chrysalis for several weeks or, in some species, right through the winter. Nothing seems to happen but, within the hard case, tremendous changes are taking place. The body tissues are completely broken down, and reassembled into the adult butterfly with antennae, wings, and other delicate features. Across these pages, you can see a blue morpho from Central and South America emerging from its chrysalis.

"THE FLIGHT FROM EGYPT"
A blue morpho butterfly is used in the border around this illustration from *Hastings Hours*, an illuminated manuscript from c.1480.

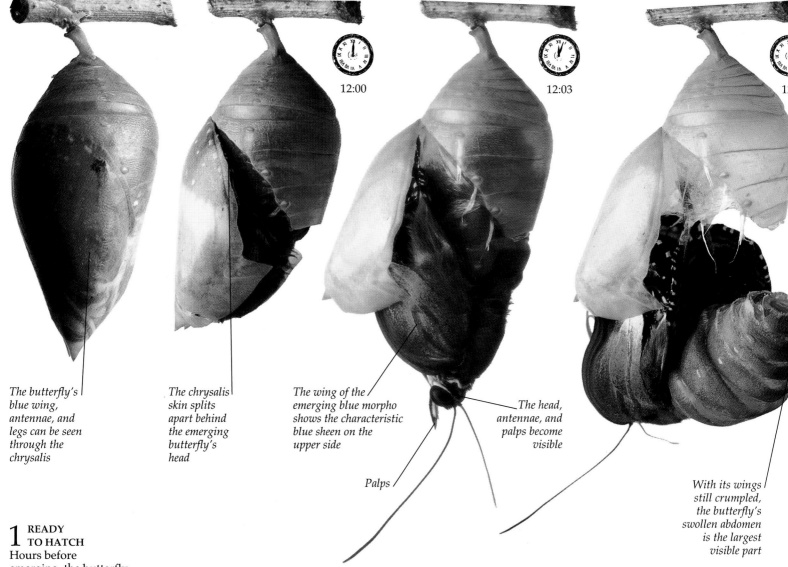

12:00

12:03

12:05

The butterfly's blue wing, antennae, and legs can be seen through the chrysalis

The chrysalis skin splits apart behind the emerging butterfly's head

The wing of the emerging blue morpho shows the characteristic blue sheen on the upper side

Palps

The head, antennae, and palps become visible

With its wings still crumpled, the butterfly's swollen abdomen is the largest visible part

1 READY TO HATCH
Hours before emerging, the butterfly is still developing. By now, some of the blue morpho's structures can be seen through the skin of the chrysalis. The dark area is the butterfly's wing, and traces of the antennae and legs are visible toward the bottom of the chrysalis. It takes about 85 days after the egg is laid for a blue morpho adult to emerge.

2 FIRST STAGE
Once the insect has completed its metamorphosis and is ready to emerge, it begins to pump body fluids into its head and thorax. This helps to split the chrysalis along certain weak points, so that the adult insect can begin to force its way out.

3 HEAD AND THORAX EMERGE
Once the skin of the chrysalis is broken, expansion can proceed more rapidly. Inflation is due not only to the body fluids in the head and thorax, but also to the air the insect takes in. Although by now the antennae, head, and palps (smaller tasting mouthparts) are visible, the wings are still too soft and crumpled for proper identification.

4 COMPLETELY FREE
Having pushed its way out of the chrysalis, the butterfly's body now hangs free. At this stage, the butterfly's exoskeleton is soft and still capable of more expansion. If for any reason the butterfly is damaged at this stage or confined, perhaps by a thoughtless collector, complete expansion is not possible. All the parts harden and a crippled butterfly results.

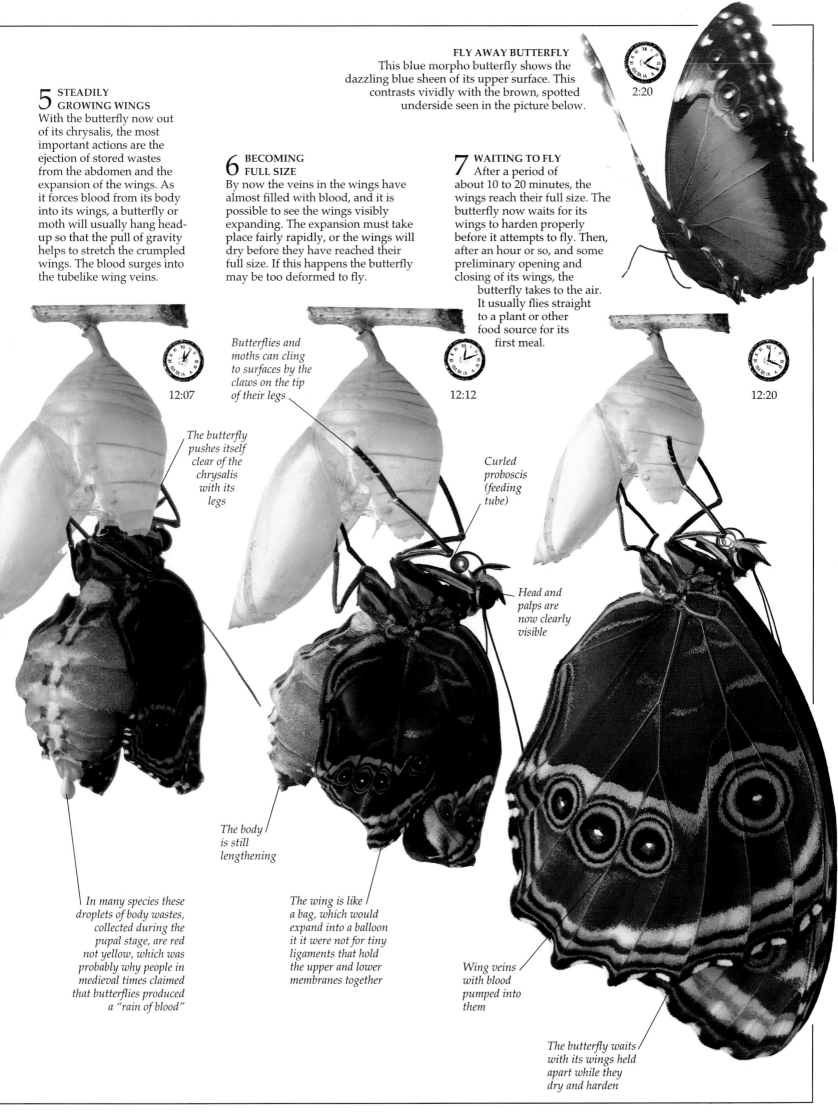

5 STEADILY GROWING WINGS

With the butterfly now out of its chrysalis, the most important actions are the ejection of stored wastes from the abdomen and the expansion of the wings. As it forces blood from its body into its wings, a butterfly or moth will usually hang head-up so that the pull of gravity helps to stretch the crumpled wings. The blood surges into the tubelike wing veins.

6 BECOMING FULL SIZE

By now the veins in the wings have almost filled with blood, and it is possible to see the wings visibly expanding. The expansion must take place fairly rapidly, or the wings will dry before they have reached their full size. If this happens the butterfly may be too deformed to fly.

7 WAITING TO FLY

After a period of about 10 to 20 minutes, the wings reach their full size. The butterfly now waits for its wings to harden properly before it attempts to fly. Then, after an hour or so, and some preliminary opening and closing of its wings, the butterfly takes to the air. It usually flies straight to a plant or other food source for its first meal.

FLY AWAY BUTTERFLY
This blue morpho butterfly shows the dazzling blue sheen of its upper surface. This contrasts vividly with the brown, spotted underside seen in the picture below.

2:20

12:07

Butterflies and moths can cling to surfaces by the claws on the tip of their legs

The butterfly pushes itself clear of the chrysalis with its legs

In many species these droplets of body wastes, collected during the pupal stage, are red not yellow, which was probably why people in medieval times claimed that butterflies produced a "rain of blood"

12:12

The body is still lengthening

The wing is like a bag, which would expand into a balloon if it were not for tiny ligaments that hold the upper and lower membranes together

Curled proboscis (feeding tube)

Head and palps are now clearly visible

12:20

Wing veins with blood pumped into them

The butterfly waits with its wings held apart while they dry and harden

Hatched at an early age

Feeding
the children

Bɪʀᴅs ᴀɴᴅ ᴍᴀᴍᴍᴀʟs, with their relatively large brains and adaptable behavior, are the two groups of animals which provide the most parental care. Birds who nest on the ground or in exposed places tend to have chicks that hatch in a well-developed state, with strong legs, eyes open, and feathers partly grown, ready to run from predators. However, the newly hatched young of the more protected tree and hole-nesters are at a much more immature stage, with bare skin, wing and leg stumps, and naked skin. But they develop almost before your eyes, as shown by these blue tit babies and their tireless parents.

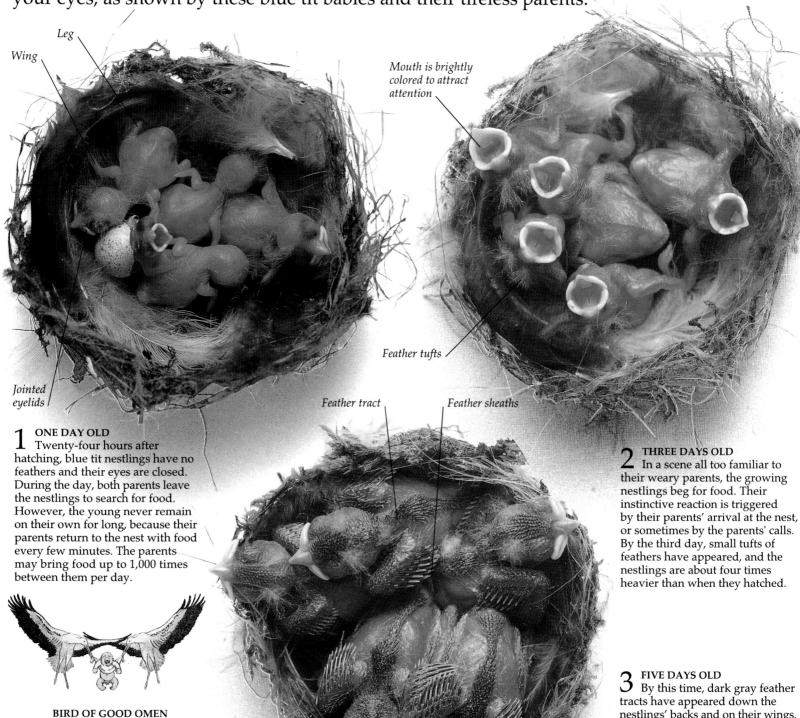

Leg

Wing

Mouth is brightly
colored to attract
attention

Feather tufts

Jointed
eyelids

Feather tract

Feather sheaths

1 ONE DAY OLD
Twenty-four hours after hatching, blue tit nestlings have no feathers and their eyes are closed. During the day, both parents leave the nestlings to search for food. However, the young never remain on their own for long, because their parents return to the nest with food every few minutes. The parents may bring food up to 1,000 times between them per day.

BIRD OF GOOD OMEN
Faithful to its mate and tireless as a parent, the stork is recognized internationally as a symbol of the birth of a new human baby.

2 THREE DAYS OLD
In a scene all too familiar to their weary parents, the growing nestlings beg for food. Their instinctive reaction is triggered by their parents' arrival at the nest, or sometimes by the parents' calls. By the third day, small tufts of feathers have appeared, and the nestlings are about four times heavier than when they hatched.

3 FIVE DAYS OLD
By this time, dark gray feather tracts have appeared down the nestlings' backs and on their wings. These are areas of skin which are destined to produce the feathers. On the wings, the tubular sheaths which will eventually produce and protect the flight feathers have already started to develop.

Feather sheaths

Emerging feather tips

ESCAPE FROM DANGER
Although most birds protect their nestlings by bluff or aggression when threatened, some parents can pick up their young and carry them away. Depending on the species, they may use either their beak, legs, or talons.

The woodcock is said to hold a chick between its legs while flying, although this has never been proved

The secretive water rail carries its chicks in its long beak

Hawks are thought to hold their nestlings in their talons as they carry them to a safer place

4 NINE DAYS OLD
As the feather sheaths grow longer, the tips of the flight feathers start to emerge. The bare skin between the feather tracts is covered up by the growing feathers. The nest is starting to get crowded, although for blue tits, five nestlings is quite a small family.

5 THIRTEEN DAYS OLD
At nearly two weeks, the nestlings are fully feathered and their eyes are open. Within another five days they will fledge, or leave the nest, but the young birds will follow their parents for some time, begging for food as they learn how to look after themselves. Independence often comes when the parents begin preparations for another clutch of eggs. Once the young birds find their parents ignoring their calls for food, they fend for themselves.

Unique to mammals

MARE AND FOAL
A mare nudges her foal toward her teats; the foal then feeds on average some 4 times each hour.

THE MAMMAL GROUP is named after the mammary glands – body parts that produce nourishing milk to feed a newborn baby. Milk is the young mammal's complete food, providing even the water it needs. No other animal possesses mammary glands, so no other mother can feed her offspring on milk. The actual glands resemble specialized sweat glands and grow into two "milk lines" on each side of the abdomen. Cats and dogs have several glands and teats along each side; in hoofed animals the teats are near the hind legs. In monkeys, apes, and humans, they are on the chest, a site that may be connected with adaptation to a tree-dwelling life and the consequent need to hold a baby with the forelimbs. Another body part unique to female mammals is the uterus, or womb. The baby develops inside this, kept warm, protected, and nourished, until ready for birth.

Mother watches and listens in case of danger

The mother lies still as her babies feed

THE NEAT TEAT
Unlike kittens, puppies usually feed from whichever teat they can find. The teat (or nipple) is a rubbery-textured lobe of tissue. It fits neatly inside the baby's mouth, to minimize loss of milk as the baby suckles. The teat also acts as a shut-off valve to prevent leakage of milk after feeding.

CONTENTED CAT AND KITTENS
Within an hour of birth, a kitten is suckling (sucking milk from its mother's teat). About 30 minutes passes between the births of successive offspring in a litter, and there are four or five kittens in an average litter, so the first-born will already be suckling when the later ones arrive. The tiny kitten, although unable to see or hear, can smell – and can feel with its whiskers, fur, nose, and feet. It moves to the milk supply by scrabbling with its feet, first locating the warmth of the mother's body, then working its way along until it finds a teat. It "kneads" the teat with its feet and face to stimulate the milk flow. After an initial free-for-all, each kitten tends to settle into a routine and suckle from its own teat. In a large litter, the young may feed in shifts.

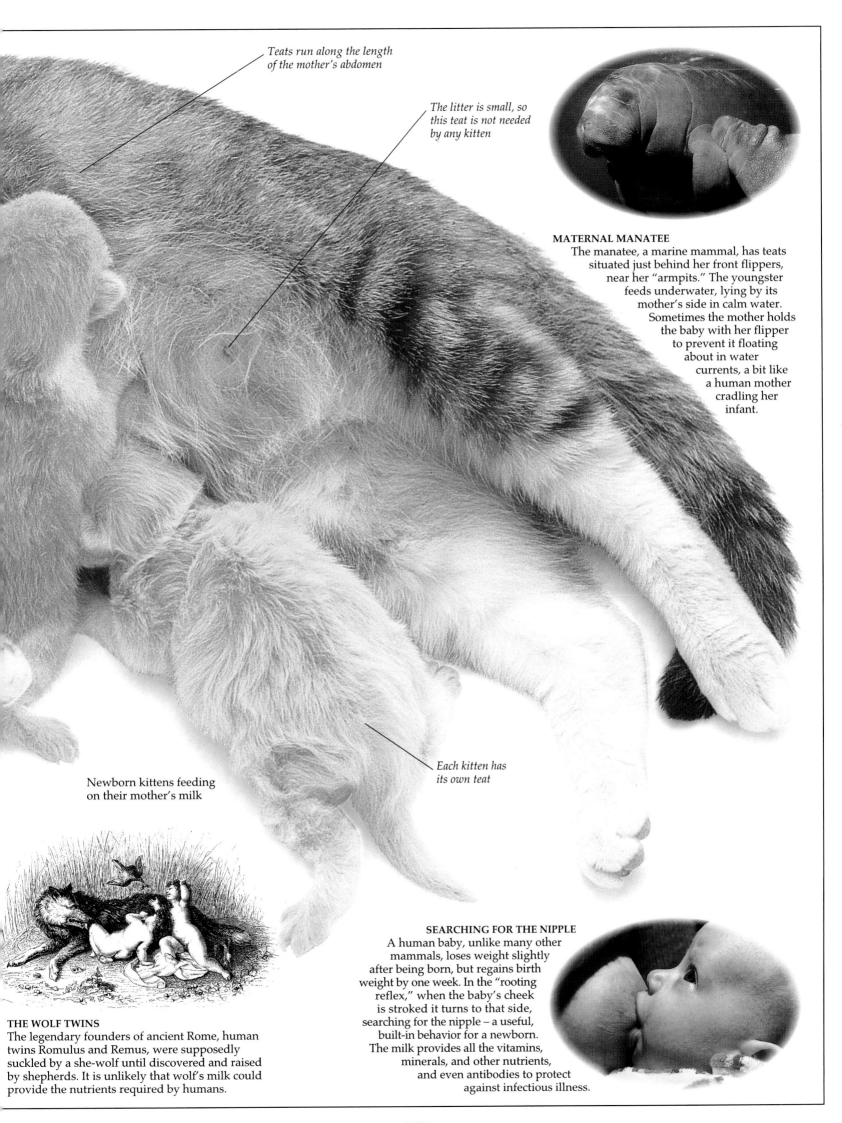

Teats run along the length of the mother's abdomen

The litter is small, so this teat is not needed by any kitten

MATERNAL MANATEE
The manatee, a marine mammal, has teats situated just behind her front flippers, near her "armpits." The youngster feeds underwater, lying by its mother's side in calm water. Sometimes the mother holds the baby with her flipper to prevent it floating about in water currents, a bit like a human mother cradling her infant.

Newborn kittens feeding on their mother's milk

Each kitten has its own teat

THE WOLF TWINS
The legendary founders of ancient Rome, human twins Romulus and Remus, were supposedly suckled by a she-wolf until discovered and raised by shepherds. It is unlikely that wolf's milk could provide the nutrients required by humans.

SEARCHING FOR THE NIPPLE
A human baby, unlike many other mammals, loses weight slightly after being born, but regains birth weight by one week. In the "rooting reflex," when the baby's cheek is stroked it turns to that side, searching for the nipple – a useful, built-in behavior for a newborn. The milk provides all the vitamins, minerals, and other nutrients, and even antibodies to protect against infectious illness.

Living in packs

HUNDREDS of mammal species, from lemmings to leopards, leave their young to make their way in the world after they have been reared by their parents. But for other mammal species, living in groups is the norm. The young may stay with their own parents for a time, as in wolves and killer whales, or the young males may move on to join other groups, as in elephants and horses. Social living has several advantages, such as hunting or defending the group as a team. In a gray wolf pack, each member knows his or her position in the scale of dominance. The only pair of wolves to mate are the dominant male and the dominant female, and after the cubs are born the father brings meat back to the den for the mother. The cubs are suckled for about ten weeks, and then the mother and the younger wolves feed them with regurgitated meat (partly digested meat returned to the mouth from the stomach) until they are old enough to start hunting with the pack. The cubs might play-fight while they are young, but in time, they too learn their place within the pack.

FOLLOW THE LEADER
This group of gray wolves is on its way to look for prey in the forest. Wolves will eat anything, from a moose to a mouse, and even insects and berries if food is scarce. Wolves range over areas up to 400 sq miles (1,000 sq km), in packs as large as 20 individuals. They can reach speeds of up to 40 mph (65 km/h) in short bursts.

Ears are erect to show that the wolf is on the alert – either for prey or foe

GRAY WOLF
Once gray wolves were found throughout most of North America. But these intelligent and sociable animals have been slaughtered by farmers and hunters for centuries. There are now only limited numbers, in Alaska, Canada, and the northern United States.

Sharp teeth enable wolf to kill its prey quickly

A WOLF OF MANY COLORS
The Arctic wolf from the far north of Canada has a very thick, white winter coat for warmth and camouflage in the snow and ice, although it can be a shade of gray or buff, or occasionally even black during the summer. It also has a short tail and small ears to keep the body as compact as possible to reduce heat loss. Arctic wolves feed on hares and birds, and if they are lucky, a pack may be able to kill a deer or a musk ox.

LITTLE RED RIDING HOOD
When there were really wolves in the forests, parents would tell their children the story of Little Red Riding Hood to warn them against going out alone.

A RARE RED WOLF
The red wolf is smaller than the gray wolf and is adapted for living in the warmer climate of the southeastern US. It was extinct in the wild but in 1988 a few were reintroduced into North Carolina.

WINNER OR LOSER
Wolves are quick to snarl at each other when they are challenging for a position of greater seniority in the pack. But it is mostly bluff, and serious fights are rare.

TROUBLE AHEAD FOR YOUNG BRAVES
According to the legends of the Nootka Indians in North America, young braves were sometimes carried away by wolves. This club may have been used as a display object to represent the powers the brave received during his captivity. Made of abalone shell, bone, and human hair, a wolf's head is carved at one end.

TERROR OF WEREWOLVES
According to folklore, a werewolf is a person who has changed into a wolf, or is capable of taking the shape of a wolf, while keeping its human intelligence. Many horror films have been made about werewolves.

The legs have to be long and very powerful so the wolf can range over huge distances in search of prey

A pack of wolves chase musk oxen on Ellesmere Island in the Arctic

The tail of this wolf is pointing down, showing it is rather wary of what is ahead

Living in prides

PERSIAN PLATE
This delightful plate from Iran shows a lion standing with the sun rising behind him. This was the symbol of Iranian kingship.

Unlike dogs and wolves, most types of cat, both big and small, are solitary hunters, except, that is, for the lions. The second largest of the big cats, lions live in family groups, or prides, of up to 12 animals. Because of their family support, they are the only cats that are able to kill animals larger than themselves. The role of the male lions is to defend their pride's territory. They do this by pacing around it, by roaring, and by marking trees and posts with their urine. The lionesses do most of the hunting. Each lioness gives birth every two years to two or three cubs. If a new lioness joins a pride, the lion will usually kill any cubs she may already have before he mates with her. Similarly, when the pride's leading male becomes old and weak, he is challenged by a younger, stronger male, who then takes over and may also kill any existing cubs. This ensures the pride rears only his own offspring, not the cubs of other males.

THE KING
The lion's body posture, facial expression, and tail communicate his mood to pride members and enemies. A threatening lion will pull back his lips, and a twitching tail indicates arousal, interest, or anger.

African lion and lioness

The lioness has no mane, probably because it would impede her efficiency as a hunter

THE PRIDE
The composition of a pride varies, but females always outnumber males. When young males reach adulthood, they either oust any older lions from the pride or, if unsuccessful, leave the pride and attach themselves to any other group of females in need of males. A pride of lions shares its territory with many other meat-eaters, competing for every scrap of meat left over when the pride has had its fill.

MATE TO KING
The lionesses are the core of any pride, sticking together with close family – sisters, daughters, and aunts. The lioness has a powerful, lithe body so she can creep stealthily up to prey before moving in for the kill.

LEO
People born under the astrological sign of Leo are said to be proud, brave, strong, and self-centered – just like the king of beasts himself.

The story of Daniel in the lions' den appears in the Old Testament

A magnificent mane, heavy body, and huge canine teeth ensure that the lion rules his world

The mane makes the lion look even bigger than he really is. It may help to frighten off other lions

THE LION AND THE UNICORN
In the Renaissance (the 15th and 16th centuries) the lion often appeared in paintings and architecture. In this beautiful French tapestry, the lion is shown to be at peace with the unicorn, symbol of purity.

HERACLES AND THE NEMEAN LION
Heracles had to perform 12 labors to pay for the killing of his family. The first was to kill the lion whose skin could not be pierced by weapons, so Heracles choked it to death. After this, he wore the skin to protect himself.

The tuft of hair at the knees makes the lion look even stronger

The still visible spots are a leftover from when the lioness was a cub

The tuft at the end of the tail is an important signal in communication when the male is challenged by a rival

Living in herds

HORSES WERE PROBABLY first domesticated for draft work and riding, over 6,000 years ago, in the Ukraine region of Europe. Gradually, wild horses were replaced by tamed ones. Today there are no truly wild horses. But there are many horses and ponies described as "feral." These feral animals are descended from domesticated stock, but are no longer under human control, and they live and breed on their own. Their behavior and social life partly revert to the truly natural lifestyle of their distant wild ancestors. Horses are social creatures, and live in groups called herds. A herd has the harem type of social organization, with a chief stallion who gathers and protects several mares and their young. Today, some feral horses, such as the American mustang and Australian brumby, are controlled by hunting, or rounded up and domesticated.

FELL PONIES
In Britain there are many breeds of pony that live on the moors, such as the Fell pony. Although Fell ponies are owned, they are allowed to live and breed with very little human control. Traditionally, the Fell ponies have been used as pack ponies, for riding, and for light draft work.

Well-proportioned head

Long face and large nose give an exceptionally keen sense of smell for detecting predators

GERMAN DÜLMEN
These rare ponies live semiwild on the Duke of Croy's estate in Westphalia in Germany. They have been bred with both British and Polish ponies, so they are not purebred. The herd dates back to the early 1300s.

Long legs for running fast on the open grasslands, where horses first evolved

THE BRUMBY OF AUSTRALIA
For 150 years there have been herds of feral horses in Australia, ever since they were abandoned during the gold rush. These horses, called brumbies, formed herds and reproduced in great numbers over large areas. They are unpopular with cattle and sheep ranchers because they compete for grazing, and usually carry many parasites. Since the 1960s, they have been hunted so extensively that there are now very few. A brumby stallion will defend his herd by kicking and biting with great vigor.

Well-formed foot with strong horn on hoof

302

SYMBOLIC HORSES
A wild running horse has often been used as a symbol of speed, power, freedom, and elegance. It has advertised many things, from banks to sports cars – such as the Mustang and Pinto in the US, and (as shown here) the Ferrari, the supreme speedster.

Ferrari

THE MUSTANGS OF AMERICA
The feral horses, or mustangs, of the Nevada desert have hard lives traveling great distances in search of enough grass and water to survive.

Star

Position of ears is important in social communication, showing fear, curiosity, and other moods

Long, straight, full mane

DAWN IN THE CAMARGUE
The beautiful white horses from the Camargue in the south of France have lived wild in the marshes of the Rhône delta for over 1,000 years. They have very wide hooves for living on soft wet grassland.

Like its ears, a horse's tail is an important social signal, as well as a useful fly whisk

Snipe

Egg-shaped eye can simultaneously focus on grass and on distant horizon to watch for enemies

Blaze

Deep chest with large heart and lungs give great stamina for sustained fast running

THE PONIES OF THE NEW FOREST
There have been herds of ponies living in the New Forest of Hampshire, England, since the 11th century. For 800 years these ponies lived wild, until attempts were made in the 19th century to improve them by bringing in stallions of other breeds. They still run semiwild in their native area, but are also reared on stud farms to provide ideal riding and working ponies.

CHAPTER 4
NATURAL SURVIVAL

IN NATURE, life is rarely easy. The list of life's problems is very long. It includes bad weather, harsh seasons, famine, drought, predators, competitors, pests, and parasites. Animals overcome these problems by a countless variety of means.

AUSTRALIAN HORN SHARK
Port Jackson sharks live on the seabed in shallow water. Many often gather in the same area where they rest on the sandy floors of caves or channels between rocks. These may offer protection against currents.

AS BRIGHT AS THE BACKGROUND
Many coral-reef fish, such as these adult (with yellow tail) and young emperor angelfish, have intensely bright colors and patterns. Isolated, as here, they seem to be inviting predation. But their natural habitat is among the equally colorful corals, seaweeds, crabs, and sponges of the reef. And while they stay together in a school, it is difficult for a predator to pick one out clearly to attack it.

AS DULL AS THE BACKGROUND
In great contrast to the coral reef, the shallow seabed in other places is dull shades of green or brown, with sand, mud, and pebbles. The spotted ray is at home here, camouflaged to blend in perfectly, thereby aiding survival.

MAKING FRIENDS
Some different species help each other.
These clownfish are protected by
the sea anemones' stinging
tentacles in return for
leftover scraps of food.

Resisting attack

SOME ANIMALS ARE UNLIKELY to become prey. No creature is likely to attack a tiger, eagle, crocodile, or shark. These beasts are large and powerful and well equipped with teeth, claws, and other weapons. They are called top carnivores, which means that in terms of food chains and food webs, they are at the summit – they can eat what they like, but nothing eats them. For the majority of animals, especially the smaller ones, a vital part of the survival game is to avoid becoming prey. There are several basic strategies: to remain quite still in the hope of not being noticed, an option which is greatly helped by being camouflaged; to escape, by fleeing at high speed; to hide in a crack or crevice; or to fight back fiercely. The first strategy has two important advantages. It uses very little energy, and it is least likely to end in physical conflict.

ATTACK AND...
A crab will usually hide under a boulder or among seaweeds. If approached out in the open, it has a well-rehearsed set of actions, as shown by this common crab. It holds its pincers forward threateningly, then rears up as though about to attack. This crab has already had a close encounter, since it has lost a leg.

STAY THEN FLEE
The day gecko, a lizard from Madagascar, lives among the bright green leaves of rainforest trees. It is difficult to spot there, because of its excellent camouflage. The gecko may even sway with the leaves to improve its disguise. As soon as it thinks it has been noticed, the gecko races away with astonishing speed and agility.

The gecko cleans its face and eyes with its tongue

Gaps between the scales allow the gecko to bend its body

Poisonous sting

NO NEED TO FLEE
Most animals know not to mess with a scorpion. This eight-legged creature is an arachnid, a relative of the spiders. When approached, the scorpion turns to face the enemy. It holds out its strong pincers threateningly and arches its tail over its head. This brings the sharp venomous sting into full view. Most scorpions use the sting mainly in self-defense. Some may use the poison to subdue struggling prey.

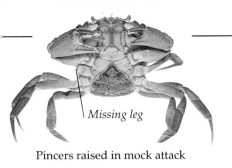

Missing leg

Pincers raised in mock attack

Crouched and curled up in defense

Preparing to escape

...THEN RETREAT
Most enemies think again when confronted by spirited resistance. When the enemy hesitates, the crab lowers itself, ready to curl into a protective ball, and then begins to crawl off sideways.

A claw on each toe gives extra grip

The underside of the toes are covered with tiny bristles for grip

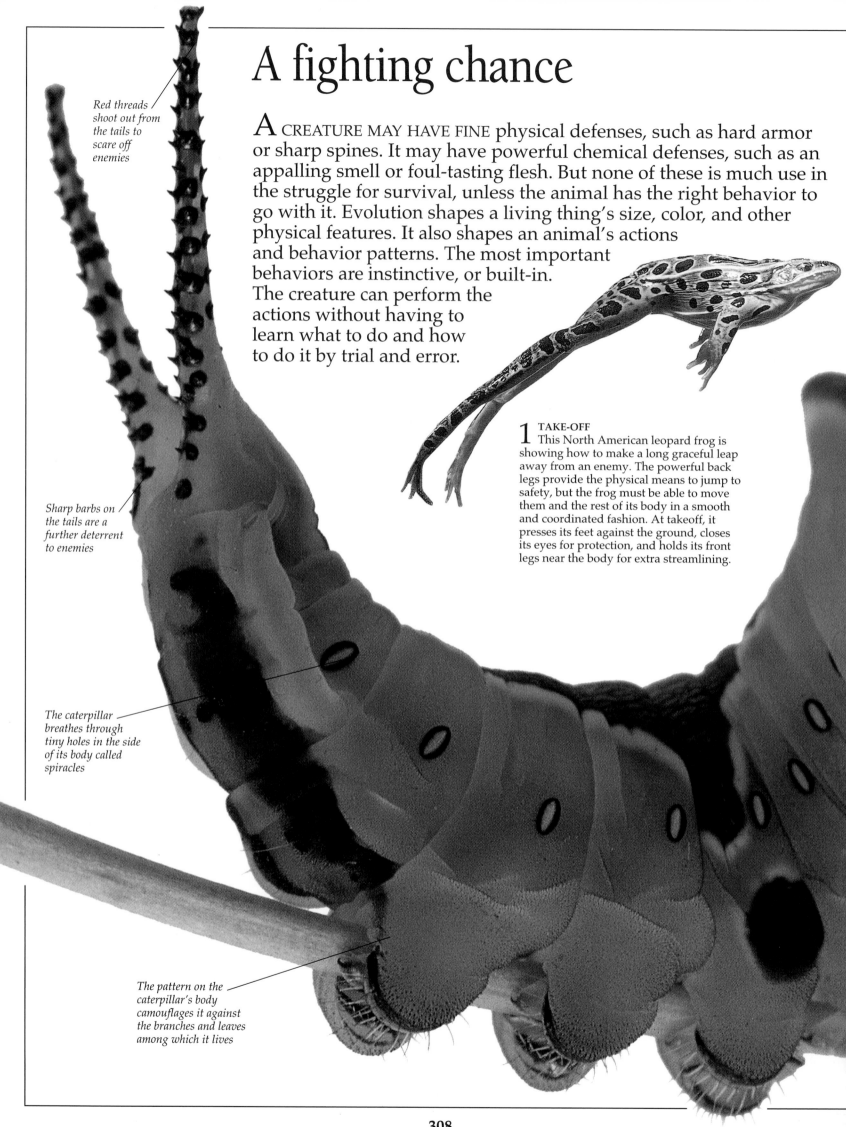

A fighting chance

A CREATURE MAY HAVE FINE physical defenses, such as hard armor or sharp spines. It may have powerful chemical defenses, such as an appalling smell or foul-tasting flesh. But none of these is much use in the struggle for survival, unless the animal has the right behavior to go with it. Evolution shapes a living thing's size, color, and other physical features. It also shapes an animal's actions and behavior patterns. The most important behaviors are instinctive, or built-in. The creature can perform the actions without having to learn what to do and how to do it by trial and error.

Red threads shoot out from the tails to scare off enemies

Sharp barbs on the tails are a further deterrent to enemies

The caterpillar breathes through tiny holes in the side of its body called spiracles

The pattern on the caterpillar's body camouflages it against the branches and leaves among which it lives

1 TAKE-OFF
This North American leopard frog is showing how to make a long graceful leap away from an enemy. The powerful back legs provide the physical means to jump to safety, but the frog must be able to move them and the rest of its body in a smooth and coordinated fashion. At takeoff, it presses its feet against the ground, closes its eyes for protection, and holds its front legs near the body for extra streamlining.

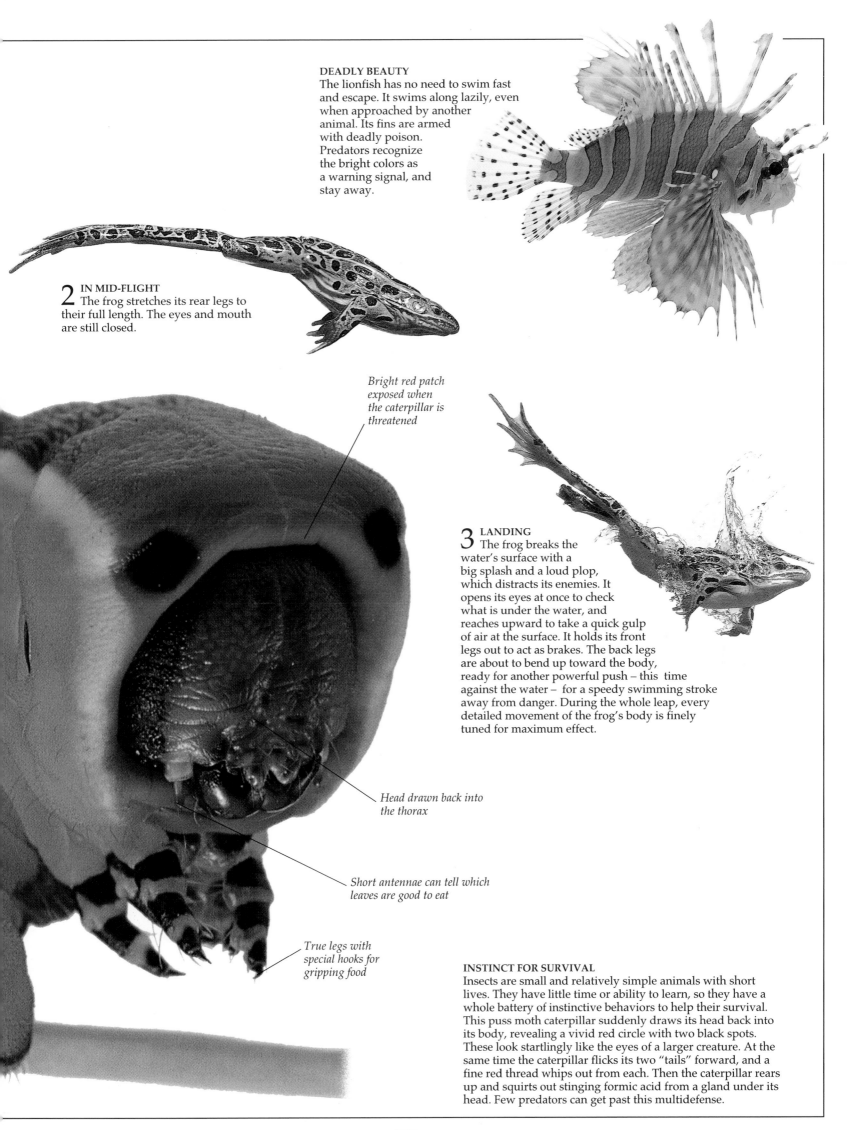

DEADLY BEAUTY
The lionfish has no need to swim fast
and escape. It swims along lazily, even
when approached by another
animal. Its fins are armed
with deadly poison.
Predators recognize
the bright colors as
a warning signal, and
stay away.

2 IN MID-FLIGHT
The frog stretches its rear legs to
their full length. The eyes and mouth
are still closed.

*Bright red patch
exposed when
the caterpillar is
threatened*

3 LANDING
The frog breaks the
water's surface with a
big splash and a loud plop,
which distracts its enemies. It
opens its eyes at once to check
what is under the water, and
reaches upward to take a quick gulp
of air at the surface. It holds its front
legs out to act as brakes. The back legs
are about to bend up toward the body,
ready for another powerful push – this time
against the water – for a speedy swimming stroke
away from danger. During the whole leap, every
detailed movement of the frog's body is finely
tuned for maximum effect.

*Head drawn back into
the thorax*

*Short antennae can tell which
leaves are good to eat*

*True legs with
special hooks for
gripping food*

INSTINCT FOR SURVIVAL
Insects are small and relatively simple animals with short
lives. They have little time or ability to learn, so they have a
whole battery of instinctive behaviors to help their survival.
This puss moth caterpillar suddenly draws its head back into
its body, revealing a vivid red circle with two black spots.
These look startlingly like the eyes of a larger creature. At the
same time the caterpillar flicks its two "tails" forward, and a
fine red thread whips out from each. Then the caterpillar rears
up and squirts out stinging formic acid from a gland under its
head. Few predators can get past this multidefense.

Sensing the surroundings

ONE OF THE CHARACTERISTIC FEATURES of any animal is its ability to detect what is happening in its surroundings, and to react appropriately to ensure survival. Many animals have the same five main senses that we do – sight, hearing, touch, taste, and smell. Amphibians show these senses very well, since they are adapted for life both on land and in the water. Some creatures, including amphibians, have extra senses, such as the ability to detect the Earth's magnetic field, or to pick up the tiny electrical signals made by the contracting muscles of an active animal.

NO ROAD SENSE
Like most wild animals, frogs and toads do not understand the danger of road traffic. However, drivers can help by taking care. Road signs like this warn motorists about migrating frogs and toads.

For ¾ mile

MYSTERY SENSE ORGAN
The wormlike amphibians called caecilians have a small tentacle below the eye. Its function is unknown, but it may be for picking up vibrations by touch, or for detecting food, predators, or a mate by smell.

Tentacle

FEELING THE PRESSURE
Frogs and toads that spend a lot of time in water have, like fishes, a lateral line – a sense system for detecting pressure changes in the water made by moving or stationary objects. The individual sense organs of the lateral line, called plaques, are easily seen on the head and along the sides of the body on this African clawed toad.

Lateral line

Lateral line

Eye of mandarin salamander (below)

Eye of marbled newt (below)

SIGHT
It is a safe guess that the larger an animal's eyes, the more it relies on eyesight. The mandarin salamander relies on vision to spot slow-moving prey in poor light. The marbled newt hunts more in water and so uses sight, smell, and taste.

TADPOLES TOO
Lateral line systems are also found in aquatic newts, salamanders, sirens, and amphibian larvae, like this American bullfrog tadpole. Its position and development varies in different species.

TOUCH

Sensitivity to touch is usually greatest on an animal's extremities, such as its hands, feet, nose, lips, and ears. The Surinam toad has long, thin tubular fingers, and the skin on them is packed with touch-sensitive nerve endings, rather like our own. The toad feels with these for worms, insect larvae, fish, and other prey in the muddy beds of rivers and streams. The fingers are covered with tiny spines that help grip the prey.

(1) Vertical pupil of red-eyed tree frog

TEMPERATURE CONTROL

Moist-skinned animals such as amphibians and worms rapidly lose body water by evaporation in hot or dry conditions. They sense temperature levels and sudden dryness through their skin and control their body temperature by basking in the sun if too cold, or moving into the shade if too hot. This painted reed frog of South Africa is reducing the area of its body exposed to the sun by tucking in its legs.

(2) Heart-shaped pupil of Oriental fire-bellied toad

(3) Horizontal pupil of Asian tree toad

PERFECT PUPILS

Eye color and pupil shape are very variable in amphibians and other animals: (1) vertical, catlike for night vision or quick response to rapidly changing light conditions; (2) heart-shaped; (3) horizontal (the more common pupil for normal daylight vision); and (4) round.

Ear of American bullfrog

(4) Round pupil of Madagascan tomato frog

HEARING

The basic design for an animal ear is a thin, taut membrane which vibrates when sound waves hit it – the eardrum. A frog's ears are plainly visible behind its eyes.

SMELL

Airborne chemicals are detected by a furry, hairlike olfactory organ inside the nose. Smells give information about food, enemies, and mates – the male newt wafts a mating scent from a gland at the base of its tail toward a female.

311

Camouflage

Black form

Speckled form

Peppered moth resting on a tree

THE THEME OF CAMOUFLAGE crops up again and again in this book because it does in nature. Colors and patterns that enable an animal to blend in with its surroundings are called cryptic (hiding) coloration. Creatures may mimic another object which is inedible, such as a twig, or distasteful, such as droppings. Or they may take on patterns and colors of local trees, rocks, or leaves. Because they are especially vulnerable in daylight hours, small edible animals, such as caterpillars and resting moths, have perfected the art of concealment. Butterflies, which are active by day, and which usually rest with their wings together over their backs, have adopted other forms of camouflage. Some forest butterflies rest like moths with their wings spread out, while other species disguise themselves as either living or decaying leaves.

CITY MOTH, COUNTRY MOTH
Some years ago, it was realized that the city form of the European peppered moth had gradually changed from a light to a black color. This helped them escape birds, which could easily spot a light-colored moth on a smoke-polluted tree. In the countryside the same moth is still speckled white.

DAMAGED LEAF
To make its camouflage more realistic, this Pyralid moth from South America has irregularly shaped clear areas in its wings. When the moth is resting these give the impression of a damaged leaf.

DECAYING LEAF
This South American leaf moth has a dead-leaf pattern on its wings, including a "skeletonized" part. When resting, the moth rolls the front part of its wings to resemble a leaf-stalk.

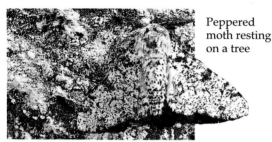

Wing looks like a torn leaf

Resemblance to stalk and veins of a leaf

INDIAN LEAF TRICK
The most dramatic example of butterfly camouflage is this Indian leaf butterfly. It frequently rests on the ground in leaf-litter, where it becomes virtually invisible.

Brown underside of leaf butterfly

Orange, brown, and blue upper side of leaf

DEAD OR ALIVE?
One of these dead leaves is the Indian leaf butterfly in its cryptic pose. Would you have noticed it in the speckled shade of a woodland? The butterfly must remain perfectly still, or the effect is spoiled – showing how behavior is also important for good camouflage.

Wings look like wood

Wings look like a dead leaf

VANISHING MOTHS
These two moths from South America are in their normal resting position and show how successful their camouflage is. In order to survive, they must not look like moths or they would soon be detected by a hungry bird or lizard.

When at rest, the undersides of the butterfly's wings are exposed, making it look like a decaying leaf

DEADLY ENEMIES
One of the main reasons why many moths and butterflies are camouflaged is to escape from predatory birds. Since birds hunt mainly by sight, rather than by sound or scent, the cryptic colors have to be especially accurate to fool them.

Light crusty-looking patches mimic the lichens which grow on old tree bark

WOOD BORER
The caterpillar of this carpenter moth from Central America bores into trees. As an adult, the moth would be almost invisible against this bark.

313

Patterns of life

ANIMALS ARE NOT ONLY CAMOUFLAGED to blend in with their surroundings. Some have specially shaped appendages which add to the effect, such as the twig-shaped legs of the stick insect. Other animals can change their own body pattern and coloration to merge in with the surroundings in which they happen to be. Among these quick-change artists are certain beetles and other insects, cuttlefish and squid, flatfish such as the plaice and sole, and reptiles such as the chameleon.

COLOR CONSCIOUS
Lizards, especially chameleons, are truly masters of camouflage. Many can make the color of their skin lighter or darker as needed. Although these changes take place so that the chameleon can match its background, many other things influence the color change. Light level, temperature, and the mood of the lizard (for example if it is frightened) can all affect the color it takes on. The chameleon's skin has several layers of color cells. Beneath these are the melanophores, cells with tentacle-like arms which extend through the other layers.

The color change is caused by the melanophores moving a dark brown pigment in and out of the upper layers of the skin

LEAF GREEN
Hard to spot against the palm trees on which they are commonly found, these tree skinks live in the forests of Indonesia, the Philippines, and the Solomon Islands. Their bright green and mottled brown bodies make them almost invisible. Green is a common color among tree-living animals active in the day.

FLOWER POWER
The head may be small, but beneath the leaves is the large body of a Murray River turtle from eastern Australia. The waterweed helps to hide the body of this powerful carnivore.

DOUBLE TROUBLE
Lying still in the leaf litter of the forests of tropical Africa, these gaboon vipers are nearly invisible in the dappled light and shade as they wait for rodents, frogs, and birds. The snake shape is disguised by the disruptive coloration and pattern. Yet when one of the snakes is removed from its natural background, its vivid markings become strikingly obvious. Although unaggressive and unlikely to attack, this viper's bite would be dangerously venomous to anyone unfortunate enough to tread on one! In fact, the fangs of the gaboon viper are the longest of any snake – up to 2 in (5 cm) in a 6 ft (1.80 m) specimen.

Gaboon viper

HIDDEN DEPTHS
Luckily for this black caiman, it could be mistaken for rocks as it lies in the muddy waters. It is hunted for its skin and is constantly threatened. But its ability to lie unseen also helps it when it is looking for food.

Hiding in the open

SMALL PLANT-EATING MAMMALS are vulnerable when feeding out in the open. They cannot take food back to a nest or burrow easily and their diet is usually not very nutritious, so they must spend long periods eating. Camouflage is therefore very important. A body covering of small parts or units with variable colors produces the best effect. The hairs on some insect and spider bodies, the tiny scales on butterfly wings, the scales on fish and reptiles, the feathers of birds, and the fur of mammals are all well suited to this purpose. A pattern may help to break up the body outline of some animals. This is called disruptive coloration.

BUILT-IN CAMOUFLAGE
The two-toed sloth of South America is very slow-moving and often completely still. In the dim forest light it merges with the foliage because it has green algae growing on its coat. Its long outer guard hairs have grooves on them in which the algae grow.

PEBBLE WITH WHISKERS
Small rodents such as mice and voles are among the most vulnerable of all animals. Their main defenses are sharp senses and a quick dive into a nearby burrow, or good camouflage if stranded out in the open. This Arabian spiny mouse's fur blends with the dry sand, light-colored pebbles, and parched wood of its semidesert home.

Extra-thick spiky hairs on its back give the spiny mouse its name

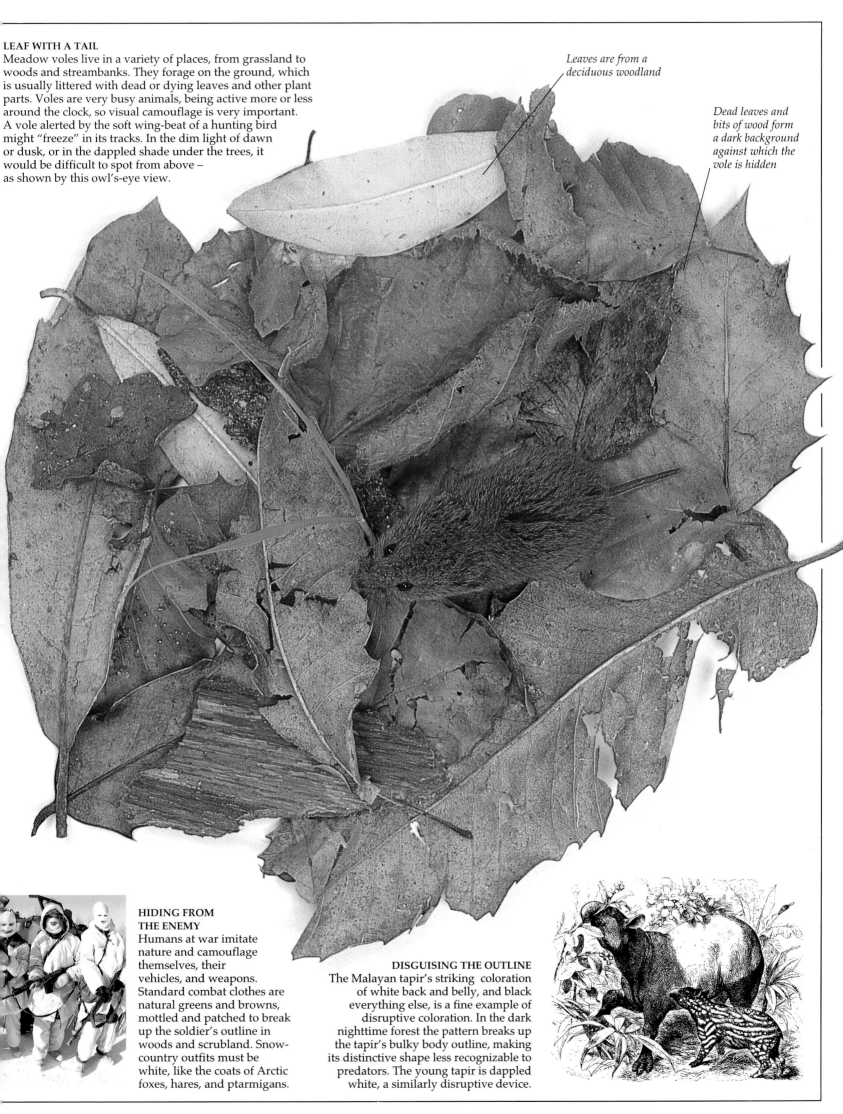

LEAF WITH A TAIL

Meadow voles live in a variety of places, from grassland to woods and streambanks. They forage on the ground, which is usually littered with dead or dying leaves and other plant parts. Voles are very busy animals, being active more or less around the clock, so visual camouflage is very important. A vole alerted by the soft wing-beat of a hunting bird might "freeze" in its tracks. In the dim light of dawn or dusk, or in the dappled shade under the trees, it would be difficult to spot from above – as shown by this owl's-eye view.

Leaves are from a deciduous woodland

Dead leaves and bits of wood form a dark background against which the vole is hidden

HIDING FROM THE ENEMY

Humans at war imitate nature and camouflage themselves, their vehicles, and weapons. Standard combat clothes are natural greens and browns, mottled and patched to break up the soldier's outline in woods and scrubland. Snow-country outfits must be white, like the coats of Arctic foxes, hares, and ptarmigans.

DISGUISING THE OUTLINE

The Malayan tapir's striking coloration of white back and belly, and black everything else, is a fine example of disruptive coloration. In the dark nighttime forest the pattern breaks up the tapir's bulky body outline, making its distinctive shape less recognizable to predators. The young tapir is dappled white, a similarly disruptive device.

317

Not what they seem

SOME OF THE MOST COLORFUL creatures are advertising their defenses to aid their survival. They have a poisonous bite or sting, or a foul smell, or they taste horrible. This is called warning coloration. Some animals with warning colors have no proper defenses at all. They are mimics copying the patterns of the truly dangerous animals so that predators avoid them too. This type of mimicry is called Batesian mimicry after the naturalist Henry Bates. It occurs especially among tropical butterflies and other insects. Mimics must not become common, because the effect of the colors on predators will weaken.

BUTTERFLY BATES
Henry Walter Bates (1825-1892) was one of the first European explorer-naturalists to study in distant parts of the world. He worked in the forests of South America, collecting butterflies, beetles, and other creatures, and sending them back to museums for description and cataloguing. His work on mimicry was an important factor in Charles Darwin's ideas about evolution.

Small postman butterfly

Flesh tastes unpleasant because the butterfly, especially as a caterpillar, feeds on poisonous plants

Mimic
Dismorphia butterfly

Distasteful
Methona butterfly

Postman butterfly

Mimic
Gazera moth

PRETEND POSTMAN
The small postman butterfly from western Brazil has red-on-black – a common combination of warning colors – coupled with light forewing patches. These tell potential predators about its poisonous flesh. A close cousin, the postman butterfly, flies in the same rainforest. It has the same warning coloration, but it is not unpalatable; it is quite edible. The postman is an impersonator. It mimics the small postman to gain protection against predation.

MORE THAN ONE MIMIC
The *Methona* butterfly in the middle of these three insects has a distasteful body, and shows off the fact with its distinctive wing patterns. The *Dismorphia* butterfly at the top looks amazingly similar, but it is a mimic, and not distasteful at all. Neither is the *Gazera* insect at the bottom; it is not even a butterfly. It is an edible moth pretending to be an inedible butterfly.

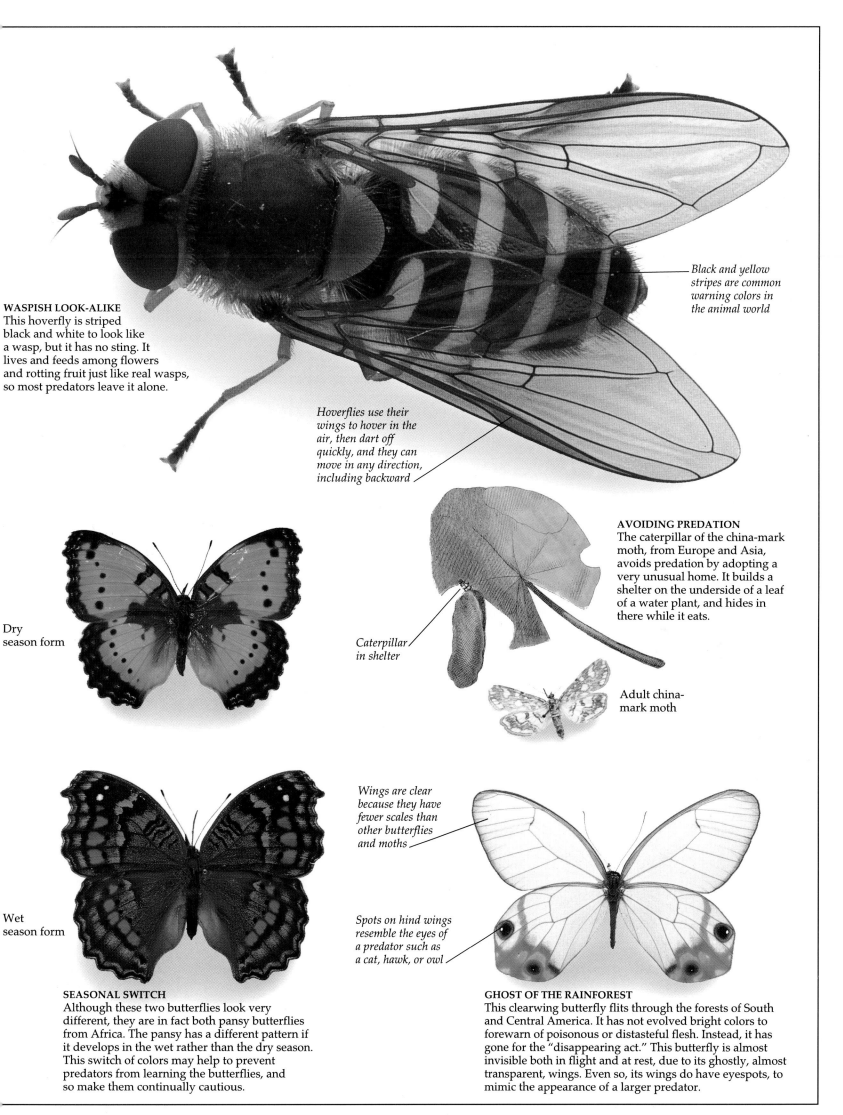

WASPISH LOOK-ALIKE
This hoverfly is striped
black and white to look like
a wasp, but it has no sting. It
lives and feeds among flowers
and rotting fruit just like real wasps,
so most predators leave it alone.

*Black and yellow
stripes are common
warning colors in
the animal world*

*Hoverflies use their
wings to hover in the
air, then dart off
quickly, and they can
move in any direction,
including backward*

Dry
season form

AVOIDING PREDATION
The caterpillar of the china-mark
moth, from Europe and Asia,
avoids predation by adopting a
very unusual home. It builds a
shelter on the underside of a leaf
of a water plant, and hides in
there while it eats.

*Caterpillar
in shelter*

Adult china-
mark moth

*Wings are clear
because they have
fewer scales than
other butterflies
and moths*

Wet
season form

*Spots on hind wings
resemble the eyes of
a predator such as
a cat, hawk, or owl*

SEASONAL SWITCH
Although these two butterflies look very
different, they are in fact both pansy butterflies
from Africa. The pansy has a different pattern if
it develops in the wet rather than the dry season.
This switch of colors may help to prevent
predators from learning the butterflies, and
so make them continually cautious.

GHOST OF THE RAINFOREST
This clearwing butterfly flits through the forests of South
and Central America. It has not evolved bright colors to
forewarn of poisonous or distasteful flesh. Instead, it has
gone for the "disappearing act." This butterfly is almost
invisible both in flight and at rest, due to its ghostly, almost
transparent, wings. Even so, its wings do have eyespots, to
mimic the appearance of a larger predator.

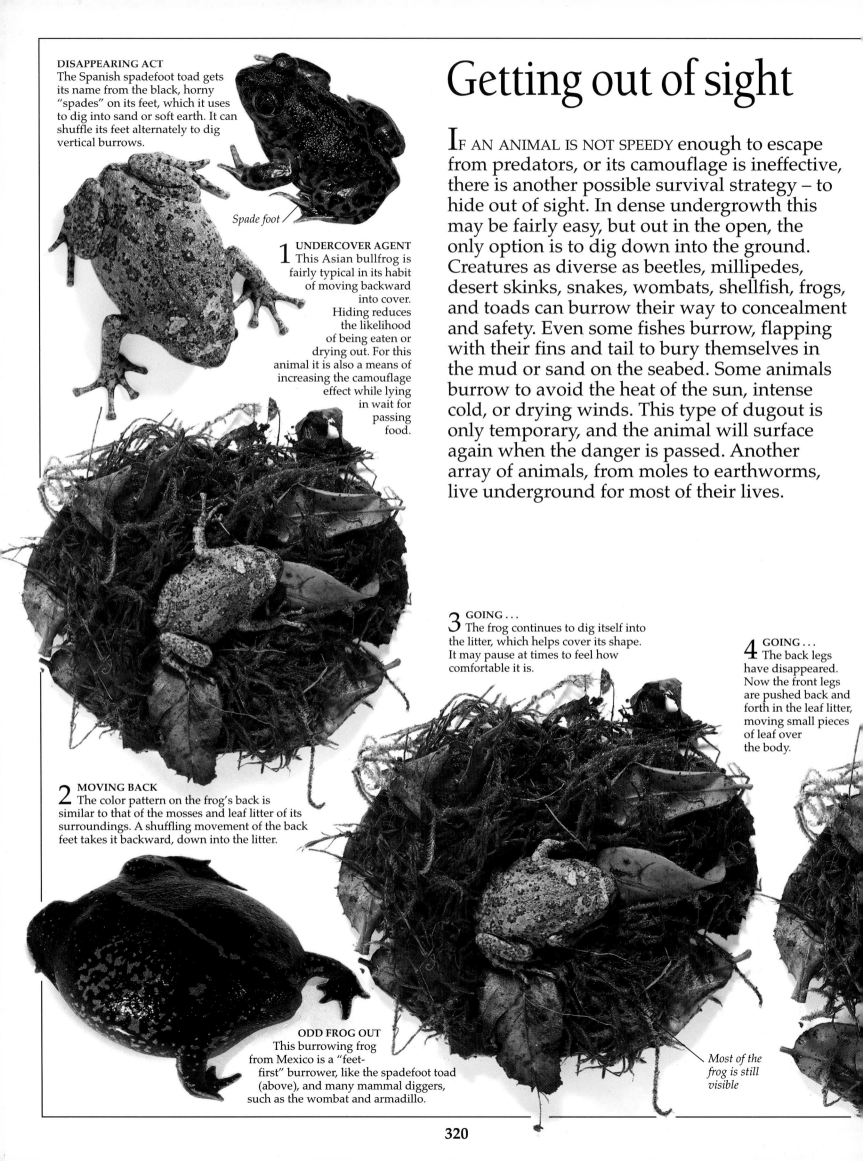

DISAPPEARING ACT
The Spanish spadefoot toad gets its name from the black, horny "spades" on its feet, which it uses to dig into sand or soft earth. It can shuffle its feet alternately to dig vertical burrows.

Spade foot

1 UNDERCOVER AGENT
This Asian bullfrog is fairly typical in its habit of moving backward into cover. Hiding reduces the likelihood of being eaten or drying out. For this animal it is also a means of increasing the camouflage effect while lying in wait for passing food.

Getting out of sight

IF AN ANIMAL IS NOT SPEEDY enough to escape from predators, or its camouflage is ineffective, there is another possible survival strategy – to hide out of sight. In dense undergrowth this may be fairly easy, but out in the open, the only option is to dig down into the ground. Creatures as diverse as beetles, millipedes, desert skinks, snakes, wombats, shellfish, frogs, and toads can burrow their way to concealment and safety. Even some fishes burrow, flapping with their fins and tail to bury themselves in the mud or sand on the seabed. Some animals burrow to avoid the heat of the sun, intense cold, or drying winds. This type of dugout is only temporary, and the animal will surface again when the danger is passed. Another array of animals, from moles to earthworms, live underground for most of their lives.

3 GOING...
The frog continues to dig itself into the litter, which helps cover its shape. It may pause at times to feel how comfortable it is.

4 GOING...
The back legs have disappeared. Now the front legs are pushed back and forth in the leaf litter, moving small pieces of leaf over the body.

2 MOVING BACK
The color pattern on the frog's back is similar to that of the mosses and leaf litter of its surroundings. A shuffling movement of the back feet takes it backward, down into the litter.

ODD FROG OUT
This burrowing frog from Mexico is a "feet-first" burrower, like the spadefoot toad (above), and many mammal diggers, such as the wombat and armadillo.

Most of the frog is still visible

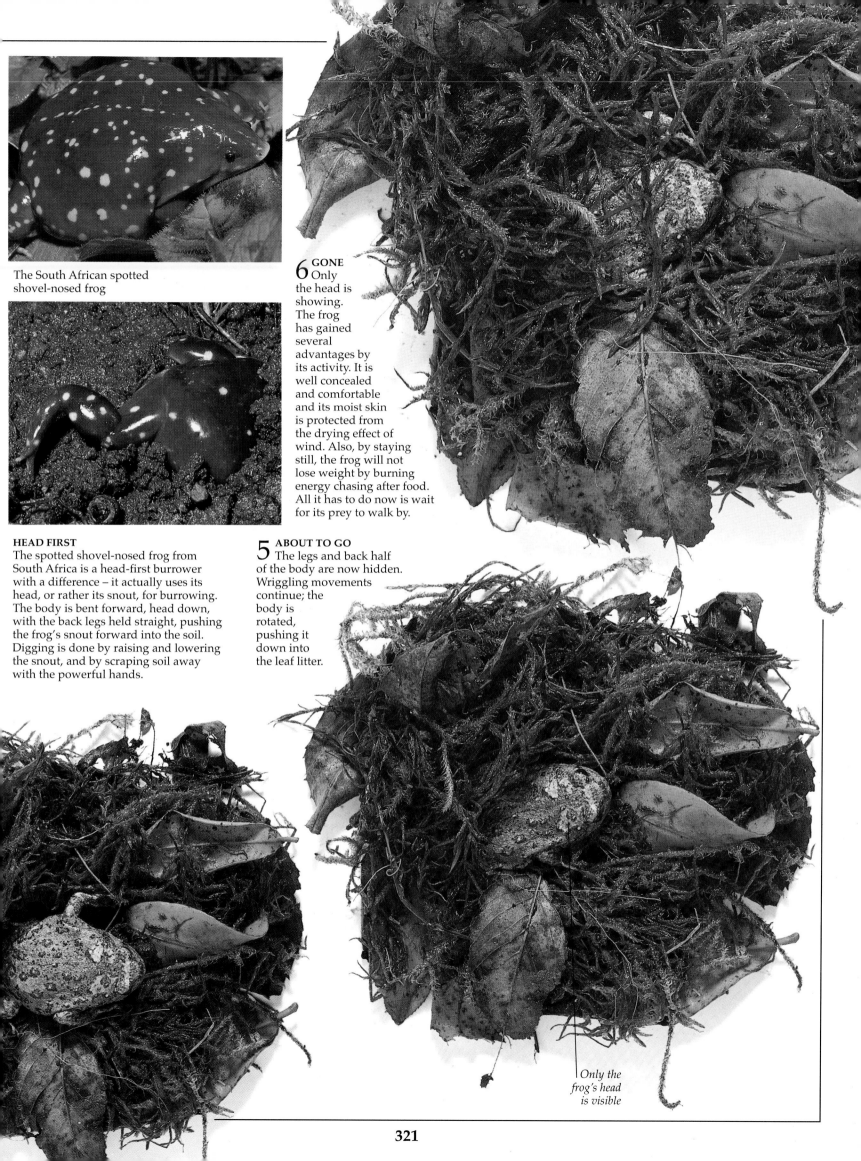

The South African spotted
shovel-nosed frog

6 GONE
Only the head is showing. The frog has gained several advantages by its activity. It is well concealed and comfortable and its moist skin is protected from the drying effect of wind. Also, by staying still, the frog will not lose weight by burning energy chasing after food. All it has to do now is wait for its prey to walk by.

HEAD FIRST
The spotted shovel-nosed frog from South Africa is a head-first burrower with a difference – it actually uses its head, or rather its snout, for burrowing. The body is bent forward, head down, with the back legs held straight, pushing the frog's snout forward into the soil. Digging is done by raising and lowering the snout, and by scraping soil away with the powerful hands.

5 ABOUT TO GO
The legs and back half of the body are now hidden. Wriggling movements continue; the body is rotated, pushing it down into the leaf litter.

Only the frog's head is visible

A spiny coat

A SPIKY SYSTEM OF SELF-DEFENSE is employed by a huge range of animals, from the hedgehog shown here to the porcupine fish, lizards such as the thorny devil, sea urchins and starfish, and insects such as thornbugs and prickly mantises. Many plants are also spiny for exactly the same reason – to ward off predators. Each of the 5,000 or so spines covering the Eurasian hedgehog is a hair modified during evolution into a sharp, stiff spike about 1 in (2-3 cm) long. As with any form of self-defense, the hedgehog's behavior has evolved in tandem with its spines, so that when in trouble it rolls into a ball shape and waits for danger to pass.

As danger passes, the head and front legs emerge

3 ALL CLEAR
The hedgehog has decided that the main threat is over and now is the time to leave. Its head straightens and is first to protrude from the ball, so that the animal can smell, hear, and see clearly. Also beginning to emerge are its front legs. The hedgehog has surprisingly long legs, usually obscured under its mantle of spines. It can run well, burrow, clamber over low walls, and swim when it needs to.

Hedgehog cautiously begins to unroll

2 CAUTIOUS PEEP
The spines physically intimidate the enemy, and they also act as a springy cushion should the hedgehog be pushed down a slope or against a tree. After a few moments of calm, the hedgehog relaxes slightly and peeks out of its prickly protection. Its eyesight is relatively poor, but its sense of smell is keen. Also, vibrations in the ground made by a creature moving nearby are transmitted via the spines and felt in the skin.

Fully rolled hedgehog has no vulnerable parts

1 ALL-OVER PROTECTION
In the face of danger, the hedgehog quickly tucks in its head, legs, and tail, and arches its back into a U-shape. A "cloak" of muscle under the loose skin comes down over the head, sides, and rear. A band of muscle running around the edge of this cloak contracts, acting like a drawstring to pull the mantle of spines together around the underparts. The spines are automatically erected in the process. This defensive behavior produces the tight ball that presents nothing but spines to the molester.

DEADLY ENEMY
The fox hunts many smaller mammals, including hedgehogs. It may poke and prod at a tightly rolled hedgehog for some time, in an attempt to make the animal uncurl and run off, whereupon the fox claws at the vulnerable belly.

Head remains tucked under

Feet barely visible

4 FLIP-OVER
Should the hedgehog continue to unroll while lying on its back, its vulnerable underparts would be exposed to any predators. To prevent attack, the hedgehog executes a quick flip-over maneuver to land on its belly, keeping its feet tucked in and its head well down for continued protection.

5 PREPARING TO MOVE OFF
If there is no sign of renewed threat, the hedgehog uncurls further. Its head emerges to reveal which end is which. Sniffing, and with whiskers quivering, it looks about for a suitable refuge, preferably a dark tangle of brambles and undergrowth.

6 QUICK EXIT
Defense gives way to escape, and the hedgehog scurries off to safety. With its body held off the ground, the animal can move surprisingly fast when at risk – at about the speed of a human's quick walk. But when foraging peacefully for slugs, worms, insects, and fallen fruit, it stays lower on the ground and shuffles among the leaves and vegetation.

Head emerges to investigate surroundings

STRANGE BEHAVIOR
Hedgehogs have often been seen to chew something foul, such as a dead toad, and then flick and spit their frothy saliva over their spines. It is not clear why. One theory is that this activity is part of the animal's defense, helping to deter predators.

BABY'S DEFENSE
A baby hedgehog's first coat of rubbery spines lies flat under its skin at birth, but pops up within a few hours. The baby cannot roll up until it is 11 days old. Its main defense is to jerk its head upward, stabbing predators on the nose.

HEDGEHOG LOOK-ALIKE
The echidna of Australia and New Guinea has a coat of defensive spines similar to those of the hedgehog. Yet it is not related, but has evolved the same system of defense separately. The hedgehog gives birth to live young, like nearly all other mammals. The echidna is one of two mammals that lay eggs (the other being the platypus) and the babies hatch from these.

Surprising the enemy

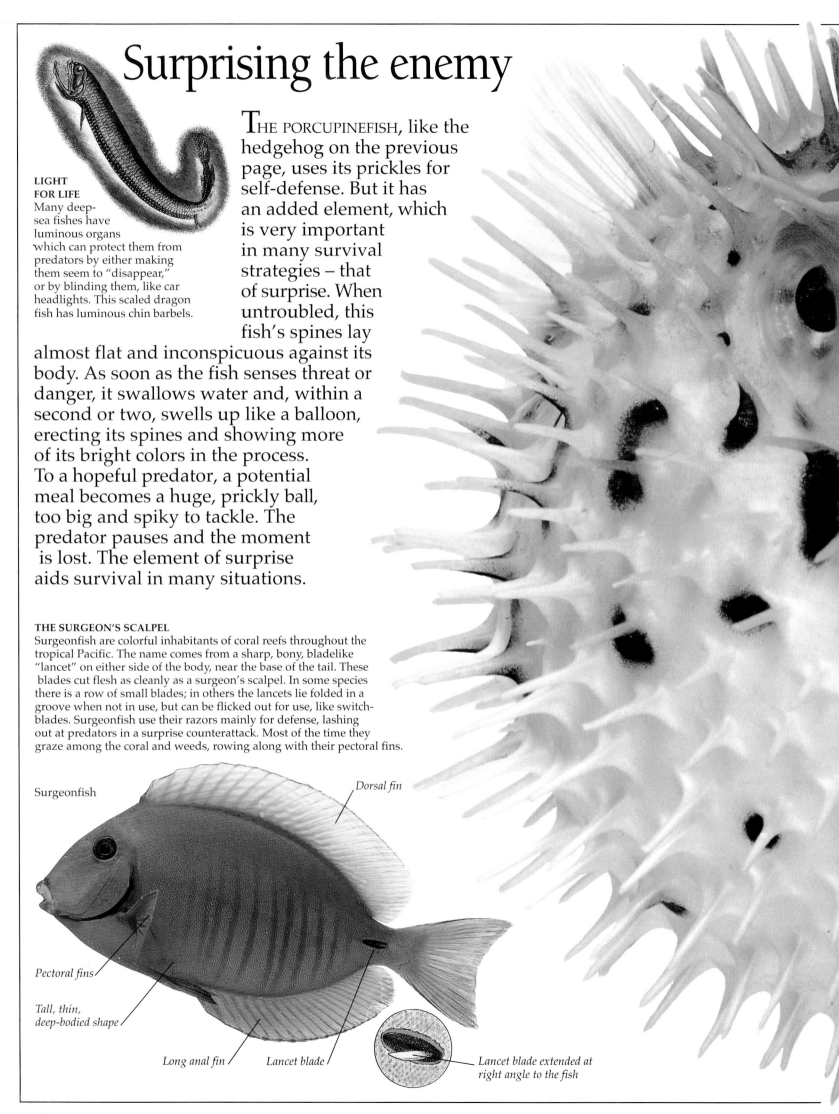

THE PORCUPINEFISH, like the hedgehog on the previous page, uses its prickles for self-defense. But it has an added element, which is very important in many survival strategies – that of surprise. When untroubled, this fish's spines lay almost flat and inconspicuous against its body. As soon as the fish senses threat or danger, it swallows water and, within a second or two, swells up like a balloon, erecting its spines and showing more of its bright colors in the process. To a hopeful predator, a potential meal becomes a huge, prickly ball, too big and spiky to tackle. The predator pauses and the moment is lost. The element of surprise aids survival in many situations.

THE SURGEON'S SCALPEL
Surgeonfish are colorful inhabitants of coral reefs throughout the tropical Pacific. The name comes from a sharp, bony, bladelike "lancet" on either side of the body, near the base of the tail. These blades cut flesh as cleanly as a surgeon's scalpel. In some species there is a row of small blades; in others the lancets lie folded in a groove when not in use, but can be flicked out for use, like switchblades. Surgeonfish use their razors mainly for defense, lashing out at predators in a surprise counterattack. Most of the time they graze among the coral and weeds, rowing along with their pectoral fins.

Surgeonfish

Dorsal fin

Pectoral fins

Tall, thin, deep-bodied shape

Long anal fin

Lancet blade

Lancet blade extended at right angle to the fish

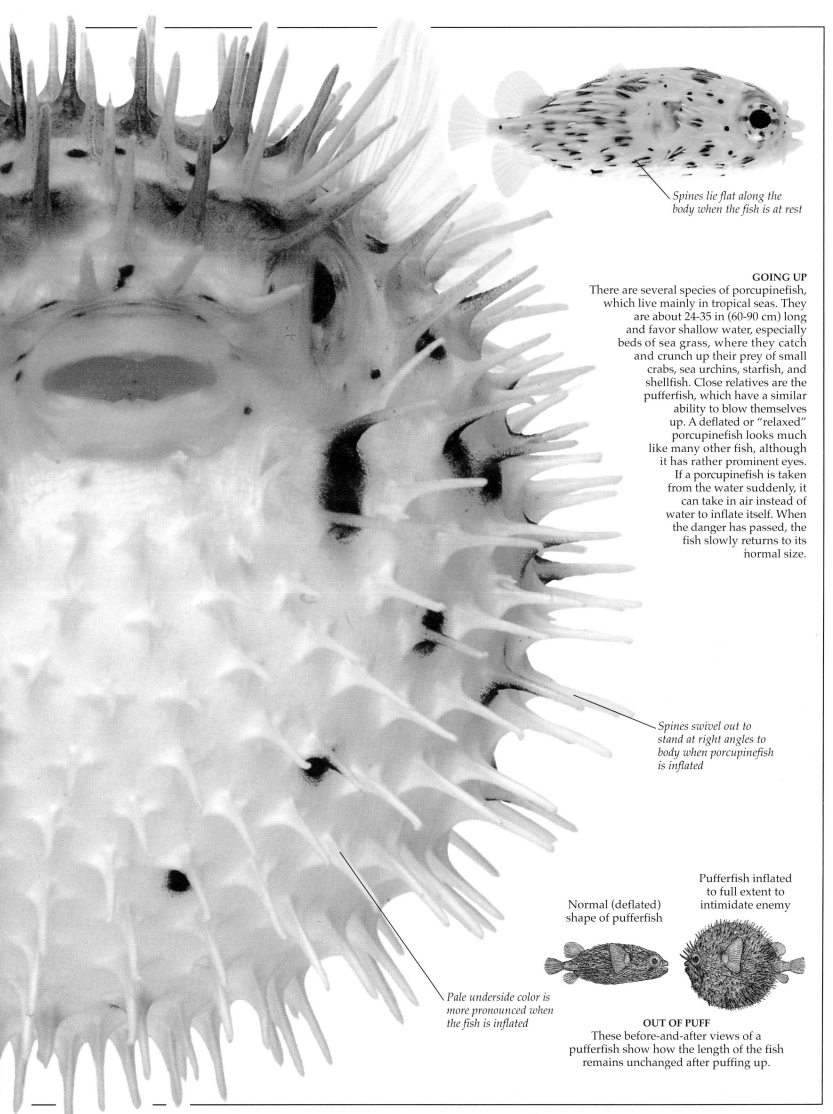

Spines lie flat along the
body when the fish is at rest

GOING UP

There are several species of porcupinefish,
which live mainly in tropical seas. They
are about 24-35 in (60-90 cm) long
and favor shallow water, especially
beds of sea grass, where they catch
and crunch up their prey of small
crabs, sea urchins, starfish, and
shellfish. Close relatives are the
pufferfish, which have a similar
ability to blow themselves
up. A deflated or "relaxed"
porcupinefish looks much
like many other fish, although
it has rather prominent eyes.
If a porcupinefish is taken
from the water suddenly, it
can take in air instead of
water to inflate itself. When
the danger has passed, the
fish slowly returns to its
normal size.

Spines swivel out to
stand at right angles to
body when porcupinefish
is inflated

Pufferfish inflated
to full extent to
intimidate enemy

Normal (deflated)
shape of pufferfish

Pale underside color is
more pronounced when
the fish is inflated

OUT OF PUFF

These before-and-after views of a
pufferfish show how the length of the fish
remains unchanged after puffing up.

Displays for defense

HAVE YOU EVER accidentally disturbed a wild animal, and jumped as it hissed or postured at you before it made off? Defense displays involve exaggerated body positions and showing off colors, spines, frills, and flaps. Other tactics designed to intimidate and scare the enemy are hissing, growling, spitting, nasty smells, and mock attacks, all done quickly for the added advantage of surprise. The aim is to frighten the foe and then make a getaway, because when the real fighting starts, survival for one or even both opponents rapidly becomes less likely. Certain features, such as the sound of a hiss, or the colors of red and yellow, seem to work throughout the animal world. They are used and understood by creatures as varied as insects, scorpions, reptiles, birds, and mammals.

STINKY STINKPOT
The skunk is a mammal that is well known for the foul smell it produces when frightened or threatened. The stinkpot from the US is a turtle that is just as evil-smelling as its name suggests. The smell is produced by a pair of glands in the soft skin of the turtle's thighs. Apart from being very smelly when frightened, it is also aggressive, so it is unlikely to be set upon by too many predators.

ON GUARD
One of the most spectacular defense displays is that of the Australian frilled lizard. This reptile is about 3 ft (1 m) long including its tail, and lives in the dry scrub where it eats grasshoppers and other small prey. The "frill" is a large flap of loose skin which is attached to the neck and is normally kept folded flat. When startled by a predator, the lizard erects this rufflike collar so that it is often more than four times the width of its body. If challenged, the lizard will also start to bob its head, lash its tail, hiss loudly, and wave its legs about.

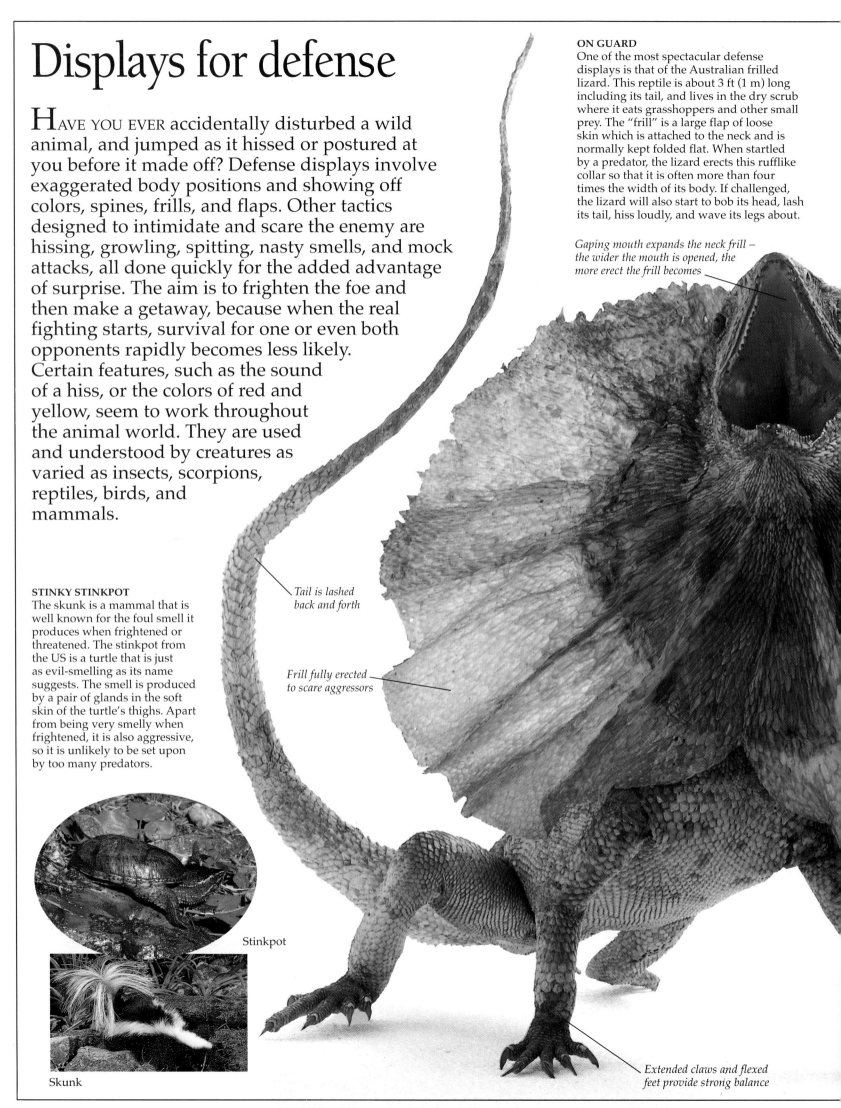

Gaping mouth expands the neck frill – the wider the mouth is opened, the more erect the frill becomes

Tail is lashed back and forth

Frill fully erected to scare aggressors

Stinkpot

Skunk

Extended claws and flexed feet provide strong balance

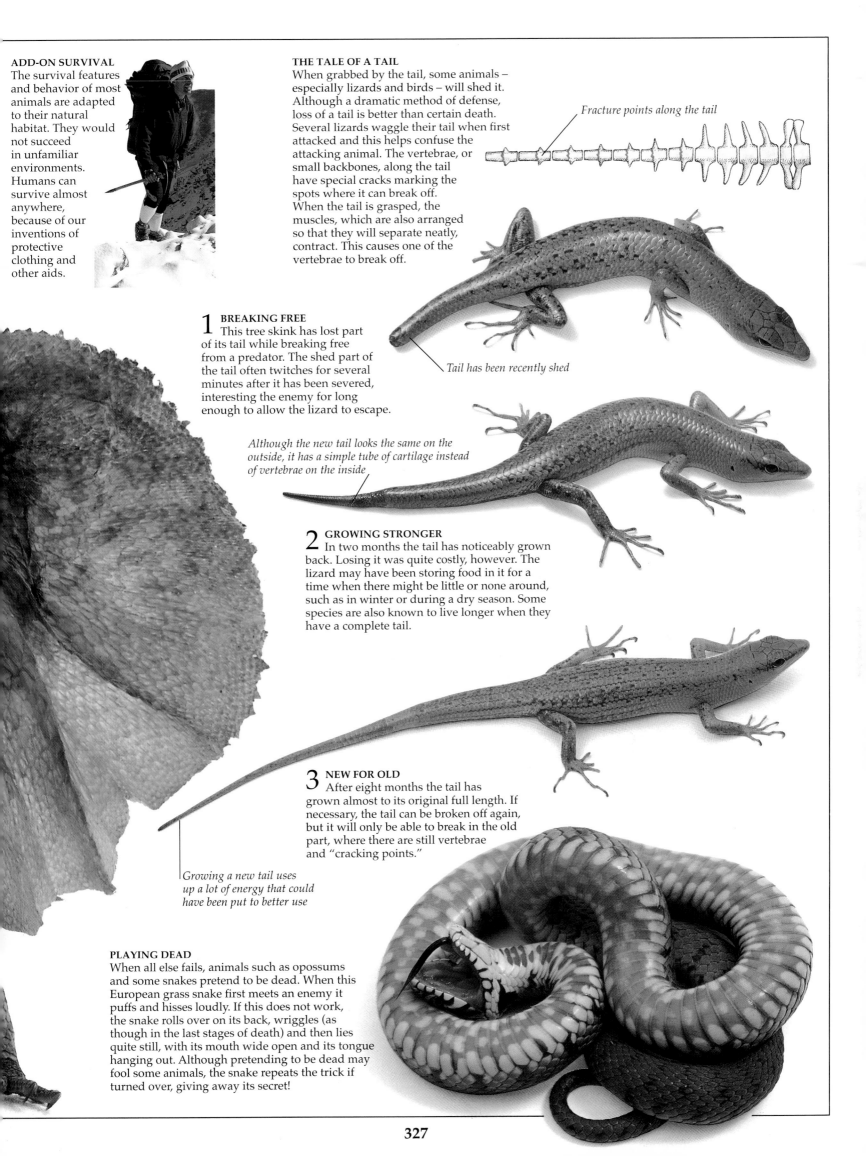

ADD-ON SURVIVAL
The survival features and behavior of most animals are adapted to their natural habitat. They would not succeed in unfamiliar environments. Humans can survive almost anywhere, because of our inventions of protective clothing and other aids.

THE TALE OF A TAIL
When grabbed by the tail, some animals – especially lizards and birds – will shed it. Although a dramatic method of defense, loss of a tail is better than certain death. Several lizards waggle their tail when first attacked and this helps confuse the attacking animal. The vertebrae, or small backbones, along the tail have special cracks marking the spots where it can break off. When the tail is grasped, the muscles, which are also arranged so that they will separate neatly, contract. This causes one of the vertebrae to break off.

Fracture points along the tail

1 BREAKING FREE
This tree skink has lost part of its tail while breaking free from a predator. The shed part of the tail often twitches for several minutes after it has been severed, interesting the enemy for long enough to allow the lizard to escape.

Tail has been recently shed

Although the new tail looks the same on the outside, it has a simple tube of cartilage instead of vertebrae on the inside

2 GROWING STRONGER
In two months the tail has noticeably grown back. Losing it was quite costly, however. The lizard may have been storing food in it for a time when there might be little or none around, such as in winter or during a dry season. Some species are also known to live longer when they have a complete tail.

3 NEW FOR OLD
After eight months the tail has grown almost to its original full length. If necessary, the tail can be broken off again, but it will only be able to break in the old part, where there are still vertebrae and "cracking points."

Growing a new tail uses up a lot of energy that could have been put to better use

PLAYING DEAD
When all else fails, animals such as opossums and some snakes pretend to be dead. When this European grass snake first meets an enemy it puffs and hisses loudly. If this does not work, the snake rolls over on its back, wriggles (as though in the last stages of death) and then lies quite still, with its mouth wide open and its tongue hanging out. Although pretending to be dead may fool some animals, the snake repeats the trick if turned over, giving away its secret!

Warning colors

A FEATURE THAT SOME ANIMALS HAVE to help them survive is poisonous (toxic) or horrible-tasting flesh. Many animals have poison for self-defense rather than for catching prey, although some animals have both. Would-be predators are warned of this by the vivid patterns, known as warning colors, which poisonous animals wear. Some of the brightest belong to the poison-dart frogs and mantella frogs of tropical forests.

DANDY FROG
This exquisitely dressed frog, looking just like a poison-dart frog in his clothes of many colors, is all puffed up and in his Sunday best.

Bright color helps to warn off predators

Red flash of color helps camouflage frog

This bright mantella has a red flash of color on the inside of its leg

This yellow mantella shows up clearly in the forest and is easily recognized as poisonous

STRANGE NAME
This species was given its common name – strawberry poison-dart frog – because of its strawberry-red color, made even brighter by deep blue-black flecks. But strawberry poison-dart frogs from different areas may be blue, green, yellow, orange, plain, spotted, and even black and white.

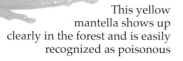

WAR PAINT
Some native peoples of North America used war paint to strike terror into the hearts of their enemies. This Hopi Indian chief wears orange, red, and yellow – the classic warning colors – in his headdress. Animals use the same colors to frighten away their enemies.

Mantellas have many color varieties so they are very difficult to identify

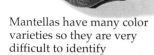

GOLDEN LOOK-ALIKE
This golden-yellow poison-dart frog has highly toxic skin. It is closely related and looks very similar to *Phyllobates terribilis* – the most toxic of all frogs.

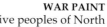

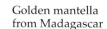

Golden mantella from Madagascar

This green mantella from Madagascar was first scientifically described in 1988. New animal species are still being discovered in remote places.

Bright black and red stripes make this frog more visible, to warn off enemies

FASCINATING FROGS

Poison-dart frogs make up a fascinating group. Some are brightly colored and highly poisonous, having complex chemicals in their skin. They range in size from 0.6 in (1.5 cm) long, to up to 2 in (5 cm) long, like these two. Poison-darts are social animals, with complex territorial, courtship, and mating behaviors.

LIFE IN THE PENTHOUSE

This spotted poison-dart frog was discovered in 1984. It is found 48–65 ft (15–20 m) up in the treetops of the cloud forests of Panama. There may be many more high-level, tree-living species of animals waiting to be discovered.

POISONED DARTS

The Choco Indians, who live in western Colombia in South America, poison the tips of the blow-pipe darts they use for hunting. They obtain the toxin by heating a live frog over a campfire. Only a few species are used, but one is so poisonous that the dart has only to be wiped against the live frog's back for it to be deadly.

Poison-dart frogs are social animals, living in small groups

HAWAIIAN HOLIDAY

This metallic-green poison-dart frog from Costa Rica, Panama, and Colombia has been introduced into the islands of Hawaii and, like some of the other species, has also been bred in captivity.

When colors develop, the poison develops too

INSECT SIZE AND SOUND

At less than 0.75 in (2 cm), this is one of the smallest poison-dart frogs. It lives in isolated patches of forest in the Andes mountains and its scientific name means buzzer – after its insectlike call.

Yellow and black are common warning colors in frogs, snakes, salamanders, wasps, and bees.

TOXIC TADPOLES

Poison-dart frogs carry their tadpoles to small isolated pools, often one at a time, where they develop their colors and skin poisons as they grow.

Underwater poison

The stargazer's poison spines are above its pectoral fins

ON LAND, a self-defensive toxin that simply oozes out on the skin, as in frogs and toads, is very effective. But in water, the poison would be rapidly diluted and washed away. So aquatic creatures often have self-defense systems where the poison is jabbed or injected into the enemy by a spike or a spine. Or they may even have poison incorporated into their flesh. Fish show both of these methods, coupled with warning coloration to advertise their venomous chemical defense.

Thin, whippy tail is of little use for swimming, but is excellent as a stinging tool

Delicate patterned tail

Three venomous anal spines

Sting is a spine-shaped, iron-hard "dagger" of bone set into the tail

Dinner or death?

Some fish have flesh that is poisonous to eat. Certain types of pufferfish are especially toxic. But the poison, tetrodotoxin, is limited to specific body parts of the fish. The flesh itself is said to be relatively safe and quite tasty. In Japan, pufferfish is served in restaurants as the delicacy "fugu," where specially trained chefs prepare and cook the catch. Even so, despite various safeguards, death has occurred when fugu has been prepared incorrectly.

Dead pufferfish awaiting preparation

THE RAY'S STING
The venom of a stingray's sting is made in shiny white tissue running along the two grooves on the spine's underside. In the European species the spine is about 5 in (12 cm) long. In larger tropical species it may reach up to 16 in (40 cm).

A pufferfish in pieces and ready for preparation. A keen eye is needed to identify the poisonous organs

STING IN THE TAIL
More than 100 species of stingray lurk in coastal shallows around the world. Some grow to great size, with a "wingspan" of more than 10 ft (3 m) and weighing well over 660 lb (300 kg). They tend to hide in the bottom sand and sediment, or glide along slowly as they search for shellfish and fish to crack and crush with their rows of blunt teeth. When in trouble, these rays bring the sting in their tail into play. Some stingrays have two or even three stings. Under threat, the ray lashes its tail to and fro or even arches it over its head, slashing with its sting and stabbing it into the enemy.

Eating fugu: compliments to the chef – if still alive afterward!

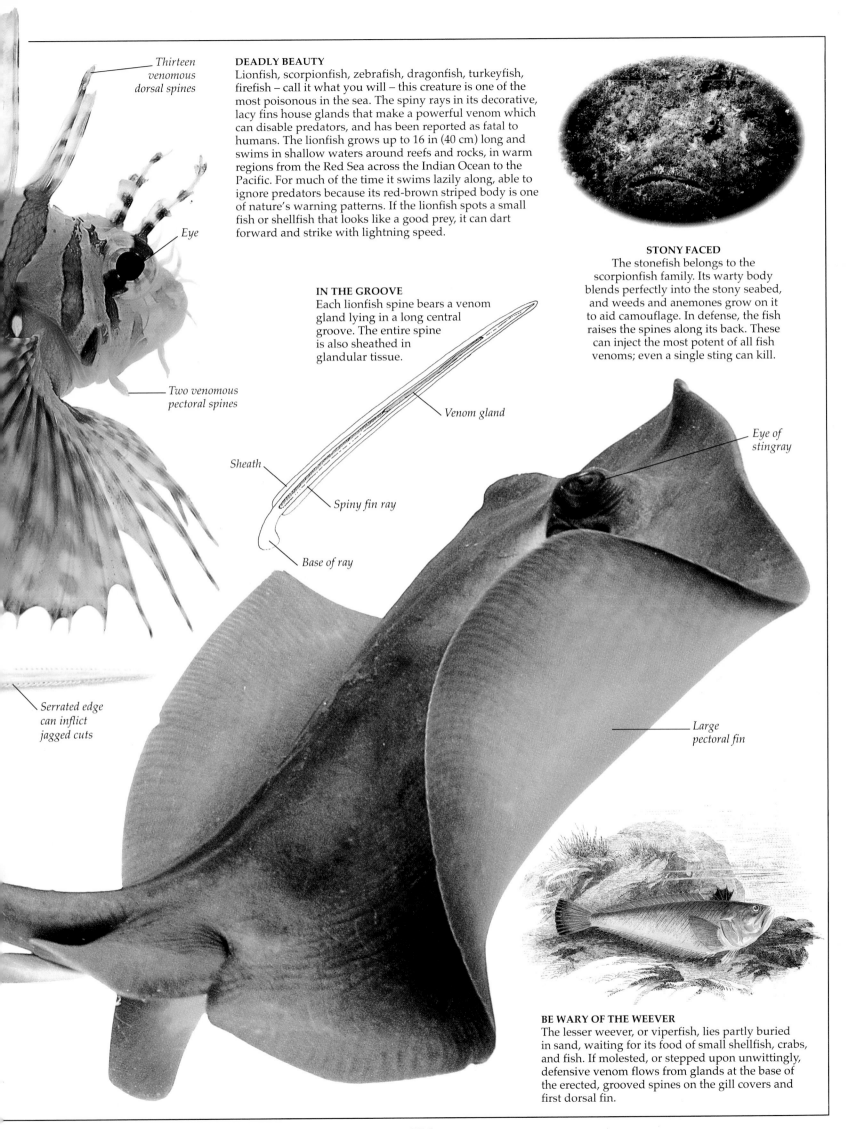

DEADLY BEAUTY

Lionfish, scorpionfish, zebrafish, dragonfish, turkeyfish, firefish – call it what you will – this creature is one of the most poisonous in the sea. The spiny rays in its decorative, lacy fins house glands that make a powerful venom which can disable predators, and has been reported as fatal to humans. The lionfish grows up to 16 in (40 cm) long and swims in shallow waters around reefs and rocks, in warm regions from the Red Sea across the Indian Ocean to the Pacific. For much of the time it swims lazily along, able to ignore predators because its red-brown striped body is one of nature's warning patterns. If the lionfish spots a small fish or shellfish that looks like a good prey, it can dart forward and strike with lightning speed.

Thirteen venomous dorsal spines

Eye

Two venomous pectoral spines

Serrated edge can inflict jagged cuts

IN THE GROOVE

Each lionfish spine bears a venom gland lying in a long central groove. The entire spine is also sheathed in glandular tissue.

Venom gland

Sheath

Spiny fin ray

Base of ray

STONY FACED

The stonefish belongs to the scorpionfish family. Its warty body blends perfectly into the stony seabed, and weeds and anemones grow on it to aid camouflage. In defense, the fish raises the spines along its back. These can inject the most potent of all fish venoms; even a single sting can kill.

Eye of stingray

Large pectoral fin

BE WARY OF THE WEEVER

The lesser weever, or viperfish, lies partly buried in sand, waiting for its food of small shellfish, crabs, and fish. If molested, or stepped upon unwittingly, defensive venom flows from glands at the base of the erected, grooved spines on the gill covers and first dorsal fin.

Escaping the cold

MANY ANIMALS ARE at their most vulnerable during the winter months. Cold temperatures, lack of food, drought, overpopulation, and other problems are best avoided with one of two options – by leaving the area, or by sleeping through the long winter season. Some fast-traveling creatures, such as birds, butterflies, and whales, go on annual long-distance migrations that tie in with the cycle of the seasons. Shorter-lived or slower-moving species such as herds of gazelle or bison may travel in a more haphazard fashion, depending on local conditions. Or they migrate in one direction, breed away from their original area, and then let their offspring make the return journey by themselves. The second option is to stay put but find a sheltered, safe place and go into a deep sleep, called hibernation. This maximizes the animal's chances of survival by saving its energy, as well as making it less conspicuous to hungry predators.

SLIPSTREAM
Flying in a V-shaped formation, like these snow geese, helps birds to save energy on a long journey. The birds following the leader fly in the "slipstream" of the bird in front. When the leader tires, another bird takes over.

SHORT SUMMER
The red-breasted goose is one of many birds that migrate to the Arctic tundra to nest in the brief summer when there is plenty of food available. As the northern winter closes in, it flies more than a thousand miles south to less harsh conditions.

UP NORTH
The cloudless sulphur is a fairly large, strong-flying butterfly. In spring, large numbers of cloudless sulphurs migrate from southern North America to more northerly areas.

MIGRATING MAMMAL
The gray whale is a famous migrant of the Pacific Ocean. In the winter months, gray whales spend their time in the warm waters off Baja California and nearby areas, where the mothers give birth to their calves in the calm coastal seas. In spring, the whales move north, following the coastline. They head for the waters off Alaska, where there is a summer flush of food, with long hours of daylight and plentiful nutrients brought by ocean currents. In the autumn they head back south again. Some individuals swim up to 12,500 miles (20,000 km) on the yearly round trip.

DOWN MEXICO WAY
Monarchs are big, powerful butterflies. As summer draws to a close, they travel from Canada and the eastern US to their warmer wintering sites in the southern US and Mexico. Here they rest in their millions on trees and rocks. As spring arrives they head up north again, to breed and continue the yearly cycle.

CAR TROUBLE
The African migrant butterfly often travels in huge swarms. Local migrations in large numbers may occur anywhere over Africa south of the Sahara. Cars driven through swarms sometimes overheat because their radiators become clogged with dead butterflies.

SILVER-Y
The silver-Y moth often journeys north from Africa and southern Europe, but the details of its travels have not been studied in depth. It cannot survive the winters in northern Europe, but moths that have survived farther south breed, and the next generation then moves north. Some fly directly to northern Europe, and others may stop and breed on the way.

BOGONG PITSTOP
The Australian bogong moth can cover buildings in Canberrra, Australia, as it rests during its migration. The moths fly to caves in the Australian Alps at about 5,000 ft (1,500 m), where they spend the hot dry months. They move north again in the cooler autumn.

LONGHAUL LADY
The painted lady is one of the most widespread of all butterflies. It is a strong flier, and individuals can travel up to 620 miles (1,000 km). In Europe, for example, it moves northward each spring, until the adults are killed off by cold weather.

Hibernation

Only warm-blooded animals – mammals and birds – are true hibernators. Hibernation is not just a long sleep. The animal's body temperature falls from 85-105°F down to perhaps 40°F. Its heart (pulse) rate drops to once every minute or less, and it may breathe only once every half-hour. This extra-deep sleep state saves huge amounts of energy, so the hibernator can survive on food reserves stored as body fats for months on end. When a cold-blooded animal becomes so cool that it cannot move and seems to be sleeping, this is called torpor.

HIBERNATING BEAR
Unlike many mammals, bears do not undergo true hibernation. Instead, a bear sleeps very deeply in winter. Its body temperature drops, and its heartbeat slows down. In this way it saves energy, yet it can rouse itself in mild winter weather and go out searching for food.

SAFE SLEEP
During the warm season, bats use great amounts of energy to fuel their small, warm-blooded body for active flight. In the cold season, when their insect prey is absent, they have little option but to hibernate. Bats like this noctule may migrate hundreds of miles to a suitable frost-free cave for winter hibernation.

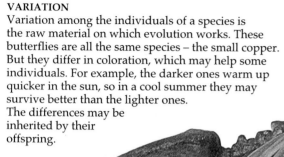

VARIATION

Variation among the individuals of a species is
the raw material on which evolution works. These
butterflies are all the same species – the small copper.
But they differ in coloration, which may help some
individuals. For example, the darker ones warm up
quicker in the sun, so in a cool summer they may
survive better than the lighter ones.
The differences may be
inherited by their
offspring.

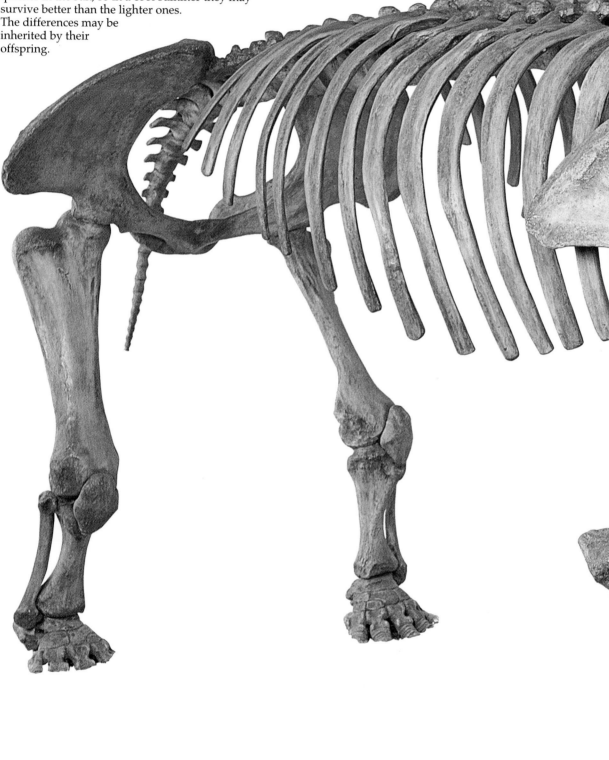

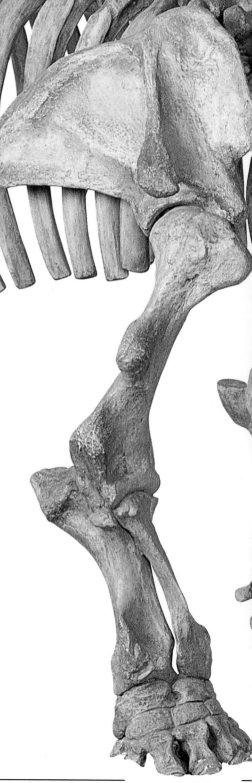

CHAPTER 5
EVOLUTION & EXTINCTION

WE LIVE IN A changing world. Nature is altering too, and has been for millions of years. The change in living things through time is called evolution. It happens mainly in response to the changing conditions here on Earth. Climates fluctuate, ice ages come and go, and long droughts are followed by wet periods. Over millions of years, new kinds of plants and animals appear, which are better suited to the new conditions. Other animals and plants are less successful. They die out and become extinct, disappearing forever.

FOSSILS
Much of the evidence for the evolution of life comes from fossils. These are the remains of animals and plants from long ago, which have been preserved in the rocks and turned to stone. Usually only the hard parts are fossilized, such as bones, teeth, horns, claws, and shells. This is the fossil skeleton of a giant rhino, *Arsinoitherium,* which lived about 30 million years ago in Egypt. By comparing its bones with those of animals today, paleontologists (fossil experts) can make good guesses about its appearance and lifestyle.

Changing for the better

THE WAY IN WHICH an animal or plant fits into its surroundings is called adaptation. The better adapted it is to the environment, the more likely it is to survive and reproduce. "Environment" here means not only physical conditions such as temperature, light, and availability of shelter; it also means biological conditions such as food, predators, competitors, and rivals for mates. Examples of how animals are adapted to their environment are everywhere in nature, from a tiger's striped camouflage to a fish's gills. Every detail of an animal's body and behavior is shaped by nature. It has evolved to maximize its chances of survival. But the environment, both physical and biological, is never constant. Other animals are always evolving and adapting to improve their own chances, which means that the food sources of carnivorous creatures change. Plants evolve to suit their surroundings and withstand being eaten, so the food sources of herbivorous animals are also changing. And so continues a never-ending struggle to avoid extinction.

Fully developed legs for walking

Short legs

Tiny legs

No legs

SKINKS LOSING LEGS
These skinks chart every stage in the evolution that led from a normal lizard to a legless one, showing how snakes may have evolved from a legged, reptile ancestor. The first stage may have involved the legs shrinking and being used only for running. Some skinks can choose to move like a snake. They straighten their legs and hold them against their body. They can then wriggle through long grass or into a crack in a rock.

PAST, PRESENT, AND FUTURE
The tiger salamander from North America is the largest of the land-living salamanders. It grows up to 16 in (40 cm) long, and feeds on worms, insects, small mammals such as mice, and some of its amphibian relations such as little frogs. As the salamander walks along, its body bends from side to side in S-shaped curves. This basic method of moving was inherited millions of years ago from the ancestors of the amphibians – fish. The same major feature has been passed along an evolutionary sequence, and been adapted to each animal's needs, according to its habits and lifestyle.

Left foot forward

Tail curves to right

Front right foot forward

Front left foot forward

Tail curves to right

Walking sequence of tiger salamander

Body curves left

When the mudskipper is on land, the gill covers are shut tight to store water inside the gill chambers

Nostrils are called nares

Mouth is shaped for snapping up insects, spiders, and even small crabs

Sharp teeth for grabbing prey

SECONDARY ADAPTATION

The first fish evolved about 500 million years ago. To breathe, they developed feathery gills to extract oxygen from the water. The mudskipper has evolved a further adaptation. This small fish lives on muddy shores and estuaries around the warm shores of the Indian and Pacific oceans. One problem with this habitat is that the retreating tide may trap it in a small pool. When a mudskipper skitters across the mud in the open air to find a better pool, it holds a quantity of water in its large gill chambers, and "breathes" the oxygen in this. Mudskippers have refined this process so that they can also absorb oxygen directly from the air, through the blood-rich skin lining the back of the mouth and throat. This means that they can stay out of water for longer.

Natural selection

EVOLUTION IS THE ADAPTATION of an animal or plant to its surroundings. In animals this usually happens when parents have more offspring that can survive. These offspring are not all the same, but vary in small details of, for example, color, size, tooth shape, and so on. In the struggle for survival, some variations may help more than others. The animals with these variations have a better chance of living to adulthood and producing their own offspring. If the helpful features are inherited, the offspring also have a better chance of surviving, and in turn passing them down the hereditary line. This process is called evolution by natural selection.

LIVING FOSSIL
The tuatara is a lizardlike reptile that lives only on a few small islands off the coast of New Zealand. It is the sole surviving species of a group of reptiles that flourished millions of years ago. The other members are now extinct. The tuatara seems to be well adapted to its island habitat. Other animals, which might win the battle for natural selection, have not been able to reach the islands because of their isolation.

CREATURE FEATURES
This colorful cricket from South America has very long, powerful back legs for jumping, and large wings. When disturbed by a predator it can leap into the air and fly away. But if its legs and wings had been even bigger, so as to escape even faster, the cricket would be impaired rather than assisted. Its body parts would be too heavy to move effectively, and use up too much energy when working, or be too obvious when the cricket was trying to hide. Each feature of a creature is a compromise. It has to fulfill many different functions, some of which may not be obvious.

Large muscles to propel back legs

Green wings provide effective camouflage

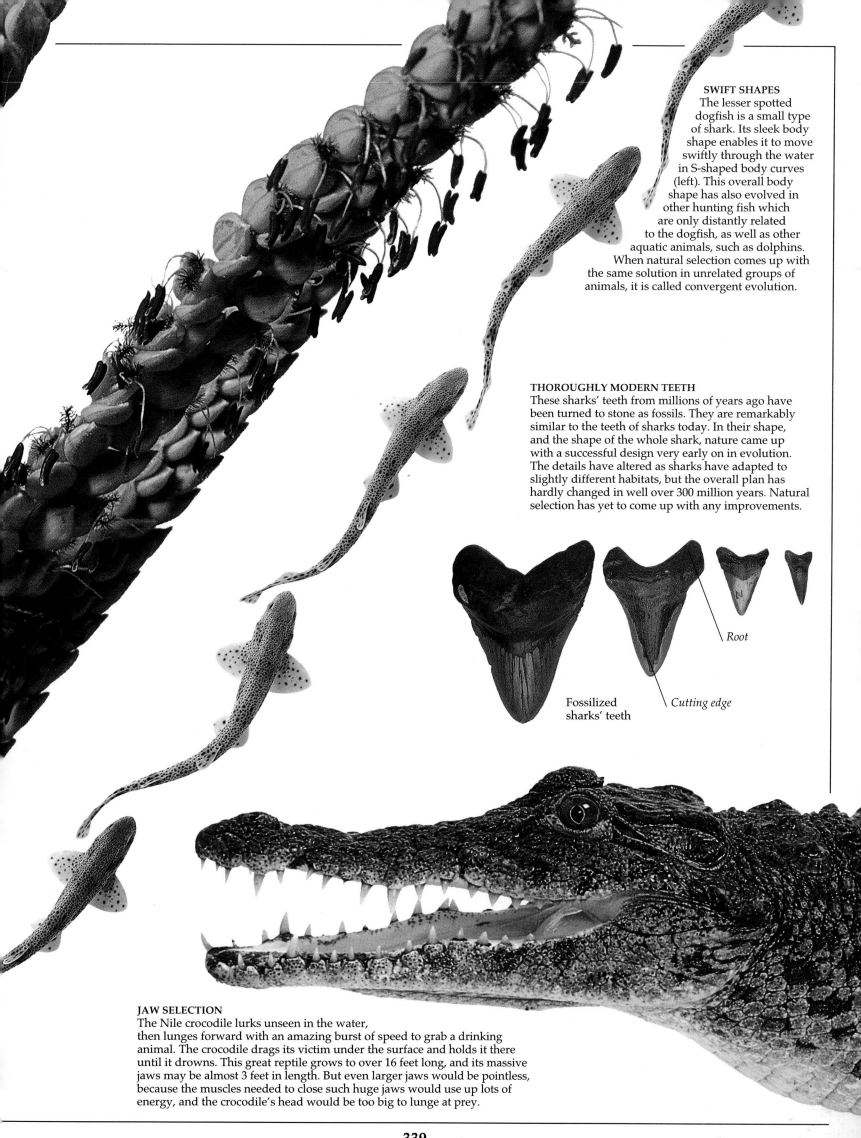

The lesser spotted dogfish is a small type of shark. Its sleek body shape enables it to move swiftly through the water in S-shaped body curves (left). This overall body shape has also evolved in other hunting fish which are only distantly related to the dogfish, as well as other aquatic animals, such as dolphins. When natural selection comes up with the same solution in unrelated groups of animals, it is called convergent evolution.

THOROUGHLY MODERN TEETH
These sharks' teeth from millions of years ago have been turned to stone as fossils. They are remarkably similar to the teeth of sharks today. In their shape, and the shape of the whole shark, nature came up with a successful design very early on in evolution. The details have altered as sharks have adapted to slightly different habitats, but the overall plan has hardly changed in well over 300 million years. Natural selection has yet to come up with any improvements.

Root

Cutting edge

Fossilized sharks' teeth

JAW SELECTION
The Nile crocodile lurks unseen in the water, then lunges forward with an amazing burst of speed to grab a drinking animal. The crocodile drags its victim under the surface and holds it there until it drowns. This great reptile grows to over 16 feet long, and its massive jaws may be almost 3 feet in length. But even larger jaws would be pointless, because the muscles needed to close such huge jaws would use up lots of energy, and the crocodile's head would be too big to lunge at prey.

Species and their origins

THE SPECIES IS THE BASIC GROUP or unit of animals (or plants) in nature. Members of a species can breed successfully with each other, but not with members of other species. Evolution is basically the appearance of new species and the extinction of others. In general, most new species arise when a group from one species becomes cut off from the rest of its kind, especially if it then lives in conditions that differ from those of the parent species. This might happen, for example, when birds are blown off course and reach distant islands or cross a mountain range. Sheer distance can also be a physical barrier. Under new conditions, natural selection means that the isolated group begins to develop new adaptations. It may develop into a new race or subspecies. In time, that subspecies can change so much and become so different from the rest of its species that the two can no longer interbreed. Once this happens, they are two distinct species.

THE COMTE DE BUFFON
Georges Buffon (1707-1788) of France was the first to define a species as a group of living things that can all potentially interbreed with each other, but not with members of other species.

Herring gull
(*Larus argentatus argentatus*)

Lesser black-backed gull (*Larus fuscus graellsii*)

ONE SPECIES OR TWO?
The herring gull (left) and the lesser black-backed gull (right) are descended from gulls that lived in eastern Siberia. These ancestral gulls spread out to both east and west. In time, the two lines of migration met on the other side of the globe, over Europe. The two ends of this circle are the herring gull and the lesser black-backed gull, which have changed so much that they rarely interbreed.

Larus argentatus vegae

Larus argentatus birulaii

Larus fuscus antellus

Larus fuscus heuglini

Larus argentatus smithsonianus

Larus argentatus omissus

Larus fuscus fuscus

Larus argentatus argentatus

Larus fuscus graellsii

RING SPECIES
Each of the different subspecies of herring gull interbreeds with its neighbors, as do the different subspecies of lesser black-backed gull. In eastern Siberia, the herring gulls interbreed with neighbors that are called black-backed gulls, but could just as well be called herring gulls. These gulls form a "ring species" and show how new species can arise through accumulated small changes.

Staying separate

A new species may develop in isolation, but then moves back to where the parent species lives. The two species may mate and produce young, which are infertile. Producing such offspring is a waste of energy for the parents, so they have learned to recognize their own species using smell, sound, color, or behavior. These signals, which keep species apart, are called "isolating mechanisms."

Chiff-chaff   Wood warbler   Willow warbler

NOT ONE, BUT THREE
The English naturalist Gilbert White (1720-1793) was the first to notice that the chiff-chaff, the willow warbler, and the wood warbler were three different species, not just one. Apart from very slight physical variations, their songs are all distinctly different. For the birds, the songs are used by the female to select a mate, so in this way they act as an isolating mechanism, separating the otherwise similar species.

Froglets set off into the wide world

THE NUMBERS GAME
A frog can lay hundreds of eggs in a single year. If all these survived to adulthood and produced young of their own, the world would be knee-deep in frogs within 10 years. Clearly, most of them die. Many of the deaths are due to chance. But any small advantage, inherited from the parents, will assist the struggle for survival. Over many generations, the advantage will gradually become more common until all members of the species have it.

PERFUMED PARTNERS
Mice, voles, and many other mammals look similar, but they can recognize their own species by characteristic scents. These are used to confirm that the correct choice of partner has been made.

Adult frog

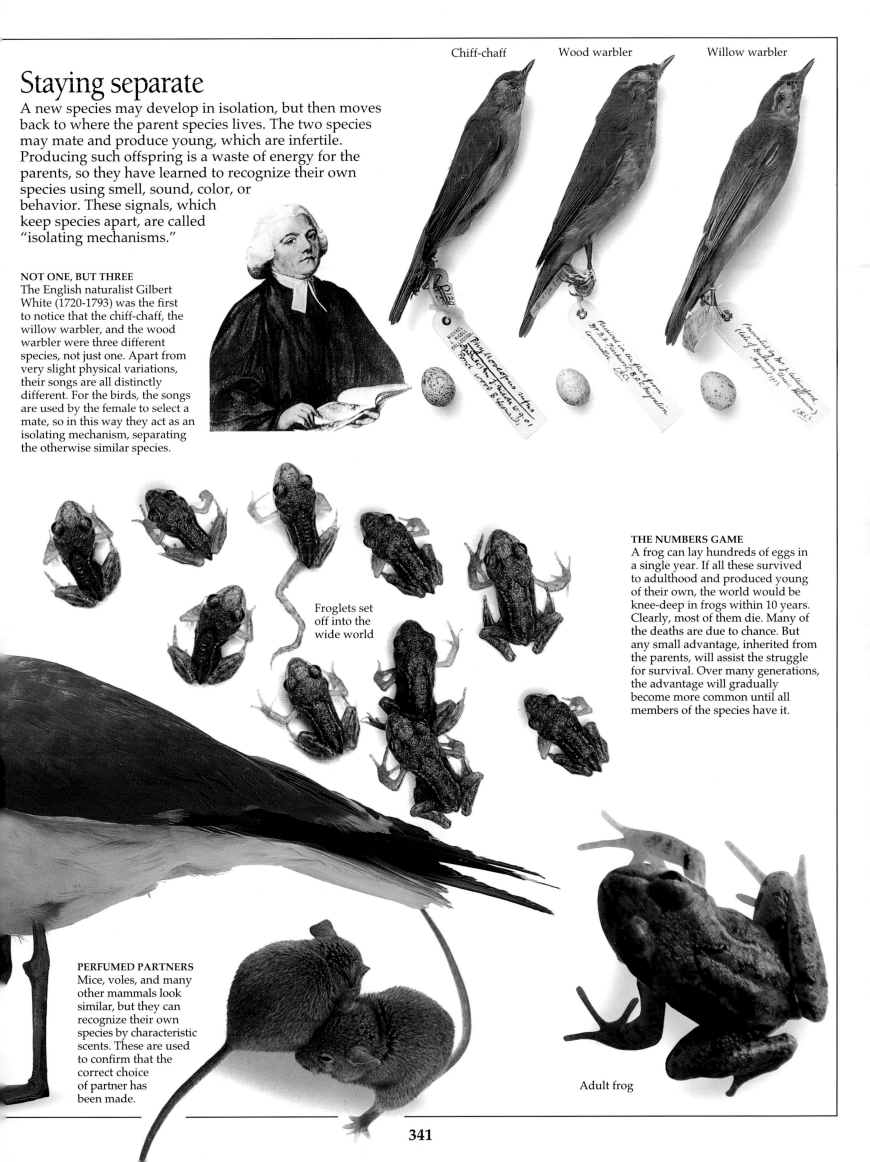

The evolution of fish

NEARLY 500 MILLION YEARS AGO, the first fish swam in the Earth's waters. They had no jaws, fins, or scales like the fish of today. But early fish did have a type of backbone (the feature that divides the animal kingdom into two groups, the vertebrates and the backboneless invertebrates). The backbone formed a firm yet flexible central brace against which muscles could pull, to propel the creature along. Fish were also the first creatures to develop jaws. This was a major advance since jaws allowed these fish to bite and chew on items that were too large to swallow in a single gulp. They were a great success. Today, all fish except the lampreys and hagfish have jaws of some kind.

FISHY LANDSCAPE
The first fish with jaws appeared 435 million years ago, during the Silurian period. This weird scene shows where they might have swum.

TINY SPINY
Ischnacanthus was an acanthodian, or "spiny shark." These ancient fish, although not true sharks, were somewhat sharklike in shape, and each fin had a strong spine along its front edge. They flourished about 400-350 million years ago and then gradually died out.

JAWLESS WONDER
Cephalaspis belonged to a group of extinct jawless fish called osteostracans, which were among the first fish to appear on Earth. This fossil is nearly 400 million years old. The large, bony shield protected the fish's head and gills.

FIRST OF THE RAY-FINS
The palaeonisciforms were the first of the bony, ray-finned fish which now include the teleosts. At first the rodlike fin rays (lepidotrichs) were parallel to the fish's body, but gradually they splayed out to make a fan shape as in the fins of most modern fish. In this fossil of *Palaeoniscus* (below), from 250 million years ago, the sculpted body scales are clearly visible.

Restoration of *Palaeoniscus*

Sculpted individual body scales

Cartilage struts

Scales

ROUNDED HOLOSTEAN
Dapedium dates from the Lower Jurassic period, some 190 million years ago. It was a holostean, a member of a group that was common at this time. Holosteans had a fully developed backbone, but the rest of the bony skeleton was poorly developed. Today there are still some living species of holosteans, including the gars of North and Central America.

Large predatory mouth

THE RISE OF THE TELEOSTS
Eurypholis has the streamlined shape, large mouth, and sharp teeth of a hunter. It is a teleost, or "true" bony fish. Teleosts make up the great majority of fish species alive today. These agile and adaptable creatures rose to success some 200-100 million years ago.

This restoration of *Eusthenopteron* shows the bones of the head and internal skeleton

ALMOST THERE
Teleost fish such as the small *Stichocentrus* gradually took over the waters from the many fish groups that had gone before. With their bony inner skeletons, flexible fins, efficient jaws, and lightweight scales, they had come a long way from the jawless, heavily armored, tanklike versions such as *Cephalaspis*.

FINS TO LEGS
The slim, predatory *Eusthenopteron* was a primitive lobe-finned fish. The base of each fin had a fleshy, muscular lobe, outwardly resembling a leg. Fish like this may have evolved into amphibians. However, *Eusthenopteron* itself was not an amphibian ancestor, but merely a fish adapted to the conditions of its time.

STRUT-FILLED WINGS
Rays have skeletons made of cartilage, which is softer and decays more quickly than bone, so it is fossilized less often. Therefore we know less about the evolution of rays and sharks, compared to that of bony fish. This specimen, *Heliobatis*, which is a kind of stingray, shows the many cartilage struts in its "wings," or pectoral fins.

Flipperlike fins

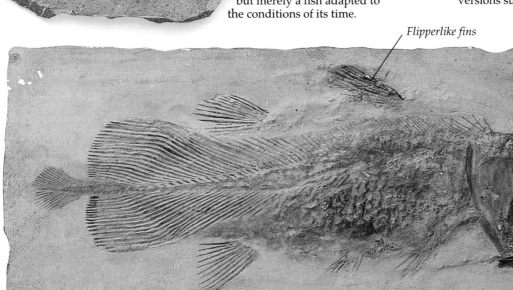

Famous fish

In 1938 scientists were startled by the discovery in South Africa of a lobe-fin fish called the coelacanth. Many fossil coelacanths were known, dating back to nearly 400 million years ago. Experts had thought they had died out 80 million years ago, but it seemed local people had been catching them for years. They are "living fossils," survivors from prehistory. More than 100 coelacanths have since been caught, and some have been filmed swimming in the sea near the Comoro Islands, off southeast Africa.

The coelacanth today – still alive and swimming

First on land

Animals had no reason to venture on land until there were plants there for food and shelter. The first plants had gained a roothold on land at the start of the Devonian period, almost 400 million years ago. They were soon followed by the first land animals, which probably resembled millipedes, centipedes, and scorpions, and then wingless insects. The first winged insects flew through the forests that covered the Earth over 300 million years ago. Early fossil remains show that a few of these insects, such as dragonflies and cockroaches, would have looked very similar to present-day species. But others represent groups that are no longer alive today. Because insects are usually small and delicate, most of them probably rotted away before they could become trapped in muddy sediments, or amber, and fossilized. And so, with very little fossil evidence, no one is yet sure how insects evolved.

INSECT JEWELRY
Amber has been looked on as precious stone for centuries. This piece of Baltic amber, cut and polished as a pendant, contains three different types of fly.

Limestone fossil of a moth's wing from southern England

SHOW YOUR COLORS
Pigments in the scales of this fossilized wing have altered the process of fossilization, so that parts of the pattern can still be seen millions of years later.

LIVING ANCESTORS?
The peripatus, or velvet worm, may represent a stage between worms and insects. It has a worm's soft, segmented body, but clawed legs like an insect and a similar heart and breathing system.

SPRINGTAILS
The wingless springtail is very similar to the first insects to evolve. Many springtails have a curious forked jumping organ folded up under their tail – hence the name. This species, on the underside of a dead limpet, lives on the seashore.

How amber is formed
Amber is the fossil resin of pine trees from millions of years ago. As the resin oozed from cracks in the tree trunks, creatures attracted by the sweet scent became trapped on its sticky surface. In time the resin, including the trapped creatures, hardened and was buried in the soil, and eventually washed into the sea. Copal looks similar to amber but is much younger.

Modern-day "sweat bee" (*Trigona* species)

Wing

Delicate legs

EARLY CRANES
About 35 million years ago in what is now Colorado, this cranefly became trapped in muddy sediment at the bottom of a lake or pond. The sediment was so fine that, when it turned to stone, even details of the wings and legs were preserved. This fossilized specimen looks very similar to modern craneflies. The weak, drifting flight and the long, floppy legs were clearly important adaptations to life long before the American continent took its present shape.

BEE IN COPAL
This piece of copal from Zanzibar (an island off the east coast of Africa) could be 1,000 to 1 million years old. It has been magnified to show the beautifully preserved "sweat bee," which looks like the present-day bee.

A STICKY END
Crawling and flying insects, attracted by the pine resin oozing from this tree trunk, are trapped forever. Scenes like this took place over 40 million years ago.

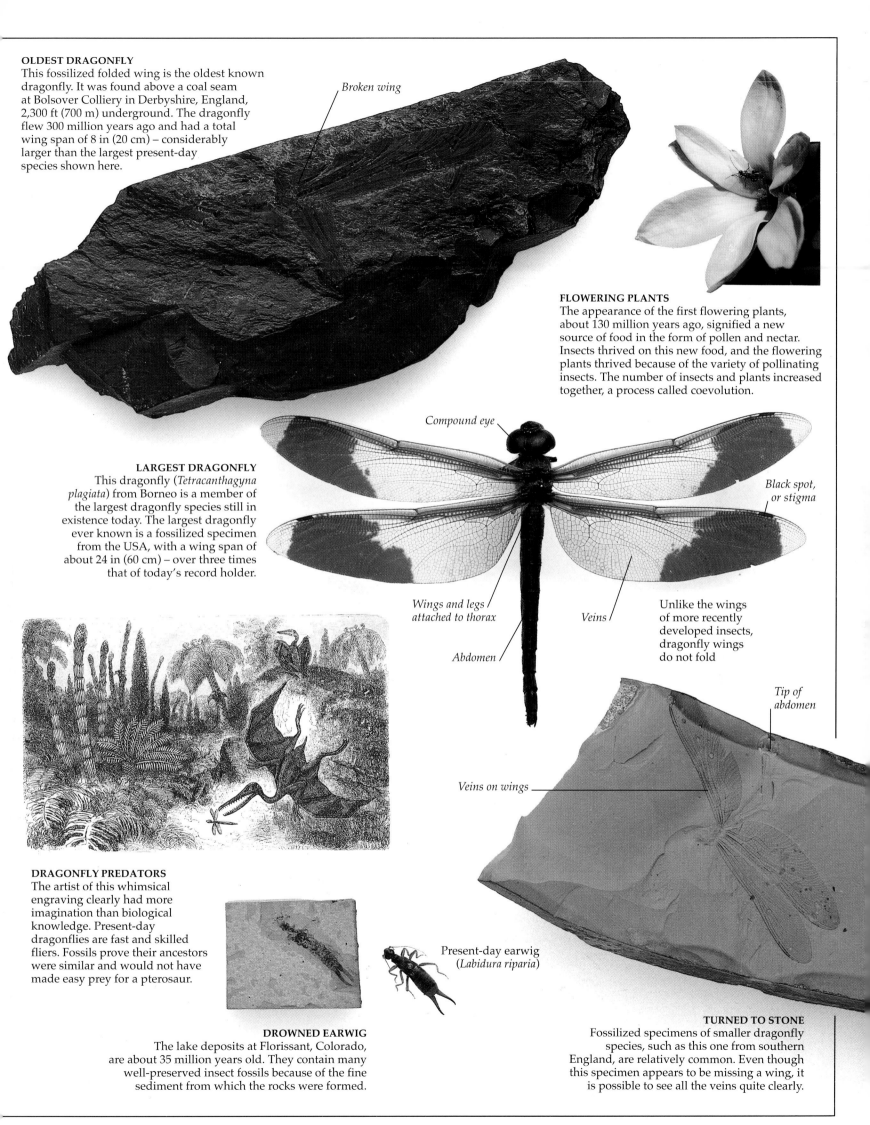

OLDEST DRAGONFLY

This fossilized folded wing is the oldest known dragonfly. It was found above a coal seam at Bolsover Colliery in Derbyshire, England, 2,300 ft (700 m) underground. The dragonfly flew 300 million years ago and had a total wing span of 8 in (20 cm) – considerably larger than the largest present-day species shown here.

Broken wing

FLOWERING PLANTS

The appearance of the first flowering plants, about 130 million years ago, signified a new source of food in the form of pollen and nectar. Insects thrived on this new food, and the flowering plants thrived because of the variety of pollinating insects. The number of insects and plants increased together, a process called coevolution.

Compound eye

Black spot, or stigma

LARGEST DRAGONFLY

This dragonfly (*Tetracanthagyna plagiata*) from Borneo is a member of the largest dragonfly species still in existence today. The largest dragonfly ever known is a fossilized specimen from the USA, with a wing span of about 24 in (60 cm) – over three times that of today's record holder.

Wings and legs attached to thorax

Veins

Unlike the wings of more recently developed insects, dragonfly wings do not fold

Abdomen

Tip of abdomen

DRAGONFLY PREDATORS

The artist of this whimsical engraving clearly had more imagination than biological knowledge. Present-day dragonflies are fast and skilled fliers. Fossils prove their ancestors were similar and would not have made easy prey for a pterosaur.

Veins on wings

Present-day earwig (Labidura riparia)

DROWNED EARWIG

The lake deposits at Florissant, Colorado, are about 35 million years old. They contain many well-preserved insect fossils because of the fine sediment from which the rocks were formed.

TURNED TO STONE

Fossilized specimens of smaller dragonfly species, such as this one from southern England, are relatively common. Even though this specimen appears to be missing a wing, it is possible to see all the veins quite clearly.

Ancient amphibians

TOAD IN THE HOLE
This mummified toad was found in England in the 1890s. The baby toad entered this hollow stone via a small hole. It grew for a time, but eventually died from a lack of food, water, and air.

THE FIRST AMPHIBIANS appeared some 360 million years ago. They evolved from fish with fleshy, lobed fins which looked like legs, and the earliest amphibians such as *Ichthyostega* still had fishlike features. They may have been attracted onto land by a good supply of food and fewer enemies to prey on them. While their fish ancestors already had lungs for breathing air and had begun to use their lobed fins for moving around on land, the early amphibians developed efficient walking limbs. The great Age of Amphibians was from the Devonian to the Permian periods. Most amphibians had become extinct by the Triassic period, leaving only a few, such as *Triadobatrachus*, to evolve into modern amphibians.

Artist's reconstruction of *Triadobatrachus*

One half of *Triadobatrachus* fossil

Skeleton of *Ichthyostega*

Reconstruction of *Ichthyostega*

FISHY FINS
These are reconstructions of *Ichthyostega*, an early amphibian from the Devonian period in Greenland. It had some fishlike features such as a tail fin and small scales in its distinctly amphibian body, but had fewer skull bones and legs suitable for walking.

AMPHIBIAN CROCODILE
This skeleton is of *Eryops*, a crocodile-like amphibian that lived in swamps in Texas about 250 million years ago. These terrestrial creatures used their strong limbs to move around on land.

ANCIENT FROG
This 20 million-year-old fossil frog, *Discoglossus*, was found in Germany. It is structurally similar to its close relative from 130 million years previously, *Eodiscoglossus*, which was found in Spain. The modern living species of *Discoglossus* show that they have remained almost unchanged over the last 150 million years. This is a good example of what is known as conservative evolution.

Wide, flat skull, like modern frogs

Outline of fossil frog

Short tail

MORE MODERN FROG
Well-preserved fossil frog skeletons such as *Rana pueyoi* from the Miocene of Spain are very like the modern European frogs that belong to the same genus, *Rana*. Fossil frogs like this help experts to date the first appearance of modern frog groups. They also show how little some groups have changed in the last 25 million years since the early Miocene period.

Fleshy, long hind legs

SLIM EVIDENCE
This fossil sandwich, which was found in France, is the only known specimen of *Triadobatrachus*, dating from the Triassic period about 210 million years ago. It has a froglike body and skull, but it is different enough from true frogs to be placed in a separate group called the proanurans.

Body shape of fossil salamander is like that of modern hellbender

Diplocaulus lived 270 million years ago

Short, stout leg supports heavy body

RELATIVE FROM ABROAD
This fossil salamander, *Cryptobranchus*, was found in Switzerland and is about eight million years old. It is a close relative of the hellbenders; the only living one, *Cryptobranchus alleganiensis*, is found in the southeastern US. Fossils like this show that some amphibians, such as these hellbenders, once had a wider distribution, and that separate land masses were once joined.

The Age of Reptiles

THE FIRST REPTILES were probably small, lizardlike creatures which evolved from amphibians more than 330 million years ago. They lived alongside the giant land-based amphibians for millions of years. But by 200 million years ago, reptiles had diversified into several different groups. Turtles, tortoises, crocodiles, and lizards were all very similar to their representatives today. Another group that was spreading and evolving rapidly was the dinosaurs. These incredibly varied and successful reptiles dominated life on land for over 120 million years. Some, like the giraffe-necked *Brachiosaurus*, weighed over 60 tons and stood as tall as a five-story building. Others were as small as a blackbird. The dinosaurs shown here belonged to the stegosaur or "roofed reptile" group, which thrived around 150 million years ago. *Stegosaurus* lived in North America and *Tuojiangosaurus* (the large skeleton) lived in what is now China.

CAUGHT IN THE RAIN
Stegosaurus, shown here caught in a downpour, probably had two rows of large upright plates in two parallel rows down its back. The plates were made of bone with honeycomb-like spaces running through – not much use as defensive armor plating.

A WEIRD STEGOSAUR
This etching shows an early attempt to reconstruct a plated dinosaur, with hedgehoglike spines instead of bony plates! It is unlikely that stegosaurs would have walked on two legs. Their front feet were adapted purely for walking.

Vertebral spine

Cone-shaped plate

Bony flange to anchor tail-swinging muscle

Heavy tail counterbalances weight of head and body

Part of hipbone (pelvis)

Chevron bone

Broad, flat feet

SPIKY TAIL
The large, cone-shaped plates on the back of *Tuojiangosaurus* give way to two pairs of sharply pointed ones, which were used as lethal weapons. Stegosaurs could swing their muscular tails from side to side with great force. The tail muscles were anchored to the bony flanges above and below each backbone (vertebra).

Sharp defensive spike

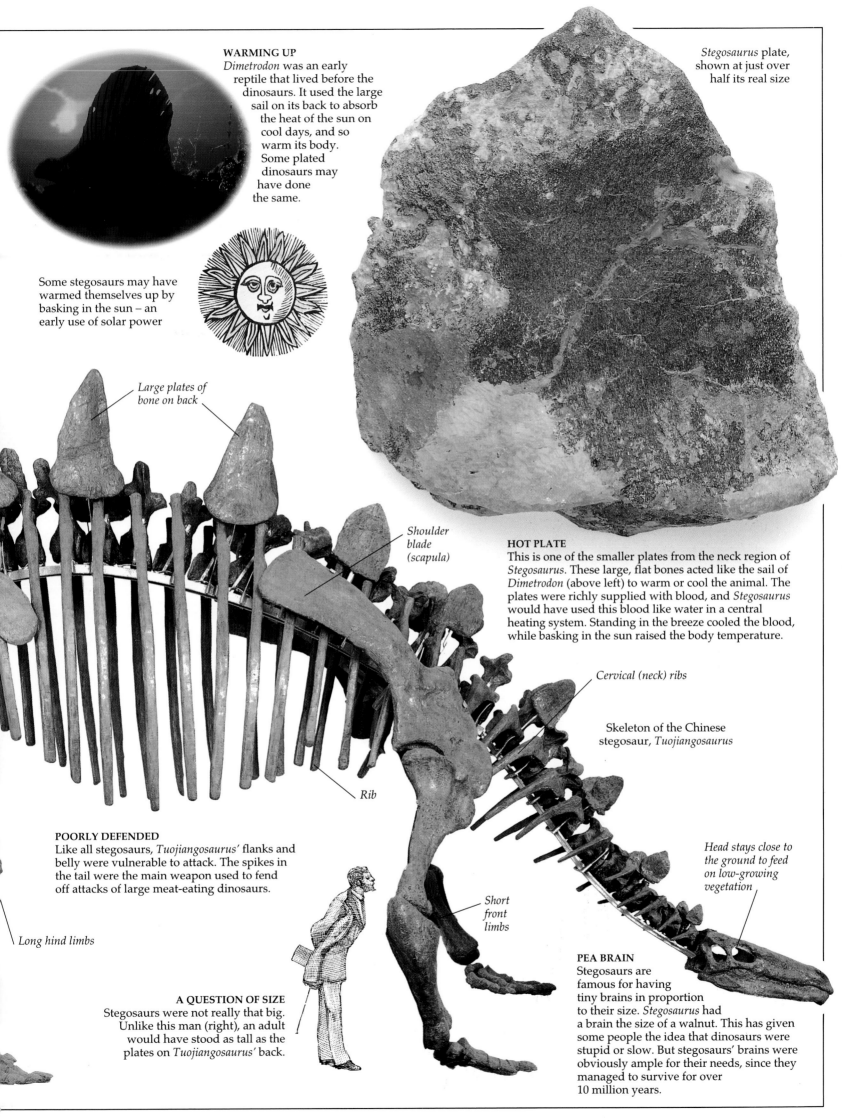

WARMING UP
Dimetrodon was an early reptile that lived before the dinosaurs. It used the large sail on its back to absorb the heat of the sun on cool days, and so warm its body. Some plated dinosaurs may have done the same.

Some stegosaurs may have warmed themselves up by basking in the sun – an early use of solar power

Stegosaurus plate, shown at just over half its real size

Large plates of bone on back

Shoulder blade (scapula)

HOT PLATE
This is one of the smaller plates from the neck region of *Stegosaurus*. These large, flat bones acted like the sail of *Dimetrodon* (above left) to warm or cool the animal. The plates were richly supplied with blood, and *Stegosaurus* would have used this blood like water in a central heating system. Standing in the breeze cooled the blood, while basking in the sun raised the body temperature.

Cervical (neck) ribs

Skeleton of the Chinese stegosaur, *Tuojiangosaurus*

Rib

POORLY DEFENDED
Like all stegosaurs, *Tuojiangosaurus'* flanks and belly were vulnerable to attack. The spikes in the tail were the main weapon used to fend off attacks of large meat-eating dinosaurs.

Head stays close to the ground to feed on low-growing vegetation

Short front limbs

Long hind limbs

A QUESTION OF SIZE
Stegosaurs were not really that big. Unlike this man (right), an adult would have stood as tall as the plates on *Tuojiangosaurus'* back.

PEA BRAIN
Stegosaurs are famous for having tiny brains in proportion to their size. *Stegosaurus* had a brain the size of a walnut. This has given some people the idea that dinosaurs were stupid or slow. But stegosaurs' brains were obviously ample for their needs, since they managed to survive for over 10 million years.

Dinosaur diets

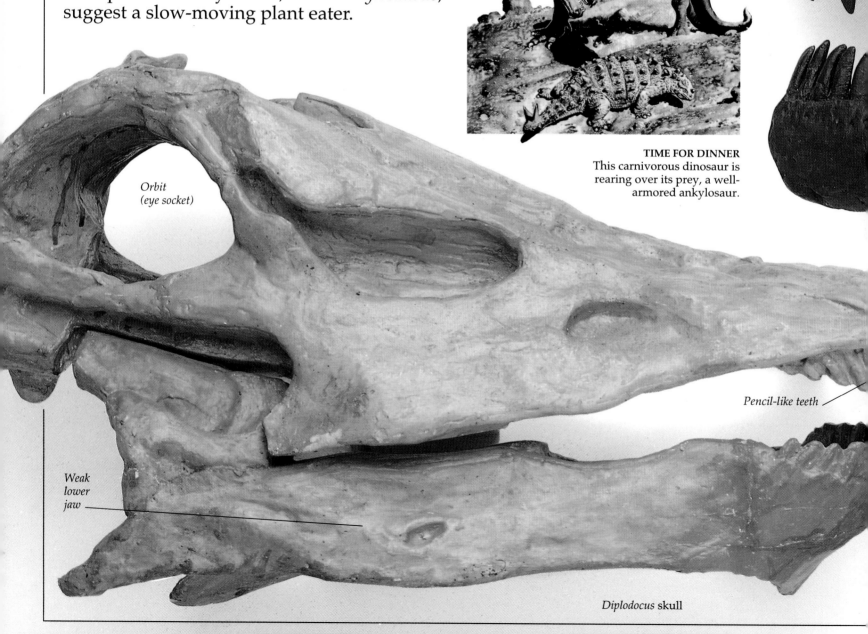

IT IS EASY TO IMAGINE DINOSAURS as being fearsome, meat-eating creatures. But some were peaceful plant eaters that simply browsed among the treetops, tearing off leaves. Other dinosaurs ate a mixed diet of meat and plants. Those that were not herbivorous did not confine themselves to dinosaur meat. They would have eaten anything that moved, including insects and birds. Fossilized dinosaur remains can tell us a lot about what the animal ate when it was alive. Scientists can compare their jaws and teeth with those of animals alive today, from horses to lions, to find similarities in structure and function. This is called comparative anatomy. Large claws on the fingers and toes show that the dinosaur was a predator; hard plates of body armor, as in *Ankylosaurus*, suggest a slow-moving plant eater.

BY THE RIVER
This scene from 190 million years ago shows meat-eating dinosaurs, swimming reptiles, and flying pterosaurs sharing the same landscape.

TIME FOR DINNER
This carnivorous dinosaur is rearing over its prey, a well-armored ankylosaur.

Orbit (eye socket)

Weak lower jaw

Pencil-like teeth

Diplodocus skull

SERIOUS TEETH
The fearsome rows of curved, serrated teeth in the *Allosaurus* skull (below) are typical of carnivores. *Allosaurus* may well have fed on the young of herbivores such as *Diplodocus* (opposite). An adult *Diplodocus* would have been too big to tackle, unless *Allosaurus* hunted in packs.

Large cavity helped reduce weight of skull

Orbit (Eye socket)

Allosaurus skull

Powerful lower jaw

VEGETARIAN SKULL
This skull belonged to a huge herbivore called *Diplodocus*. All of the thin, pencil-like teeth are at the front of the mouth. *Diplodocus* would have used them like a rake to draw in conifer needles and leaves. Unable to chew, *Diplodocus* simply swallowed what it raked in.

Diplodocus

Fern leaf

Massospondylus skull (below)

DIPLODOCUS DINNER
Diplodocus may have raked in plants like this fern leaf. Because it never chewed, it did not need a strong lower jaw.

DUAL DIET DINOSAUR
The skull above belonged to *Massospondylus*. Its teeth, being neither serrated and stabbing, nor rakelike or grinding, were multipurpose. Small and coarse-edged, they could chew either meat or plants. Animals who can eat like this are called omnivores.

Death of the dinosaurs

DINOSAURS DISAPPEARED from the Earth quite suddenly, and why this happened is still a mystery. Around 70 million years ago, the dinosaurs ruled the Earth. Yet about five million years later, they had all died out, perhaps only in a matter of months. Scientists have various theories to explain their sudden extinction, but many ignore one vital point: dinosaurs were only one of a whole range of creatures that died out at the same time, including all the swimming and flying reptiles. So any theory to explain dinosaur extinction must explain the disappearance of these groups as well. Some people think that small mammals ate all the dinosaur eggs. This is very unlikely – for how would it account for the extinction of other species that disappeared at the same time? Others believed that diseases were responsible, affecting only certain groups.

POISONOUS BITE
It has been suggested that the dinosaurs died out because they ate new kinds of poisonous plants, including the deadly nightshade (above), that began to grow on Earth.

Stony meteorite fragment

ROCKS FROM SPACE
A likely reason for the sudden extinction is that a massive meteorite from space collided with the Earth. This would have been catastrophic, causing a huge steam and dust cloud which darkened the Earth for a long time, killing off many plants and the animals that fed on them.

Fossilized ammonite shell

A MASS EXTINCTION
Many other creatures died out at the time of the dinosaur extinction. Whatever happened seemed to affect some creatures, while leaving others unscathed. Ammonites, a type of mollusk, became extinct, as did the mosasaurs, plesiosaurs, and ichthyosaurs, groups of meat-eating marine reptiles. Sea crocodiles died out but the river crocodiles survived. The flying reptiles – pterosaurs – disappeared, but birds were unaffected.

Iron meteorite fragment

Iguanodon ischium (part of hipbone)

Unaffected part of bone

Shaft of ischium bent forward after repair

Section of
hadrosaur backbone

Vertebral
spine —

**THE BEGINNING
OF THE END**
A *Tyrannosaurus rex* is
shown fleeing in terror
as a meteor hits the Earth.
The impact would have had
an effect rather like that of a
massive nuclear war. Dense black
clouds of dust and soot would have
cut out the sun for months.

A GROWTH
Dinosaurs could contract cancer. This
section of backbone belonged to a hadrosaur,
or "duck-billed" dinosaur that walked upright
on its back legs, and shows a swollen area
that was a cancerous tumor in the bone.

Part of ischium that
formed hip joint
with thighbone —

Swollen area of
tumor growth

Point of
fracture

Vertebral
body

Thickening of
bone around break

BROKEN BONE
During their reign, dinosaurs were not immune to diseases
and accidents. The *Iguanodon* hip bone (above) shows a
fracture that healed itself during the creature's lifetime.

Mammoths and mastodons

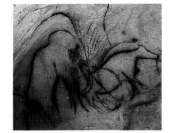

Stone Age painting found in a cave in France

WHEN THE DINOSAURS and many other animals died out 65 million years ago, they left opportunities for others to take over. The main group which responded very quickly was the mammals. Small, shrewlike mammals had first appeared with the dinosaurs, over 200 million years ago. During the dinosaurs' reign they did not evolve very much, and none was bigger than a pet cat. But by 50 million years ago, all manner of weird and huge mammals walked the Earth, while others took to the water as whales. The elephant group of mammals arose over 40 million years ago. It produced some of the biggest of all land mammals, the mammoths and mastodons. These animals lived until relatively recently alongside Stone Age humans, and some of their bodies have been found deep-frozen in the ice of the far north. We do not know why mammoths and mastodons became extinct, but computer studies of their decline in numbers suggest that it was a combination of overhunting by humans and changes in the climate that led to their final disappearance 10,000 years ago.

HAIRY LEGS
It is very rare to be able to see the hair, skin, and muscles of long-extinct creatures. Usually only bones and teeth are fossilized, but when frozen mammoths thaw out of the permafrost (permanently frozen ground) in Siberia, we can learn – as with this mammoth leg – about their shaggy coat and long "toenails."

SNOW PLOWS
Mammoth tusks curve much more than those of living elephants, and are the biggest teeth of any known creature. Some grew to lengths of 16 ft (5 m). Mothers, as in this reconstruction, would have used them to protect their calves from predators. Mammoths probably also used them to sweep aside snow when feeding on the grassy plains.

Body squashed flat by weight of frozen earth and snow

FAST-FROZEN MAMMOTH
Perhaps 40,000 years ago, this baby mammoth died in a Siberian marsh just as the ground froze. In 1977, his frozen body was recovered by scientists, and nicknamed "Dima." One scientist tried to use genes from cells in Dima's best-preserved organs to clone mammoth cells in a test tube. The plan was to implant these cells in a female Asian elephant's womb, in the hope that she would give birth to a bouncing baby mammoth. It did not work.

MAMMOTH TASK
The first whole mammoth to be studied by scientists was found in 1900 beside the River Berezovka in Siberia. A shed was built over the thawing carcass while it was excavated and dissected.

SIMILAR BUT DIFFERENT
Reconstructions of mammoths and mastodons may look alike, but mastodons differed in several ways from mammoths. Mastodons were stockier, and did not have a steeply sloping back. Some had two small tusks in the lower jaw as well as the big upper tusks.

Mammoths had small ears which helped reduce loss of body heat in cold conditions

MAMMOTH ANCESTORS
Mammoths evolved in the cold of the frozen north. But their ancestors originated in what is now the Middle East, over 40 million years earlier.

Mammoth stamp from Manama, Bahrain, in the Middle East

IVORY MISSILES
During the Stone Age, ivory was used for making household implements, tools, and weapons. This mammoth-ivory boomerang, found in Poland, dates back 23,000 years. The growth lines in the mammoth's tusk show as cones, one inside the other, along the length of the whole tusk.

A long, woolly coat protected mammoths from freezing temperatures

Reconstruction of an adult female mammoth with her baby at her side

Broad feet spread body weight for walking in soft snow

Adapting to habitats

MOLES HAVE STRONG, BROAD front feet for digging through soil. Ducks have webbed feet for swimming. It is clear that all plants and animals are superbly adapted to their climate and way of life. The English naturalist Charles Darwin (1809-1882) proposed that these adaptations were an outcome of natural selection. Each creature is also adapted to a particular location where conditions suit it best, from a pine forest to a stony desert. These surroundings are called habitats. Some animals, such as the fox, can tolerate a wide range of habitats, from mountains and moors to city parks. It manages this because of its body design and adaptable behavior. Other creatures need a specialized habitat. The olm, a strange, wormlike salamander, lives in complete darkness in underground streams and caves in southern Europe, and is highly sensitive to disturbances in the air and water.

PALEY'S WATCH
An English clergyman, William Paley (1743-1805) believed in "natural theology" – a theory that all adaptation was evidence of the Creator's handiwork. He published his ideas in a book which began with the example of himself walking across a heath and finding a watch among the stones. Unlike the stones, the watch had moving parts that worked together for a purpose. Paley said that the existence of the watch proved that there was a watchmaker, so an animal or plant proved the existence of a Creator. By studying natural history, the nature of God could be better understood.

FACE FOR THE HABITAT
Leaf-nosed bats from different habitats have varying face shapes. This may be connected with the difficulty they have in navigating around obstacles, using their sense of echolocation. Bats hunting in woodlands must avoid branches, which bats flying over open water or grasslands do not encounter.

Faces of leaf-nosed bats

SUITED FOR THE SOIL
The European mole is well suited for life in the soil. It has tiny eyes, since it rarely uses them; its broad, shovel-like front paws dig through the soil; and its sensitive snout smells and feels for worms, grubs, and other food. Yet this mole would probably not survive underground in a desert or on a moorland. Its habitat is under woodlands, meadows, and lawns. Other species of burrowing mammals are better adapted to different habitats.

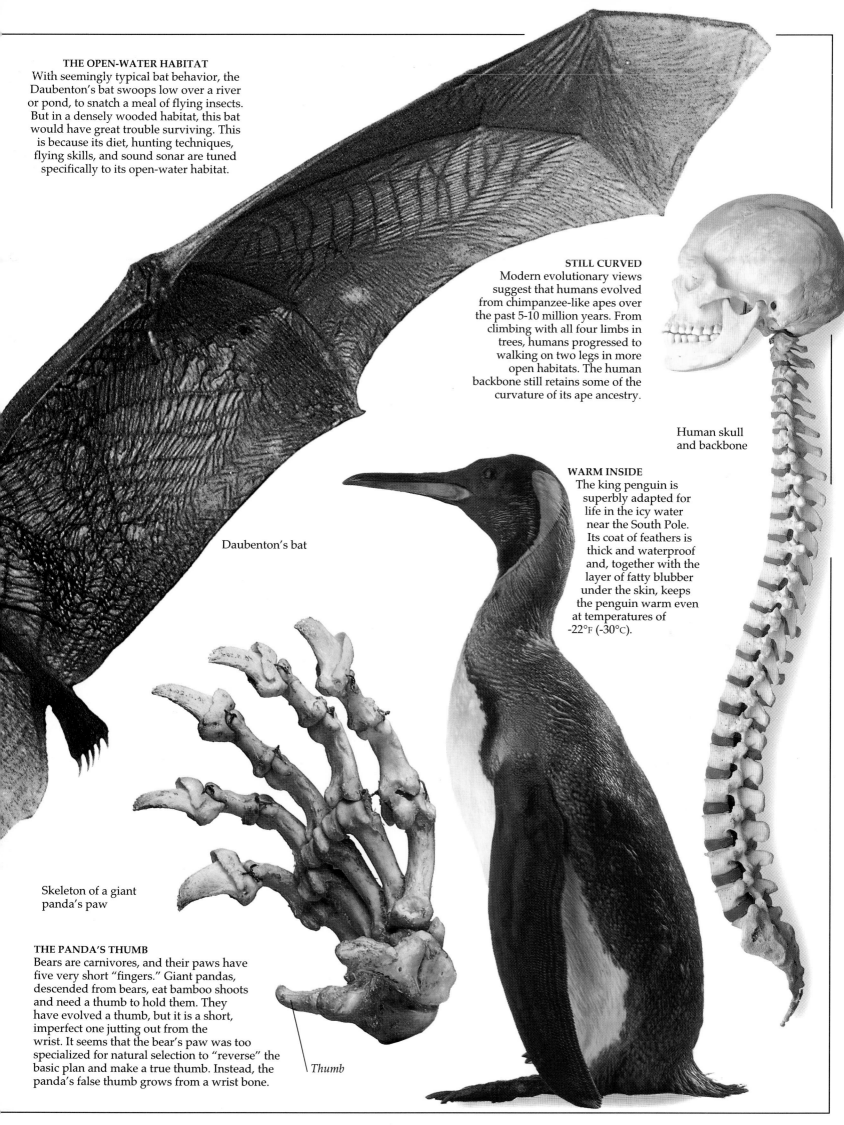

THE OPEN-WATER HABITAT
With seemingly typical bat behavior, the
Daubenton's bat swoops low over a river
or pond, to snatch a meal of flying insects.
But in a densely wooded habitat, this bat
would have great trouble surviving. This
is because its diet, hunting techniques,
flying skills, and sound sonar are tuned
specifically to its open-water habitat.

STILL CURVED
Modern evolutionary views
suggest that humans evolved
from chimpanzee-like apes over
the past 5-10 million years. From
climbing with all four limbs in
trees, humans progressed to
walking on two legs in more
open habitats. The human
backbone still retains some of the
curvature of its ape ancestry.

Human skull
and backbone

Daubenton's bat

WARM INSIDE
The king penguin is
superbly adapted for
life in the icy water
near the South Pole.
Its coat of feathers is
thick and waterproof
and, together with the
layer of fatty blubber
under the skin, keeps
the penguin warm even
at temperatures of
-22°F (-30°C).

Skeleton of a giant
panda's paw

THE PANDA'S THUMB
Bears are carnivores, and their paws have
five very short "fingers." Giant pandas,
descended from bears, eat bamboo shoots
and need a thumb to hold them. They
have evolved a thumb, but it is a short,
imperfect one jutting out from the
wrist. It seems that the bear's paw was too
specialized for natural selection to "reverse" the
basic plan and make a true thumb. Instead, the
panda's false thumb grows from a wrist bone.

Thumb

Life in the ocean

LIFE BEGAN IN THE OCEANS millions of years ago. Today, oceans cover 71 percent of the planet and provide homes for countless animals, including fish, seals, sharks, and jellyfish. Ocean wildlife is at its richest in the warm shallow waters of coral reefs, where dazzlingly colorful fish such as clown triggerfish and angelfish live. In deeper waters, whales, dolphins, and porpoises are found. Most animals live close to the water's surface, where sunlight filters through the water, allowing microscopic plants such as diatoms to flourish. An intricate food web exists here: microscopic animals feed on the diatoms; small animals feed on these; larger sea creatures eat the smaller ones, and all the way up the food chain, to predators such as sharks.

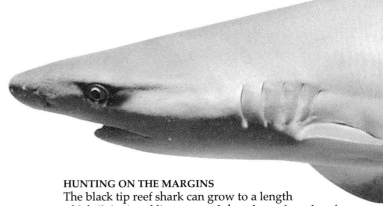

RAY'S WAVES
A ray "flies" through the water by vertical waves that pass along its winglike pectoral fins, from head to tail.

HUNTING ON THE MARGINS
The black tip reef shark can grow to a length of 8 ft (2.4 m) and lives around the edges of coral reefs. It does not have the slim body and maneuverability of fish that usually dwell in the coral reef. Instead, it is streamlined and is adapted for a deep-water lifestyle. This top predator patrols the waters near the reef, taking advantage of the plentiful plant and animal life there by picking off the occasional unwary victim.

MOLLUSK WITH A DIFFERENCE
Like the snail, this squid is a mollusk. It can camouflage itself rapidly, sending waves of color down its body, and squirting out a cloud of dark ink to cover its escape.

SPIDER IN THE FOOD WEB
Crabs, such as this spider crab, tend to inhabit shallow water, where there is sufficient light to encourage plant growth and so feed animal life.

WATER SKATER
Garfish live in shoals in the open ocean. They have beaklike jaws and sharp teeth, and feed on small fish. The garfish escapes predators by vibrating its tail and skittering across the sea's surface, with the front part of its body raised out of the water.

Black tip reef shark

A FUNNY FISH
Bizzare patterns and hues are not only there to look pretty. The clown triggerfish has a dramatic set of broken patterns that breaks up the outline of its body , confusing predators long enoough for the fish to get away. The triggerfish takes its name from the second fin spine on its back, which, like a gun's trigger, can lock or release the first spine into an upright position to deter a predator's attack.

Clown triggerfish

INVISIBLE LINKS IN THE CHAIN OF LIFE
The microscopic world of plankton forms the base of the ocean food chain. Phytoplankton, tiny plants such as diatoms and algae, are eaten by zooplankton (magnified above), minuscule animals that drift in the ocean currents. These in turn are eaten by filter feeders from mollusks up to blue whales.

WELL WRAPPED UP
With their streamlined bodies, seals and sea lions are well equipped for life in the ocean. Their oily, glossy fur keeps them warm in cold waters, helped by a thick layer of fat, or blubber, under the skin. Seals use their front flippers like oars as they speed after fish in the sea. There are more than 30 kinds of seals and sea lions in the world, including this gray seal (above).

Freshwater habitats

FRESHWATER MAKES UP only three percent of all water on Earth, the rest being salty seawater. But freshwater habitats are more variable than ocean habitats, varying from foaming streams to sluggish rivers, and tiny puddles and pools to vast lakes. The chemical content of the water is often affected by the rock type underneath it. Where there is a rich supply of nutrients, encouraging the growth of plants, there is a large number and variety of animals, such as insect larvae, fish, aquatic mammals, and birds. Water from highland areas is often clear and rich in oxygen, but lacks nutrients and so is poor in aquatic life. The ecology of freshwater is therefore complicated by these different factors. Some animals are able to live in clear fast-flowing rivers, while others need the still, murky waters of a lake.

TAGGED FISH
Fish are caught and tagged with small metal or plastic clips, to study their growth rate, migration, and life spans. Scientists also tag individual fish to determine the size of the population. This can be calculated using a formula based on the frequency with which the tagged fish are recaptured. By regularly weighing and measuring the tagged fish, scientists can see how each one grows over time.

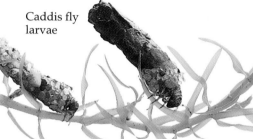
Caddis fly larvae

Water shrimp

Minnows

POSITIVE INDICATORS
In all rivers there is a profusion of small creatures under stones and among the plants. Many, such as the caddis fly larva, mayfly nymph, and bloodworm, are the larval form of flying insects. Some of these animals are sensitive to pollution. Scientists can tell if a river is polluted by counting the numbers of each species found. The presence of caddis fly larvae, mayfly nymphs, and water shrimps indicates clean water, so they are called positive indicators.

Mayfly nymphs

MIDDLE WATERS
As a river widens, bends begin to develop, and patches of silt and mud accumulate. Plants such as the water crowfoot (right) thrive in this less rapid water. Small invertebrates that live among the weeds provide a rich source of food for bottom-feeding minnows.

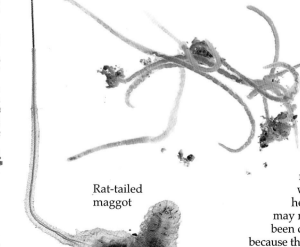
Tubifex worms

Rat-tailed maggot

Bloodworm

NEGATIVE INDICATORS
If a stretch of river supports only such species as rat-tailed maggots, bloodworms, and tubifex worms, this shows that the water is heavily polluted. Other forms of life may not survive because their gills have been clogged by particles in the water or because they have been unable to tolerate low oxygen levels. The rat-tailed maggot (the larva of a fly) can survive because it takes in air using a specialized breathing tube rather like a snorkel.

WATER CROWFOOT
Like plants found in streams and rivers, the water crowfoot is adapted to resist the pull of the current. It puts down strong roots in the river bed, and its leaves have long, thin stems, which bend with the flow of the water.

Rainbow trout

FASTER WATERS
The upper reaches of a
river are often fast flowing
and well oxygenated, providing
perfect conditions for rainbow trout
and a few other small fish that can cope
with this environment. These creatures are
powerful swimmers, and can cope with the swift
current. They save energy by resting near the edge of the
river or by a boulder, where the water flows more slowly.

SLOWER WATERS
In the lower reaches of the river, the gradient is less steep and the water flows
more slowly. Silt and nutrients tend to settle on the river bed, providing a
foothold for a diversity of plants. These enrich the food supply for other
organisms so the lower reaches contain a variety of fish. Within
this zone, different parts of the river attract different species.
The barbel occupies the clearer,
faster-flowing parts, for
example below weirs.
Tench prefer slower,
muddier water, and
pike live wherever
there is enough
weed to hide
them as they
lie in ambush.

Tench

Barbel

*Barbels for
locating food*

*Flattened underside for
bottom-dwelling lifestyle*

*Forward-facing
eyes for distance*

*Powerful tail and
fins for rapid
acceleration*

*Camouflaged
coloring*

Juvenile pike

The woodland habitat

THE WOODLANDS in temperate regions (between the tropics and the polar circles) provide shelter for a large wildlife community. Every tree supports its own web of life: insects feed on the leaves, birds and mammals nest in the trunk and branches, and sowbugs and beetles live in the leaf litter. Seasonal weather changes affect animal behavior. In the warm spring days insects emerge, birds begin to nest, and young mammals are born. In the hot summer months the young animals grow quickly. Most trees lose their leaves in the autumn, and the animals feast on berries or store food for the winter. The cold nights and short days make winter a difficult time: many animals grow thick coats and spend more time in their burrows or tree holes, while many birds fly away to spend the winter in warmer climates.

GALL STORY
Forest food chains can be complicated. Insects such as moths and wasps lay their eggs in buds, leaves, and fruits, where the larvae develop inside swellings called galls. The chalci wasp searches out the larvae and lays its eggs in them.

GREEN WOODPECKER
The forest food chain continues when, in turn, both the larvae inside the galls and the chalci wasp (above) are eaten by insect-hunting birds such as this green woodpecker.

The short tail is made of stiff feathers which support the woodpecker as it climbs up trees

Canopy: gets full strength of Sun

Litter layer: plants that thrive in moist, shady conditions

Shrub layer: tall bushes and small trees

Herb layer: plants that can cope with low light levels

Topsoil

Subsoil

Bedrock

WOODEN HOSTS
Trees provide a variety of smaller habitats, in vertical layers in the forest. Flying creatures such as birds and butterflies frequent the upper layers, where leaves and fruits are profuse. On the forest floor conditions are cool, shady, and damp, which suits worms, snails, and similar small creatures.

NIGHT FLIER
An unmistakable hoot in the night reveals that there is a tawny owl in the woods. During the day, the owl sits quietly in the trees. It is hard to spot because its mottled coloring blends in with the bark and leaves. Its sharp hearing and silent flight make it an excellent hunter of mice, voles, and other small mammals, as well as small birds, amphibians, fish, and insects.

LEAF LITTER CARNIVORE
Centipedes scurry through the leaf litter on the forest floor. They seize small prey such as worms, grubs, and larvae in their large fangs and inject poison to subdue the victim. Centipedes have one pair of legs per body segment; their plant-eating cousins, millipedes, have two pairs.

Fur, feathers, and bones

Vole's skull

Rodent's hipbone

OWL PELLETS
Some birds, such as owls and members of the crow family, bring up the indigestible parts of their food as pellets. The pellet contains bones, teeth, fur, claws, feathers, and other hard parts.

BROWSERS
Deer are typical woodland animals. They browse on the tree leaves at dawn and dusk, and rest in the middle of the day in the deep shade of thickets.

Mountain life

The MOUNTAIN HABITAT is a harsh one, and the greater the altitude, the harsher it becomes. The temperature falls by about 2°F (1°C) for every 500 ft (150 m), the winds blow harder, and the atmosphere becomes thinner and less rich in oxygen. Only insects can survive at the high altitudes of the mountain peaks. They feed on plant spores, pollen, and other insects swept up from the lower plains. Most animals live farther down the slopes in the forests and meadows. Many of the mountain mammals have thick fur and large lungs to help them survive the cold, the wind, and the thin air. High-altitude animals, such as pumas, usually move down to the lower slopes and valleys in winter. Others, such as marmots and bears, hibernate during the coldest months.

Thick dense fur is a blue-gray color

Brushlike tail

WELL WRAPPED UP
The Andes mountains of South America are home to the chinchilla – a mountain mammal with a luxurious fur coat. At one time, wild chinchillas were quite common. Today, they are rare because too many have been hunted for their valuable fur.

ALPINE ZONES
Whatever the climate, the increasing altitude on a mountain creates zones of different habitats. These layers show the changing vegetation in the European Alps. Deciduous woodlands in the foothills give way to coniferous forest, which can tolerate the increasing cold. At 8,500 ft (2,600 m) the alpine meadow is the main vegetation. Between the meadow and the snow at the top lies the alpine tundra, with rocky scree above it.

Snow field to summit

14,000 ft (4,200 m)

Rocky scree

Alpine tundra

Alpine meadow

8,500 ft (2,600 m)

Deciduous woodland

BLOOD AND HONEY
Many mountain insects have a varied diet, eating whatever they can find during the different seasons. This fly from the Himalayan region has dual-purpose mouthparts. Its short, strong, biting "jaws" can pierce the skin of mammals such as yaks to feed on the blood, just like the horsefly of meadows and pastures. Its long, thin "tongue" can sip nectar from flowers, when these bloom in the brief mountain summer.

SKY FIGHTER
Fast and agile in the air, with a keen eye and rapid reflexes, the merlin is one of the top predators in the mountain food chain. It takes small birds, such as meadow pipits and snow buntings, in midair. In winter, as food sources dwindle, it extends its feeding range to include pastures, marshes, and coasts. Birds are particularly successful in mountain habitats because they can range over huge distances to look for food, and quickly fly to the lowlands to avoid bad weather and when winter arrives.

FUR AND FEET
Mammals that live on mountains cope with the cold by having an extra-thick coat of fur. They also have sturdy legs and flexible, rubbery hooves or paws to grip and clamber on steep slopes and over boulders. The mountain goat shows both of these adaptations. One advantage of mountain life is that predators are less common than on the lowlands, and more easily seen in the open landscape.

ELUSIVE PUMA
The puma is also called the cougar or mountain lion. It is as much at home on the slopes of the Adirondacks in the eastern United States as on the inhospitable, windswept shores at the tip of South America. It hides in rocky places and so it is seldom seen, even though it hunts by day as well as by night.

The desert life

THE FEATURES THAT CHARACTERIZE all deserts are a lack of water – less than 10 in (250 mm) of rain per year – and generally harsh conditions. Desert conditions are found in many parts of the world. Most deserts receive some rain, though it is highly unpredictable, and it is this potential source of water that makes life possible in this arid environment. Temperatures fluctuate widely, too. Many deserts are very hot in the day, but they can be extremely cold at night. Food is limited compared with most other habitats. However, a range of animals has adapted to living with a slight and irregular supply of water, and to conserving precious energy. By day, most desert animals hide from the searing sun in burrows or under rocks. They emerge to feed at night, when the air is cooler and damper.

Black band marks the position of the hood, which is extended when the cobra feels threatened

Diadem snake

Gray banded king snake

WAITING WITH VENOM
The red spitting cobra lurks in palm groves at oases in eastern Africa. When attacking its prey of small reptiles and mammals, the cobra bites to inject venom. Reptiles such as snakes, lizards, and tortoises do well in a desert habitat because they control their body temperature by gaining or losing heat from their surroundings. And compared to amphibians such as toads, with their permeable skin, reptiles are better suited to desert habitats because they have scaly skin to help them conserve moisture.

SPECIAL SNAKES
Like all snakes, the diadem snake uses its tongue to pick up scents from the air and the ground. The scents are then transferred to a sensory organ in the roof of the mouth which detects chemicals. The gray banded king snake has also adapted to desert life; its enormous eyes help it to spot prey during the night when it hunts to escape the daytime heat.

SHIP OF THE DESERT
The camel has long been used to carry people and goods across the sandy sealike dunes, earning its name "ship of the desert." This mammal is admirably adapted to desert life with wide feet like sandshoes, thick fur to keep out heat and cold, and specialized body chemistry to conserve water.

Sharp beak
to tear flesh

Sting

Small pincers

Wide tail helps
the hawk to
control gliding

Protective scales

SLOW AND DRY
Scorpions that live in deserts are
especially venomous: this is so that they
do not waste precious energy fighting
in self-defense or subduing larger prey.
The hard body casing, or exoskeleton,
of creatures such as scorpions, spiders,
and insects cuts down loss of valuable
water from the body in the desert heat.

Powerful talons

EQUIPPED FOR THE KILL
The Harris' hawk is a top predator in the deserts
of North America. Seeking a diet consisting
mainly of reptiles, which may be thin on the
ground, each individual needs a vast area as its
hunting ground. The powerful talons grip the
squirming prey, and long legs with protective
scales keep the bird's body out of harm's way.

Overlapping scales
allow for rapid and
agile movement

Life at its richest

FROG BEETLE
This Malayan frog beetle has powerful back legs for jumping, just like its amphibian namesake.

BEETLING ABOUT
Most beetles, including this leaf beetle, live in the forests of warm regions. There are over 300,000 beetle and weevil species – more than in any other insect family.

TROPICAL FORESTS, or jungles, are among the richest places on Earth for wildlife. This is partly because jungles grow where there is year-round warmth and moisture and plenty of sunlight. These conditions provide an ideal habitat for all sorts of animals: in fact, there may be more animal species lurking in a couple of miles of jungle than there are in the whole of Alaska (591,000 sq miles). Because a tree provides different living conditions, from the leaf litter at its base to the highest branch, the types of animals that live in each part also vary greatly. The top of a tree, or canopy, takes most of the sunlight, while the forest floor is surprisingly gloomy because the dense foliage blocks out the light. Jungle animals are sustained by a continuous supply of food from blossoms and fruit all through the year. They are some of the most bizarre creatures to be found anywhere in the world.

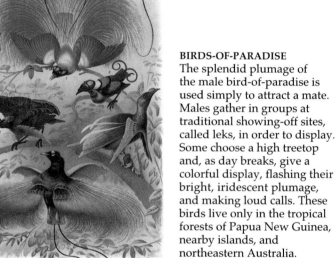

BIRDS-OF-PARADISE
The splendid plumage of the male bird-of-paradise is used simply to attract a mate. Males gather in groups at traditional showing-off sites, called leks, in order to display. Some choose a high treetop and, as day breaks, give a colorful display, flashing their bright, iridescent plumage, and making loud calls. These birds live only in the tropical forests of Papua New Guinea, nearby islands, and northeastern Australia.

HIGH FLIER
Creatures that live in the high canopy have evolved accordingly. This flying gecko usually relies on its camouflage to hide in the leaves and branches. If spotted, it launches itself into the air and glides to safety. Loose flaps of skin along its body and limbs spread out to form a broad swooping surface.

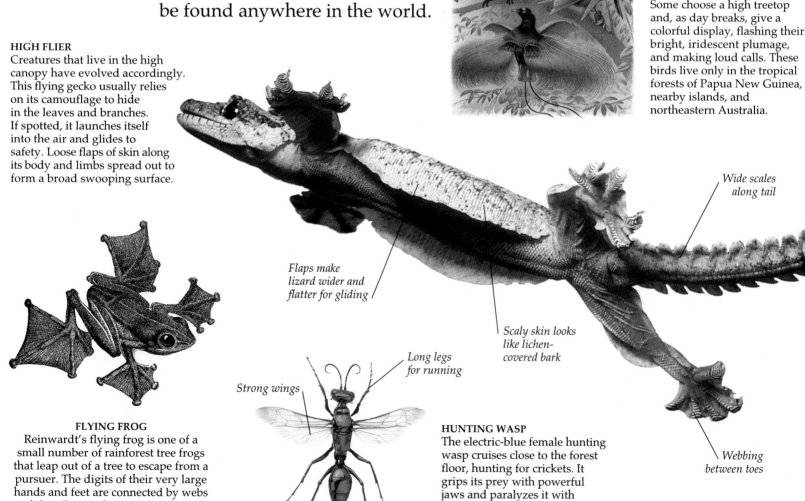

Flaps make lizard wider and flatter for gliding

Wide scales along tail

Scaly skin looks like lichen-covered bark

Long legs for running

Webbing between toes

Strong wings

FLYING FROG
Reinwardt's flying frog is one of a small number of rainforest tree frogs that leap out of a tree to escape from a pursuer. The digits of their very large hands and feet are connected by webs of skin. During long, gliding leaps, these behave like parachutes.

HUNTING WASP
The electric-blue female hunting wasp cruises close to the forest floor, hunting for crickets. It grips its prey with powerful jaws and paralyzes it with venom injected by its sting. It drags the insect into a burrow and lays a single egg in it so that, when the larva hatches, it has food until it pupates.

Blue-and-yellow macaw
from South America

SMASH THE FRUIT
The beaks of macaws and parrots
are hooked and extremely powerful.
They are adapted for piercing the
tough husks and skins of fruits,
and hooking the juicy flesh and
seeds within. These birds live in
tropical forests, although some species
have become adapted to drier habitats.

FLYING SNAKE
This flying tree snake is one of five species
from southeast Asia that can glide through the
air. By raising its ribs upward and outward,
the snake flattens its body and so manages to
travel distances of up to 160 ft (50 m) from
one tree to another. When it lands on the
ground it resumes its usual shape.

FLYING DRAGON
The flying dragon is a type of lizard
that has achieved its parachute
shape in a different way to the
flying gecko opposite. Six or seven
pairs of very long rib bones covered
with thin skin act as "wings." These
are usually folded against the
lizard's body, but open out so
it can glide long distances.

MOST MASSIVE MOTH
The atlas moth is one of the largest of all
butterflies and moths, with a wingspan
of 12 in (30 cm). It survives in woods
and forests across India and Sri Lanka
to Malaysia, Indonesia, and China. But
like other endangered jungle creatures,
it is illegally collected and sold as an
exotic pet, or even as a dead specimen.

*Wing pattern
and colors
help males
and females
find each other*

Animal classification

ALMOST EVERY ASPECT of studying nature involves classification – placing living things into groups. Classification, is constantly evolving as we learn more about living things. Most modern schemes start with five main groups, or kingdoms – monerans and protists (microscopic and single-celled animals), fungi, plants, and animals. The animal kingdom divides into two subgroups – the invertebrates and the vertebrates. These groups are divided into phyla which encompass animals with basic similarities in body structure, such as reptiles or mammals. Each phylum is then divided into classes, a class into orders, an order into families, a family into genera. Finally, each genus is divided into species. There are at least another 20 minor phyla, mostly of invertebrates which resemble worms or shellfish.

Invertebrates

Invertebrate species outnumber the larger, more familiar vertebrates by at least twenty to one. The vast majority of invertebrates are insects, class Insecta, with more than one million described and catalogued species, and perhaps several million more yet to be identified. Insects, along with spiders, crabs and other crustaceans, and millipedes and centipedes, make up the largest phylum in the animal kingdom – the arthropods, or "jointed-legged" animals. Their basic common feature is a hard outer body casing, or exoskeleton, and legs which can be bent at the joints.

Sea anemone

Earthworm

Snail

Spider

Crab

Starfish

INSECTA
All insects belong to one class. They have six legs when adult, and most have two or four pairs of wings. The largest subgroup of insects is the beetles and weevils.

Red admiral butterfly

CNIDARIA
This is a subphylum of Coelenterata. Cnidarians have a jellylike body and tentacles, and include jellyfish, corals, and sea anemones.

ANNELIDA
There are several phyla of worms. This one contains worms with many body segments, such as the earthworm.

MOLLUSCA
This phylum includes snails, slugs, octopuses, squids, mussels, and clams and similar shellfish. Most of them have a hard outer shell.

ARACHNIDA
Spiders, scorpions, and mites form this class in the phylum Arthropoda. Their basic feature is four pairs of walking legs.

CRUSTACEA
This class of arthropods includes sea-living crabs, lobsters, prawns, shrimps, and barnacles, and a few land-dwellers such as sowbugs.

ECHINODERMATA
Echinoderms are a phylum of sea-dwellers with a circular body plan, such as starfish, sea urchins, sea lilies, and feather stars.

Vertebrates

All vertebrates have a backbone, also known as a vertebral column, and a supporting skeleton inside the body, rather than around it as in many invertebrates. It is generally assumed that a structure as complicated as the backbone arose only once during evolution, so all vertebrates are related by their common ancestry. Most vertebrates are large, compared to invertebrates, with keen senses and a relatively large brain, and show variable and adaptable behavior. The main phylum of vertebrates is Chordata, containing the classes of fish, amphibians, reptiles, birds, and mammals.

AVES
This class contains the birds. The key feature that makes a bird is its feathers. All birds are warm blooded, have a toothless beak, and forelimbs adapted as wings.

Lanner falcon

Tiger

Snake

Frog

Yellow cichlid

Dogfish

MAMMALIA
Mammals are warm blooded, like birds. They have a body covering of fur, apart from a few exceptions, and feed their babies on mother's milk.

REPTILIA
Reptiles have a dry, scaly skin, and most lay tough-shelled eggs. They include lizards, snakes, turtles and tortoises, and crocodiles and alligators.

AMPHIBIA
The amphibian class includes frogs, toads, salamanders, and newts. They have moist, scaleless skin, and lay jelly-covered eggs called spawn.

OSTEICHTHYES
This class of fish contains the bony fish, which number well over 20,000 species. They have a skeleton made of bone and most have flexible fins called ray fins.

CHONDRICHTHYES
Cartilaginous fish make up the second main class of fish. They have a skeleton made of cartilage, not bone. They all live in the sea and include sharks, skates, and rays.

The history of life

Paleozoic era

The history of the Earth is divided into major time periods called eras. In the first, the Precambrian era, life forms were mostly microscopic single cells. In the second, the Paleozoic era, larger and more complex animals evolved with shells, backbones, jaws, and legs. We know this from the evidence of fossils. Paleozoic means "ancient life."

Era	Period	Million years ago
Cenozoic	Holocene (Epoch)	0.01
Cenozoic	Pleistocene (Epoch)	2
Cenozoic	Pliocene (Epoch)	5
Cenozoic	Miocene (Epoch)	25
Cenozoic	Oligocene (Epoch)	38
Cenozoic	Eocene (Epoch)	55
Cenozoic	Paleocene (Epoch)	65
Mesozoic	Cretaceous	144
Mesozoic	Jurassic	213
Mesozoic	Triassic	248
Paleozoic	Permian	286
Paleozoic	Carboniferous	360
Paleozoic	Devonian	408
Paleozoic	Silurian	438
Paleozoic	Ordovician	505
Paleozoic	Cambrian	590
	Precambrian (about seven times longer than all the other periods put together)	4,600 (origin of the earth)

Prehistoric time scale

TRILOBITE
Trilobites were distant cousins of crabs and lobsters. They all lived in the sea, appearing almost 600 million years ago but dying out by 200 million years ago.

NAUTILOIDS
Nautiloids and the similar ammonites were mollusks. Each had a body with many tentacles protruding from its coiled shell. Ammonites died out, but one nautiloid species, the nautilus, survives.

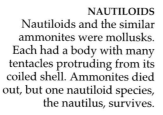

FISH
The first fish had no proper jaws or paired fins. This is a fossil of *Birkenia,* only 3 in (7 cm) long, which lived 420 million years ago.

AMPHIBIANS
The first land vertebrates were amphibians, which evolved during the Devonian period. The soft parts and skin are unusually well preserved in this fossil frog.

THE PREHISTORIC TIME SCALE
This chart shows the main eras and periods, plus the smaller time spans of the Cenozoic era, and how many millions of years ago they occurred. Fossils are dated from the type of rock in which they are embedded, the other fossils found with them, and by measuring the tiny amounts of radioactivity or magnetism in the fossil rock.

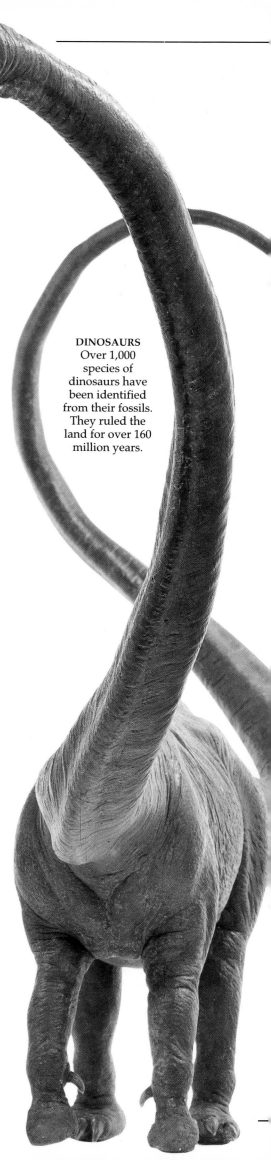

DINOSAURS
Over 1,000 species of dinosaurs have been identified from their fossils. They ruled the land for over 160 million years.

Mesozoic era

In the era of "middle life," the land was dominated by reptiles, and especially by dinosaurs. Reptiles also flourished in the seas and, as pterosaurs, in the air. Mammals had appeared, but they were insignificant. A mass extinction at the end of the Cretaceous period meant the end of many plants and animals.

BIRDS
The earliest bird, *Archaeopteryx*, lived nearly 150 million years ago. Bird bones are light, hollow, and fragile, and rarely fossilize.

ICHTHYOSAURS
These sharp-toothed, dolphin-shaped reptiles terrorized the seas for much of the Mesozoic era. Other Mesozoic marine reptiles included plesiosaurs and mosasaurs.

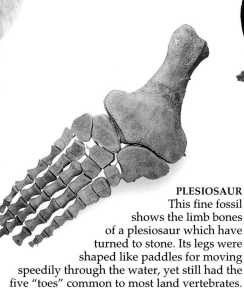

PLESIOSAUR
This fine fossil shows the limb bones of a plesiosaur which have turned to stone. Its legs were shaped like paddles for moving speedily through the water, yet still had the five "toes" common to most land vertebrates.

Cenozoic era

The era of "recent life," from 65 million years ago and into the present, has been marked by the rise of mammals to be the dominant large animals on land, while birds have taken over the sky. But through all the eras, many groups of animals and plants have diversified. These include crustaceans, worms, fish, and insects.

HORSES
The earliest horse, *Hyracotherium*, was about the size of a pet cat. It lived in the forests of North America and Europe aboutl 55 million years ago. Horses and other hoofed mammals form the ungulate group of mammals.

APES
The skull of the Miocene ape, *Proconsul*, has several similarities to today's chimps. Its blunt teeth indicate that it ate fruits and leaves. Apes, along with monkeys, lemurs, tarsiers, and bushbabies, form the primate group of mammals.

CATS
The saber-toothed tiger, *Smilodon*, had fearsome canine fangs to slash and slice at victims. It lived from about 1.6 million to only 8,000 years ago in North and South America. Cats, along with dogs, bears, raccoons, and mongooses, are in the carnivore group of mammals.

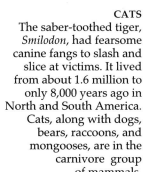

ELEPHANTS
Mammoths like this whole specimen, which was deep-frozen in Siberian ice, belonged to the elephant (proboscid) group of mammals.

GLYPTODONTS
The armored *Glyptodon* lived in South America. Like many there, it became extinct when continental drift joined South to North America, and invading species from the North forced many South American mammals into extinction.

Skull of *Homo erectus*

EARLY HUMANS
Fossil skulls give a clear picture of how upright-walking, large-brained creatures called hominids evolved from an apelike ancestor. Modern humans, *Homo sapiens*, may have appeared as little as 100,000 years ago. This skull belonged to *Homo erectus*, or upright man, an early ancestor of modern humans.

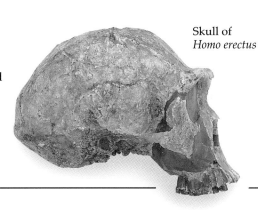

Glossary

ABDOMEN In insects, spiders, and crustaceans, the section of the body farthest away from the head. It is attached to the thorax.

ANTENNA One of the paired sense organs, on the head of an invertebrate, used to feel or taste.

BINOCULAR VISION Vision using two eyes to gauge depth.

BLOOD A fluid that flows around the body, distributing nutrients and many other substances, and collecting wastes. The "blood" of invertebrate animals is more correctly known by other names, such as endolymph.

BONE A hard body substance that forms the skeleton or supporting framework of most vertebrate animals. It is made chiefly of minerals, especially calcium and phosphorus, and the protein collagen.

BRAIN A mass of interconnected nerves which is the body's control and coordination center. Usually found in the head region, and in the skull of vertebrate animals.

CAMOUFLAGE The means by which an animal escapes the notice of predators, usually because it resembles its surroundings. *See also Disruptive Coloration.*

CARNIVORE An animal that eats mainly other animals or their body parts. This term is usually used for animals that consume large chunks of animal flesh, such as lions and wolves. *See Insectivore, Piscivore.*

CARPAL To do with the part where the forelimb of a land vertebrate animal joins the hand or front foot. Commonly called the wrist.

CARTILAGE A smooth, rubbery, or gristly body substance. In some animals it forms the whole skeleton. In others, such as mammals, it forms the coverings of the bones in a joint, and the framework of parts such as the ears.

CATERPILLAR The larva of a butterfly or moth.

CELL The microscopic unit that makes up most living things. It consists of jellylike cytoplasm held in by a membrane. At the center of most cells is a nucleus.

CHITIN A tough carbohydrate found in the external skeleton of insects, crustaceans, and spiders.

CHRYSALIS The hard skin covering the pupa of a butterfly or moth. *See also Pupa.*

COLD-BLOODED ANIMAL One that cannot warm itself up, as a warm-blooded animal can, and whose temperature depends on its surroundings. In warm sunshine, cold-blooded animals are warm.

DETRIVORE An animal that eats detritus, which includes the remains of dead animals, plants, and other living things. Sometimes called a scavenger or carrion-feeder.

DIGESTION The breakdown of food into nutrients (tiny parts) small enough to be absorbed into the body. This usually happens by a combination of physical and chemical means.

DIGIT A finger, toe, or equivalent, such as a horse's hoof.

DISRUPTIVE COLORATION A means of camouflage whereby an animal's markings, such as bold stripes or spots, break up its body shape in order to confuse predators. *See also Camouflage.*

DIURNAL Active by day.

ECOLOGY The study of how animals and plants live together and fit into the world around them.

ECOSYSTEM All the living things in a particular region such as a forest, lake, or river, as well as the soil, water, and nonliving things they use.

EGG CELL A female sex cell, in both animals and plants. *See also Sexual Reproduction.*

EMBRYO A very young plant or animal, still inside the mother (in mammals), its egg (in birds and reptiles), or its seed (in plants).

ENAMEL The hard substance that covers the surface of teeth.

ENDOSKELETON A skeleton that is mainly on the inside of the body, and covered by softer parts such as muscles, as in humans and all vertebrates. *See Skeleton and Exoskeleton.*

EVOLUTION A very slow process of change that affects all living things. It can gradually change the characteristics of a species, and produce new species from existing ones. The main driving force behind it is natural selection.

EXOSKELETON A skeleton which is mainly on the outside of the body, enclosing and encasing the softer body parts such as muscles, as in insects, crabs, and similar invertebrates. *See also Skeleton and Endoskeleton.*

FEMUR The main upper hindlimb bone in land vertebrate animals, as in the human thigh. Also used to describe thighlike structures in the legs of some invertebrate animals, such as insects.

FERTILIZATION In sexual reproduction, the stage at which male and female sex cells join together to form a single cell.

FIBULA One of two lower hindlimb bones in a land-dwelling vertebrate animal, as in the human shin. *See also Tibia.*

FOOD CHAIN A food pathway that links different species in a community, passing down energy and nutrients from one organism to another. The amount of energy passed on diminishes at each stage.

FOOD WEB A collection of food chains in a community of living things. Each species is usually involved in several different food chains. Different food chains often interconnect to form a large network, or food web.

FOSSIL The ancient remains of an animal or plant found preserved in rock.

FRUGIVORE An animal that eats mainly fruits, as well as other soft plant parts such as leaves and buds.

GILL Feathery structures in fish and other aquatic animals that extract oxygen from water for the purposes of respiration.

GRAMNIVORE An animal that eats mainly grains, seeds, nuts, and similar tough plant materials and fibers.

HABITAT The environment needed by a particular species for its survival.

HEART A muscular organ that pumps blood or an equivalent body fluid, making it flow around the body.

HERBIVORE An animal that eats mainly plant material, especially leaves, buds, shoots, fruits and stems, and flowers. *See also Gramnivore, Frugivore.*

HIBERNATION A winter sleeplike state entered into by many small animals. During hibernation, the animal's body enters a state of torpor; its body temperature drops, and its metabolic rate slows down.

HUMERUS The main upper forelimb bone in a land-dwelling vertebrate animal, as in the human upper arm.

INSECTIVORE An animal that eats mainly insects, especially small ones such as ants, termites, flies, and gnats. This diet may also include insectlike animals such as sowbugs and millipedes.

INSTINCTIVE BEHAVIOR A pattern of behavior, such as a spider spinning its web, that is inherited, or built into the animal's nervous system.

INTESTINES Usually tubelike body parts that digest food and absorb it into the body. *See Digestion.*

INVERTEBRATE An animal without a backbone (spinal column), such as a worm, spider, insect, or crab. *See Vertebrate.*

KERATIN The protein that makes up skin, hair, fur, nails, hooves, and feathers.

KIDNEY One of a pair of organs in an animal's body that removes waste from the blood and regulates its water content.

LARVA The young stage of an insect or other invertebrate that looks quite different from its parent.

LATERAL LINE A line of pressure sensors found along the side of a fish's body.

LIGAMENT A strong, flexible material that holds two bones together where they meet in movable joints.

LIVER A body part that processes digested nutrients and other body chemicals, changing, storing, and releasing them according to the body's needs.

LUNG One of a pair of organs used by most vertebrates to breathe, and so exchange oxygen and carbon dioxide inside the body.

MANTLE In snails, oysters, and other mollusks, a layer of the body that makes calcium carbonate (chalk) and so builds up the shell.

METABOLISM All the chemical reactions that occur inside a living organism.

METAMORPHOSIS A complete change in body shape, such as when a caterpillar changes into a pupa and then into a butterfly.

MIGRATION A regular journey by many animals from one place to another.

MIMICRY Imitation of one living thing by another, in order to gain protection or hide from predators.

MINERAL A simple chemical, such as iron, that living things need to stay alive.

MOLLUSK A soft-bodied invertebrate that is often protected by a hard shell. Mollusks are the second largest group of invertebrates. Most mollusks have shells and live in the water, although some live on land. The three main mollusk groups are the gastropods, the bivalves, and the cephalopods.

MOLTING The process of shedding skin, feathers, or fur.

MUSCLE A body part which can contract to move part or all of the body.

NATURAL SELECTION The process by which many different natural factors, from climate to food supply, steer the course of evolution.

NECTAR A sugary liquid produced by animal-pollinated flowers. The sweet nectar attracts animals, which help spread the plant's pollen as they feed on different plants.

NOCTURNAL An animal that is active at night and inactive during the day.

NYMPH The young stage of an insect, such as a grasshopper, that looks like a small version of its parents.

OMNIVORE An animal that eats any kind of food, whether of plant, animal, or fungal origins.

ORGANISM Any living thing.

PARASITE Any organism that lives on or inside another (its host) and from which it takes food.

PECTORAL To do with the part of a land vertebrate animal where the forelimb joins the main body – the "shoulder" – or the equivalent position in a fish.

PELVIC To do with the part of a land vertebrate animal where the hindlimb joins the main body – the "hip" – or the equivalent position in a fish.

PHEROMONE A chemical released by one animal that has an effect on another. Insects, for example, use pheromones for many different functions, including marking trails, signaling alarm, or attracting members of the opposite sex.

PHOTOSYNTHESIS The process by which plants use the energy in sunlight.

PISCIVORE An animal that eats mainly fish.

PLANKTON The mass of microscopic plants and animals that floats near or at the surface of seas and lakes.

PREDATOR An animal that hunts other animals.

PREY The animals that are hunted and eaten by a predator. *See also Predator.*

PROTEIN An organic compound that performs many functions in living things, from controlling chemical reactions to building structures such as hair. Some proteins also act as hormones.

PUPA The stage in the life cycle of an insect during which the larva turns into an adult. *See also Metamorphosis.*

RADIUS One of the two lower forelimb bones in a land vertebrate animal, as in the human forearm. *See also Ulna.*

SEED A tough package containing a plant embryo and food reserves for it to use. Following the process of germination, each seed can develop into a new plant.

SEXUAL REPRODUCTION A way of producing young that needs two parents. One, the female, produces an egg cell, while the other, the male, produces sperm.

SKELETON The hard, strong supporting framework of an animal's body, which is usually jointed to allow movement. *See Endoskeleton, Exoskeleton.*

SKULL The set of fused bones or cartilages in the head of a vertebrate animal that enclose the brain and house the main sense organs.

SPECIES A group of living things whose members can breed successfully with each other to produce fertile offspring, but who cannot breed with any other living things.

SPERM CELL A male sex cell.

SPIRACLE A tiny air hole that allows air to enter an insect's tracheae. It is surrounded by a ring of muscle that enables the spiracle to open and close. A land-dwelling insect has several pairs of spiracles on the sides of its thorax and abdomen.

STOMACH A body part that stores eaten food and begins the digestive process. *See Digestion.*

SWIM BLADDER A balloonlike organ that contains gas. It allows a fish to be neutrally buoyant in the water, which means that it does not rise or sink. When a fish dives, it increases the amount of gas in its swim bladder so that the bladder will not be squashed by water pressure.

TADPOLE The larva of a frog or toad, which lives entirely in water and breathes through gills.

TARSAL To do with the part where the hindlimb of a land vertebrate animal joins the foot. Commonly called the ankle. Also used to describe similar structures in invertebrate animals such as insects and spiders.

TENDON A tough cord or band of white inelastic tissue that attaches a muscle to a bone or some other part of an animal's body.

THORAX In insects, spiders, and crustaceans, the middle part of the body. In insects, it carries the legs and wings.

TIBIA One of the two lower hindlimb bones in a land vertebrate animal, as in the human shin. *See also Fibula.*

ULNA One of the two lower forelimb bones in a land vertebrate animal, as in the human forearm. *See also Radius.*

VERTEBRA One of the short, pillarlike bones that makes up the backbone. Together, the vertebrae form a hollow rod that contains and protects the spinal cord. Humans usually have 33 vertebrae. Some frogs have fewer than a dozen vertebrae, while snakes can have over 400.

VERTEBRATE An animal with a backbone (spinal column). There are five main groups of vertebrates: fish, amphibians, reptiles, birds, and mammals.

WARM-BLOODED ANIMAL An animal that can make its own heat by burning up food. This means that it can be warm even if its surroundings are cold.

Index

A

abdomen, 208, 374
acanthodians, 342
adaptation, 336-7
adder, 284
African egg-eating snake, 254-5
African elephant, 233, 262
African house snake, 271
albatross, 224
Albertosaurus, 240
algae, 206, 207, 359
Allosaurus, 351
amber, 344
ammonites, 352, 372
amphibians:
  classification, 371
  eggs and tadpoles, 286-7
  evolution, 343, 346-7
  eyes, 311
  fossils, 372
  hunting and feeding, 250-1
  metamorphosis, 286, 288-9
  senses, 310-1
  skeleton, 220-1
  temperature control, 311
amplexus, 288
angelfish, 304, 358
Ankylosaurus, 350
Annelida, 370
antennae, 208, 209, 374
ants:
  jays, 229
  and aphids, 245
  metamorphosis, 290
  nests, 278
apes:
  evolution, 357, 373
  feeding, 261
  mammary glands, 296
aphids, 245, 257
Arachnida, 370
Archeopteryx, 224, 373
Arctic fox, 317
Arctic hare, 317
Arctic wolf, 298
armor, 204-5
Arsinoitherium, 335
Asian elephant, 232, 262-3
Asian tree toad, 311
atlas moth, 369
Aves, 371
avocet, 257

B

babies *see* reproduction
backbone:
  fish, 218, 342
  humans, 357
  mammals, 230
  snakes, 223
  vertebrates, 371
badger, 230, 261
barbel, 361
barbs, feathers, 229
barbules, 229
barnacles, 214
barracuda, 247
basking shark, 216, 248
Bates, Henry, 318
Batesian mimicry, 318
bats:
  echolocation, 240-1, 356

evolution, 356-7
hibernation, 333
beaks, 256-9, 281
bears:
  claws, 265
  hibernation, 333, 364
  paws, 357
bees:
  in amber, 344
  anatomy, 208
  metamorphosis, 290
  nests, 278
  warning colors, 329
beetles:
  anatomy, 208
  burrowing, 320
  camouflage, 314
  courtship, 276
  feeding, 245
  metamorphosis, 290
  tropical forests, 368
  woodland habitat, 362
binocular vision, 374
birds:
  beaks, 256-9
  butterfly and moth
  camouflage, 313
  chicks, 271, 294-5
  classification, 371
  colonies, 281
  courtship, 268, 280-1
  desert habitats, 367
  eggs, 271, 284
  feathers, 228-9
  fossils, 373
  hibernation, 333
  migration, 332
  mountain habitats, 365
  nests, 278
  skeleton, 224-5
  species, 340-1
  tropical forests, 368-9
  wings, 226-7
  woodland habitats, 362-3
birds-of-paradise, 281, 368
Birkenia, 372
birth, mammals, 284
  see also eggs
black-backed gull, 340
black-footed cat, 266
black panther, 266
black tip reef shark, 358, 359
blackcap, 257
blood system, 206, 374
  frogs, 221
  sharks, 219
bloodworm, 360
blowflies, 245
blubber, 357, 359
blue-and-yellow macaw, 369
blue-footed booby, 281
blue mormon butterfly, 277
blue morpho butterfly, 292-3
blue tit, 294-5
bone, 374
  see also skeleton
booby, 281
bowfin, 278
Brachiosaurus, 348
brain, 206, 374
  dinosaurs, 349
  insects, 208
  sharks, 218, 219
bream, 246
breathing
  see respiratory system
brittlestar, 212, 213
brown squirrel, 264
brumby, 302
Buffon, Comte Georges, 340

bogong moth, 333
bugs, 245
  courtship, 276
  metamorphosis, 290
bullfrog:
  burrowing, 320-1
  ears, 311
  skeleton, 221
  tadpoles, 310
burrowing, 320-1
burrowing frog, 320
bush cricket, 244
butterflies:
  Batesian mimicry, 318
  camouflage, 312-3
  courtship, 276-7
  defenses, 318, 319
  eggs, 277
  evolution, 334
  metamorphosis, 290-3
  migration, 332-3
  proboscis, 245
  woodland habitats, 362
  see also caterpillars
buzzards, 258

C

cabbage white butterflies, 277
caddis fly, 360
caecilians, 220
  hunting and feeding, 251
  senses, 310
  skeleton, 221
caiman:
  babies, 284
  camouflage, 315
  hunting and feeding, 239
  skeleton, 222
calcium carbonate, 282, 283
Camargue horses, 303
camel, 366
camouflage, 304, 312-5, 374
  Arctic wolf, 298
  birds, 280, 281
  eggs, 271
  frogs, 286
  fur, 234
  geckoes, 306
  mammals, 316-7
  mimicry, 312, 318
cancer, dinosaurs, 353
canine teeth, 261
capercaillie, 256
carnivores, 238, 374
  amphibians, 250
  mammals, 261
  reptiles, 252
  top carnivores, 306-7
carpal, 374
carpenter moth, 313
cartilage, 374
  fish, 216, 218-9, 248-9
cascadura, 216
caterpillars, 374
  camouflage, 312, 313
  defenses, 308-9, 319
  feeding, 244-5
  metamorphosis, 290-1
  spiracles, 209
cats:
  claws, 235
  evolution, 373
  fur, 234, 235
  hunting and feeding, 266-7
  mammary glands, 296-7
  skeleton, 233
cave paintings, 354
cells, 374

Cenozoic era, 372, 373
centipedes, 363
  evolution, 344
  as food, 257, 259
  weapons, 240
Cephalaspis, 342, 343
chalci wasp, 362
chameleon:
  camouflage, 314
  hunting and feeding, 253
  skeleton, 222
cheetah, 267
chelonians, 223
chicks, 271, 294-5
chiff-chaff, 341
chimpanzee, 261
china-mark moth, 319
chinchilla, 364
Chirostenotes, 240
chitin, 208, 214, 374
Choco Indians, 329
Chondrichthytes, 371
Chordata, 371
chrysalises, 290-3, 374
cichlid, 371
citrus swallowtail butterfly, 290-1
clams, 206-7
classification, 370-1
clawed toad, 310
claws:
  bears, 265
  cats, 235
  dinosaurs, 240, 350
  lobsters, 214
clearwing butterfly, 319
cloaca, 218
cloudless sulphur butterfly, 332
clown triggerfish, 358, 359
clownfish, 305
cnidarians, 242-3, 370
cobras, 366
cockles, 210, 257
cockroaches, 290, 344
cod, 216-7
coelacanth, 343
coelenterates, 242-3
coevolution, 345
cold-blooded animals, 333, 374
cold conditions, 332-3
colonies, birds, 281
color:
  camouflage, 312-3, 314
  courtship, 276-7
  warning, 318-9, 328-9
comparative anatomy, 350
compound eyes, 209
conches, 205, 210
conchiolin, 282
coniferous forests, 364
conservative evolution, 347
convergent evolution, 339
coot, 259
copal, 344
coral reefs, 247, 304, 358
corals, 242
cormorant, 258
cougar, 365
courtship:
  birds, 268, 280-1
  colors and scents, 276-7
coyote, 261
coypu, 260
crabs, 358, 370
  defenses, 306-7
  eggs, 271
  as food, 257
  shells, 205, 214, 283
crane fly, 344

Cretaceous period, 373
crickets:
  feeding, 244
  as food, 253
  metamorphosis, 290
  natural selection, 338
crocodiles, 306
  babies, 284
  eggs, 285
  evolution, 346, 348
  extinction of sea crocodiles, 352
  hunting and feeding, 252
  jaws, 222
  natural selection, 339
crows:
  feeding, 259
  pellets, 363
  skeleton, 224, 225
crustaceans, 214-5, 370
  reproduction, 276
  shells, 205
cryptic coloration, 312
Cryptobranchus, 347
cushion star, 213
cuttlefish, 210, 314

D

damselfly, 272-3
dances, courtship, 281
dandy frog, 328
Daniel, 301
Dapedium, 343
daphnia, 214
Darwin, Charles, 318, 356
Darwin's frog, 287
Daubenton's bat, 357
day gecko, 306
dead, playing, 327
deadly nightshade, 352
deciduous woodlands, 364
deer, 363
defenses *see* natural survival
desert habitats, 366-7
desert skinks, 320
detrivores, 374
Devonian period, 344, 346
diadem snake, 366
diatoms, 358
diet *see* hunting and feeding
digestion, 206, 374
  frogs, 221
  insects, 208
  sharks, 218, 219
digits, 374
Dimetrodon, 349
dinosaurs, 224, 372
  claws, 240, 350
  diet, 350-1
  evolution, 348
  extinction, 352-3, 354
Diplocaulus, 347
Diplodocus, 350, 351
Discoglossus, 347
Dismorphia butterfly, 318
displays, defensive, 326-7
disruptive coloration, 374
diurnal, 374
divers, 224
dodo, 224
dogfish, 279, 339, 371
dogs:
  feeding, 261
  mammary glands, 296
  muscles, 206, 207
dolphin, 358
doves, 256
down feathers, 228, 229

376

Acknowledgments

Dorling Kindersley would like to thank:

David Pickering and Helena Spiteri for editorial assistance; and Alex Arthur, David Burnie, Dr. Barry Clarke, Juliet Clutton-Brock, Linda Gamlin, Theresa Greenaway, Miranda MacQuitty, Colin McCarthy, Dr. Angela Milner, Laurence Mound, Dr. David Norman, Steve Pollock, Ian Redmond, and Paul Whalley for contributing to the book.

Special photography
Geoff Brightling, Jane Burton and Kim Taylor, Peter Chadwick, Geoff Dann, Richard Davies (Oxford Scientific Films,) Philip Dowell, Mike Dunning, Andreas von Einsiedel, Neil Fletcher, Frank Greenaway, Colin Keates and Harry Taylor (Natural History Museum,) Dave King, Karl Shone, and Jerry Young; all the photographers at the British Museum.

Illustrators
Stephen Bull, Peter Chadwick, Will Giles, Mick Loates, Andrew Macdonald, Coral Mula, Richard Ward, Dan Wright, John Woodcock.

Model makers
Graham High, Jeremy Hunt

Index
Hilary Bell

Picture research
Fiona Watson

Picture credits
t=top b=bottom c=center l=left r=right

Ardea 284tl/Jean-Paul Ferrero 298t, 314 br
Zedenek Berger 346c
G.I. Bernard 297tr
Biofotos/Heather Angel 285tr, 311tl, 344c, 345tr
Bridgeman Art Library/Alan Jacobs Gallery, London 214tr, 280tl, 280cl, 280c, 292tr, 300bl, 301tc
British Library 266bl
Prof. Edmund Brodie Jnr. 286bl, 328c
Danny Bryantowich 317bl
Zdenek Burian/Artia Foreign Trade Corp 350c
Dr. Barry Clarke 311tc
Bruce Coleman/Kim Taylor 243tr, 245tl, 252tl, 252cl, 266br, 267c/Michael Fogden 286clb, 300cl/A.J. Stevens 321tl, 321cl, 326cl/Jane Burton 348tl, 349tl, 365tl, 365cr
Mary Evans 214br, 218tr, 224b, 226tl, 226cl, 226bl, 228bl, 230tr, 230tl, 242tl, 252cr, 256tr, 259tl, 265cl, 276tl, 286tr, 294bl, 297bl, 298cb, 328tl, 329cr, 342tl, 348cl, 349cb
F.L.P.A/Leo Batten 257c
Giraudon 340tl
Robert Harding Picture Library/Philip Craven 209tr, 327t, 331tr
Eric and David Hosking 281tr, 281cr
Dave King/courtesy of National Motor Museum at Beaulieu 303tr
Kobal Collection 266t, 299cr
Bob Langrish 303tl
Mike Linley 286cl, 320tr
The Mansell Collection 224tl, 226clb, 231tl, 341tl
Military Archive and Research 316br Musée
National d'Histoire Naturelle, Paris 346tr, 347tl, 354c
Natural History Museum, London 354br
N.H.P.A./Peter Johnson 234cl, 260cr, 260bl, 261tr, 262tr, 302bl
Only Horses 303c
Naturhistoriska Riksmuseet 346cl
Oxford Scientific Film/Alistair Shay 244tl/Doug Perrine 249tl/Fred Baverdam 249cl/Jack Dermid 249cr/Zig Leszczynski 264tr, 277 bl, 312cl, 326bl, 344cl, 359bl, 360tl
Planet Earth/Brian Pitkin 248tl/Ken Lucas 248cr, 261br, 299bl, 343br, 360br, 367tl/Ian Redmond 263br
Science Photo Library/Sinclair Stammers 224c
David A. Hardy 353tl
Frank Spooner 330cl, 330bl, 330cbl
A. Tanner 301tr
Werner Forman Archive 299cr
Zefa/K. and H. Benson 251cl, 267bl, 302cl, 328crb
Dr. Eric Zimen 299tr